HEAT TRANSMISSION

Heat
Transmission

BY

WILLIAM H. McADAMS
Professor of Chemical Engineering at the Massachusetts
Institute of Technology

Sponsored by the
Committee on Heat Transmission,
National Research Council

SECOND EDITION
REVISED AND ENLARGED
FOURTH IMPRESSION

McGRAW-HILL BOOK COMPANY, INC.
NEW YORK AND LONDON
1942

THE MAPLE PRESS COMPANY, YORK, PA.

PREFACE TO THE SECOND EDITION

A survey of the developments in the broad field of heat transmission indicates that greater progress has been made during the last ten years than in any previous decade. However, the new material is so buried in the general literature that it is in a large degree unavailable to the student and the practicing engineer. The purpose of this revision has been to remedy this situation.

One of the most important developments of the decade has been new insight into the mechanisms of heat transfer across boundary surfaces, secured through modern experimental methods of laboratory study. Many of these improvements have a photographic basis. Thus, shadow photography and use of the interferometer have added considerably to the knowledge of natural convection in gases. Photographic investigation has likewise thrown light on such phenomena as film-type and dropwise condensation of vapors, nuclear and film boiling of liquids outside tubes, and dry-wall vapor binding due to spray formation with liquids boiling inside tubes. These studies have already resulted in the development of better methods of correlating data.

The next important development consists of improved methods of computation. Thus, it is now realized that the calculation of unsteady conduction for many special shapes can readily be made by proper combination of well-established values for such common shapes as the slab, cylinder, and sphere. For the evaluation of net radiation between gray surfaces in an enclosure, a new and more rigorous treatment yields a simple equation for cases which in the past seemed too complex for analytical solution. The use of the enthalpy-potential concept in the design of cooling towers and dehumidifiers, in which simultaneous heat flow and mass transfer are involved, has been greatly broadened. The mathematical treatment of problems of optimum velocity has been generalized and improved, and equations and charts for mean temperature difference are now available for many cases hitherto unsolved. The general methods of formulating convenient design procedures for exchangers are illustrated by developing relations for a number of typical cases, such as fixed velocity, fixed pressure drop, and fixed heated length.

From an engineering point of view, the expansion of graphical methods of correlating data and organizing them for easy and effective use in design has been highly significant. Illustrations in the text include the graphical treatment of two-dimensional steady conduction through complex shapes, the application of the method of finite increments to unsteady conduction in cases involving complex boundary conditions, and the extensive use of alignment charts. The revision has attempted not only to present these graphical methods but to give them in forms of greatest utility to the design engineer, thus eliminating trial and error computation.

Owing to the wealth of new data, it has been possible to extend the correlations of the first edition and to include many new ones. Thus in the field of heating and cooling, new correlations cover flow in tubes for the streamline and transition regions, streamline and turbulent flow in ducts, turbulent flow in annuli, flow parallel to planes, gravity flow of liquids in layer form, flow across banks of tubes, flow past finned surfaces, turbulent flow past spheres, and natural convection from planes. Some of these new correlations may require modification as new data become available. Throughout the text effort has been made to indicate clearly the order of dependability of the recommended relations and to cite the sources of the supporting data.

For emphasis, the basic assumptions and general background of the derivations are divorced from the mathematical presentation and are given in the main text, and a clear outline of the mathematical manipulations is given in fine print. This edition continues the policy of including the solution of illustrative cases in the text, but an innovation is the introduction of a large number of practice problems designed to test the reader's grasp of principles and methods.

Thanks are due Prof. G. C. Williams for extensive assistance in the preparation of manuscript and illustrations, Prof. H. C. Hottel for permission to include Chapter III, T. H. Chilton for furnishing abstracts of articles and for permission to reproduce a number of alignment charts, J. H. Perry for the use of charts and tables, Profs. J. H. Keenan and F. G. Keyes for permission to include an abstract of their steam tables, J. A. Lane for amplifying tables of thermal conductivities, F. E. England for help in the preparation of the bibliography and some of the graphs, and various manufacturers for furnishing drawings or photographs. A number of research workers kindly furnished unpublished material, as listed in the bibliography. Nearly all the nomenclature is taken from the lists of the American Standards Association and the American Institute of Chemical Engineers.

WILLIAM H. McADAMS.

CAMBRIDGE, MASS.,
June, 1942.

PREFACE TO THE FIRST EDITION

This book is designed to serve both as a text for students and as a reference for practicing engineers. The problem of heat transmission is encountered in almost every industry, and because of the diversity in the fields of application there exist countless differences in detail. However, the principles underlying the problem are everywhere the same, and it is the purpose of this book to present fundamentals rather than to deal with the details of individual problems and special cases. This is done not merely because the discussion of individual cases would involve excessive space but because, in the first place, the solution of no individual problem can be adequate without a mastery of the principles underlying the whole field, and, in the second place, the solution of the specific problem becomes relatively easy once those fundamental principles are understood.

Because of the large number of fields in which heat transmission plays a part, the literature on the subject is extremely diffuse. Important data are often found in most unexpected places, and results are expressed in unfamiliar forms. Reliable data from the most diverse sources, including many unpublished results, have been reduced to a common basis for purposes of comparison and have been correlated in the light of the most helpful theoretical analyses. The results of these critical studies are presented as formulas and graphs carefully constructed to give due weight to all the data and at the same time to make the results readily available for use in engineering design. Because in many important cases the formulas represent not the results of a single investigation but concordant data from varied sources, it is believed that they afford the most dependable basis for engineering design.

The technique of employing the formulas is made clear by the solution of illustrative problems characteristic of the most important engineering uses to which the formulas are likely to be put. Where the general equations, based on the data for a number of fluids, contain a number of factors, calculations are simplified by the use of alignment charts, whereby the several physical properties are evaluated in terms of temperature of the fluid.

This book may be divided into three parts: conduction, radiation, and convection.

The section on conduction consists of two chapters, the first dealing with steady conduction of heat, thermal conductivities, the effect of the shape of bodies, and resistances in series and in parallel. In the second chapter, unsteady conduction, as in the heating and cooling of solids, is considered, and problems are solved by the use of charts involving four dimensionless ratios.

The second section treats radiation between solids for a number of important specific cases, radiation from nonluminous and luminous flames, and the general problem of furnace design, where heat is transferred simultaneously by several mechanisms.

The third section consists of seven chapters. The first of these deals with dimensional similarity. Because of the important relation between fluid motion and forced convection, a chapter is devoted to fluid dynamics. The third chapter serves as an introduction to convection and treats the relations between over-all and individual coefficients of heat transfer, the effect of deposits of scale, mean temperature difference in heat exchangers involving counterflow, multipass and cross flow, and the measurement of surface temperatures. The four remaining chapters deal with heat transfer by forced and free convection under the general headings of fluids inside pipes, fluids outside pipes, condensation, and evaporation. Photographs of convection currents and charts of distribution of velocity and temperature illustrate the mechanisms involved. The original data of a number of reliable investigators are plotted to develop the relations recommended for the various cases, and the experimental ranges of the various factors are tabulated. Optimum operating conditions are considered, and methods are given for determining the economic velocity of fluid in a heat exchanger and the optimum temperature difference in the recovery of waste heat.

The Appendix contains tables and charts of thermal conductivities, specific heats, latent heats of vaporization, and viscosities, and miscellaneous tables, such as steam tables, conversion factors, and dimensions of steel pipe.

In the text, reference numbers are used to designate the literature citations tabulated alphabetically in the Bibliography. Text page references are cited in the Bibliography, which thus serves as the Author Index.

This book has been written under the auspices of the National Research Council, Heat Transmission Committee; and the author wishes to express his appreciation of the active cooperation and assistance of the individual members of this Committee, particularly for the help of Paul Bancel of the Ingersoll Rand Company, Prof. C. H. Berry of Harvard University, John Blizard of the Foster Wheeler Corporation, W. H. Carrier of the Carrier Engineering Corporation, T. H. Chilton and A. P. Colburn of E. I. du Pont de Nemours & Company, Inc., H. N. Davis of Stevens Institute of Technology, H. C. Dickinson of the Bureau of Standards, W. V. A. Kemp, formerly Secretary of the Committee on Heat Transmission, H. Harrison of the Carrier Engineering Corporation, C. F. Hirschfeld of the Detroit Edison Company, Prof. L. S. Marks of Harvard University, G. A. Orrok of New York, R. J. S. Pigott of the Gulf Companies, W. Spraragen of the National Research Council, T. S. Taylor of the Bakelite Corporation, M. S. VanDusen of the Bureau of Standards, and D. J. VanMarle of the Buffalo Foundry and Machine Company.

Help has also been received from so many individuals at such diverse times that it would be impossible to name them all, but this does not mean that the author fails to appreciate the value of such help and to be grateful for it. However, it is desired to mention the work of certain of my professional associates who have given freely of time and energy during the course of the work. In this group it is desired to mention T. B. Drew, J. J. Hogan, Prof. H. C. Hottel, C. R. Johnson, Prof. W. K. Lewis, W. M. Nagle, Prof. C. S. Robinson, Prof. W. P. Ryan, Prof. T. K. Sherwood, Prof. W. H. Walker, and Prof. G. B. Wilkes. Thanks are due to V. C. Cappello for the reading of proof.

WILLIAM H. McADAMS.

CAMBRIDGE, MASS.,
December, 1932.

INDEX TO PRINCIPAL RELATIONS

FOR CONVECTION

PAGE

Over-all coefficient of heat transfer, defined................................ 134
Individual coefficient of heat transfer, defined............................. 135
Relation between over-all and individual coefficients................... 136
Allowances for scale deposits.. 138
Mean temperature difference.. 141–148
Usual ranges of over-all coefficients..................................... 251

HEATING AND COOLING, FLOW PARALLEL TO AXIS

Turbulent flow in tubes, general case............................... 168, 196
   Simplified equation for gases..................................... 174–176
   Simplified equation for water...................................... 183–186
   Coiled tubes.. 177
Streamline flow in tubes.. 190–191
Transition region, flow inside tubes....................................... 196
Rectangular sections.. 198–199
Annular sections.. 202
Gravity flow of liquid in layer form............................... 203–206
Flow parallel to a single plane..................................... 206–207

HEATING AND COOLING, FLOW NORMAL TO AXIS

Single tubes, general case.. 221, 226
   Simplified equation for gases....................................... 223
Banks of tubes... 230, 357
   Simplified equation for water.. 230
Finned tubes... 234–235
Gravity flow of liquid in layer form....................................... 206
Spheres, general case.. 236–237
Streamline shapes... 236

NATURAL CONVECTION, HEATING, AND COOLING

Horizontal tubes, general case... 243
Vertical planes, general case.. 248
Inside vertical tubes.. 185, 191
Simplified equations for various shapes........................... 240, 250
$h_c + h_r$ for horizontal pipes.. 247
U for coils and jacketed vessels................................ 249–250

CONDENSING VAPORS

Film-type condensation of pure vapor...................................... 268
   Alignment chart for streamline flow................................ 269
Dropwise condensation of stream... 276
U, steam to water... 273, 278
Refrigerants to water, U.. 271–275
Mixtures of vapors.. 281–283
Dehumidification.. 284–285
Cooling towers.. 289–290
Humidifiers.. 292

BOILING LIQUIDS

Outside tubes... 319–321
Inside tubes.. 333–334

CONTENTS

	PAGE
PREFACE TO THE SECOND EDITION	V
PREFACE TO THE FIRST EDITION	ix
INDEX TO PRINCIPAL RELATIONS FOR CONVECTION	xii
INTRODUCTION	1

CHAPTER I
CONDUCTION 5

CHAPTER II
HEATING AND COOLING OF SOLIDS 27

CHAPTER III
RADIANT HEAT TRANSMISSION 45

CHAPTER IV
DIMENSIONAL ANALYSIS 87

CHAPTER V
FLOW OF FLUIDS 99

CHAPTER VI
INTRODUCTION TO HEAT TRANSFER BETWEEN FLUIDS AND SOLIDS 133

CHAPTER VII
HEATING AND COOLING FLUIDS INSIDE TUBES 154

CHAPTER VIII
HEATING AND COOLING FLUIDS OUTSIDE TUBES 210

CHAPTER IX
CONDENSING VAPORS 254

Page

CHAPTER X
Heat Transfer to Boiling Liquids 294

CHAPTER XI
Applications of Design. 340

Appendix (Tables and Charts of Data) 379

Bibliography and Author Index. 419

Subject Index 449

HEAT TRANSMISSION

INTRODUCTION

The laws of heat transmission are of controlling importance in the design and operation of many diverse forms of heaters, coolers, condensers, evaporators, and the like, found in many different industries. It is well understood that heat may flow by three distinct mechanisms, which may be defined as follows.

MODES OF HEAT TRANSMISSION

1. Conduction.—Conduction is the transfer of heat from one part of a body to another part of the same body, or from one body to another in physical contact with it, without appreciable displacement of the particles of the body.

2. Convection.—Convection is the transfer of heat from one point to another within a fluid, gas or liquid, by the mixing of one portion of the fluid with another. The motion of the fluid may be entirely the result of differences of density resulting from the temperature differences, as in natural convection; or the motion may be produced by mechanical means, as in forced convection.

3. Radiation.—A hot body gives off heat in the form of radiant energy which is emitted in all directions. When this energy strikes another body, part may be reflected. Part may be transmitted unchanged through the body, in which case the body is said to be diathermanous. The remainder is absorbed and quantitatively transformed into heat.* If two bodies, one hotter than the other, are placed within an enclosure, there is a continuous interchange of energy between them. The hotter body radiates more energy than it absorbs; the colder body absorbs more than it radiates. Even after equilibrium of temperature is established, the process continues, each body radiating and absorbing energy.

Since in most cases any actual transfer of heat is accomplished by more than one of the three modes, it is preferable to use the

---

* Except in the relatively rare cases in which photochemical reactions are induced or energy is consumed in other special ways.

1

terms *transfer* or *transmission* to describe the process, reserving the use of the terms *radiation, convection*, and *conduction* for that fraction of the heat transmission accomplished by the mechanism designated.   The term *radiation* is probably the most generally misused of the three, such expressions as radiation through furnace walls, etc., being common.

ILLUSTRATIONS

Thus, in considering the brick walls of a dwelling, heat will be conducted through the solid from the warmer to the colder face. Also, when one end of an insulated iron bar is held in the fire, heat will be conducted through the metal toward the colder end, although a part will be conducted through the insulation and dissipated to the room by the mechanisms of convection and radiation.   When heat is transmitted through a cellular or porous solid, the heat may flow not only by conduction but also both by convection within the gas pockets and by radiation from surface to surface of the individual cells within the nonhomogeneous solid.

In the heating of a tank of liquid, if the steam coil is located near the top of the tank, the heated liquid, because of its reduced density, would not tend to mix readily with the colder, more dense liquid at the bottom of the tank.   In order to promote the thermo-siphon circulation of the liquid, due to differences in density, the heating coil should be located near the bottom of the tank.   For similar reasons, the heating element of the so-called "steam radiator" should be placed near the floor of the room rather than near the ceiling.   Instead of depending wholly on this natural convection, an increased rate of circulation can be obtained by mechanical means such as a pump or fan, giving what is known as *forced convection*.

In a cold room heated only by a fireplace, an occupant near the fire may receive too much heat on one side, because of the radiant energy emitted by the fire, and yet be unpleasantly cold on the other side.   Radiant energy from the sun travels through space, penetrates the earth's atmosphere, is partially absorbed, and the remainder reaches the surface of the earth, where part is reflected and the residue is transformed into heat.   In the generation of steam, radiation from the fire bed to the tubes of the boiler plays an important part.   The hot flue gases pass over the boiler tubes, and thus additional heat is transferred to the tubes by convection. The carbon dioxide and water vapor of the flue gases radiate energy directly to the tubes. Hence the heat conducted through the metal walls of the tubes is supplied by radiation from warmer solids, by convection from the warm gases, and by radiation from certain constituents of the flue gases.

It is thus seen that in most, if not all, actual cases of heat transmission more than one mechanism is involved. Therefore it will be necessary not only to present the laws of heat transmission governing the three mechanisms, together with auxiliary data, but also to develop proper methods for calculating the total heat flow due to the combined effects.

Although the entire book is devoted to a study of the laws of heat transfer, it is interesting at this point to make a preliminary inspection of the basic equations. The law of conduction, which is well understood, states that the instantaneous rate of heat of heat transfer dq is proportional to the area dA through which heat flows at right angles and to the temperature gradient $-dt/dx$,

$$dq = -k \, dA \, \frac{dt}{dx} \tag{1}$$

The proportionality factor k is called the *thermal conductivity*, and in a given set of units the values for various substances cover a range of ten thousandfold.

The law of thermal radiation is equally well established, and the gross emission is proportional to the fourth power of the absolute temperature T of the body:

$$dq = \sigma\epsilon \, dA \, T^4 \tag{2}$$

The dimensionless factor ϵ is called the *emissivity* and ranges from zero for the perfect reflector to unity for the ideal radiator or black body, and the proportionality factor σ is a dimensional constant whose size depends only on the units employed.

On the other hand, the transfer of heat from the surface of a solid at temperature t_s to a fluid having bulk temperature t flowing past it is extremely complex, since both conduction and convection are involved; and the situation is handled by defining a coefficient of heat transfer h that appears in Newton's law of cooling:

$$dq = h \, dA \, (t_s - t) \tag{3}$$

where dq is the local rate of heat transfer through a surface element dA. It will be found that the coefficient h depends not only on the units employed but on certain physical properties of the fluid, dimensions of the apparatus, velocity of the fluid past the surface, and whether or not the fluid is changing phase. In a given set of units the values of h cover a range of one hundred thousandfold, as shown in Table I.

TABLE I.—APPROXIMATE RANGE OF VALUES OF h ORDINARILY ENCOUNTERED

	Btu/(hr)(sq ft)(deg F)
Steam, dropwise condensation	10,000–20,000
Steam, film-type condensation	1,000– 3,000
Water boiling	300– 9.000
Organic vapors condensing	200– 400
Water, heating or cooling	50– 3,000
Oils, heating or cooling	10– 300
Steam, superheating	5– 20
Air, heating or cooling	0.2– 8

CHAPTER I

CONDUCTION

Introduction.—In the great majority of cases arising in engineering practice, heat flows from some medium into and through a solid retaining wall and out into some other medium. The flow through each medium is, therefore, but one step in a more complicated process, and the resistance to the conduction of heat through the retaining wall is only one of a series of resistances. A clear understanding of the mechanism of heat transfer by conduction through a single homogeneous solid is essential to the solution of the more complex problems.

This chapter deals with the basic differential equation for heat conduction and integrated equations for the steady conduction of heat through homogeneous bodies of various shapes. Equations are given for the conduction of heat through more than one resistance, for both series and parallel flow. The chapter contains a number of illustrative problems.

TABLE I.—NOMENCLATURE*

A Area through which heat flows at right angles, square feet; $A_a = (A_1 + A_2)/2$; A_m is true mean value.

a Temperature coefficient of thermal conductivity, reciprocal degrees Fahrenheit.

a_1 Dimensionless constant in equation $a_1 = k/c_v \mu$.

b_1 Constant in Eq. 23, reciprocal weight per cent.

c Specific heat, Btu/(lb)(deg F).

c_p Specific heat at constant pressure, Btu/(lb)(deg F).

c_v Specific heat at constant volume, Btu/(lb)(deg F).

C Conductance, Btu/(hr)(deg F).

C' Conductance per unit area, Btu/(hr)(sq ft)(deg F).

C_s Sutherland constant, degrees Fahrenheit absolute.

d Prefix, indicating differential.

e Base of natural logarithms, 2.718 · · · · .

k Thermal conductivity at temperature t, Btu/(hr)(ft)(deg F); k_a att $a = (t_1 + t_2)/2$; k_o at 0°F.

TABLE I.—NOMENCLATURE.*—(*Continued*)

L Length of cylinder, feet.
M Molecular weight, a ratio.
M' Actual weight of one molecule, grams.
N Number of spaces; N_L is number of lanes.
Q Quantity of heat, Btu.
q Steady rate of heat flow, Btu per hour.
R Thermal resistance $x/k_m A_m$, (deg F)(hr)/Btu.
R_G Special gas constant, in heat units.
R_T Total thermal resistance, $\Sigma(x/k_m A_m)$.
T Absolute temperature, degrees Fahrenheit absolute.
t Thermometric temperature, degrees Fahrenheit.
V_a Acoustic velocity in a liquid, feet per hour.
x Length of conduction path, radius, feet.
x_w Per cent by weight of a solute in an aqueous solution, dimensionless.
y Length of any inside edge of a parallelepiped, feet; y_{max}, largest value of y.
z_c Mean distance between centers of molecules of a liquid, feet; in centimeters $z_c' = (M'/\rho)^{1/3}$.
z Width, feet.

Greek
Δt Temperature difference, degrees Fahrenheit.
θ Time, hours.
κ c_p/c_v, dimensionless.
μ Absolute viscosity, lb/(hr)(ft).
μ' Absolute viscosity, centipoises.
π 3.1416 · · · , a pure number.
ρ Density, grams per cubic centimeter.
ρ' Density relative to water, dimensionless.
Σ Prefix, indicating a summation.

* The symbols used in this book have, in general, been taken from the lists of the American Standards Association and of the American Institute of Chemical Engineers.[16]

THERMAL CONDUCTION THROUGH A SINGLE HOMOGENEOUS SOLID

Basic Equation.—Fourier's law[231]* for the conduction of heat states that the instantaneous *rate* of heat flow $dQ/d\theta$ is equal to the product of three factors: the area A of the section, taken at right angles to the direction of heat flow; the temperature gradient $-dt/dx$, which is the rate of change of temperature t with respect to the length of path x; and a proportionality factor k, known as the *thermal conductivity*. Mathematically expressed, Fourier's law is as follows:

* Literature references are given in the Bibliography and Author Index, p. 419.

$$\frac{dQ}{d\theta} = -kA \frac{dt}{dx} \tag{1}$$

where dQ is the amount of heat flowing in differential time $d\theta$.

The differential form given in Eq. 1 is general for unidirectional conduction and may be applied to cases in which the temperature gradient $-dt/dx$ varies with time as well as with the location of the point considered. In every case of heat flow by conduction, a temperature gradient must exist. If the temperature of a given point in the body varies with time, the rate of heat flow will also vary with time. The process of heat flow in a case in which temperature varies with both time and position is called *heat conduction* in the *unsteady state*, and problems involving the integration of the differential equations for this case are treated in Chap. II.

As contrasted with heat conduction in the complicated unsteady state, heat conduction in the *steady state* refers to those cases in which the temperature at any given point in the system is independent of time. Fortunately, many cases in industrial practice fall under this heading, simplifying the quantitative treatment of such problems in heat conduction. Thus, the temperature at a point in a furnace wall, although rising during the first period of firing, eventually becomes substantially constant and so remains as long as the furnace is in continuous operation under steady conditions.

Basic Equation for Thermal Conduction in the Steady State.— Since for conduction in the steady state, the temperature at any point does not vary with time, it follows that the temperature gradient $-dt/dx$ and, consequently, the rate of heat flow $dQ/d\theta$ are likewise independent of time. Hence, the rate $dQ/d\theta$ equals Q/θ and is designated by q, and Eq. 1 becomes

$$q = -kA \frac{dt}{dx} \tag{2}$$

In the English system involving the units of feet, pounds, hours, degrees Fahrenheit, and British thermal units, k is expressed as British thermal units per hour per square foot taken at right angles to the direction of heat flow, per unit temperature gradient, degrees Fahrenheit per foot of length of path. This is often improperly abbreviated to "Btu per hr per sq ft per deg F per ft," but it should be remembered that the units of k are

$$\frac{(Btu)/(hr)(sq\ ft)}{(deg\ F/ft)} = \frac{Btu}{(hr)(ft)(deg\ F)}$$

Throughout the text, unless otherwise specified, numerical values of k are expressed in these units, but factors are given on page 379 for converting the numerical values of k from one system of units to another.

Thermal Conductivities of Solids.—The thermal conductivities of various solids differ widely. Thus, k for copper is approximately 220, whereas k for corkboard is about 0.025. For a given solid, k is a function of temperature, and for most homogeneous solids hitherto investigated this temperature relationship is nearly linear over a considerable range in temperature: $k = k_0(1 + at)$, k being the value at $t°F$, k_0 at $0°F$, and a the temperature coefficient. The temperature coefficient is positive for many insulating materials, a notable exception being magnesite brick, as shown by Table IV, page 382. On the other hand, for good conductors, such as most metals, the temperature coefficient is usually negative, aluminum and brass being exceptions. At a given temperature, the thermal conductivity of commercial samples of a metal may differ widely, probably because of the variation in the content of certain elements or compounds present in small amounts. In 1853, Wiedemann and Franz[763] advanced the theory that the ratio of the thermal conductivity to the electrical conductivity was practically constant for all metals, and in 1882 Lorenz[446] proposed that this ratio should be proportional to the absolute temperature. The deviation from the Lorenz rule for metals is generally less than 50 per cent, with an average deviation of 11 per cent.[336] According to Thornton,[717] the thermal conductivity of a nonmetallic solid is proportional to the product of the density and elasticity, but it is doubtful if the relation is of general validity.

For nonhomogeneous solids the thermal conductivity at a given temperature is a function of the apparent or bulk density. Thus, at 32°F, k for asbestos wool is 0.052 when the bulk density is 24.9 lb per cu ft, and is 0.111 for a density of 43.6 lb per cu ft. In determining the apparent thermal conductivity of granular solids, such as granulated cork or charcoal grains, Griffiths[265] found that air circulates within the mass of granular solid. Under a certain set of conditions, the apparent thermal conductivity of charcoal grains was 9 per cent greater when the test section was vertical than when horizontal. When the apparent conductivity of a cellular or porous nonhomogeneous solid is determined, the apparent temperature coefficient may be much larger than for the homogeneous solid alone, because of the fact that heat is transferred not only by the mechanism of conduction but also by convection in the gas pockets and by radiation from surface to surface of the individual cells. If internal radiation is an important factor, a plot of the apparent conductivity as ordinates *vs.* temperature should show a curve concave upward, since radiation increases with the fourth power of the absolute temperature. Griffiths notes that cork, slag wool, charcoal, and wood fibers, when of good quality and dry, have thermal conductivities of about 2.2 times that of still air, whereas a highly cellular form of rubber, 7 lb per cu ft, had a thermal conductivity only 1.6 times that of still air. In connection with the apparent thermal conductivity of fibrous materials, Finck[221] gives interesting conclusions regarding the effect of apparent density, arrangement of fibers, and the roles played by conduction, convection, and radiation. A lightweight thermal insulation* consists of very thin layers of aluminum foil (0.0003 in. thick) spaced about $\frac{1}{3}$ in. apart in either flat or crumpled sheets, the apparent density being only 0.19 lb per cu ft. For a given thickness, this material is said to have a thermal resistance at low temperatures equal to that of cork and higher than magnesia at 400°F. The low apparent thermal conductivity is due to the small air spaces and to the low emissivity of the metal, approximately 5 per cent of that of a black body. In cases in which heat is transferred through a porous solid by the combined mechanisms of conduction, convection, and radiation, it is preferable to express the results as conductances (see page 25) rather than as apparent thermal conductivities. In measuring the apparent thermal conductivity of diathermanous substances such as quartz, especially when exposed to radiation emitted at high temperatures, it should be remembered that a part of the heat is transmitted by radiation.

Tables and plots of thermal conductivities of various solids, liquids, and gases are given in the Appendix, pages 380 to 392.

In order to be of practical use, Eq. 2 must be integrated, and for this purpose the variation of k with t and of A with x must be known. As stated above, experimental data on the variation of k with temperature can often be expressed by the linear relationship

$$k = k_0(1 + at) \tag{3}$$

where k is the instantaneous value of the thermal conductivity at the

* Breitung,[88] Anon,[15] Gregg,[260] Naumann,[502] Schmidt,[632] Wilkes,[764] and Wilkes *et al.*[765]

temperature t, and k_0 and a are constants.   Combining Eqs. 2 and 3,

$$-k \, dt = -k_0(1 + at) \, dt = q \, dx/A. \tag{4}$$

Integrating between the temperature limits t_1 and t_2,

$$-\int_{t_1}^{t_2} k \, dt = (t_1 - t_2)(k_0)\left[1 + a \, \frac{(t_1 + t_2)}{2} \right] = q \int_1^2 \frac{dx}{A}$$

Hence, where k is linear in t, one may use the equation

$$k_a(t_1 - t_2) = q \int_1^2 dx/A \tag{5}$$

where k_a is the arithmetic mean of k_1 at t_1 and k_2 at t_2, or k_a is evaluated at the arithmetic mean of t_1 and t_2.

If k is not linear in t, some mean value k_m will apply.   Irrespective of the relation between A and x

$$k_m = \frac{1}{(t_1 - t_2)} \int_{t_1}^{t_2} k \, dt$$

In many practical cases, however, the cross-sectional area A varies appreciably with the length of path x, so that the shape of the solid through which the heat is flowing must be known before Eq. 5 may be integrated.   Four such cases will now be discussed, of which the first two include most of the problems arising in engineering practice.[740]

Case I.   *Conduction of Heat through a Solid of Constant Cross Section.*—For this case, where A is constant, integration of Eq. 5 between the limits of x_1 and x_2, gives

$$q = \frac{k_m A (t_1 - t_2)}{x_2 - x_1} = \frac{k_m A \, \Delta t}{x} \tag{6}$$

For convenience, the temperature difference $t_1 - t_2$ has been replaced by Δt, and the thickness $x_2 - x_1$ by x.   Equation 6 states that the rate of heat flow in Btu per hour is directly proportional (1) to the mean thermal conductivity of the substance in question, (2) to the cross-sectional area of the path in square feet, and (3) to the temperature difference in degrees Fahrenheit between the points from and to which the heat is flowing and is inversely proportional to the length of the path in feet.

Illustration 1.—Calculate the heat loss through a 9-in. brick and mortar wall ($k_m = 0.4$), 10 ft high and 6 ft wide, when the inner and outer surface temperatures are 330 and 130°F, respectively.

Solution.—By Eq. 6,

$$q = \frac{k_m A \, \Delta t}{x} = \frac{(0.4)(60)(330 - 130)}{\frac{9}{12}} = 6400 \text{ Btu/hr}$$

On account of its simplicity, Eq. 6 is usually employed even when the cross section of path is a variable quantity, average values A_m for the area being then employed. The next three cases resolve

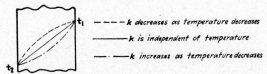

FIG. 1.—Temperature gradients in flat walls.

themselves into the problem of deriving rules for obtaining correct mean values of this area for various special shapes, employing the equation

$$q = k_m \, A_m \, \Delta t / x \tag{7}$$

Case II. *Cross Section of Path Proportional to Linear Dimension (Lagged Pipes).*—Where heat is flowing through the sides of a closed cylindrical body of circular section, the direction of flow is at all points radial and perpendicular to the axis, and the cross section of the path is proportional to the distance from the center of the cylinder. It will now be shown that in such cases the logarithmic-mean area is the proper average value.

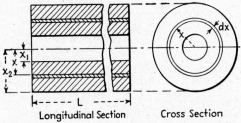

Longitudinal Section   Cross Section

FIG. 2.—Diagram for case II: logarithmic-mean area.

Consider the flow through a section of thickness dx, at a distance x from the center (see Fig. 2).

By Eq. 5, $\int dx/A = k_m(\Delta t)/q$. The cross section of path is $A = 2\pi x L$ where L is the length of the cylinder. This gives

$$\int_1^2 \frac{dx}{x} = \frac{k_m \, \Delta t 2\pi L}{q}. \tag{8}$$

On integration and substitution of limits, this becomes

$$q = \frac{k_m 2\pi L (\Delta t)}{\ln_e (x_2/x_1)}. \tag{9}$$

As stated above, it is desired to employ the simple form of Eq. 7, using a mean value of that area, A_m, which will give the correct heat flow. Equating Eqs. 9 and 7, one obtains

$$q = \frac{k_m 2\pi L \, \Delta t}{\ln_e (x_2/x_1)} = k_m A_m \frac{\Delta t}{x_2 - x_1} \tag{10}$$

whence,

$$A_m = \frac{2\pi x_2 L - 2\pi x_1 L}{\ln_e (2\pi x_2 L / 2\pi x_1 L)} \tag{11}$$

$$A_m = \frac{A_2 - A_1}{\ln_e (A_2/A_1)} = \frac{A_2 - A_1}{2.3 \log_{10} (A_2/A_1)}. \tag{12}$$

Equation 12 requires that the area of cross section through which the heat is flowing in such a case be computed by dividing the difference of the external and internal areas by the natural logarithm of their ratio. For any two quantities, the average so obtained is called the *logarithmic mean* and is, as will later appear, a value frequently used in problems on the flow of heat. Equation 11 indicates that A_m may also be computed by multiplying the logarithmic-mean radius by 2π times the length of pipe in feet instead of calculating A_2 and A_1 separately. For a given material and boundary temperatures, Eq. 9 indicates that the rate of heat conduction per unit length of hollow cylinder depends only on the ratio of outer and inner radii and is independent of thickness.

When the value of A_2/A_1 does not exceed 2, the arithmetic-mean area

$$A_a = (A_1 + A_2)/2 \tag{12a}$$

is within 4 per cent of the logarithmic-mean area; this accuracy is considered sufficient for problems in heat conduction.

Optimum Thickness of Pipe Covering.—The heat loss from an insulated steam pipe involves the coefficient of heat transfer from steam to metal, the conductivity and thickness of both the pipe wall and the insulation, and the coefficient of heat transfer from the surface of the insulation to the surroundings. This case will be treated in Chap. XI after the surface coefficients have been studied in detail. As the thickness of the insulation is increased the investment charges increase, but the heat loss usually decreases, and the optimum thickness of insulation corresponds to a minimum total annual cost.

Case III.   *Cross Section of Path Proportional to Square of Linear Dimension.*

Consider a hollow sphere bounded by radii x_1 and x_2, through which heat is flowing radially in all directions at a uniform steady rate.   At any radius x the cross-sectional area A equals $4\pi\ x^2$; upon integrating Eq. 5 between the limits x_1 and x_2, one obtains

$$\frac{q}{4\pi}\left(\frac{1}{x_1}-\frac{1}{x_2}\right) = k_m\ \Delta t \tag{13}$$

or

$$q = \frac{4\pi\ k_m\ x_1 x_2 (\Delta t)}{x_2 - x_1} \tag{13a}$$

If it is desired to employ Eq. 7, involving a suitable mean area A_m, one may equate Eqs. 7 and 13a to obtain

$$A_m = 4\pi x_1 x_2 = \sqrt{A_1 A_2} \tag{14}$$

In case, therefore, the cross-sectional area be proportional to the square of the linear dimension, the average area to be employed in calculating the heat flow is the *geometric* mean of the internal and external surfaces, as indicated by Eq. 14.   In the case of beehive coke ovens of commercial size, the geometric mean theoretically applies, but the arithmetic mean is within less than 1 per cent of the geometric.   Were the outside diameter twice the inside, the arithmetic mean of the inside and outside areas would be 25 per cent too high, but such cases do not occur in industrial practice.   It is to be noted that both the logarithmic- and geometric-mean values are always lower than the arithmetic.

In the flow of heat through the walls of hollow cubes, such as cubical furnaces, the area of cross section is proportional to the square of the linear dimension, but all this area does not receive heat flow at right angles.   Hence, the flow calculated from the geometric-mean area for a cube would be too high.   The flow of heat through cubes and the more general case of flow through rectangular bodies having walls relatively thick compared with the inside dimensions are treated in the next special case.

Case IV.   *Rectangular Bodies Having Walls at Least One-half as Thick as the Shortest Inside Dimension.*—This special case is very important as applied to the loss of heat from furnaces which have walls at least one-half as thick as the shortest inside dimension.

If in Eq. 7, the area be taken as the inside area, the heat loss so calculated will be a great deal too low.   On the other hand, if the outer area or even the arithmetic-mean area be used, the heat loss calculated will be too high.   Not only does heat flow at right angles to the entire inside area but it also flows at various angles through the edges and corners of the outside walls. For such cases, the integration of the basic differential equation becomes difficult. Langmuir[423] solved the problem by experimentally determining the electrical conductance of a solution of copper sulphate in a container of the desired shape and, by comparing this with the electrical conductance of the same solution in a container of constant cross section, deduced the equations given below for an approximation to the average area A_m to be used in Eq. 7. This procedure is a good example of the theory of models (page 95); since the basic equations for the conduction of electricity and of heat are identical in form, the results are applicable to both phenomena. The empirical equations given below agree closely with those which Langmuir obtained from theoretical analyses based on isothermal surfaces at the boundaries. The results are also supported by subsequent data.[519]

Consider only bodies bounded by rectangular parallelepipeds, corresponding inner and outer surfaces being parallel and in all cases the same distance x apart. All faces intersect at right angles. Five special cases are given, and it is believed that an understanding of these will enable the reader to handle any set of conditions of this type met in practice.

Case IVa. The Lengths y of All Inside Edges Are between One-fifth and Twice the Thickness x of the Walls.—The sum total of the lengths of all the inside edges is Σy. To the actual inside area A_1 must be added $0.54x\,\Sigma y$ to correct for the edges and $0.15x^2$ for each of the eight corners, this sum being called the average area A_m:

$$A_m = A_1 + 0.54x\,\Sigma y + 1.2x^2 \tag{15}$$

Case IVb. Length y of One Inside Edge Is Less than One-fifth the Thickness x of Walls.—In this case, the lengths of the four inside edges, less than $x/5$, are neglected in determining Σy. Then

$$A_m = A_1 + 0.465x\,\Sigma y + 0.35x^2 \tag{16}$$

where Σy is the sum total of all the remaining eight inside edges, each of which is greater than $x/5$.

Case IVc. Lengths of Two Inside Edges Are Each Less than One-fifth the Thickness x of the Walls.

$$A_m = \frac{2.78 y_{max}\, x}{\log_{10}(A_2/A_1)} \tag{17}$$

where y_{max} is the longest dimension of the interior.

Case IVd. All Three Interior Dimensions Are Less than One-fifth the Thickness of the Walls.—Using the same nomenclature,

$$A_m = 0.79\sqrt[3]{A_1 A_2} \tag{18}$$

Case IVe. When the Walls Are Not of Uniform Thickness.—Should one encounter a furnace, the various walls of which are not of uniform thickness, the total heat loss should be obtained by adding together the heat loss for each individual wall; *i.e.*, A_m should be calculated for each wall and then substituted separately in Eq. 7. The edge corrections will thus be figured twice and the corner corrections three times. Hence, for this case, Eq. 15 should read

$$A_m = A_1 + 0.271x\Sigma y + 0.4x^2 \tag{19}$$

and Eq. 16 should read

$$A_m = A_1 + 0.233x^2\Sigma y + 0.12x^2 \tag{20}$$

The total heat loss for the furnace is, therefore, Σq, *i.e.*, the sum of the heat losses from the individual walls.

Steady Flow from an Insulated Heat Source.—One is sometimes interested in the exchange of heat (or electricity) by conduction between a heat source and its surroundings of much smaller conductivity k. Examples include a pipe line buried in the ground and submerged heating elements, sometimes used in horticulture. A number of such cases have been solved mathematically by Ruden-

TABLE II.—RESISTANCE FACTORS R BETWEEN VARIOUS HEAT SOURCES AND
A SEMI-INFINITE BODY OF LOW THERMAL CONDUCTIVITY k

Description	Equation for $R = (t_1 - t_\infty)/q$
Sphere of diameter D with center at distance z below surface	$R = \dfrac{1}{2\pi Dk}\left(1 + \dfrac{D}{4z}\right)$
Horizontal cylinder of length L and diameter D with axis at distance z below surface	$R = \dfrac{1}{2\pi Lk}\ln_e \dfrac{2L}{D}\left(1 + \dfrac{\ln_e \dfrac{L}{2z}}{\ln_e \dfrac{2L}{D}}\right)$ $D \ll z; \quad z \ll L$
Horizontal thin circular disk of diameter D, well below surface	$R = \dfrac{1}{4Dk}$
Horizontal torus of mean diameter D_m and thickness y, with axis at distance z below surface	$R = \dfrac{1}{2\pi^2 D_m k}\ln_e \dfrac{8D_m}{y}\left(1 + \dfrac{\ln_e \dfrac{2D_m}{z}}{\ln_e \dfrac{8D_m}{y}}\right)$ $y \ll z; \quad z \ll D_m$
Thin horizontal rectangle with larger and smaller sides D_1 and D_2, well below surface	$R = \dfrac{1}{2\pi D_1 k}\ln_e \dfrac{4D_1}{D_2}$
Vertical circular wire of length L and Diameter D, with one end at surface	$R = \dfrac{1}{2\pi Lk}\ln_e \dfrac{4L}{D}; D \ll L$

berg,[613a] and the results may be reported in terms of a resistance factor R in the equation $q = (t_1 - t_\infty)/R$, wherein q is the rate of heat exchange by conduction between the source at t_1 and the surroundings at t_∞ measured at a large distance from the source. Values of R are given in Table II in terms of the pertinent dimensions describing the body and its location in the medium, which is treated as semi-infinite in size, and hence t_∞ is constant. Clearly the equation and values of R apply for flow in either direction, *i.e.*, t_1 may be larger or smaller than t_∞.

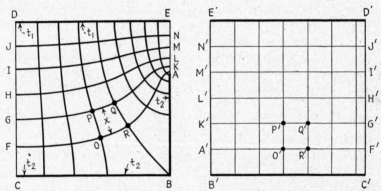

FIG. 3.—Diagram for Awbery and Schofield[21] problem in steady two-dimensional heat conduction.

Graphical Solution for Complex Cases.—A number of writers* give graphical methods that can be employed to solve complex problems in steady conduction, such as a slab of conductivity k_A with two isothermal faces at t_1 and t_2, with ribs of conductivity k_B imbedded at right angles to the faces[21]; a slab of conductivity k_A with isothermal faces at t_1 and t_2, containing a cylindrical heat source[646] at t_3. The method depends on the fact that the flow lines must cross isotherms at right angles.

Two-dimensional Heat Flow.—The left-hand part of Fig. 3 shows the application of the method to an insulator of thickness CD bounded on the surface DE by an isothermal metal plate at temperature t_1 and on the other by a colder isothermal metal plate CB at t_2; at intervals of $2CB$ the lower part of the insulator is penetrated by metal ribs BA, also at t_2. There is no heat flow in the longitudinal direction L, measured at right angles to the plane of Fig. 3.

* Lehman,[429] Wedmore,[751] Awbery and Schofield,[21] Schofield,[646] and Stodola.[701]

In applying the method, one may arbitrarily subdivide the integral $\int_1^2 k\,dt$ into any convenient number N of *equal* parts, $k\,\Delta t_x$.* The heat may be visualized as flowing in series through a narrow lane starting at the isotherm DE, representing t_1 and ending somewhere along the isotherm ABC, representing t_2. Heat flows at the steady rate q_L through each such lane. For any small part, such as $OPQR$, of any lane, the heat is flowing at right angles to the area Ly, where L is the length of the body, and y is the mean width of the quadrilateral $OPQR$, *i.e.*, y equals $(PQ + OR)/2$. The conduction equation is $q_L = kA_m\,\Delta t_x/x = k(Ly)(\Delta t_x)/x$, and since $k\,\Delta t_x$ from one isotherm to the next is the same, and q_L and L are also constant throughout the lane, the equation shows that the ratio y/x must be constant throughout the lane although both y and x may vary. In other words, where the isotherms are crowded close together, as in the vicinity of AE, x and consequently y must be small. If the construction used in drawing each lane is such that y equals x, as is the case in Fig. 3, the heat flow per lane is $kL(t_1 - t_2)/N$, and the total flow carried by the total number of lanes, N_L, is $N_L kL(t_1 - t_2)/N$. Therefore, one may fix N and, by trial, so locate the isotherms and flow lines that they intersect at right angles to form quadrilaterals such that y is substantially equal to x, *i.e.*, the ratio of the sums of opposite sides closely approaches unity. Such quadrilaterals are called *curvilinear squares.*†

Inspection of Fig. 3 shows that 9 lanes were obtained. Thus if $t_1 - t_2$ is 120°F, k_{12} is 0.35,‡ and L is 10, q equals $(9)(0.35)(10)(120)/6 = 630$ Btu/hr.§

If the rib had been omitted, as shown in the right-hand part of Fig. 3, and N is again taken as 6, since the heat flow is now uniform, $O'P'Q'R'$ must be square, and one finds that N_L is 6.3 instead of 9. Hence the use of the rib increased the heat flow by 43 per cent.

Instead of arbitrarily fixing the number of equal parts into which the $k_{12}(t_1 - t_2)$ is divided, in some cases it may be more convenient

---

* If k is independent of t, each Δt_x equals $(t_1 - t_2)/N$, and where k varies with t, each $k\,\Delta t_x$ product equals $\dfrac{1}{N}\displaystyle\int_1^2 k\,dt$.

† A curvilinear square is a figure that, upon further subdivision by isothermals and normal flow lines, would yield a very large number of true squares and a relatively small number of other-sided figures.

‡ k_{12} represents the mean value of k, *i.e.*, $k_m = \dfrac{1}{(t_1 - t_2)}\displaystyle\int_1^2 k\,dt$.

§ Clearly, more accurate results would be obtained by using more isotherms and flow lanes, so that the quadrilaterals would more closely approach squares.

to fix the number of lanes. In either event, the isothermals and flow curves must intersect at right angles to form curvilinear squares and q equals $N_L k_{12} L(t_1 - t_2)/N$.

Since the diagram is purely geometrical and is valid regardless of how k varies with t, it applies equally well when the direction of heat flow is reversed by interchanging the positions of the source and sink. Furthermore, if now the surfaces ABC and DE are made adiabatic and the source and sink are located at AE and CD (or at CD and AE), the diagram again applies, giving nine isotherms and six lanes of equal flow; hence if $t_1 - t_2$ is 120, k_{12} is 0.35[*] and L is 10, $q = 6(0.35)(10)(120)/(9) = 280$ Btu/hr.

Since the form of the law for the flow of electricity is the same as that for heat, one may deal with electricity rather than heat in making experimental measurements with scale models containing an electrolyte in a solution of gelatin. The results obtained graphically agree well with those obtained experimentally.[423,519]

Three-dimensional Heat Flow.—Complex cases may be handled by an extension of the graphical method described above; the geometrical construction must now satisfy the equation

$$dq = -k \, dy \, dL \, \frac{dt}{dx}$$

instead of $-ky \, dL \, dt/dx$. Empirical solutions for certain shapes are available.

THERMAL CONDUCTION IN FLUIDS

The law for the conduction of heat is the same for liquids and gases as for solids, the values of k being, however, very small. At room temperature, for example, k, expressed as Btu/(hr)(sq ft) (deg F/ft) is 0.34 for stationary water, and 0.015 for stationary air, as compared with 220 for copper and 0.7 for firebrick. In both liquids and gases, it is difficult, and under engineering conditions impossible, to eliminate the effect of convection, *i.e.*, the transfer of heat by the movement of the fluid itself, and hence heat transfer in liquids and gases by conduction goes hand in hand with that by convection. This joint effect will be discussed in later chapters.

Thermal Conductivity of Liquids.—In attempting to measure the thermal conductivity of various liquids, many of the early

---

[*] For some substances, such as wood, k along the grain is not equal to that across the grain.

experimenters used such thick layers of liquid and large temperature differences that convection currents were set up, and hence conduction was not the sole process by which heat was transferred. Therefore, reliable data on the thermal conductivities of liquids are rare, accurate data on the temperature coefficient of thermal conductivity being especially scarce. By employing thin layers and small temperature differences, it is inconceivable that convection currents could form. Bridgman[90]* employed a liquid layer $\frac{1}{64}$ in. in thickness and a temperature difference of about 1°F, and obtained reliable values. For his experiments with water at 167°F, Bridgman estimated that the maximum amount of heat radiated through the water would be less than 0.6 per cent of the heat transferred through the water by conduction. Bates[50] has developed an improved guard-ring apparatus, in which large temperature differences are used, for determining k for thick layers of liquids; the heat is supplied at the top and removed at the bottom.

The thermal conductivities of practically all nonmetallic liquids† lie between 0.050 and 0.150 Btu/(hr)(sq ft)(deg F/ft), although the value for water at 68°F is 0.344. The thermal conductivities of most liquids decrease with increased temperature, although water and certain aqueous solutions are exceptions, as shown on page 389. The effect of pressure on the thermal conductivities of liquids has been studied by Bridgman, who found that an increase from 1 to 2000 atm increased the thermal conductivities of 28 liquids from 11.1 to 15.3 per cent, and that at 12,000 atm the conductivities were approximately doubled. Values of k are given on page 389.

In 1923, Bridgman[90] proposed the theoretical dimensionless equation for liquids

$$k = 2R_G V_a/z_c^2 \tag{21}$$

k being the thermal conductivity, R_G gas constant in heat units, V_a the acoustic velocity in the liquid, and z_c the mean distance of separation of centers of molecules, if there is assumed an arrangement cubical on the average and if z_c in centimeters is calculated by the equation $z_c = (M'/\rho)^{1/3}$, wherein M' represents the weight in grams of one molecule. The values of k calculated by means of Eq. 21 are shown to approximate Bridgman's experimental data for 11 liquids, the deviation being from −13 to +38 per cent. The

* J. F. D. Smith[675,677] later used the same apparatus.

† In the region of absolute zero, the apparent k of liquid helium II is reported[163a] to exceed that of any other substance.

velocity of sound in the liquids was not measured but calculated from the known compressibility. The agreement is remarkable in view of the fact that the equation involves no empirical constant.

The 1936 empirical equation of Smith, based on data for water, 6 paraffin alcohols, 13 pure hydrocarbons, 6 petroleum fractions, and 20 miscellaneous liquids, is recommended for estimating the thermal conductivities of nonmetallic liquids at 86°F and 1 atm pressure, in those cases in which measured values are not available:

$$k = 0.00266 + 1.56(c - 0.45)^3 + 0.3(\rho'/M)^{1/3} + 0.0242(\mu'/\rho')^{1/6} \tag{22}$$

In this equation, k is in Btu/(hr)(sq ft)(deg F/ft); c is the specific heat; ρ' is the specific gravity relative to water; M the molecular weight; μ' the viscosity in centipoises. For petroleum products at 86°F, Smith recommends k be taken as 0.079, instead of using Eq. 22 or that of Cragoe.[159]

The form of equation proposed by Barratt and Nettleton[47] for estimating data for the thermal conductivity of a mixture of liquids was checked by the most recent data of Bates *et al.*,[50] who found excellent agreement with experimental values for ethanol-water, methanol-water, and glycerol-water mixtures. It was necessary, however, to use new values[50] of the constant b rather than those previously given.[47] The average error was less than 1 per cent.

$$k \sinh (100b_1) = k_1 \sinh (x_{w1}b_1) + k_2 \sinh (x_{w2}b_1) \tag{23}$$

where b_1 is a constant depending on components considered; k, k_1, and k_2 are the thermal conductivities of the mixture and of the pure components, respectively; x_{w1} and x_{w2} are the concentrations in weight per cent. (Hyperbolic sines must be used.)

As an approximation for both mixtures of miscible liquids and for aqueous solutions, k may be taken as a linear function of the fraction of solute by weight.

Thermal Conductivity of Gases.—The relation of the thermal conductivity to the viscosity of a gas is of particular theoretical interest in that the data support to a remarkable degree the theoretical relation deduced from the kinetic theory.[350] Maxwell[474] early derived the dimensionless equation

$$k = a_1\mu c_v \tag{24}$$

where μ is the absolute viscosity of the gas, c_v is the specific heat at constant volume, and a_1 is a constant, consistent units being employed. Maxwell predicted a value of 2.5 for a_1, which has been found to be nearly correct for monatomic gases. However, for diatomic gases, a_1 is about 1.90 and for triatomic gases, about 1.72. Eucken[212] has suggested the empirical relation

$$a_1 = 0.25(9\kappa - 5) \tag{24a}$$

where κ is the ratio of the specific heat at constant pressure to that at constant volume. Elimination of a_1 from Eqs. 24 and 24a gives the recommended relation for estimating a dimensionless group $c_p\mu/k$ of importance in convection:

$$\frac{c_p\mu}{k} = \frac{4}{9 - \dfrac{5}{\kappa}} \tag{24b}$$

Values of the term $c_p\mu/k$ for gases at atmospheric pressure are shown on page 415. Although data are lacking, in practice the term $c_p\mu/k$ is assumed independent of pressure (page 243).

Apparently most of the attempts to measure experimentally the thermal conductivities of gases and vapors failed to eliminate heat transmission by convection and radiation, especially the former. In other words, improvements in apparatus for measuring thermal conductivity of gases have not kept pace with those made in the apparatus for determining the thermal conductivities of liquids. However, the values of k for gases are probably in error not more than 10 to 20 per cent. **Tables of thermal conductivities of gases and vapors are given in the Appendix,** pages 391 to 392.

The variations, with temperature, of k for gases follows, in general, the Sutherland type of equation

$$k = k_{492}\left(\frac{492 + C_s}{T + C_s}\right)\left(\frac{T}{492}\right)^{3/2} \tag{25}$$

where T is the temperature in degrees Fahrenheit absolute, and C_s is an empirical constant, called the *Sutherland constant*. Incidentally, an equation of the same form is used for viscosity μ of gases, and for a given gas the same value of C_s applies in calculating both k and μ. The effects of pressure and temperature on μ are given on page 410.

According to the kinetic theory of gases, if the mean free path of the gas molecule is small compared with the thickness of the conducting layer, the thermal conductivity of a gas should be independent of pressure. Few experimental data are available as to the effect on k of pressures materially above normal atmospheric pressure, but at pressures sufficiently low an effect is predicted from kinetic theory.*

As pointed out previously, heat transfer between a gas and solid involves not only conduction but also convection and radiation. Practical problems in heat transfer between gas and solid can, therefore, be solved not merely by reference to tables of thermal conductivities of gases. These practical problems are treated in later chapters.

CONDUCTION THROUGH SEVERAL BODIES IN SERIES: RESISTANCE CONCEPT

The steady flow of heat through each of several bodies in series is of more practical interest than heat flow through a single solid.

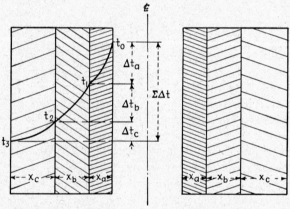

FIG. 4.—Temperature distribution in walls of three concentric cylinders.

With reference to Fig. 4, heat is being conducted at a steady rate through a wall composed of three different solids, a, b, and c. By applying Eq. 7 separately to each solid, it will now be shown that, for the steady state, the rate of heat flow may be calculated either by dividing the temperature drop through any individual resistance by the resistance of the body, $R = x/k_m A_m$, or by dividing the total temperature drop by the sum of the individual

* Kundt and Warburg[416] and Smoluchowski.[678] For effects of reduced pressures on the apparent values of k. see P. Lasareff,[424] W. Mandell and J. West,[467] and E. Schneider.[645]

resistances. For the steady conduction of heat through a single homogeneous body, Eq. 7 may be written as follows:

$$q = \frac{\Delta t}{x/(k_m)(A_m)} = \frac{\Delta t}{R} \tag{26}$$

Applying Eq. 26 in turn to each solid,

$$q = \frac{t_0 - t_1}{R_a} = \frac{t_1 - t_2}{R_b} = \frac{t_2 - t_3}{R_c} \tag{26a}$$

wherein R_a, R_b, and R_c are the **individual** resistances of the three solids, respectively. By adding the expressions $qR_a = t_0 - t_1$, and $qR_b = t_1 - t_2$, one obtains $q(R_a + R_b) = t_0 - t_2$. Hence

$$q = \frac{t_0 - t_2}{R_a + R_b} = \frac{t_0 - t_3}{R_a + R_b + R_c} \tag{26b}$$

which may be written

$$q = \frac{\Sigma(\Delta t)}{R_T} = \frac{(\Delta t)_a + (\Delta t)_b + (\Delta t)_c}{R_a + R_b + R_c} \tag{26c}$$

wherein R_T is the **total** series resistance, *i.e.*, the sum of the individual resistances. Or

$$q = \frac{\Sigma(\Delta t)}{\dfrac{x_a}{k_a A_a} + \dfrac{x_b}{k_b A_b} + \dfrac{x_c}{k_c A_c}} \tag{26d}$$

It should be noted that k_a, k_b, and k_c represent the **mean** thermal conductivities of a, b, and c; and A_a, A_b, and A_c the mean areas taken at right angles to the direction of heat flow. Thus, if the walls were concentric cylinders, each average area should be the logarithmic mean of the outer and inner surfaces of that hollow cylinder (page 12).

Illustration 2.—A standard 2-in. steel pipe (page 416) carrying superheated steam is insulated with 1.25 in. of a molded high-temperature covering made of diatomaceous earth and asbestos ($k = 0.058$). This covering is insulated with 2.5 in. of laminated asbestos felt ($k = 0.042$). In a test, the temperature of the surroundings was 86°F, the average temperature of the steam inside the pipe was 900°F and the temperature of the outer surface of the lagging was 122°F.

    a. Calculate the heat loss, expressed as Btu/(hr)(ft of length of pipe).

    b. Calculate the temperature at the interface between the two layers of insulation.

c. Calculate the surface coefficient of heat loss h, expressed as Btu/(hr) (sq ft of outside lagging surface)(deg F difference from surface to room).

Solution.—The following diameters are needed: i.d. of pipe, 2.07 in.; o.d. of pipe, 2.37 in.; mean diameter of pipe, 2.22 in.; o.d. of first covering, 4.87 in.; logarithmic mean diameter, 3.48 in.; o.d. of second covering, 9.87 in.; mean diameter 7.07 in. The heat loss per foot is calculated from Eq. 26*d*, page 23, using k of 23.5 for wrought iron, page 380, and a wall thickness of 0.154 in.

$$q = \frac{900 - 122}{\dfrac{0.154/12}{(23.5)(2.22\pi/12)} + \dfrac{1.25/12}{(0.058)(3.48\pi/12)} + \dfrac{2.5/12}{0.042(7.07\pi/12)}}$$

$$= \frac{778}{0.00094 + 1.97 + 2.68} = \frac{778}{4.65} = 167 \text{ Btu/(hr)(ft)}$$

b. Since temperature drop is proportional to resistance, $900 - t_i = 778$ $(1.97/4.65) = 330$; whence t_i equals 570°F.

c. $h = \dfrac{q}{A_0(\Delta t)} = \dfrac{167}{\dfrac{9.87\pi(1)(122 - 86)}{12}} = 1.8 \text{ Btu/(hr)(sq ft)(deg F)}$

Contact Resistance.—In the preceding example, in which two solids were in contact, no allowance was made for a temperature drop at the boundary, which presupposes perfect contact. However, this requires the absence of gases or vacant spaces caused by those blowholes, bubbles, rough surfaces, etc., which are very likely to be present where two solids are brought together. Even traces of poorly conducting material between metals, such as oxide films on the surface, will cause abrupt drops in the temperature.[46,711] It is usually impossible to estimate accurately the thickness of such films, but their effect may be serious.

Instead of attempting to determine separately the conductivities of brick and mortar, it is often customary to measure the average conductivity of a brick-and-mortar wall. Van Dusen and Finck[731] report experimentally determined over-all thermal resistances of a number of walls and also individual resistances of the various components. In general, fairly satisfactory agreement was found between the predicted values and observed results. Over-all resistances for large walls in service may be determined by the use of the *heat meter*,[509] which measures the temperature drop through the known resistance of the meter, simultaneously measuring the temperature gradient through the wall itself. In this way the thermal conductivity of the whole wall, or of any layer, may be measured, even though the use of the meter reduces the heat flow compared with that from the bare wall. Precautions should be taken to secure data under steady conditions.

Conductance.—Where heat is transferred by more than one mechanism through a structure having a mean cross-sectional area A_m, the conductance is defined as the gross rate of heat transfer Σq divided by the temperature drop Δt between its faces:

$$C = \Sigma q / \Delta t \tag{27}$$

The unit conductance C', or the conductance of a unit area, is defined by the equation

$$C' = \Sigma q / A \, \Delta t \tag{27a}$$

and equals C/A.* Where heat flows through a structure solely by conduction, $q = k_m A_m (\Delta t)/x$, the conductance would reduce to $k_m A_m / x$, and the resistance $x/k_m A_m$ would be equal to the reciprocal of the conductance. For cases in which heat is flowing through a hollow enclosure by conduction through one wall, thence by convection and radiation acting in parallel across the gas space to the other wall, and out by conduction, the concept of unit conductance is preferred (Eq. 27a), although some writers report the results as apparent conductivities, based on Eq. 7. The conductance of some structures is independent of their thickness, and in such cases the apparent conductivity would be a function of thickness.

Other Applications of the Basic Conduction Equation.—The basic conduction equation of Fourier (Eq. 1, page 7) is the starting point in the theoretical treatment of numerous problems in heat transfer other than steady-state conduction in solids. Among these problems are unsteady-state heat conduction in solids (page 29); heat transfer to fluids in streamline flow in pipes (page 187) and in wetted-wall heaters (page 205); heat transfer to fluids moving by free convection (page 237). Additional applications of Eq. 1 to problems in steady flow are conduction along fins (page 232) and heat transfer from condensing vapors (page 259).

Problems

1. The plane wall of a furnace consists of two layers: 4.5 in. of firebrick ($k = 1.0$) and 9.0 in. of red brick ($k = 0.4$). In steady operation, the flame side of the firebrick was at 1305°F, and the outside of the red brick was at 265°F.

To reduce heat loss, the outside surface of the red brick was covered with a 1.5-in. layer of magnesia ($k = 0.049$); when steady conditions had been attained, the temperature of the outer surface of the magnesia was 190°F and the tem-

* Although C' has the same dimensions as the coefficient h of heat transfer (p. 3), the temperature difference $(t_s - t)$ used in defining h is that between the surface and the body of fluid flowing past the boundary, whereas the Δt employed in the definition of C' is that across the two faces of the structure.

perature of the flame side of the firebrick was 1355°F.   Assume all conductivities independent of temperature.

    a. Calculate the heat flux, Btu/(hr)(sq ft) before and after insulating.

    b. For the insulated wall, calculate the temperatures at the junction of the
        firebrick and the red brick and at the junction of the red brick and
        magnesia.

    2. A bare pipe line carrying steam under pressure loses 1 million Btu/hr.
If insulated, it would lose 170,000 Btu/hr.

    Calculate the time required for the actual savings to equal the initial cost
of the insulation.

    Data and Notes.—The first cost of the insulation, installed, will be $600 and
the line will be used 8400 hr per year.   With the bare pipe line, the fuel costs
$20 per hour of operation and fixed charges on the power house and pipe line
amount to $20 per hour of operation.   After passing through the bare line, the
steam delivered per hour contains 100 million Btu of latent heat, all of which is
needed to meet the requirements of the plant.

    3. A standard 1-in. horizontal steel pipe (page 416) carrying steam under
pressure is insulated with a 2-in. layer of magnesia pipe covering (page 387).
The average temperatures on the inner and outer surfaces of the insulation are
350 and 125°F, respectively.

    a. Estimate the Btu per hour conducted through the covering per 100 ft of
        pipe.

    b. What per cent error results if the arithmetic mean area instead of the
        logarithmic mean area is used?

    4. A vertical flat wall of the combustion chamber of a furnace is made up of
an inner layer of 9 in. of magnesite brick (density = 158 lb/cu ft., k = 2.2 at
400°F, k = 1.1 at 2200°F) followed by an outer layer of 4.5 in. of kaolin insulating brick (density of 27 lb/cu ft, k = 0.15 at 932°F, k = 0.26 at 2100°F).
The average surface temperatures of the inner face of the magnesite brick wall
and the outer face of the kaolin brick wall are 2200 and 330°F, respectively.

    If the thermal conductivities of magnesite and kaolin are assumed to be
linear functions of the temperature, what is the heat flux through the furnace
wall, expressed in Btu/(hr)(sq ft)?

    5. Referring to Problem 4, what would be the heat flux if the kaolin layer
were on the furnace side of the wall and the magnesite layer on the outside, the
inside and outside face temperatures again being 2200°F and 330°F, respectively?

    6. Sulphuric acid is stored in a rectangular tank constructed of lead ⅛-in.
thick, outside of which are placed silica bricks 2½ in. thick, which, in turn, are
supported by an outer shell of steel ¼ in. thick.   With the inside surface of
lead at 190°F and the room at 80°F, the temperature of the outside of the steel
shell is 140°F.   Because of the danger of burns to workmen, the management
of the plant considers 140°F to be the maximum allowable outside temperature
of the steel.

    If the temperature of the inside surface of the lead is raised to 280°F, what
is the corresponding minimum thickness of silica brick that could be used for a
room temperature of 80°F?   Assume thermal conductivities independent of
temperature.

CHAPTER II

HEATING AND COOLING OF SOLIDS

Introduction.—In the transfer of heat by conduction, the case of the *steady* state, where the temperature at a given point is independent of time, has been treated in Chap. I. The heat conduction is said to be in the *unsteady* state when the temperature at a given point varies with time. Unsteady-state conduction is involved in the quenching of billets, the annealing of solids, the manufacture of

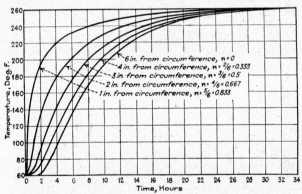

Fig. 5*.—Time-temperature relations for unsteady-state heating of round timbers in steam bath. (*Based on data of MacLean.*[463])

glass, the burning of bricks, the steaming of wood, and the vulcanization of rubber. Where chemical reactions occur during the heating period, as in the vulcanization of rubber, heat transfer plays a particularly important role, because the rate of the reaction increases rapidly with small increases in temperature. As heat flows into the rubber, a temperature gradient is established from the heated surface to the interior, bringing about vulcanization or curing to varying degrees at successive cross sections. As a result, if the center is properly cured, the surface will be overcured. One remedy consists in a gradual "stepping up" of the temperature of the surroundings. Figure 5 shows diagrammatically the types of curves obtained upon exposing a homogeneous solid to surroundings at a uniform

* Courtesy of the American Wood Preservers' Association.

base temperature t_b.   As the heating is continued, the temperature at a given point asymptotically approaches the temperature of the heating medium.   Whereas points near the surface quickly approach the temperature of the surroundings, those in the interior lag far behind.   Figure 6 shows the same data with $Y = (t' - t)/(t' - t_b)$ plotted to a logarithmic scale $vs.$ time to a uniform scale.

The following section outlines the mathematics involved in calculating the relations between temperature and time for various points or sections of solids of several shapes and includes graphical solutions of the important equations.   The relation involves the

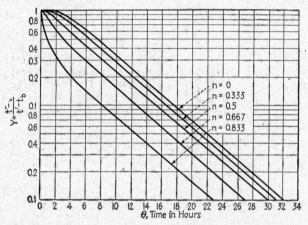

FIG. 6.—Data of Fig. 5, replotted as Y $vs.$ θ, on semilogarithmic paper.

thermal conductivity, density, and specific heat of the body, its shape and size, and the external conditions, including the temperature of the surroundings and the coefficient of heat transfer between surroundings and the surface.

The following section on Theory (pages 28 to 30) outlines the procedure by which the integrated relations are obtained but may be omitted by readers interested only in applications of the theory.

Theory.—As introduction, a simple limiting case of unsteady-heat conduction is discussed.   Consider a thin slab of metal of volume V, total surface area A, and thickness $2r_m$, at temperature t, in contact with warmer air at uniform temperature t'.   At any time θ from the start of the heating operation, the quantity of heat dQ transferred in the short time $d\theta$ depends upon the surface area of the slab, the difference in temperature between the air and the surface of the metal, and a factor h, called the *coefficient* of heat transfer from the surroundings to the surface,

$$dQ/d\theta = hA(t' - t_s). \tag{1}$$

Under such conditions the numerical value of h will be relatively small, and for a reasonable value of the temperature difference $t' - t_s$ the corresponding rate of heat transfer per unit area $dQ/A\ d\theta$ will be small. Consequently, because of the high value of the thermal conductivity k of the metal and its small thickness, the metal temperature t will be substantially uniform and equal to t_s. Then, by a heat balance on the slab, having density ρ and specific heat c_p,

$$dQ = hA(t' - t)\ d\theta = V\rho c_p\ dt \qquad (2)$$

Assuming $hA/V\rho c_p$ constant, integration from $t = t_b$ to $t = t$ and $\theta = 0$ to $\theta = \theta$ gives

$$\ln_e\left(\frac{t' - t_b}{t' - t}\right) = \frac{hA\theta}{V\rho c_p} \qquad (3)*$$

where $\ln_e$ represents a Napierian logarithm equal to $2.3 \log_{10}$. The same result could be obtained by using a *logarithmic*-mean value of the temperature difference $t' - t$ in the expression

$$\frac{Q}{\theta} = hA(t' - t)_m = \frac{V\rho c_p(t - t_b)}{\theta} \qquad (4)$$

The general case involving an appreciable temperature gradient through the solid is solved by application of an appropriate form of the conduction equation.

Derivation of Differential Equation for Unsteady-state Conduction.— The general differential equation for unsteady-state conduction of heat is obtained from the familiar basic Fourier equation for the conduction of heat and a heat balance. Consider an element of volume with area $dy\ dz$ and thickness dx. The heat entering along the x-axis is $-k_x(dy\ dz)(\partial t/\partial x)(d\theta)$, and that leaving is

$$(dy\ dz)\left[k_x\frac{\partial t}{\partial x} + \frac{\partial}{\partial x}\left(k_x\frac{\partial t}{\partial x}\right)dx\right]d\theta$$

The difference between that entering and leaving along all three axes is equated to that stored in the element

$$dx\ dy\ dz\left[\frac{\partial}{\partial x}\left(k_x\frac{\partial t}{\partial x}\right) + \frac{\partial}{\partial y}\left(k_y\frac{\partial t}{\partial y}\right) + \frac{\partial}{\partial z}\left(k_z\frac{\partial t}{\partial z}\right)\right]d\theta$$
$$= (dx\ dy\ dz)\left(\rho c_p\frac{\partial t}{\partial\theta}\right)d\theta, \qquad (5)$$

giving the general differential equation for unsteady-state heat conduction, expressed in rectangular coordinates:

$$\frac{1}{\rho c_p}\left[\frac{\partial}{\partial x}\left(k_x\frac{\partial t}{\partial x}\right) + \frac{\partial}{\partial y}\left(k_y\frac{\partial t}{\partial y}\right) + \frac{\partial}{\partial z}\left(k_z\frac{\partial t}{\partial z}\right)\right] = \frac{\partial t}{\partial\theta}. \qquad (5a)$$

Upon neglecting variations of k with temperature, and assuming the substance

* If h is constant, a plot[138] of $\ln_e(t' - t)$ vs. θ would give a straight line having a negative slope equal to $hA/V\rho c_p$.

to be homogeneous and isotropic, k is taken outside the parenthesis of Eq. 5, giving the term $k/\rho c_p$, called the *thermal diffusivity*:

$$\alpha = k/\rho c_p.$$

The desired temperature-time-position relations for the heating or cooling of various shapes are obtained by integration of Eq. 5, substituting the necessary boundary conditions for the case in question. For example, in the case of the infinite slab, *i.e.*, one having a very large ratio of surface to thickness, the heat flow is unidirectional, and Eq. 5 reduces to

$$\frac{k}{\rho c_p}\left(\frac{\partial^2 t}{\partial x^2}\right) = \frac{\partial t}{\partial \theta} \tag{5b}$$

For the special case of a slab having a thickness $2r_m$ and a negligible surface resistance, corresponding to an infinite value of the surface coefficient h, the surface temperature changes to the temperature of the surroundings immediately at zero time. The boundary conditions are then $t = t'$ at $x = 0$ and at $x = 2r_m$; $t = t_b$ at $\theta = 0$, and $t = t'$ at $\theta = \infty$. A solution is given by the rapidly converging infinite series

$$\frac{t' - t}{t' - t_b} = \frac{4}{\pi}\left(e^{-a_1 X}\sin\frac{\pi x}{2r_m} + \frac{1}{3}e^{-9a_1 X}\sin\frac{3\pi x}{2r_m} + \frac{1}{5}e^{-25a_1 X}\sin\frac{5\pi x}{2r_m} + \cdots\right) \tag{6}$$

where a_1 equals $(\pi/2)^2$, and X represents the dimensionless ratio $\alpha\theta/r_m^2$. The total heat absorbed by the slab up to any time θ is obtained by evaluating the integral of $(t' - t_b)\rho c A\, dx$, from 0 to $2r_m$, giving

$$\frac{Q}{2r_m A\rho c(t' - t_b)} = 1 - \frac{8}{\pi^2}\left(e^{-a_1 X} + \frac{1}{9}e^{-9a_1 X} + \frac{1}{25}e^{-25a_1 X} + \cdots\right) \tag{7}$$

For a slab having a thickness $2r_m$ and a *finite* surface resistance, corresponding to a definite and constant value of h, the boundary conditions become

$$k\left(\frac{\partial t}{\partial x}\right)_{x=0} = h(t_s - t'); \qquad k\left(\frac{\partial t}{\partial x}\right)_{x=2r_m} = -h(t_s - t')$$

$t = t_b$ at $\theta = 0$; $t = t'$ at $\theta = \infty$. Integration of Eq. 5b for this case leads to a relation between t, θ, x, and h. Solutions for solids of various shapes have long been available in the literature,* but computations directly from the equations are very tedious because of the large number of terms.

APPLICATIONS

A number of writers† have plotted the theoretical relations for a number of shapes, in terms of the dimensionless ratios involved.

The significance of all terms is given in Table I, wherein any consistent units may be employed. For illustration, the symbols

---

* For example, see Fourier,[231] Carslaw,[109] Ingersoll and Zobel,[334] Gurney,[275] Byerly,[102] Newman,[506] Schack,[628] and Fischer.[222]

† Williamson and Adams,[768] Gurney and Lurie,[276] Grober,[272] Schack,[627] Fishenden and Saunders,[224] and Goldschmidt and Partridge.[253]

are defined in the system involving feet, pounds, hours, degrees Fahrenheit, and Btu.

TABLE I.—NOMENCLATURE FOR UNSTEADY-STATE CONDUCTION

A	Surface of body exposed to heat, square feet.
a_1	Constant, equal to $(\pi/2)^2$.
c_p	Specific heat of solid, Btu/(lb)(deg F).
d	Prefix, indicating derivative.
h	Coefficient of heat transfer between surroundings at t' and surface at t_s, Btu/(hr)(sq ft)(deg F).
k	Thermal conductivity of solid, Btu/(hr)(sq ft)(deg F per ft).
L	Total thickness of slab, or $2r_m$, feet.
m	Resistance ratio $R_s/R_m = k/r_m h$, dimensionless. For Fig. 13, $m = k/hx$.
n	Position ratio r/r_m, dimensionless; not involved for the semi-infinite solid.
N	Number of imaginary slices, each ΔL ft thick, in a slab.
Q	Quantity of heat, Btu.
r	Radius, normal distance from midplane to point in body, feet.
r_m	Normal distance from midplane to surface, feet; for the brick-shaped solid, the midplane distances along the three coordinate axes are designated as x_m, y_m, and z_m, respectively.
R	Local thermal resistance of a unit area $= x/k$.
R_m	Midplane thermal resistance $= r_m/k$.
t'	Temperature of surroundings, degrees Fahrenheit.
t	Temperature at position n or x at time θ, degrees Fahrenheit.
t_a	Space-average temperature of slab at time θ, degrees Fahrenheit.
t_b	Original uniform (base) temperature of solid, degrees Fahrenheit.
t_c, t_h	Temperatures of cold and hot ambient fluids, degrees Fahrenheit.
t_s	Temperature at surface, *i.e.*, t for $n = 1$ or $x = 0$, degrees Fahrenheit.
t_0, t_1	Temperatures at sections 0 and 1, degrees Fahrenheit.
t_0', t_1'	Values of t_0 and t_1 after elapse of a finite increment $\Delta\theta$ in time, degrees Fahrenheit.
$t^\star$	Temperature of fictive layer, defined by Eq. 11, degrees Fahrenheit.
V	Volume of solid, cubic feet.
x	Normal distance from surface to point, feet.
X	"Relative time" ratio $= \alpha\theta/r_m^2$, Fourier number, dimensionless; for the semi-infinite solid $X = \alpha\theta/x^2$.
Y	Temperature-difference ratio $(t' - t)/(t' - t_b)$, dimensionless.
y	Coordinate at right angles to x- and z-axes, feet.
z	Coordinate at right angles to y- and z-axes, feet.
α	$k/\rho c_p =$ thermal diffusivity, square feet per hour $= 3.87$ times diffusivity in square centimeters per second.
∂	Prefix, indicating partial derivative.
ΔL	Thickness of a finite slice of a slab, $\Delta L = L/N$, feet.
$\Delta\theta$	Finite time increment, $\Delta\theta = (\Delta L)^2/2\alpha$, hours.
ρ	Density of solid, pounds per cubic foot.
θ	Time, from start of heating or cooling, hours.
∞	Symbol for infinity.

The predicted relations are plotted with Y as ordinates on a logarithmic scale *vs.* X as abscissas to a uniform scale, in Figs. 7 to 14, inclusive.* If the surface resistance were zero, the surface temperature would immediately reach that of the surroundings, giving the line marked $m = 0$, $n = 1$, coincident with the Y-axis. With infinite surface resistance, $m = \infty$, the surface temperature would remain at the original value, giving the curve marked $m = \infty$, identical with the X-axis. For intermediate values of m, a number

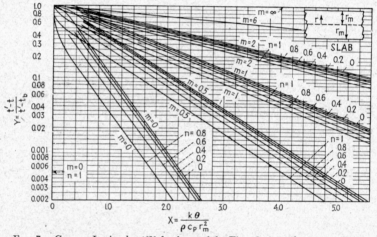

Fig. 7.—Gurney-Lurie chart[275] for large slab; Figs. 8, 9, and 10 give values of Y_m, Y_s, and Y_a for a larger range of values of m and X. For small values of X, such that the change in midplane temperature is negligible, greater accuracy is obtained by evaluating Y from Fig. 13. Results for the brick-shaped solid may be obtained from Fig. 7 by use of the Newman method, page 38.

of curves are shown in Figs. 7, 11, and 12, and for each particular m a family of six curves is drawn, corresponding to each of six different positions: $n = 0$, 0.2, 0.4, 0.6, 0.8, and 1.0. The curves show, for a given X, that the temperatures at the midplane, $n = 0$, and at the surface, $n = 1$, differ considerably when m is small and slightly when m is large. The curves given in Figs. 7 to 14 are based on the assumption of constancy in t', m, and $\alpha = k/\rho c_p$. Olsen and

* Figures 7 and 8 show values of Y at the midplane ($n = 0$), and Figs. 7 and 9 give Y at the surface ($n = 1$); where the values of Y, for a given m, n and X, differ, those of Figs. 8 and 9 are preferred, since the scale of the graphs in Figs. 8 and 9 are larger than in Fig. 7, and it is certain that the values plotted in Figs. 8 and 9 were obtained by employing an adequate number of terms in the series. Practically all of the charts and tables for the slab contain errors at small values of X, and it is believed that the values given in Figs. 8 and 9 are the best available.

Schultz[535] give interpolation tables of values of X ranging from 0 to 0.4, with increments of 0.001, and the corresponding values of Y for the cylinder and slab.

Consider two runs heating slabs of the same material, the thickness in the first case being twice that in the second, and $m = 0$. For a given Y and a given position ratio n, it is seen from Fig. 7 that

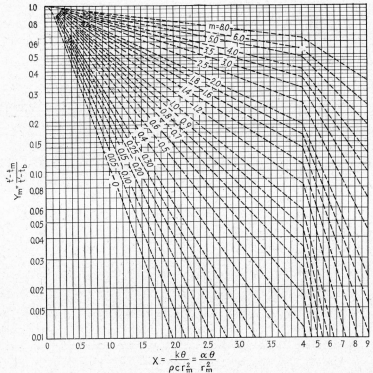

FIG. 8.—Hottel chart[319b] for large slab, for evaluation of midplane temperature.

the value of X would be the same in both cases. However, $X = \alpha\theta/r_m^2$, and since the diffusivity α is the same in both cases, it is clear that the actual heating time θ will be directly proportional to the *square* of the thickness. In other words, it would take four times as long to heat the thick slab as the thinner one. This is as would be expected, since the thicker slab contains twice as much material and the heat must penetrate twice as far. This brings out the disadvantage of heating thick layers and, by inference, the advantage of heating both faces compared to heating only one. If m

were finite, the foregoing relation would not hold unless m were the same in both cases, which would require that hr_m be constant.

The following examples illustrate the method of using the charts.

Illustration 1.—A flat slab of rubber, 0.5 in. thick, initially at 80°F, is to be placed between two electrically heated steel plates maintained at 287°F.

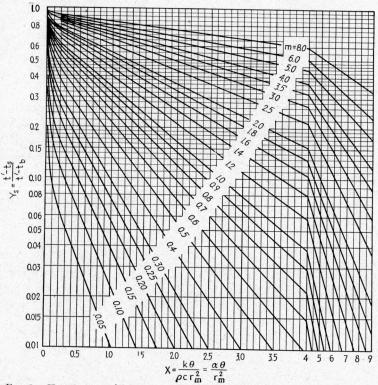

FIG. 9.—Hottel chart[319b] for large slab, for evaluation of surface temperature.

The heating is to be discontinued when the temperature at the center line of the rubber slab reaches 270°F.

a. Calculate the length of the heating period.

b. At the end of the run, what would be the temperature of the rubber in a plane 0.1 in. from the center line?

c. How long, from the start of the heating, is required for the temperature to reach 270°F at the plane specified in part (b)?

d. Repeat part (a) on the assumption that the rubber is heated from one face only, the other being perfectly insulated.

Data.—Using the units of Table I, page 31, for the rubber, $k = 0.092$ and $k/\rho c_p = 0.0029$. Assume a constant coefficient h from metal to rubber of 1000.

Solution.—a. All quantities will be expressed in the units mentioned above. Noting that the midplane distance r_m is $\frac{1}{48} = 0.0208$ ft, $m = k/hr_m = 0.092/(1000)(0.0208) = 0.00442$. At the end of θ hr of heating, $Y = (287 - 270)/(287 - 80) = 0.0821$. At the center line of the rubber slab, $n = r/r_m = 0$. Since $Y = 0.0821$ and $n = 0$ on Fig. 7, interpolation to $m = 0.0044$ gives $X = 1.13 = k\theta/\rho c_p r_m^2 = 0.0029\theta/(0.0208)^2$, whence $\theta = 0.169$ hr, the answer to part (*a*).

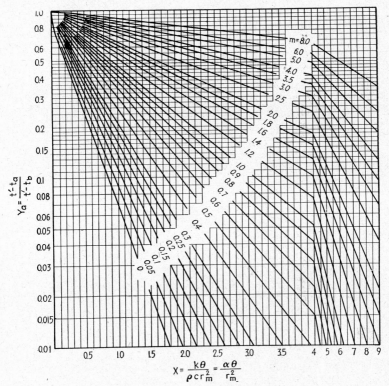

Fig. 10.—Hottel chart[319b] for large slab, for evaluation of space-mean temperature.

b. For the point 0.1 in. from the center line, $n = 0.1/0.25 = 0.4$, and, as before, $m = 0.0044$ and $X = 1.13$; from Fig. 7, Y is found to be 0.065. By definition, $Y = (287 - t)/(287 - 80)$, whence $t = 273.5°F$, the answer to part (*b*).

In part (*c*), where $Y = 0.0821$, $m = 0.0044$, and $n = 0.4$, Fig. 7 shows that $X = 1.03$. Since by definition, $X = 0.0029\theta/(0.0208)^2$, $\theta = 0.153$ hr.

d. When heated from one side only, $r_m = 0.5/12 = 0.0417$ ft, $m = k/hr_m = 0.092/(1000)(0.0417) = 0.00221$. At the center line of the slab, n is 0.5, and $Y = (287 - 270)/(287 - 80) = 0.0821$. From Fig. 7, X is $0.955 = 0.0029\theta/(0.0417)^2$, whence $\theta = 0.573$ hr when heated from one side only, as compared with 0.169 hr when heated from both sides.

In Figs. 7, 11, and 12, in order to facilitate extrapolation to values of m above 2, the approximate positions of curves for $m = 6$ are

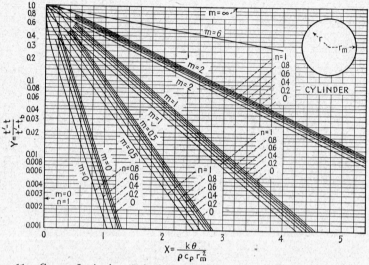

Fig. 11.—Gurney-Lurie chart[275] for long cylinder; values of Y_m for a short cylinder may be obtained from Figs. 7 and 11 by use of the Newman method, page 38.

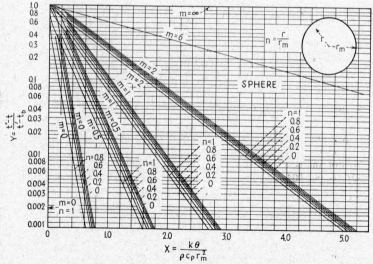

Fig. 12.—Gurney-Lurie chart[275] for sphere.

shown. The curves for $m = 6$ were based on the approximate Eq. 3, which was obtained on page 29 by ignoring the temperature

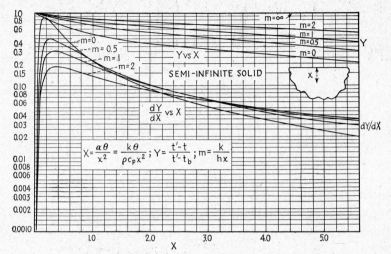

FIG. 13.—Gurney-Lurie chart[275] for semi-infinite solid; this chart may also be used for the slab for that portion of the operation in which the midplane temperature remains unchanged.

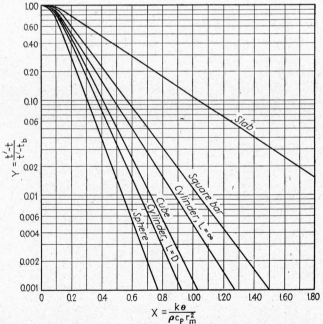

FIG. 14.—Williamson-Adams chart[768] for midplane or midpoint of various solid shapes, having negligible surface resistance ($m = 0$).

gradient in the solid. Substituting Y for the dimensionless ratio of temperature differences $(t' - t)/(t' - t_b)$, X for the dimensionless term $k\theta/\rho c_p r_m^2$, and m for the dimensionless term k/hr_m, Eq. 3 becomes

$$- \ln_e Y = \left(\frac{Ar_m}{V}\right)\left(\frac{1}{m}\right)(X) \tag{8}$$

For various shapes the dimensionless ratio Ar_m/V has the following values:

	Ar_m/V
Slab having a large ratio A/r_m	1
Cylinder having a large ratio A/L	2
Cube or sphere	3

When heating a relatively thick body for a relatively short time, it is clear that the heat would penetrate only a short distance in a zone near the surface and that the temperature of the interior would not be affected. This case corresponds to a semi-infinite solid, and it is obvious that the midplane distance becomes indefinite. However, for this case, the results may be plotted as Y *vs.* X if X is defined as $\alpha\theta/x^2$, where x represents distance from the surface to the point in question. Figure 13 shows the corresponding curves plotted in the upper part of the chart as Y *vs.* X, and it is seen that position ratios n are not involved.* In solving certain problems, it is advantageous to know the rate of change of Y with X; hence, in the lower part of Fig. 13, for the semi-infinite solid, the derivative dY/dX is shown plotted *vs.* X, using the same scale as ordinates as used for Y *vs.* X. Similar curves or derivatives for the other shapes have been plotted by Gurney.[275]

For a brick-shaped solid, having total thicknesses $2x_m$, $2y_m$, and $2z_m$, the value of Y at a given time and position may be evaluated by the method of Newman,[507] in which Y equals the product $Y_x Y_y Y_z$, where Y_x is evaluated from Fig. 7 at $X_x = k\theta/\rho c r_m^2$, at $n_x = r/r_m$

---

* Where greater accuracy is desired than is obtainable from Fig. 13, for m of zero, one may use the equation of the curve:

$$Y = \frac{2}{\sqrt{\pi}} \int_0^\beta e^{-z^2} dz$$

wherein $\beta = 1/2 \sqrt{X} = x/2 \sqrt{\alpha\theta}$; values of the Gauss "error integral," Y, are given in mathematical tables:

Y	0.9953	0.9103	0.8427	0.7421	0.6778	0.5205	0.4284	0.2227
X	0.0625	0.1737	0.2500	0.3907	0.5102	1.0000	1.5625	6.2500

and $m_x = k/hr_m$; similarly, Y_y and Y_z are read for the same θ at X_y, n_y, and m_y and at X_z, n_z, and m_z, corresponding to y_m and z_m.

Limitations.—In many cases, the actual operating conditions may not correspond exactly to the conditions for which the curves apply. Thus, the various factors that were assumed constant, such as the temperature t' of the surroundings and h, may vary during the period of heating or cooling; in such cases, the curves given are not strictly applicable. If the shape of a body does not correspond exactly to one of those given in Figs. 7 to 14, examination of the difference in shapes will show qualitatively the results to be expected. For conditions widely different from those considered, it is sug-

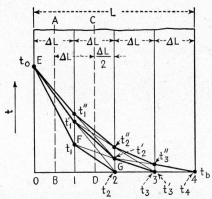

Fig. 15.—Graphical method of Schmidt,[631] applied to the case in which the temperature on one side is suddenly increased from t_b to t_0 while that on the other side is held at t_b.

gested that experimental data be plotted as log Y *vs.* X to facilitate the interpretation of the data.

Graphical Methods.—In a pioneer paper Schmidt[631] developed a graphical method for the approximate solution of complex problems, many of which have not yet been solved analytically. The approximation resides in replacing a differential by a finite increment. A derivation is given below.

Derivation.—Visualize a slab of uniform thickness, having physical properties independent of temperature. The problem is to determine the temperature distribution at any time θ.

Imagine the slab divided into a finite number N of slabs having equal thickness, $\Delta L = L/N$. If the surface resistance is negligible ($1/h = \infty$), after the finite time $\Delta\theta$ has elapsed the temperatures at cross sections 0, 1, and 2 will have the temperatures t_0, t_1, t_2 shown diagrammatically by points E, F, and G of Fig. 15. Consider the first two layers each bisected by imaginary planes AB

and CD. As an approximation the temperature gradient at AB is equal to $(t_0 - t_1)/\Delta L$; similarly, at CD, $-dt/dL = (t_1 - t_2)/\Delta L$. At the given instant the rate of heat conduction into AB exceeds the rate out at CD by the amount $kA(t_0 - t_1)/\Delta L - kA(t_1 - t_2)/\Delta L$, and during a time increment $\Delta\theta$ this excess heat will raise the average temperature of the solid lying between AB and CD from t_1 to t_1'. The heat balance gives

$$\frac{kA(t_0 - t_1)}{\Delta L} - \frac{kA(t_1 - t_2)}{\Delta L} = \frac{A(\Delta L)\rho c(t_1' - t_1)}{\Delta\theta} \tag{9}$$

Designating the diffusivity $k/\rho c$ as α, rearrangement of Eq. 9 gives

$$\frac{(t_0 + t_2)}{2} - t_1 = \frac{(\Delta L)^2(t_1' - t_1)}{2\alpha(\Delta\theta)} \tag{9a}$$

By a proper choice of the size of $\Delta\theta$, the ratio $\dfrac{(\Delta L)^2}{2\alpha\Delta\theta}$ will be made equal to one, and Eq. 9a then becomes

$$t_1' = \frac{t_0 + t_2}{2} \tag{10}$$

Thus it is seen that, after the elapse of a time unit $\Delta\theta$, the new temperature at section 1 is the arithmetic mean of the temperatures previously prevailing at sections 0 and 2. This same reasoning holds for all sections ΔL apart.

Illustration 2.—Consider a large wall of uniform thickness of 13.5 in. and at a uniform base temperature t_b of 100°F. Let the temperature of one face be suddenly increased to t_0 of 1000°F, but the other side is to be maintained at t_4 of 100°F. The average values of k, ρ, and c, assumed constant, are 0.80, 151, and 0.23, respectively. What would be the approximate distribution of temperature in the wall at the end of 6.88 hr, if t_0 is maintained constant?

If N is taken as 4, $\Delta L = 0.281$ ft; since $\alpha = 0.8/(151)(0.23) = 0.023$ sq ft/hr, the corresponding $\Delta\theta = (0.281)^2/(2)(0.023) = 1.72$ hr, and $6.88/1.72 = 4$ time increments are required.[*]

The temperature distribution at the end of the first time increment can be obtained[224] from the relation for the semi-infinite solid, since the heat has not yet reached the other side of the slab. Thus at the plane F, the distance x from the heated surface is ΔL, $X = \alpha\theta/x^2 = \alpha \Delta\theta/(\Delta L)^2$; noting that $\Delta\theta = (\Delta L)^2/2\alpha$, X equals $\frac{1}{2}$. Since h is infinite, the resistance ratio m or k/hx is zero, and Fig. 13 shows that Y is 0.683; hence the accomplished temperature rise $t_1 - t_b$ is $1 - Y_1$ or 0.317 times the initial temperature difference $t_h - t_b$, or $t_1 = t_b + (1 - Y)(t_h - t_b)$.

Similarly, at $x = 2\Delta L$, $1 - Y_2$ is 0.045, and at $x = 3 \Delta L$, $1 - Y_3$ is negligible.

Thus if t_h is 1000° and t_b is 100°, $t_1 = t_b + (1 - Y_1)(t_h - t_b) = 100 + 0.317(900) = 385°$; similarly $t_2 = 100 + 0.045(900) = 140°$.

The temperatures t_3 and t_4 are unchanged at t_b of 100°.

One now uses the Schmidt rule, $t_1' = (t_0 + t_2)/2$. This can be done graphically by drawing a straight line through t_0 and t_2, points E and G of Fig. 15, and

---

[*] Less error would be introduced by using more slices and consequently shorter time increments, but the use of four slices will suffice to illustrate the method.

reading t_1' at the intersection of EG with plane 1; t_2' is found similarly at plane 2 by joining t_1 and t_3. This procedure is repeated until the sum of the time increments corresponds to the desired total time θ.

Alternatively, one could use an algebraic method of solution illustrated by Table II. The second horizontal line was computed above by use of Fig. 13. The third line is obtained from the Schmidt rule $t_1' = (t_0 + t_2)/2$, $t_2' = (t_1 + t_3)/2$, etc.; the fourth line, from $t_1'' = (t_0' + t_2')/2$, $t_2'' = (t_1' + t_3')/2$, etc.

TABLE II

θ	t_0 at $0°(\Delta L)$	t_1 at $1(\Delta L)$	t_2 at $2(\Delta L)$	t_3 at $3(\Delta L)$	t_4 at $4(\Delta L)$
$0(\Delta\theta)$	1000	100	100	100	100
$1(\Delta\theta)$	1000	385	140	100	100
$2(\Delta\theta)$	1000	570	243	120	100
$3(\Delta\theta)$	1000	622	345	172	100
$4(\Delta\theta)$	1000	673	397	222	100
∞	1000	775	550	325	100

The preceding example treated the case in which both surface temperatures were constant. Schmidt also treats the case for finite boundary coefficients with the hot and cold ambient fluids constant at t_h and t_c. In the following example h is assumed infinite on the hot side and finite on the cold side; hence the temperature on the cold surface varies with time; t_b and t_c are constant; ΔL will be taken as $L/4$.

A heat balance at the cold surface gives $h_c A(t_4 - t_c) = -kA(dt/dL)_4$.

Now imagine that a fictitious layer of the same solid, of thickness ΔL, be added to the system and that the temperature of the outer surface of the fictive layer is $t^\star$, defined by the relation $-(dt/dL)_4 = (t_4 - t^\star)/\Delta L$. Elimination of $-(dt/dL)_4$ from the last two equations gives

$$\frac{t_4 - t^\star}{t_4 - t_c} = \frac{\Delta L}{k/h} \tag{11}$$

Hence if t_c is plotted as an ordinate at a distance k/h to the right of plane 4 and a straight line is drawn from t_c to t_4, $t^\star$ is the ordinate at plane 5, which is at a distance of ΔL from plane 4. The construction is shown in Fig. 16. The Schmidt rule $t_4' = (t_3 + t^\star)/2$ is then applied by connecting t_3 and $t^\star$ by a straight line, and t_4' is the ordinate at plane 4.*

Illustration 3.—The following example is based on $h_h = \infty$, $h_c = 2.2$, $t_h = 1700°F$, $t_b = 70°F$, $t_c = 70°F$, $L = 13.5/12 = 1.124$ ft, $k = 0.8$, $\rho = 151$, $c = 0.23$; hence $\alpha = 0.8/(151)(0.23) = 0.023$. It is desired to determine the approximate distribution of temperature 8 hr after the furnace is fired.

* Since the fictive layer has no heat capacity it is theoretically incorrect to apply the Schmidt rule to determine t_4', but the approximation is satisfactory as long as the ratio of ΔL to k/h is small. If ΔL exceeds k/h a better approximation is to obtain t_4' by aligning t_3 with t_c, thus abandoning the concept of the fictive layer.

Solution.—$\Delta L = 1.124/4 = 0.281$ ft, $\Delta \theta = (0.281)^2/(2)(0.023) = 1.715$ hr, and $k/h = 0.364$.

$$t^\star = \left(1 - \frac{h\,\Delta L}{k}\right) t_4 + t_c \frac{h\,\Delta L}{k} = 0.228 t_4 + 54 \qquad (11a)$$

The details of an algebraic solution are given in the following table, with temperatures expressed in degrees Fahrenheit.

TABLE III

$\Delta\theta$	θ	t at 0	t at 1	t at 2	t at 3	t at 4	$t^\star$ (Eq. 11a)	Line
0	0	70	70	70	70	70	70	1
1	1.72	1700	587	143	75	70	70	2
2	3.46	1700	922	331	107	73	71	3
3	5.15	1700	1015	514	202	89	74	4
4	6.86	1700	1107	609	302	138	85	5
5	8.58	1700	1154	705	374	194	98	6
∞	∞	1700	1392	1084	776	468	160	7

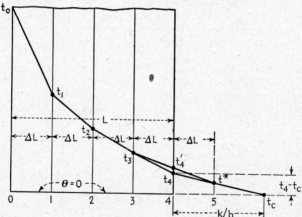

Fig. 16.—Schmidt approximate method of allowing for a finite surface resistance $(1/h)$ on the cold side.

The values in line 1 were given, and those in line 2 were obtained from Fig. 13, as explained on page 40. In lines 3 to 6, inclusive, the temperatures at planes 1, 2, 3, and 4 were obtained from temperatures in the line immediately preceding, using Eq. 10, whereas $t^\star$ was obtained from t_4 (in the same line) and Eq. 11a. The derived temperature distribution at the end of 8 hr could then be interpolated from those given in the table. At infinite time, when the steady state has been established, $k(t_0 - t_4)/L$ must equal $h(t_4 - t_c)$, whence t_4 is 468°F and the steady flux is 876 Btu/(hr)(sq ft). The corresponding constant temperature gradient is shown in line 7.

If h_c varies with temperature or temperature difference, the abscissa of t_c is permitted to vary. If the initial temperature of the solid is not uniform but is known, the procedure is the same as given above, except that one omits the use of Fig. 13 and applies the Schmidt rule immediately. Schmidt also treats the case of a composite wall. Allowance for the variation of thermal diffusivity may be made either graphically[664] or analytically.[624]

Miscellaneous Methods.—A mechanical integrator has been described by Nessi and Nisolle[505] and by Nessi.[504] Moore[487] devised the "hydrocal," a calculating machine for solving complex problems in unsteady-state heat transfer; Paschkis[550a,550b] describes an electrical method of solving such problems.

Wood.—MacLean,[463] in a study of the data of Wirka[773] on the steaming of green southern-pine timbers, found that the integrated relations (see Fig. 11 for the long cylinder) correlated the data on temperature gradients at various periods in the batch operation and obtained an average value of $k/\rho c_p = 0.00678$ sq ft/hr for the thermal diffusivity of the wood. The diameters of the 33 specimens ranged from 6.74 to 12 in., the average moisture content was 63 per cent by weight, and the average density was 65.4 lb/cu ft.

Rubber.—Perks and Griffiths,[556] Shepard and Wiegand,[653] and Sherwood[658] give methods of computation of the rate of vulcanization of rubber as a function of temperature. Sherwood shows the substantial advantage, in the curing of rubber tires, of applying heat to both inner and outer surfaces.

Miscellaneous.—Ice formation on pipes is discussed by several writers* and data[357] are available on the freezing and thawing of fruit juices. Harbert *et al.*[280] treat unsteady flow of heat in porous solids.

Periodic Variation in Temperature of Surroundings.—Solutions are available in the literature.†

Blast-furnace Stoves and Heat Regenerators.—When hot gases are intermittently turned into a chamber partly filled with cooler solids or when cold air is allowed to flow intermittently over warmer solids, the mathematical relations become quite involved.‡ Methods for approximate calculations are available.§ The Lungstrom preheater is treated by Ruhl.[614]

* Elmer,[210] Planck,[564] and Pekeris and Slichter.[555]

† Carslaw,[109] Ingersoll and Zobel,[334] Grober,[271] Schack,[627] Goldschmidt and Partridge,[253] and Houghten *et al.*[326]

‡ Heiligenstaedt,[295] Nusselt,[529] Hausen,[289] Lubojatzky,[450] Ackermann,[1a] and others.

§ For example, see Schack,[626,627] Rummel and Schack,[617] Rummel,[616] Hausen,[290] and Trinks.[721]

An approximate result may be obtained from the equation of Rummel:[615]

$$\frac{Q}{A} = \frac{(\Delta t_1 - \Delta t_2)/(\ln \Delta t_1/\Delta t_2)}{\dfrac{1}{h_A\theta_A} + \dfrac{1}{h_G\theta_G} + \dfrac{1}{2.5c_p\rho L'} + \dfrac{L'}{k(\theta_A + \theta_G)}}$$

in which Δt_1 and Δt_2 are the average differences in temperature between gas and air at the two ends of the regenerator, c_p, ρ, and k are, respectively, the specific heat, density, and thermal conductivity of the brick, L' is the ratio of the total volume to the exposed surface of the bricks, θ_G and θ_A are the length of the gas and air blows, and h_G and h_A are the individual heat-transfer coefficients from gas to bricks and from bricks to air, respectively, values of which are given by Rummel.

Problems

1. Long cylindrical logs 6 in. in diameter, initially at a uniform temperature of 60°F, are to be placed in a bath of saturated steam at 212°F. The thermal diffusivity may be taken as constant at 0.0068 sq ft/hr, and h may be taken as 1000 Btu/(hr)(sq ft)(deg F).

Calculate the time required for the temperature at the axis to reach 160°F and the corresponding temperature at a point 1 in. below the surface.

2. A canvas belt 1.8 in. thick is heated between two steam-heated steel plates in a press. The belt, initially at 60°F, is to be heated from both sides of the press, which is maintained at 280°F until the temperature at the axis is 270°F.

   a. How long must the belt be heated, and what will be the final temperature at a plane 0.54 in. below the surface?
   b. How long would be required for a belt 3.6 in. thick, heated as above, to reach a midplane temperature of 270°F?

Data and Notes.—α for the belt material = 0.0058 sq ft/hr; neglect surface thermal resistance between press and belt.

3. A refractory wall 1.13 ft thick, having initially a uniform temperature of 100°F, is suddenly exposed on one side to surroundings at a constant temperature of 1100°F. The resistance to heat flow between the surroundings and the surface of the wall is negligible. The other side of the wall is maintained at a temperature of 100°F.

How long will be required for the temperature at a plane 3.4 in. beneath the 1100°F surface to reach a temperature of 737°F?

Data.—$c = 0.15$, $\rho = 100$, $k = 1.2$.

CHAPTER III

RADIANT HEAT TRANSMISSION

By Hoyt C. Hottel

The relative importance of the several mechanisms of the transfer of heat from one body to another differs greatly with the temperature level of the system. At very low temperatures the transfer is chiefly by conduction, the passing along, from one layer of molecules to another, of the kinetic energy of the molecules in excess of that of the adjacent layer—kinetic energy that the molecules have by virtue of their temperature. Superposed on this phenomenon, when the system is fluid, is that of convection, the transfer of energy by mass motion of a large portion of the fluid—large, that is, compared with molecular magnitudes. Even at moderate temperature levels, however, another phenomenon becomes appreciable. The molecules or atoms, through some sort of excitation caused by temperature, give rise to radiant energy, emitted in an amount determined by the temperature level of the molecules and capable of passage with more or less absorption to a distant receiver of the radiation. If the phenomena of conduction and convection on the one hand are contrasted with thermal radiation on the other, it is found that the former are affected by temperature difference and very little by temperature level, whereas the latter increases rapidly with increase in temperature level. It follows that at very low temperatures, conduction and convection are the major contributors to the total heat transfer; at very high temperatures, radiation is the controlling factor. The temperature at which radiation accounts for roughly one-half of the total heat transmission depends on such factors as the emissivity of the surface or the magnitude of the convection coefficient. For large pipes losing heat by natural convection, this is room temperature; for fine wires of low emissivity, it is above a red heat.

Subject matter will be divided into (1) the nature of thermal radiation (pages 47–51), (2) radiant-heat interchange between the surfaces of solids separated by a nonabsorbing medium (pages 51–64), (3) radiation from nonluminous gases (pages 64–73),

45

(4) radiation from clouds of particles (pages 73–77), and (5) the combined effect of all these mechanisms in the combustion chamber of a furnace (pages 77–84). Nomenclature is summarized in Table I.

TABLE I.—NOMENCLATURE

A Area of surface, square feet; A_c of cold body (sink); A_e of small (enclosed) body; A_p for fictitious plane; A_R, for refractory; A_1 and A_2 for surfaces 1 and 2.

a, b Radii of smaller and larger disks, respectively, feet.

C_1 Dimensionless factor to allow for partial pressure of water vapor, Fig. 30.

$(c_p)_m$ Mean specific heat of combustion gas, Btu/(lb)(deg F).

c_1, c_2 Dimensional constants in Planck's law (Eq. 2).

F A dimensionless geometrical factor, to allow for **direct** interchange between surfaces 1 and 2; F_{12} from surface 1 to 2 based on A_1; F_{21} from surface 2 to 1, based on A_2; see Eqs. 6, 7 and 10 and Figs. 23–26.

$\bar{F}$ A dimensionless geometrical factor, to allow for net flow between *black* surfaces 1 and 2, including the effect of refractory surfaces; Eqs. 11–12 and Figs. 25 and 26.

$\mathfrak{F}$ A dimensionless factor to allow for interchange between *gray* surfaces, defined by Eq. 14 and expressed in terms of $\bar{F}$'s, ϵ's, and A's by Eq. 15; $\mathfrak{F}_{12}$ is based on A_1, $\mathfrak{F}_{21}$ on A_2.

h Coefficient of heat transfer by convection, Btu/(hr)(sq ft)(deg F); h_c in general, h_C at sink, h_R at inside surface of refractory, h_o at outside surface of refractory.

h_r Coefficient of heat transfer by radiation between surfaces, Btu/(hr)(sq ft)(deg F).

I Intensity of incident radiation, Btu/(sq ft)(hr).

i Enthalpy (heat content) of the entering fuel, air, and recirculated flue gas (if any) above a base temperature T_o (water as vapor), Btu per hour.

KL Factor in ordinate of Fig. 33.

K_2 Normal distance between disks a and b, feet.

k_w/x_w Thermal conductivity of furnace wall, Btu/(hr)(sq ft)(deg F/ft), divided by wall thickness, in feet.

L Beam lengths for gas radiation, feet (see Table II).

M Average molecular weight.

P Partial pressure of gas in atmospheres, P_c for carbon dioxide, P_w for water vapor.

q Rate of heat transfer by radiation; Btu per hour; where necessary to distinguish, q_c for convection and q_r for radiation; q_F, from flame by all mechanisms; q_L, lost to surroundings.

r Radial distance, feet; r_1 and r_2 are total radii of disks 1 and 2.

r_{af} Weight ratio of air to fuel, dimensionless.

r_f Ratio of average billet-pushing rate over a period of several hours to pushing rate during periods of steady operation, dimensionless.

S Ordinate of Fig. 32.

TABLE I.—NOMENCLATURE.—(*Continued*)

T Absolute temperature; Rankine, Fahrenheit absolute (460 + degrees Fahrenheit); T_c of cold body (sink); T_e of enclosure; T_F of flame; T_G of gas; T_g for green-brightness temperature; T_r for red-brightness temperature; T_s of surface; T_o, base temperature in enthalpy balance; T_1 and T_2, of surfaces 1 and 2; in Figs. 33 and 34, T is in degrees Kelvin (273 + deg C).

t Thermometric temperature, degrees Fahrenheit; for subscripts see T.

U_R Over-all coefficient of heat transfer through refractory, Btu/(hr) (sq ft)(deg F).

W Total emissive power, Btu/(hr)(sq ft); W_B for black body; $W_{B\lambda}$ for monochromatic emissive power, [(Btu)/(hr)(sq ft)]/cm.

w_A Firing rate, defined on page 81.

w_G Combustion-gas rate, pounds per hour.

x, y, z Distances, in feet, defined in Fig. 24.

Y, Z Dimension ratios, defined in Fig. 24.

Greek

α Absorptivity, dimensionless.

Δ $T_g - T_r$ (see Fig. 33).

ϵ Emissivity, dimensionless. Values are given in the Appendix, Table XIII.

θ Angle.

λ Wave length, in Eq. 2.

η Dimensionless ratio (see page 81).

ρ_1, ρ_2 Local radii of disks b and a, respectively, feet.

ρ_e Specific electrical resistance.

σ Dimensional constant in Stefan-Boltzmann law, page 49.

ϕ Plane angle.

ψ Plane angle.

ω Solid angle.

γ Dimensionless exponent, defined on page 76.

THE NATURE OF THERMAL RADIATION

When a body is heated, radiant energy is emitted at a rate, and of a quality, dependent on the temperature of the body. Thus, when the filament of an incandescent lamp is heated electrically, both the quantity of energy emitted per unit time and the proportion of visible radiation (light) emitted are found to increase rapidly with increase in temperature of the filament. At temperatures below approximately 1000°F, the radiation is not perceived by the human eye but may be recognized by the sense of warmth experienced when the hand is held near a slightly warmer body. When both the quality and quantity of radiant energy emitted per unit time depend solely on the temperature of the given body, the radiation is called *thermal radiation*. Certain materials, when suitably excited by electric discharge, bombardment by electrons, or exposure to radiation of suitable wave length, emit a *characteristic* radiation, which, when dispersed by a prism or the equivalent, shows a discontinuous spectrum, with energy concentrated in certain wave lengths characteristic of the emitting substance. Examples of characteristic radiation include the mercury-arc and neon lamps. Certain solids and liquids, when illuminated by light of suitable wave length without rising appreciably in temperature, emit a characteristic radiation described as *fluorescence* if emission ceases with the illumination and as *phosphorescence* if emission continues an appreciable time after illumination ceases. Usually the exciting light has shorter wave length than the visible emitted radiation. This section will deal only with radiation resulting directly from thermal excitation, which hereinafter will be referred to merely as *radiation* rather than by the more descriptive term *thermal radiation*.*

If two small bodies of areas A_1 and A_2 are placed in a large evacuated enclosure perfectly insulated externally, then, when the system has come to thermal equilibrium, the bodies will emit radiation at the rates A_1W_1 and A_2W_2, respectively, where W is the total emissive power,† energy per unit time per unit area of the surface [Btu/(sq ft)(hr)] emitted throughout the hemisphere above each element of surface. The intensity‡ of energy impinging on the small bodies, due to radiation from the enclosure, is I. If the bodies have *absorptivities* (fraction of incident radiation that is absorbed) of α_1 and α_2, then energy balances on the bodies will have the form

$$IA_1\alpha_1 = A_1W_1 \quad \text{and} \quad IA_2\alpha_2 = A_2W_2$$

from which $W_1/\alpha_1 = W_2/\alpha_2 (= W_x/\alpha_x$, where x is *any* body). This generalization, that at thermal equilibrium the ratio of the emissive power of a surface to its absorptivity is the same for all bodies, is known as *Kirchhoff's law*. Since α cannot exceed unity, Kirchhoff's law places an upper limit on W, called W_B; and any surface having this upper limiting emissive power is called a *perfect radiator*. Since such a surface must have an absorptivity of unity and there-

---

* It should perhaps be noted here that some writers reserve the term *thermal* to describe radiation that depends only on the temperature and in no way on the character of the emitter. The term will be used here, however, in its broader sense.

† Sometimes called *emittance, total hemispherical intensity*, or *radiant flux density*.

‡ In the field of illumination, J rather than I, is often used for intensity.

fore a reflectivity of zero, the perfect radiator is more commonly referred to as a *black body*. The ratio of the emissive power of an actual surface to that of a black body is called the *emissivity* ϵ of the surface. Kirchhoff's law restated is as follows: *At thermal equilibrium the emissivity and absorptivity of a body are the same.*

The emissive power of a black body depends on its temperature only, and the second law of thermodynamics may be used to prove a proportionality between emissive power and the fourth power of the absolute temperature. The relation

$$W_B = \sigma T^4 \tag{1}$$

is known as the *Stefan-Boltzmann law;* and the proportionality constant σ is known as the Stefan-Boltzmann constant [0.173 $\times$ 10^{-8} Btu/(sq ft)(hr)(deg R)^4; 5.71×10^{-5} ergs/(sq cm)(sec)(deg K)^4; 4.92×10^{-8} kg-cal/(sq m)(hr)(deg K)^4].*

Consider two opaque parallel plane surfaces A_B and A, large in extent compared with the distance between them. The first is a black body absorbing all incident radiation, and the second is a gray body having an absorptivity of less than unity. Both surfaces are at the same temperature, and the space between the planes is evacuated. The black surface emits W_B; of this, the gray surface absorbs $W_B\alpha$ and reflects $W_B(1 - \alpha)$ and emits $W_B\epsilon$. The black surface absorbs all the incident radiation $(W_B)(1 - \alpha) + W_B\epsilon$ and emits W_B. Since there can be no net transfer of heat from two surfaces at the same temperature, $W_B(1 - \alpha) + W_B\epsilon$ must equal W_B, whence ϵ equals α, as noted above. If now a peephole were made in the black body, the amount of energy per unit time streaming through the peephole (the sum of the emission and reflection from the gray body) must equal that emitted from a black body at the same temperature. In fact, the isothermal enclosure provided with a peephole is used experimentally to obtain black-body radiation and, together with Eq. 1, is the primary temperature standard above the range of the gas thermometer.

Other properties of black-body radiation of interest in heat transmission are related to the nature of its distribution in the spectrum and the shift of that distribution with temperature. If $W_{B,\lambda}$ is the *monochromatic emissive power* at wave length λ such that $W_{B,\lambda} \cdot d\lambda$ is the energy emitted from a surface per unit area

* Deg R designates degrees Fahrenheit absolute, and deg K designates degrees centigrade absolute.

per unit time in the wave-length interval λ to $\lambda + d\lambda$, the relation among $W_{B,\lambda}$, λ, and T is given by *Planck's law,*

$$W_{B,\lambda} = \frac{c_1\lambda^{-5}}{e^{\frac{c_2}{\lambda T}} - 1} \tag{2}$$

$c_1 = 3.27 \times 10^{-12}$ [Btu/(sq ft)(hr)] (cm)^4 or 0.885×10^{-12} (cal) (sq cm)/(sec); $c_2 = 2.58$ (cm)(deg R) or 1.433 cm deg K. According to Planck's law, the monochromatic emissive power at any temperature varies from 0 at $\lambda = 0$ through a maximum and back to 0 at $\lambda = \infty$; at any wave length it increases with temperature, but values at shorter wave lengths increase faster so that the maximum value shifts to shorter wave lengths as the temperature rises. The

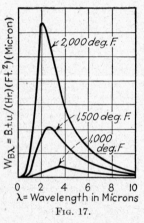

FIG. 17.

position of the maximum is inversely proportional to the absolute temperature (*Wien's displacement law*), derivable from Eq. 2. The relation is: $\lambda_{max}T = 0.5193$ cm deg R, or 0.2885 cm deg K. Figure 17 is a plot of the monochromatic emissive power of a black body *vs.* wave length for several different temperatures. The total emissive power for a given temperature is the area under the curve

$$W_B = \int_0^\infty W_{B\lambda} \, d\lambda \tag{2a}$$

The emissivity ϵ of a surface (more properly the total hemispherical emissivity, to differentiate it from monochromatic emissivity ϵ_λ, the ratio of radiating powers at the wave length λ, and from directional emissivity ϵ_θ, the ratio of radiating powers in a direction making the angle θ with the normal to the surface) varies with its temperature, its degree of roughness, and, if a metal, its degree of oxidation. Table XIII (page 393) gives the emissivities of various surfaces and emphasizes the large variation possible in a single material. Although the values in the table apply strictly to normal radiation from the surface (with few exceptions), they may be used with negligible error for hemispherical emissivity except in the case of well-polished metal surfaces, for which the hemispherical emissivity is 15 to 20 per cent higher than the normal value.[63a]

A few generalizations may be made concerning the emissivity of surfaces: (1) The emissivities of highly polished metals have been shown[642] to be very low and to be a function of the product term $\rho_e T$, in which ρ_e is the specific electrical resistance and T is the absolute temperature. A correlation on this basis, however, is possible only when extraordinary pains are taken to prevent any possibility of oxidation or imperfection of polish. A poorly polished specimen may have several times this theoretical minimum emissivity. (2) The emissivities of nearly all substances increase with temperature. (3) The low-temperature emissivity of most nonmetals is above 0.8. (4) Iron and steel vary widely with the degree of oxidation and roughness, clean metallic surfaces having an emissivity of 0.05 to 0.45 at low temperatures to 0.4 to 0.7 at high temperatures; oxidized and/or rough surfaces, 0.6 to 0.95 at low temperatures to 0.9 to 0.95 at high temperatures.

The absorptivity α of a surface depends on the factors affecting emissivity and, in addition, on the quality of the incident radiation, measured by its distribution in the spectrum. One may assign two subscripts to α, the first to indicate the temperature of the receiver and the second that of the incident radiation. It has already been seen that, according to Kirchhoff's law, the emissivity of a surface at temperature T_1 is equal to the absorptivity $\alpha_{1,1}$ which the surface exhibits for black radiation from a source at the same temperature; *i.e.*, a surface of low radiating power is also a poor absorber (or good reflector or transmitter) of radiation from a source at its own temperature. If the monochromatic absorptivity α_λ varies considerably with wave length and much less with temperature (which is generally the case), it follows that the total absorptivity $\alpha_{1,2}$ will vary more with T_2 than with T_1. For most surfaces of industrial importance (but not all), α_λ increases towards short wave lengths, from which $\alpha_{1,2}$ increases as T_2 increases. This also explains the effect of temperature on emissivity (see above).

If α_λ is a constant independent of λ, the surface is called *gray*, and its total absorptivity α will be independent of the spectral-energy distribution of the incident radiation; then $\alpha_{1,2} = \alpha_{1,1} = \epsilon_1$; *i.e.*, emissivity ϵ may be used in substitution for α even though the temperatures of the incident radiation and the receiver are not the same.

RADIATION BETWEEN THE SURFACES OF SOLIDS SEPARATED BY A NONABSORBING MEDIUM

The net loss of energy by radiation from a body at temperature T_1 in *black* surroundings at T_2 is given by

$$q_{1,\text{net}} = 0.173A_1\left[\epsilon_1\left(\frac{T_1}{100}\right)^4 - \alpha_{1,2}\left(\frac{T_2}{100}\right)^4\right] \text{Btu/(hr)} \qquad (3)$$

when A_1 is square feet and T is degrees Rankine.

When $\alpha_{1,2}$ equals ϵ_1 (see above), this reduces to

$$q_{1,\text{net}} = 0.173A_1\epsilon_1\left[\left(\frac{T_1}{100}\right)^4 - \left(\frac{T_2}{100}\right)^4\right] \qquad (4)$$

The intensity of thermal radiation from a black body of any shape, measured at a given distance and direction from the body, is identical with that which would be emitted from any other black body at the same temperature, the elements of whose perimeter, when viewed from the measuring point, are identical in direction to the corresponding elements of the original black body.[741]

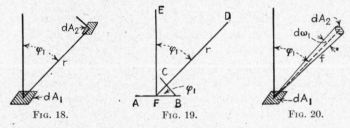

Fig. 18.　　　　　　Fig. 19.　　　　　　Fig. 20.

Derivation of General Differential Equation.—Visualize a small black-surface element dA_1 of total emissive power W_B radiating in all directions from one side. The problem is to determine what portion of its radiation is intercepted by some other small black surface of element dA_2. Figure 18 presents the details of the problem. The radiation per unit time $dq_{1\to2}$ from dA_1 intercepted by dA_2 is proportional to the *apparent* area dA_1' as viewed from dA_2. Furthermore, the interception of the emitted beam is proportional to the *apparent* area dA_2' of dA_2, taken normal to the beam. Also the radiation received at dA_2 will vary inversely as the square of the distance or radius r separating dA_1 and dA_2. Algebraically stated, these relations give the equation

$$dq_{1\to2} = I_1(dA_1')(dA_2')/r^2 \qquad (5)$$

where I_1 is a proportionality constant. This is the "square-of-the-distance law," familiar from physics experiments in illumination. Since dA_1' equals $dA_1 \cos \phi_1$* and similarly dA_2' equals $dA_2 \cos \phi_2$, this may be written

$$dq_{1\to2} = I_1(dA_1 \cos \phi_1)(dA_2 \cos \phi_2)/r^2 \qquad (5a)$$

* This may be seen from Fig. 19, which shows an enlarged view of dA_1 having side AB, and of dA_1' having side BC. Since AB and BC, enclosing angle ABC, are, respectively, perpendicular to EF and DF, BC/AB equals $\cos ABC$. Since BC/AB equals dA_1'/dA_1, dA_1' equals $dA_1 \cos \phi_1$.

This equation is sometimes expressed in a different form. Let the small *solid angle* subtended by dA_2 at dA_1 be called $d\omega_1$ (see Fig. 20). By definition a solid angle is numerically the area subtended on a sphere of unit radius, or, for a sphere of radius r, the intercepted area divided by r^2. Hence one may write $d\omega_1 = dA_2'/r^2 = dA_2 \cos \phi_2/r^2$, and Eq. 5a becomes

$$dq_{1\to2} = I_1 \, dA_1 \cos \phi_1 \, d\omega_1 \qquad (5b)$$

Since Eq. 5a is symmetrical with respect to dA_1 and dA_2, and to $\cos \phi_1$, and $\cos \phi_2$, a third way of writing Eq. 5a is

$$dq_{1\to2} = I_1 \, dA_2 \cos \phi_2 \, d\omega_2 \qquad (5c)$$

The various forms of Eq. 5 are completely equivalent; the choice among them in subsequent use will depend on the particular problem. The proportionality factor I_1 of Eq. 5 is known as the **intensity of radiation** from the surface dA_1.

The rate of radiation dq_1 in *all* directions from one side of dA_1 is given by integration of Eq. 5b over the complete hemispherical angle 2π above dA_1; $dq_1 = dA_1 I_1 \int d\omega_1 \cos \phi_1$. Since by definition W_{B1} equals dq_1/dA_1, the relation between W_{B1} and I_1 is obtained by

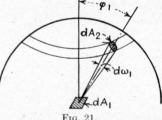

$$W_{B1} = I_1 \int \cos \phi_1 \, d\omega_1 \qquad (5d)$$

Referring to Fig. 21, describe a hemisphere of radius r around dA_1.

Fig. 21.

Let dA_2 be a small surface element of the surface of the hemisphere, the radius r making the angle ϕ_1 with the normal to dA_1. Considering as an element of area of the hemisphere a ring of width $r \, d\phi_1$ and a length of $2\pi r \sin \phi_1$, the area dA_2 is $2\pi r^2 \sin \phi_1 \, d\phi_1$. Substitution of this value of dA_2 in Eq. 5d gives

$$W_{B1} = 2\pi I_1 \int_0^{\frac{\pi}{2}} \sin \phi_1 \cos \phi_1 \, d\phi_1 = \pi I_1 \left(\sin^2 \phi_1 \right)_0^{\frac{\pi}{2}} = \pi I_1$$

Thus the intensity I of the cosine law is found to be the total emissive power of a black body, divided by π:

$$I = W_B/\pi = \sigma T^4/\pi \qquad (5e)$$

The same result is obtained by considering the upper surface to be an infinite plate parallel to dA_1, rather than the hemisphere considered above.

Of the radiation emitted per unit time by the black element dA_2, the amount $dq_{2\to1}$ intercepted by dA_1 is given by equations like Eqs. 5a, 5b and 5c, except that I_1 is replaced by I_2. Since for black bodies, all radiation intercepted is absorbed, the net rate of interchange, dq_{net}, or $dq_{1\rightarrow2}$, minus $dq_{2\rightarrow1}$, is given by equations like Eqs. 5a, 5b and 5c, except that I_1 is replaced by $I_1 - I_2$, which equals $(W_{B1} - W_{B2})/\pi$.

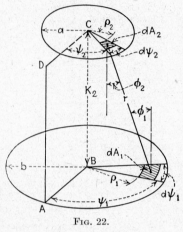

FIG. 22.

Net Rate of Direct Radiation between Two Finite Black Bodies.—The application of this relation to the evaluation of the *net* interchange between finite black surfaces will be illustrated by a simple case, that of two parallel disks directly opposed, separated by the distance K_2. Figure 22 shows the details of the problem. The larger and smaller disks have radii a and b and areas A_1 and A_2, respectively. The angles ψ_1 and ψ_2 are measured from the reference plane $ABCD$. The elementary surfaces dA_1 and dA_2 lie at local radii ρ_1 and ρ_2, respectively. Equation 5, with the replacement of I by the term $(W_{B1} - W_{B2})/\pi$, is convenient to use:

$$dq_{net} = \frac{(W_{B1} - W_{B2}) \, dA_1 \cos \phi_1 \, dA_2 \cos \phi_2}{\pi r^2} \tag{5f}$$

By examination of Fig. 22, the terms in this equation may be identified as follows:

$$dA_1 = d\rho_1 \, \rho_1 \, d\psi_1; \qquad dA_2 = d\rho_2 \, \rho_2 \, d\psi_2;$$
$$\cos \phi_1 = K_2/r; \qquad \cos \phi_2 = K_2/r;$$
$$r = \sqrt{\rho_1^2 + \rho_2^2 - 2\rho_1\rho_2 \cos (\psi_2 - \psi_1) + K_2^2}$$

Substituting these five relations in Eq. 5f and inserting limits to cover the whole area of each disk give the relation

$$q_{net} = (W_B - W_{B2}) \int_0^{2\pi} \int_0^{2\pi} \int_0^a \int_0^b \frac{\rho_1\rho_2 K_2^2 \, d\rho_1 \, d\rho_2 \, d\psi_1 \, d\psi_2}{\pi[\rho_1^2 + \rho_2^2 - 2\rho_1\rho_2 \cos (\psi_2 - \psi_1)^2 + K_2^2]}$$

$$= (W_{B1} - W_{B2}) \left\{ \frac{\pi}{2} [(b^2 + a^2 + K_2^2 - \sqrt{(b^2 + a^2 + K_2^2)^2 - 4a^2b^2})] \right\} \tag{5g}$$

Since the radiant-heat interchange between the disk of area A_1 and an infinite parallel plane replacing A_2 is $(W_{B1} - W_{B2})A_1$, it is seen that the bracket in Eq. 5 represents $A_1 F_{1\rightarrow2}$, where $F_{1\rightarrow2}$ represents the fraction of the radiation leaving one side of A_1 in all directions, which is intercepted by disk A_2. By the symmetry of the problem, the bracket may alternatively be considered to be represented by $A_2 F_{2\rightarrow1}$. Since either $A_1(= \pi b^2)$ or $A_2(= \pi a^2)$ may be factored out of the bracket, the choice of A_1 gives one value to $F_{1\rightarrow2}$ and the choice of A_2 another value of $F_{2\rightarrow1}$.

The Geometrical Factor *F.*—The general equation of *direct* radiant-heat interchange between two black surfaces, exclusive of the effects of any other partially reflecting surfaces that augment the interchange between the black surfaces, is consequently

$$q_{net} = (W_{B1} - W_{B2})AF = 0.173 \left[\left(\frac{T_1}{100} \right)^4 - \left(\frac{T_2}{100} \right)^4 \right] AF \quad (6)$$

in which A is the area of one of the surfaces and F is a geometrical factor dependent only on the shape and relative orientation of the

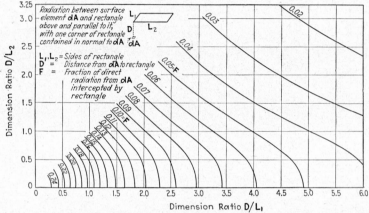

Fig. 23.—Geometrical factor F for direct radiation between an element dA and a parallel rectangle, in terms of the dimension ratios.

two surfaces and on which one of the two surfaces is used in evaluating A.

Equation 6 covered the case of two surfaces, with no indication of the method of treatment of a complete multisurface enclosure. The latter, in general, involves the use of a number of interchange factors F_{nm} defined above. Values of F have been calculated for various surface arrangements on the assumption that emissivity ϵ_θ is constant, independent of θ (exact for black surfaces, quite good for most nonmetallic or tarnished or rough metal surfaces). These values of F for a surface element dA and a rectangle in a parallel plane appear in Fig. 23; for adjacent rectangles in perpendicular planes in Fig. 24; for opposed parallel rectangles and disks of equal size as lines 1 to 4 of Fig. 25; for an infinite plane parallel to a system of parallel tubes as lines 1 and 3 of Fig. 26. Other cases are treated in the literature.* Important and useful concepts in

* References 318, 319, and 650.

evaluating F's are that

$$F_{12}A_1 = F_{21}A_2 \tag{7}$$

since otherwise there would be a net heat flux between A_1 and A_2

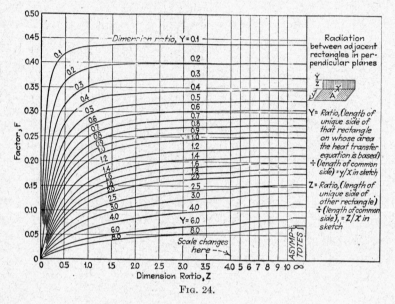

Fig. 24.

when at the same temperature; that

$$F_{11} + F_{12} + F_{13} \cdots = 1 \tag{8}$$

that, of course, when A_1 can "see" no part of itself:

$$F_{11} = 0 \tag{8a}$$

The radiation from a **black** surface A_1 to **black** surface A_2 is now $A_1F_{12}\sigma T_1^4$; from A_2 to A_1, it is $A_2F_{21}\sigma T_2^4$; the net interchange is their difference, which may be written

$$q = \sigma A_1 F_{12}(T_1^4 - T_2^4) \tag{9}$$
$$q = \sigma A_2 F_{21}(T_1^4 - T_2^4) \tag{9a}$$

One thus reaches the important conclusion that interchange may be obtained by evaluating the one-way radiation from either surface to the other, whichever is more convenient, and then replace the emissive power by the difference of emissive powers of the two surfaces.

In an *enclosure of black surfaces* the net heat flux from A_1 is then given by

$$q_{1,\text{net}} = (A_1 F_{12}\sigma T_1^4 - A_2 F_{21}\sigma T_2^4) + (A_1 F_{13}\sigma T_1^4 - A_3 F_{31}\sigma T_3^4) + \cdots \tag{10}$$

$$\equiv A_1 F_{12}\sigma(T_1^4 - T_2^4) + A_1 F_{13}\sigma(T_1^4 - T_3^4) + \cdots \tag{10a}$$

$$\equiv A_1\sigma T_1^4 - (A_1 F_{11}\sigma T_1^4 + A_2 F_{21}\sigma T_2^4 + A_3 F_{31}\sigma T_3^4 + \cdots) \tag{10b}$$

Allowance for Refractory Surfaces. The Factor $\bar{F}$.—Consider an enclosure consisting in part of black heat sources and sinks A_1,

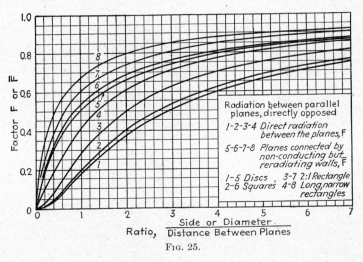

Fig. 25.

A_2, A_3 $\cdots$, and in part of refractory surfaces A_R, A_S $\cdots$, from which there is no *net* radiant heat flux (fulfilled by the average refractory wall where difference between internal convection and external loss is minute compared to incident radiation). The unknown refractory surface temperatures may be eliminated by heat balances, yielding an equation that expresses the net flux $q_{1 \rightleftharpoons 2}$ from A_1 to A_2 by the combined mechanisms of direct radiation plus reradiation from the refractory surfaces:

$$q_{1 \rightleftharpoons 2} = A_1 \bar{F}_{12}\sigma(T_1^4 - T_2^4) \equiv A_2 \bar{F}_{21}\sigma(T_1^4 - T_2^4) \tag{11}$$

The factor $\bar{F}$ has been determined exactly for a few geometrically simple cases[322] and may be approximated for others. If A_1 and A_2 are equal parallel disks, squares, or rectangles connected by non-conducting but reradiating refractory walls, then $\bar{F}$ is given by

Fig. 25, lines 5 to 8. If A_1 represents an infinite plane and A_2 is one or two rows of infinite parallel tubes in a parallel plane and if the only other surface is a refractory surface behind the tubes, $\bar{F}_{12}$ is given by line 5 or 6 of Fig. 26. If an enclosure may be divided into several radiant heat sources or sinks A_1, A_2, etc., and the rest of the enclosure (reradiating refractory surface) may be lumped together as A_R at a uniform temperature T_R, then the

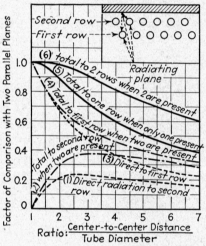

FIG. 26.—Radiation between a plane and one or two rows of tubes parallel to the plane.

factor $\bar{F}_{12}$ is given in terms of the direct geometrical factors F by the expression

$$\bar{F}_{12} = F_{12} + \frac{F_{1R}F_{R2}}{1 - F_{RR}} \tag{12}$$

If there are but two source-sink-type surfaces, A_1 and A_2, by application of the principles expressed in Eqs. 7 and 8, the foregoing expression reduces to the more readily used form

$$\bar{F}_{12} = F_{12} + \frac{1}{\dfrac{1}{F_{1R}} + \dfrac{A_1}{A_2} \cdot \dfrac{1}{F_{2R}}} \tag{12a}$$

If this case is further simplified by considering that neither A_1 nor A_2 can "see" itself (*i.e.*, has no negative curvature), using Eqs. 7, 8, and 8a the foregoing expression reduces to

$$\bar{F}_{12} = \frac{A_2 - A_1 F_{12}^2}{A_1 + A_2 - 2A_1 F_{12}} \tag{12b}$$

which necessitates the evaluation of but one geometrical factor F. This case covers a major fraction of problems of radiant-heat interchange between source and sink in a furnace enclosure and is in error only to the extent to which the assumption of uniform refractory temperature is not permissible. More complicated expressions are available, permitting approach to the exact answer to any desired degree of accuracy, depending on the number of zones into which the refractory is divided.

It is sometimes desirable to find the equilibrium value of refractory surface temperature. For the conditions for which Eq. 12b is valid, the refractory surface temperature is given by

$$T_R = \sqrt[4]{\frac{(A_1 - A_1F_{12})T_1^4 + (A_2 - A_1F_{12})T_2^4}{(A_1 - A_1F_{12}) + (A_2 - A_1F_{12})}} \tag{13}$$

Allowance for Nonblack Surfaces. The Factor $\mathfrak{F}$.—Exact allowance for the departure of surfaces from black or ideal radiating characteristics is in general too complicated for engineering use. However, if the assumption that *all surfaces are gray* is permitted, a simple and adequate treatment is possible. If nomenclature is as for $\bar{F}$ except that A_1, A_2, etc., are now surfaces having emissivities (and absorptivities) ϵ_1, ϵ_2, etc., it is found that the net radiant interchange between A_1 and A_2 (due now to the combined mechanisms of direct radiation, reradiation from refractory surfaces, and multiple reflection inside the enclosure) may be expressed in the form

$$q_{1 \rightleftharpoons 2} = A_1\mathfrak{F}_{12}\sigma(T_1^4 - T_2^4) \equiv A_2\mathfrak{F}_{21}\sigma(T_1^4 - T_2^4) \tag{14}$$

Just as the factor $\bar{F}$ could be evaluated from F, so the factor $\mathfrak{F}$ may be evaluated from $\bar{F}$. For the case of two nonrefractory surfaces A_1 and A_2 and however many refractory zones,

$$\mathfrak{F}_{12} = \frac{1}{\dfrac{1}{\bar{F}_{12}} + \left(\dfrac{1}{\epsilon_1} - 1\right) + \dfrac{A_1}{A_2}\left(\dfrac{1}{\epsilon_2} - 1\right)} \tag{15}$$

It is to be noted that the emissivity of the refractory surfaces forming the system is not a factor, *i.e.*, that whether a refractory surface maintains its equilibrium by complete absorption and blackbody reradiation or by complete diffuse reflection and no radiation is immaterial.

The limitation of Eq. (15) to conditions for which the division of source- and sink-type surfaces into but two zones A_1 and A_2

must be kept in mind; it is valid only when all elements of surface on A_1 (or A_2) "see" substantially the same picture, *i.e.*, when $F_{dA_1 \to 2}/F_{dA_1 \to R}$ is about the same for all points on A_1.

As in the case of $\bar{F}$, $\mathfrak{F}$ may be evaluated to any desired degree of accuracy by dividing the system into a sufficient number of zones; but most furnace problems do not justify going beyond the expression given above.

Recommended Procedure.—The use of the preceding principles is best illustrated by some examples.

Illustration 1.—What is the heat transfer by radiation between an oxidized nickel tube 4 in. o.d., at a temperature of 800°F and an enclosing chamber of silica brick at 1800°F, the brick chamber being (*a*) very large relative to the tube diameter and (*b*) 8 in. square inside?

a. Since the surroundings are large compared to the enclosed tube, it is unnecessary to allow for the emissivity of the silica brick, because the surroundings, viewed from the position of the small enclosed body, appear black; hence Eq. 3 is used. The emissivity of oxidized nickel at 800°F is, by interpolation from Table XIII, about 0.43; its absorptivity for radiation from a source at 1800° is approximately its emissivity at 1800°F, which by extrapolation is about 0.58. The tube area per foot is $\pi 4/12 = 1.05$ sq ft/ft. From Eq. 3

$$q(\text{per foot length}) = 0.173 \times 1.05 \left[0.43 \left(\frac{800 + 460}{100} \right)^4 - 0.58 \left(\frac{1800 + 460}{100} \right)^4 \right]$$

$$= -25,540 \text{ Btu}/(\text{hr})(\text{ft of tube})$$

The more usual procedure of using a single value for α and ϵ (Eq. 4) would give, for $\epsilon = 0.58$, q per foot $= -24,840$.

Had one employed Eq. 15, with $\bar{F}_{12} = F_{12} = 1$, since A_1/A_2 approaches zero, the value of $\mathfrak{F}_{12}$ is found to be

$$\mathfrak{F}_{12} = \frac{1}{\dfrac{1}{\bar{F}_{12}} + \left(\dfrac{1}{\epsilon_1} - 1 \right)} = \epsilon_1$$

i.e., the interchange factor $\mathfrak{F}_{12}$ is independent of the emissivity of the surroundings when A_1/A_2 approaches zero, and Eq. 3 applies.

b. Since the enclosure is not large, compared with the tube, it is necessary to allow for the emissivity of the silica brick, using Eq. 14.

As before, $\bar{F}_{12} = 1$. When $\epsilon_1 = 0.58$ and $\epsilon_2 = 0.8$, Eq. 15 gives

$$\mathfrak{F}_{12} = \frac{1}{1 + \left(\dfrac{1}{0.58} - 1 \right) + \dfrac{1.05}{2.67} \left(\dfrac{1}{0.8} - 1 \right)} = 0.549$$

Therefore $q = -24,840 \times 0.549/0.58 = -23,500$.

If one wished to allow for the difference between ϵ and α, an approximation for this case would be to use

$$q_{net} = A_1 \mathfrak{F}_{12} \sigma T_1^4 - A_1 \mathfrak{F}_{12} \sigma T_2^4$$

and to evaluate $\mathfrak{F}_{12}$ in the first term, using ϵ_1 and ϵ_2 at $T_1(\mathfrak{F}_{12} = 0.412)$, and in the second term, using ϵ_1 and ϵ_2 at $T_2(\mathfrak{F}_{12} = 0.549)$.

$$q_{net} = 0.173 \times 1.05(0.412 \times 12.6^4 - 0.549 \times 22.6^4) = -24,100$$

Illustration 2.—A muffle-type furnace in which the carborundum muffle forms a continuous floor of dimensions 15 by 20 ft has its ultimate heat-receiving surface in the form of a row of 4-in tubes on 9-in centers above and parallel to the muffle and backed by a well-insulated refractory roof; the distance from the muffle top to the row of tubes is 10 ft. The tubes fill the furnace top, of area equal to that of the carborundum floor. The average muffle-surface temperature is 2100°F; the tubes are at 600°F. The side walls of the chamber are assumed substantially nonconducting but reradiating and are at some equilibrium temperature between 600 and 2100°F, such that they radiate just as much heat as they receive. The tubes are oxidized steel of emissivity 0.8; the carborundum has an emissivity of 0.7. Find the radiant-heat transmission between the carborundum floor and the tubes above, taking into account the reradiation from the side walls.

Call the area of the roof tubes A_1, that of the carborundum floor A_3, that of the refractory side walls of the furnace A_R. The problem must be broken up into two parts, first considering the roof with its refractory-backed tubes. To an imaginary plane A_2 of area 15 by 20 ft located just below the tubes, the tubes emit radiation $A_1\mathfrak{F}_{12}T_1^4$, equal to $A_2\mathfrak{F}_{21}T_1^4$. To obtain $\mathfrak{F}_{21}$, one must first evaluate $\overline{F}_{12}$, which comes from Fig. 26, line 5, from which $\overline{F}_{21} = 0.84$. From Eq. 15

$$\mathfrak{F}_{21} = \cfrac{1}{\cfrac{1}{0.84} + \left(\cfrac{1}{1} - 1\right) + \cfrac{9}{4\pi}\left(\cfrac{1}{0.8} - 1\right)} = 0.73*$$

This amounts to saying that the system of refractory-backed tubes is equal in radiating power to a continuous plane A_2 replacing the tubes and refractory above them, having a temperature equal to the tubes and an equivalent or effective emissivity of 0.73.

The new simplified furnace now consists of an enclosure formed by a 15- by 20-ft rectangle A_3 of emissivity 0.7, above and parallel to it a 15- by 20-ft rectangle A_2 of temperature T_1 and emissivity 0.73, and refractory walls A_R to complete the enclosure. The desired heat transfer is $q_{2 \rightleftharpoons 3}$.

$$q_{2 \rightleftharpoons 3} = \sigma(T_1^4 - T_3^4)A_2\mathfrak{F}_{23}$$

Normally to evaluate $\mathfrak{F}_{23}$, one would find F_{23} first, then evaluate $\overline{F}_{23}$ by Eq. 12 —an approximation to the extent that it assumes a constant side-wall temperature. For the present case, however, Fig. 25, line 6, presents an exact allowance for the continuous variation in side-wall temperature from top to bottom. The interchange factor between parallel 15- by 20-ft rectangles separated by 10 ft may be taken as the geometric mean of the factors for 15-ft squares

---

* The use of Eq. 15 was hardly justifiable here, since the "views" from spots on the top and the bottom of the tubes comprising the area A_1 are so different; but when A_1 is divided into two zones, the value of $\mathfrak{F}_{21}$ is raised to only 0.74.

separated by 10- and 20-ft squares separated by 10 ft. Then, from Fig. 25, line 6, $\bar{F}_{23} = \sqrt{0.63 \times 0.69} = 0.66$. From Eq. 15,

$$\mathfrak{F}_{23} = \cfrac{1}{\cfrac{1}{0.66} + \left(\cfrac{1}{0.73} - 1\right) + 1 \cdot \left(\cfrac{1}{0.7} - 1\right)} = 0.433 = \mathfrak{F}_{32}$$

i.e., the floor and tubes interchange 43.3 per cent as much radiation as parallel black planes close together, each of area equal to the floor. The net interchange is

$$q_{net} = 0.173 \times (15 \times 20)(25.6^4 - 10.7^4)0.433 = 9,380,000 \text{ Btu/hr}$$

Illustration 3.—The distribution of radiant heat to the different rows of tubes in a tube nest irradiated from one side is desired when the tubes are 4.0 in. o.d. on 8-in. triangular centers. Let the area of the continuous plane below the tube nest be A_1 and the area of the tubes, A_2. According to Fig. 26, curve 3, the first row of tubes will intercept directly 0.66 of the total. According to curve 1, the second row will intercept 0.21 of the total, leaving $1 - 0.66 - 0.21 = 0.13$ to be intercepted by the remaining rows.

Suppose the tube nest replaced by a single row of tubes A_2 with refractory back wall A_R. Equation 12 gives $\bar{F}_{12}$. For the present case $F_{RR} = 0$ and $F_{1R} = 1 - F_{12}$ and $F_{R2} = F_{12}$; so Eq. 12 becomes

$$\bar{F}_{12} = F_{12} + (1 - F_{12})F_{12} = 0.66 + 0.34 \times 0.66 = 0.88$$

a value that could have been read from Fig. 26, curve 5. A single tube and back wall will therefore be 88 per cent as effective a heat receiver as an infinite number of rows, so far as radiant-heat transmission is concerned.

Suppose the one plane had been replaced by two rows of tubes with refractory back wall, instead of by a single row. According to Fig. 26, curves 4 and 2, the total radiation to the first row is 0.69, to the second 0.29, to both 0.69 + 0.29, or 0.98 as much as to an infinite number of rows (or to a continuous plane).

From Fig. 26, it is seen that only when the tubes are of small diameter relative to their distance apart is there any considerable quantity of radiant-heat penetration beyond the second row. The solution of a three- or four-row problem may be made readily by a method described elsewhere.[319]

Simplified Radiation Equation.

—In dealing with radiation between surfaces separated by a nonabsorbing medium, under certain circumstances (page 217) convection transfer from gas to solid may be substantial compared with that transferred by radiation. This case arises when a steam pipe having surface area A_s is exposed to colder surroundings. The rate q_c of transfer by convection is computed by the relation $q_c = h_c A_s(t_s - t_G)$, where t_G is the bulk temperature of the ambient gas; values of h_c are given on pages 240 to 250. The rate q_r of heat transfer by radiation from the surface of the pipe to the walls of the enclosure at T_e may be computed from Eq. 4 (page 52): $q_r = 0.173\epsilon_s A_s[(T_s/100)^4$

$- (T_e/100)^4]$. The total rate of heat loss, by the combined mechanisms of convection and radiation, is $q_c + q_r$, sometimes written q_{c+r}. Instead of using Eq. 4, which involves the fourth powers

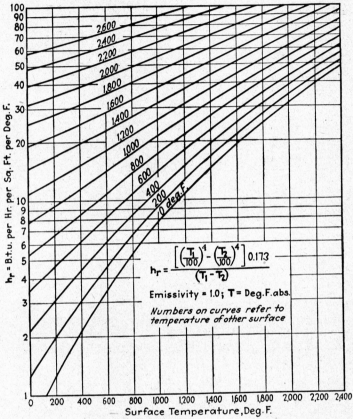

Fig. 27.—Coefficient of heat transfer by radiation, for $\epsilon = 1.0$, to be used in Eqs. 16 and 17, page 63.

of the absolute temperature on the surfaces, it is convenient to compute q_r from a simplified equation for radiation:

$$q_r = h_r(A_s)(t_s - t_e) \qquad (16)$$

which involves the first power of the difference in temperature, where h_r is defined by the relation

$$h_r = \frac{q_r}{A_s(t_s - t_e)} = \frac{0.173\epsilon_s[(T_s/100)^4 - (T_e/100)^4]}{(T_s - T_e)} \qquad (17)$$

Figure 27 shows h_r (for $\epsilon = 1$) as a function of the two temperatures involved. Since the equation is symmetrical in the two temperatures, the numbers of the abscissas may be identified with the temperature of either surface (t_s or t_e) and those on the curves as the other (t_e or t_s). Use is made of Eq. 16 and Fig. 27 on page 63.

It is sometimes convenient to replace Eq. 4, $q_r = \sigma\epsilon_1 A_1(T_1^4 - T_2^4)$ by the relation $q_r = 4\sigma\epsilon_1 A_1 T_{\text{av.}}^3 (T_1 - T_2)$, using $T_{\text{av.}} = (T_1 + T_2)/2$, which approximation introduces an error of only 10 per cent for $T_1 = 2T_2$.

At times it may simplify algebraic computation to make both convection and radiation conform to the algebraic form of the latter rather than the former; in that case, one replaces $q_c = h_c A_s(t_s - t_G)$ by $0.173\mathfrak{F}'A_s[(T_s/100)^4 - (T_G/100)^4]$, where $\mathfrak{F}'$ allows for the effect of transfer by convection, $\mathfrak{F}' = h_c(T_s - T_a)/(0.173)$ $[(T_s/100)^4 - (T_G/100)^4]$.

RADIATION FROM NONLUMINOUS GASES

If black-body radiation passes through a gas mass containing, for example, carbon dioxide, absorption occurs in certain regions of the infrared spectrum. Conversely, if the gas mass is heated it radiates in those same wave-length regions. This infrared spectrum of gases has its origin in simultaneous quantum changes in the energy levels of rotation and of interatomic vibration of the molecules[10] and, at the temperature levels reached in industrial furnaces, is of importance only in the case of the heteropolar gases. *Of the gases encountered in heat-transfer equipment, carbon monoxide, the hydrocarbons, water vapor, carbon dioxide, sulphur dioxide, ammonia, hydrogen chloride, and the alcohols possess emission bands of sufficient magnitude to merit consideration.* The gases with symmetrical molecules, hydrogen, oxygen, nitrogen, etc., have been found not to show absorption bands in those wave-length regions of importance in radiant-heat transmission at temperatures met in industrial practice.

Consider a hemispherical gas mass of radius L containing carbon dioxide of partial pressure P_c, and let the problem be the evaluation of radiant-heat interchange between the gas at temperature T_G and a black element of surface at temperature T_s, located on the base of the hemisphere at its center. Per unit of surface the emission of the gas to the surface is $\sigma T_G^4 \epsilon_G$, where ϵ_G denotes gas emissivity, the ratio of radiation from gas to surface to the radiation from a black body at the same temperature. For carbon dioxide ϵ_G depends on T_G, the total pressure, and the product term P_cL, and is given in Fig. 28, which applies for the usual case of total pressure constant at 1 atm. The absorption by the gas of radiation from the surface is $\sigma T_s^4 \alpha_G$, where α_G is the absorptivity of the gas for black-body radiation from the surface. Approximately α_G is obtained from the gas emissivity chart at the same

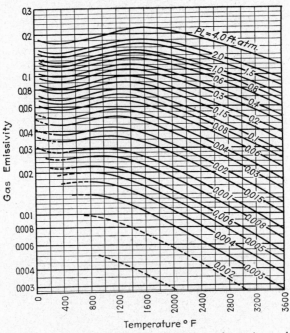

Fig. 28.—Emissivity of carbon dioxide, *vs.* temperature, for various values of P_cL.

value of P_cL as before but at the temperature T_s instead of T_G. Such an approximation is adequate if the gas is hotter than the surface and the absorption term consequently of secondary importance. If the reverse is the case, an accurate value of α_G may be obtained if one reads an emissivity from Fig. 28 at T_s, as before, but at $P_cL(T_s/T_G)$ instead of P_cL, and then multiplies the result by $(T_G/T_s)^{0.65}$.

The net radiant-heat interchange between the gas and a unit area of black bounding surface is then

$$(\sigma T_G^4 \epsilon_G - \sigma T_s^4 \alpha_G) \tag{18}$$

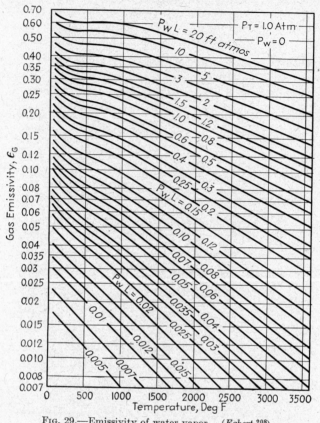

Fig. 29.—Emissivity of water vapor. (*Egbert.*[208])

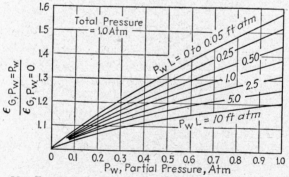

Fig. 30.—Factor C_1 vs. P_w, for various values of $P_w L$. (*Egbert.*[208])

In the case of water vapor the gas emissivity ϵ_G depends on T_G and P_wL, as before, and in addition somewhat on the partial pressure of water vapor P_w. Correlation of the data of various experimenters is found possible by reducing all measured emissivities to values corresponding to an idealized case where $P_w = 0$, by the use of a factor depending on P_w and P_wL. The smoothed curves through the resulting corrected data appear in Fig. 29 as a plot of ϵ_G vs. T_G for the various values of P_wL, for the "ideal" system at zero partial pressure of water vapor. Allowance for the finite value of P_w is then made by multiplying ϵ_G as read from Fig. 29 by a factor C_1 read from Fig. 30 as a function of P_w and P_wL.

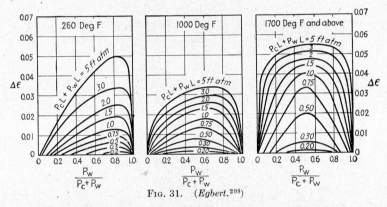

FIG. 31. (*Egbert.*[208])

Although absorption of black-body radiation by water vapor is dependent to some extent on the gas temperature, an adequate approximate value for absorptivity α_G is obtained in a manner similar to that for carbon dioxide, *i.e.*, α_G is approximately equal to gas emissivity ϵ_G calculated at P_wL and at T_s rather than T_G. The same correction C_1 for partial pressure is made as before.

When carbon dioxide and water vapor are present together, the total radiation due to both is somewhat less than the sum of the separately calculated effects, because each gas is somewhat opaque to the other. The correction for this effect may be read from Fig. 31, which gives the amount $\Delta\epsilon$ by which to reduce the sum of ϵ_G for CO_2 and ϵ_G for H_2O (each evaluated as if the other gas were absent) to obtain the ϵ_G due to the two together. The same type of correction applies in calculating α_G.

Relation 18 was restricted to interchange between a gas and its bounding surface when the latter is black. If the surface is gray, with an emissivity (and absorptivity) equal to ϵ_s, multiplication of Relation 18 by ϵ_s would make proper allowance for reduction in the primary beams from gas to surface and surface to gas, respectively; but some of the gas radiation initially reflected from the surface would have further opportunity for absorption at a surface, because the gas is but incompletely opaque to the reflected beam. Consequently, the factor by which Relation 18 is to be multiplied lies between ϵ_s and 1, the nearer the latter the more transparent the gas (*i.e.*, the lower P_cL and P_wL) and the more convoluted the surface. Rigorous treatment of the problem is tedious for engineering use. Fortunately, in the emissivity range of most industrial surfaces, 0.7 to 1.0, an adequate approximation consists in multiplying Relation 18 by an effective or pseudoemissivity ϵ_s' lying halfway between the actual value of ϵ_s and unity.

The final formulation of radiant interchange between a gas and its bounding surface when the gas contains CO_2 and H_2O is now

$$q/A \,=\, \sigma\epsilon_s'(\epsilon_G T_G^4 - \alpha_G T_S^4) = 0.173\epsilon_s'\left[\epsilon_G\left(\frac{T_G}{100}\right)^4 - \alpha_G\left(\frac{T_s}{100}\right)^4\right] \quad (19)$$

where $\epsilon_s' = (\epsilon_s + 1)/2$.

To keep straight on nomenclature, a series of subscripts will be appended to the value of ϵ read from Fig. 28 or 29, the first representing the gas (whether CO_2 or H_2O) the second the temperature on the plot (whether T_G or T_s), the third the value of PL at which ϵ is read. In this nomenclature, terms in Eq. 19 are defined as follows:

$$\epsilon_G = \epsilon_{CO_2,T_G,P_cL} + \epsilon_{H_2O,T_G,P_wL}C_1 - \Delta\epsilon_{T_G}$$
$$\alpha_G = \alpha_{CO_2} + \alpha_{H_2O} - \Delta\alpha$$
$$\alpha_{CO_2} = \epsilon_{CO_2,T_s,P_cLT_sT_G}(T_G/T_s)^{0.65}$$
$$\alpha_{H_2O} = \epsilon_{H_2O,T_s,P_wL}C_1, \text{ approximately}$$
$$\Delta\alpha = \Delta\epsilon_{T_s}$$

As previously pointed out, the error in q/A is negligible when α_{CO_2} is evaluated as ϵ_{CO_2,T_s,P_cL}, if $T_s \ll T_G$. The maximum error so introduced is about 10 per cent when T_s equals $0.8T_G$.

Relation 18 (or 19) was formulated for the case of interchange between a gas hemisphere and a spot on its base, *i.e.*, for the case in which the length of path L of the radiant beam is the same in all directions. For gas shapes of industrial importance, it is found that any shape is approximately representable by an "equivalent" hemisphere of proper radius, or that there is a mean beam length that can be used in evaluating gas emissivities and absorptivities from Figs. 28 and 29. As PL approaches zero, the mean beam length approaches as a limit the value four times the ratio of gas volume to bounding area, or four times the mean hydraulic radius. For the range of PL encountered in practice, L is always less; 85 per cent of the limiting value is generally a satisfactory approximation.[568] Table II summarizes the results of tedious graphical or analytical treatment of various special shapes.

TABLE II.—BEAM LENGTHS FOR GAS RADIATION

Shape	Characterizing dimension D	Factor by which D is multiplied to obtain mean beam length L	
		When $PL = 0$	For average values of PL
Sphere........................	Diameter	⅔	0.60
Infinite cylinder.................	Diameter	1	0.90
Same, radiating to center of base...	Diameter	......	0.90
Right circular cylinder, height = diameter, radiating to center of base........................	Diameter	......	0.77
Same, radiating to whole surface...	Diameter	⅔	0.60
Infinite cylinder of half-circular cross section. Radiating to spot on middle of flat side...........	Radius	......	1.26
Space between infinite parallel planes......................	Distance between planes	2	1.8
Cube........................	Edge	⅔	0.60
1 × 2 × 6 rectangular parallelepiped, radiating to...	Shortest edge		
2 × 6 face....................	....	1.18 ⎫	
1 × 6 face....................	....	1.24 ⎪	1.06
1 × 2 face....................	....	1.18 ⎬	
All faces.....................	....	1.20 ⎭	
Space outside infinite bank of tubes with centers on equilateral triangles; tube diameter = clearance......................	Clearance	3.4	2.8
Same as preceding, except tube diameter = one-half clearance...	Clearance	4.45	3.8
Same, except tube centers on squares; diameter = clearance...	Clearance	4.1	3.5

In some problems (page 78) it is desirable to evaluate an equivalent gray-body emissivity of a gas mass or flame, ϵ_F, which serves both as emissivity and as absorptivity, such that for radiant interchange with black surroundings $q/A = \sigma\epsilon_F(T_G^4 - T_S^4)$. Comparison with Eq. 19 indicates that

$$\epsilon_F = \frac{\epsilon_G - \alpha_G(T_s/T_G)^4}{1 - (T_s/T_G)^4} \qquad (20)$$

If gas radiation occurs in equipment in which there is a continuous change in temperature of the gas and the surface from one end to the other of the interchanger, exact allowance therefor can be made by conventional graphical integration. To a generally adequate degree of approximation, however, one may use a mean surface temperature equal to the arithmetic mean, and a mean gas temperature equal to the mean surface temperature plus the logarithmic mean of the temperature difference, gas to surface, at the two ends:

$$t_{s,\mathrm{av}} = \frac{(t_{s1} + t_{s2})}{2} \qquad (21)$$

$$t_{G,\mathrm{av}} = t_{s,\mathrm{av}} + \frac{(t_{G1} - t_{s1}) - (t_{G2} - t_{s2})}{2.3 \log \dfrac{(t_{G1} - t_{s1})}{(t_{G2} - t_{s2})}} \qquad (22)$$

Effect of Presence of Two Surfaces at Different Temperatures.— When a radiating gas fills a chamber, the walls of which consist of the ultimate heat-receiving surface and of an intermediate heat receiver and reradiator such as a refractory surface, the question arises as to how to evaluate the total heat interchange between gas and ultimate heat receiver by the combined mechanisms of direct radiation from the gas to the ultimate receiver and radiation from the gas to the refractory surface and thence to the ultimate receiver. This problem, in its general form involving heat balances, external heat losses from the furnace, and convection heat transfer inside the chamber, is treated in detail in the last part of the present section (page 78). As an approximation, however, the total heat transfer to the ultimate receiver may be estimated by assuming that its effective area is that of itself plus a certain fraction f of that of the refractory and that the only temperatures involved are those of the gas and the ultimate receiving surface. The fraction f, the effectiveness of the refractory surface, varies from zero when the ratio of refractory surface to ultimate receiving surface is very high, to unity when the ratio is very low and the value of ϵ_F is low. When the refractory-surface area and ultimate heat-receiving surface area are of the same order of magnitude, a value of 0.7 may be used for f, although for more exact calculations the method of the last section of this chapter should be used.

Radiation from Sulphur Dioxide.—In the design of sulphur burners and of sulphur-dioxide coolers, the radiation from the gas may be a major factor in the evaluation of the total heat transferred.

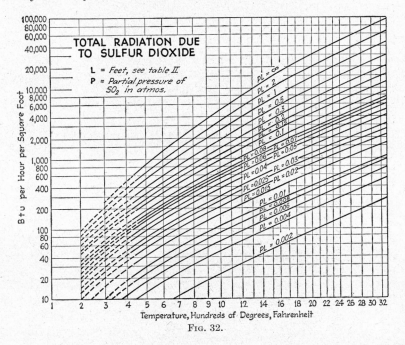

Fig. 32.

The data of Coblentz[131] on the infrared absorption spectrum of sulphur dioxide, although hardly adequate as a basis for quantitative calculations, have been used for want of something better. The results are presented in Fig. 32, by Guerrieri, in a form similar to the water-vapor and carbon-dioxide plots. The equation of radiant-heat transfer is

$$q/A = \epsilon_s(S_g - S_s) \tag{23}$$

in which q/A is Btu /(sq ft bounding surface)(hr); ϵ_s, emissivity of the surface; S_g, the sulphur-dioxide radiation, as read from Fig. 32 corresponding to the gas temperature; S_s the same, but corresponding to the surface temperature and representing, therefore, the amount of radiation from the surface that is absorbed by the gas.

Radiation from Other Gases.—Measurements of total radiation from carbon monoxide have been made by Ullrich,[724] who found that the gas emissivity is a maximum at around 1600°F, that at $PL = 2$ its emission is about half that of carbon dioxide at all temperatures from 600 to 2500°F, and that at $PL = 0.01$ its emission varies from 40 to 90 per cent of that of carbon dioxide as the temperature varies from 600 to 2500°F.

Measurements of total radiation from ammonia have been made by Port,[568] who found that the gas emissivity is very high compared with carbon dioxide or water vapor, that it decreases continuously from room temperature up, that at $PL = 2$ it varies from one to two times that of water vapor, and that at $PL = 0.01$ it varies from 1.5 to four times that of water vapor over the range, room temperature to 2000°F.

For other gases of interest one must rely on evaluations similar to those on SO_2 above, based on the infrared absorption spectra of the gases in question. For the method of such calculation and for a more complete story on gas radiation see Schack,[625] Hottel,[317] Schmidt,[635] Fishenden,[223] Hottel and Mangelsdorf,[323] Hottel and Smith,[324] Eckert,[207] and Hottel and Egbert.[321]

Illustration 4.—Flue gas containing 6 per cent carbon dioxide and 11 per cent water vapor by volume (wet basis) flows through the convection bank of an oil tube still consisting of rows of 4-in. tubes on 8-in. centers, nine 25-ft tubes in a row, the rows staggered to put the tubes on equilateral triangular centers. The flue gas enters at 1600 and leaves at 1000°F. The oil flows countercurrent to the gas and rises from 600 to 800°F. Tube-surface emissivity is 0.8. What is the average heat input rate, due to gas radiation alone, per square foot of external tube area?

In addition to the direct radiation from gas to tubes, there will be some reradiation from the refractory walls bounding the chamber, the effect of which may be determined approximately by the method discussed on page 71. With each row of tubes there is associated $8/12 \times \sqrt{3}/2$ or 0.577 ft of wall height, of area $(8/12 \times 9 \times 2 + 25 \times 2) \times 0.577 = 35.8$ sq ft. One row of tubes has an area of $\pi \times 4/12 \times 25 \times 9 = 25$ sq ft. If the recommended factor of 0.7 on the refractory area is used, the effective area of the tubes is $\dfrac{235 + 0.7 \times 35.8}{235}$ $= 1.11$ sq ft/sq ft of actual area. The exact evaluation of outside tube temperature from the known oil temperature would involve a knowledge of oil-film coefficient, tube-wall resistance, and rate of heat flow into the tube, the evaluation usually involving trial and error. However, for the present purpose the temperature drop through the tube wall and oil film will be assumed 75°F, making the tube surface temperatures 675 and 875°F; average 775°F. The radiating-gas temperature is

$$t_g = 775 + \frac{(1600 - 875) - (1000 - 675)}{2.3 \log \dfrac{1600 - 875}{1000 - 675}} = 775 + 499 = 1274°F$$

According to Table II, $L = 2.8 \times$ the clearance between tubes, or $2.8 \times \frac{4}{12}$ $= 0.935$ ft. $P_w L = 0.11 \times 0.935 = 0.102; P_c L = 0.06 \times 0.935 = 0.056; P_c L$ $(T_s/T_G) = 0.056(775 + 460)/(1274 + 460) = 0.040$. From Fig. 28 for CO_2, ϵ_{CO_2} (at $t_G = 1274$, $P_c L = 0.056) = 0.064$; α_{CO_2} (at $t_s = 775$, $PL = 0.040$) $= 0.0535 \times (1734/1235)^{0.65} = 0.067$. From Figs. 29 and 30 for H_2O, ϵ_{H_2O} (at $t_G = 1274$, $PL = 0.102$, $P_w = 0.111) = 0.064 \times 1.07 = 0.068$; at $t_s = 775$, $P_w L = 0.102$, $P_w = 0.11$, $\alpha_w = 0.085 \times 1.07 = 0.091$. From Fig. 31, by interpolation $\Delta\epsilon = 0.001$, and $\Delta\alpha = 0$ (both negligible). Substituting in Eq. 19, $q/A = 0.9 \times 0.173$ $[17.34^4(0.064 + 0.068 - 0.001)$ $- 12.35^4(0.067 + 0.091)] = 1275$ Btu/(sq ft)(hr), exclusive of effect of refractory surfaces, or approximately $1275 \times 1.11 = 1415$ Btu/(sq ft tube area) (hr). This is equivalent to a convection coefficient of $1415/499$, or 2.8, which is the order of magnitude expected of the convection coefficient itself.

RADIATION FROM CLOUDS OF PARTICLES

The treatment of radiation from powdered-coal flames, from dust particles in flames, and from flames made luminous by the thermal decomposition of hydrocarbons to soot involves the evaluation of radiation from clouds of particles. Powdered-coal flames contain particles varying in size from 0.01 to 0.0 in., with an average size in the neighborhood of 0.001 in., and a composition varying from a high percentage of carbon to nearly pure ash. The suspended matter in luminous gas flames has its origin in the thermal decomposition of hydrocarbons in the flame due to incomplete mixing with air before being heated, consists of carbon and of very heavy hydrocarbons, and has an initial particle size of about 0.000012 in. The powdered-coal particles are sufficiently large to be substantially opaque to radiation incident on them, whereas the particles of a luminous flame* are so small as to act like semitransparent bodies with respect to thermal or long wave-length radiation. This difference in transparency of the individual particles justifies a separate treatment of the two types of flames.

Luminous Flames.—There are two methods of attacking the problem of developing a suitable method for predicting the radiation to be expected from a luminous flame. The first is to collect data

---

* The term *luminous flame*, as used in this section, always refers to a flame made luminous by soot particles formed in the flame, not to the presence of macroscopic dust or powdered-coal particles or metal vapors or to the bluish gas flames obtained with a high degree of primary aeration.

on actual flames under varying conditions of aeration, fuel-gas composition, flame volume, etc., and to use the data as a basis for calculations. Unfortunately the published data of this sort are woefully inadequate, usually consisting of a measurement of total radiation from small laboratory flames, with no basis for determining the opacity of the flame or, consequently, the radiation from a larger flame of similar type. The changes in soot concentration attending changes in burner design, shape of combustion chamber, degree of primary and secondary aeration, fuel-gas composition, and draft regulation all make the estimation of the luminous-flame radiation to be expected in a proposed installation exceedingly uncertain.

.It is possible to show, however, how data may be obtained from a furnace with known conditions of combustion, and applied to a different size or shape of furnace in which the conditions of combustion are roughly the same. From a quantitative investigation of the variation, with wave length of the monochromatic absorptivity of luminous flames, it has been shown by Hottel and Broughton[320] that the absorptivity (and emissivity) decreases with increase in wave length and that the total emissivity is less than the emissivity in the visible spectrum. This makes direct visual estimation of luminous-flame emissivity very misleading. However, by the use of an optical pyrometer containing color screens of different wave lengths (red and green), it is shown that two apparent temperatures, the red brightness temperature T_r and the green brightness temperature T_g may be obtained, which permit a calculation of both true flame temperature and total flame emissivity. Figure 33 is a working plot (in degrees Kelvin) from which the true temperature may be obtained, given T_r and $\Delta(= T_g - T_r)$. On the same plot one obtains the value of the absorption strength $K_1 L_F$, in which K_1 is a term measuring the soot concentration of the flame, and L_F is the thickness of flame through which the pyrometer is sighted. With absorption strength known, Fig. 34 may be used to determine the effective emissivity of the flame envelope. The transfer of heat from the flame envelope of area A and true flame temperature T_F to the confining walls of temperature T_s is given by

$$q = 0.173A \left[\left(\frac{T_F}{100} \right)^4 - \left(\frac{T_s}{100} \right)^4 \right] \cdot \epsilon_F \cdot \epsilon_s' \qquad (24)$$

in which ϵ_F is the emissivity of the flame envelope as determined by Fig. 34, and ϵ_s' is the effective emissivity of the surroundings.

If an optical pyrometer with both red and green screens is not available, Fig. 33 may still be used to determine absorption strength: (1) if the red brightness temperature T_r is determined with an ordinary optical pyrometer and the true temperature T_F with a high-velocity thermocouple; or (2) if a mirror is held behind the flame in the line of sight of the optical pyrometer. The first method is open to the serious objection that the absorption strength K_1L_F changes rapidly with a change in the usually small quantity

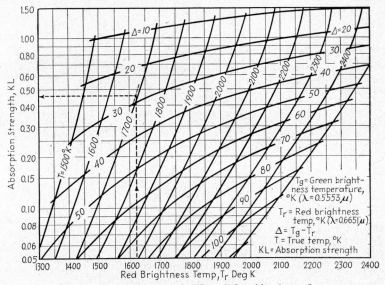

Fig. 33.—Absorption strength KL or K_1L_F of luminous flames.

$T_F - T_r$ representing the difference between the temperature readings of two entirely different kinds of instruments.

In using the two-color principle for determining the true temperature and total emissivity of a flame, it should be borne in mind that the pyrometer must not "see" anything but the flame itself; *i.e.*, the background of the flame should be an open peephole in the back wall of the furnace or a cold nonreflecting surface, never a hot refractory surface. When temperature measurements have been made on an industrial flame of one size to determine its absorption strength K_1L_F, for the purpose of estimating the emissivity ϵ_F of a similar but larger flame, the absorption strength (K_1L_F), determined from Fig. 33 should be multiplied by the dimension ratio L_2/L_1 before Fig. 34 is used. In addition, the value of K_1L_F should correspond to the particular shape of flame under consideration, in accordance with the principles discussed in connection with the use of Table II.   An example will be found on page 77.

The data available on luminous flames in industrial furnaces indicate that radiation from the soot is frequently of a greater order of magnitude than nonluminous gas radiation.   Lent[430] has made a blast-furnace gas flame practically black by addition of benzene to form soot.   Haslam and Boyer[285] found that a luminous acetylene flame radiated roughly four times as much heat as when nonluminous and the size of their experimental flame was such as to indicate

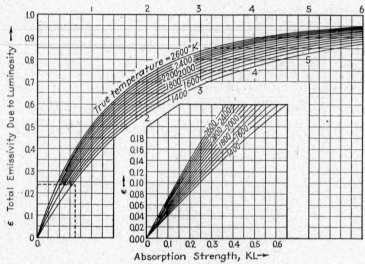

Fig. 34.—Emissivity of luminous flames.

that maximum blackness had not been obtained.   Sherman[654] has measured emissivities of luminous gas flames in an experimental furnace.

Powdered-coal Flames.—The radiation from powdered-coal flames has been treated analytically by Wohlenberg and his associates[776,775] by Haslam and Hottel[286] and by Lindmark et al.[438] Experimental studies have been conducted by Lindmark (ibid.) and by Sherman.[655]

It may be shown that the emissivity of a cloud of opaque particles, based on the area of the envelope of the whole cloud, is of the form $(1 - e^{-\gamma})$, in which γ is the product term, (concentration of particles) (time-average cross section of a particle) (length of radiant beam through cloud), the last term being defined as in

Table II. By making suitable assumptions as to the laws of particle-size distribution in pulverized coal and the rate of combustion of individual particles, one may use the foregoing exponential relation to calculate the emissivity of a pulverized-coal flame. Values so obtained, however, are almost invariably considerably lower than measured flame emissivities. The discrepancy is probably due to the contribution of cracked hydrocarbons producing luminosity as well as to residual ash particles not allowed for in the theoretical derivation. Fortunately, modern pulverized-coal installations involve such large flames that their emissivity is not far from unity.

Illustration 5.—It is desired to determine approximately the radiation from a proposed luminous-flame burner installation, from measurements made on a similar combustion chamber all the dimensions of which are one-half those of the proposed installation. It is intended to keep aeration and mixing conditions as similar as possible in the two chambers. The flame in each case is roughly spherical in form. An optical pyrometer with red and green screens is sighted through the smaller flame at its diameter, the apparent temperatures obtained being $T_r = 2699°F$ ($= 1755°K$), and $T_g = 2740°F$ ($= 1778°K$). (a) What are the emissivity and true temperature of the smaller flame? (b) What will be the probable rate of heat transfer per square foot of flame envelope of the proposed larger installation if the flame temperature is the same and the surrounding walls are at 2600°F and black?

a. From Fig. 33, when the red brightness temperature T_r of the flame is 1755°K and the difference between T_g and T_r is $1778 - 1755 = 23°K$, the true-flame temperature is found to be 1811°K and the absorption strength $K_1 L_F$ is 0.7. This value of $K_1 L_F$, however, corresponds to length of radiant beam L equal to the diameter of the flame sphere. According to Table II, the average value of L is 0.6 times the diameter when the radiating shape is spherical. Then the average absorption strength is $0.7 \times 0.6 = 0.42$. From Fig. 34, when $K_1 L_F = 0.20$ and true-flame temperature $= 1811°K$, the flame emissivity is 0.20.

b. If the flame dimensions are doubled, other things being equal, the absorption strength $K_1 L_F$ will double. When $K_1 L_F = 2 \times 0.42 = 0.84$, Fig. 34 indicates that the flame emissivity will be 0.365 (not double the value 0.20). The net radiation per square foot of flame envelope will be

$$\frac{q}{A} = 0.173 \times 0.365 \times \left[\left(\frac{1811 \times 1.8}{100} \right)^4 - \left(\frac{2600 + 460}{100} \right)^4 \right] = 16{,}100 \frac{\text{Btu}}{(\text{sq ft})(\text{hr})}$$

The General Problem of Heat Transfer in a Combustion Chamber.—One of the most complex problems of heat transmission is the evaluation of the performance of a combustion chamber of a furnace, in which heat is being transmitted simultaneously by all or most of the mechanisms so far discussed. Two methods of treatment of this problem are possible: either (1) the theoretical one in which the attempt is made to consider the various individual factors, each acting in accordance with the principles discussed previously, and to combine them; or (2) the empirical one in which furnace test data are analyzed in the attempt to detect the effect of factors suspected of being of importance. These methods will be considered in order.

Allowance is to be made for the combined actions of direct radiation from the flame to the stock or heat sink; radiation from flame to refractory surfaces, thence back through the flame (with partial absorption therein) to the sink, convection; and external losses. A solution of the problem is possible if the following assumptions are accepted: (1) external losses from refractory walls equal convection from flame to refractory; (2) the flame is gray and has an emissivity ϵ_F, evaluated as discussed on page 70; (3) all refractory surfaces have a common average (but unknown) temperature; (4) a mean temperature T_F is assignable to the flame and combustion products in the chamber; (5) the heat sink or ultimate receiver has a uniform surface temperature T_C and is gray, with emissivity ϵ_C and area A_C. The solution of the problem, giving the net rate of heat transfer q_F from the flame by all mechanisms, is

$$q_F = \underbrace{\sigma(T_F^4 - T_C^4)A_C\mathfrak{F}_{CF}}_{\text{Radiation to sink}} + \underbrace{h_C A_C'(T_F - T_C)}_{\text{Convection to sink}} + \underbrace{U_R A_R(T_F - T_O)}_{\text{External loss*}} \quad (25)$$

in which

$$\mathfrak{F}_{CF} = \cfrac{1}{\cfrac{1}{\overline{F}_{CF}} + \cfrac{1}{\epsilon_C} - 1} \quad (26)$$

$$\overline{F}_{CF} = \epsilon_F\left(1 + \cfrac{A_R/A_C}{1 + \cfrac{\epsilon_F}{1 - \epsilon_F} \cdot \cfrac{1}{F_{RC}}}\right) \quad (27)$$

$$U_R = \cfrac{1}{\cfrac{1}{h_R} + \cfrac{x_w}{k_w} + \cfrac{1}{h_o}} \quad (28)$$

In these equations h_C, h_R, and h_o represent convection coefficients at the sink, inside refractory, and outside refractory surfaces, respectively; x_w and k_w are wall thickness and thermal conductivity of the refractory; T_O is outside air temperature; A_C' differs from A_C in excluding that cold surface or ultimate-receiver area that, though in view of the flame and receiving radiation, does not receive heat by convection from the gases until they leave the chamber.

It is to be noted that, as in the case of radiation in an enclosure containing no radiating or absorbing gas (page 59), $\mathfrak{F}$ is built up from $\overline{F}$ and ϵ_C and $\overline{F}$ from F; but here the flame emissivity ϵ_F is in addition involved Some simplification is possible if the geometrical factor F_{RC}—the fraction of the radiation leaving refractory surfaces that is directed toward the "cold" surface or heat sink—is replaced by $A_C/(A_R + A_C)$—a fair approximation when the refrac-

* The external loss has been assumed equal to the convection to the refractory.

tory and cold surfaces are not completely segregated from each other. Then

$$q_F = \sigma(T_F^4 - T_C^4)A_C\left[\cfrac{1}{\cfrac{1}{\epsilon_C} + \cfrac{A_C}{A_C + A_R}\left(\cfrac{1}{\epsilon_F} - 1\right)}\right] + h_c A_C'(T_F - T_C)$$

$$+ U_R A_R(T_F - T_O) \quad (29)$$

From this simplified form much more readily than from the more general Eq. 25 it is to be noted that increasing the flame emissivity increases the heat transmission, but not proportionately; that decreasing surface emissivity (and absorptivity) from unity when the flame is very transparent produces almost no effect on the heat transmission; but that decreasing ϵ_C from unity when the flame is substantially opaque ($\epsilon_F = 1$) produces a proportional decrease in heat transmission.

The derivation of Eq. 25 (or Eq. 29) was based on the assumption that A_C was composed of plane areas. Suppose instead that A_C is a row of tubes mounted in front of a refractory wall. A little consideration will show that the value of A_C to use in the radiation term of the foregoing equations is the continuous plane A_p in which the tubes are located, multiplied by the proper factor $\bar{F}$ for tubes with a refractory background (see Fig. 26), and that the refractory surface A_R should be increased by the amount $(1 - \bar{F})A_p$.

Equation 25 (or Eq. 29) expresses a relation between two unknowns T_F and q_F, and a second relation is necessary if a solution is to be obtained. The other relation is an energy balance. If one assumes turbulence to be so great that the mean flame temperature T_F used for calculation of radiation is the same as the temperature T_G of the gas leaving the chamber, then

$$q_F = i - w_G(c_p)_m(T_F - T_0) \quad (30)$$

where i represents the hourly enthalpy or heat content of the entering fuel, air, and recirculated flue gas, if any, above a base temperature T_0 (water as vapor); and $(c_p)_m$ represents the mean heat capacity (evaluated between T_F and T_0) of the gas leaving the chamber, at hourly mass rate w_G. Equation 25 (or Eq. 29) and 30 may be solved by trial and error or by graphical methods involving superimposed plots.

The pair of equations just discussed applies strictly to one of two limiting furnace types—that one in which the assignment of a mean flame temperature equal to the temperature of the gases leaving is justifiable. For this to be the case, combustion must be relatively slow, delayed by retarded mixing of secondary air with the flame and progressing uniformly at all points in the chamber. Better agreement between predicted and experimental results is obtained on some furnaces when the assumption is made that flame temperature and exit gas temperature are not the same but differ by a constant amount. In a number of furnace tests the difference was about 300°F.

The other extreme in furnace types is that one in which combustion occurs substantially instantaneously at the burners (through complete premixing of fuel and air); the temperature attained is that generally known as *theoretical flame temperature* or *adiabatic-combustion temperature;* and the temperature falls continuously as the gases flow from burner to outlet. When such a furnace is long compared to its cross section normal to the direction of gas flow, Eq. 29 (or Eq. 25) may be considered as applying to a differential length of furnace, and the solution of the problem involves either a tedious but straightforward graphical integration or the use of a suitable mean of T_{F_1} and T_{F_2} in Eq. 29. Equation 30, of course, becomes $q_F = i - w_G(c_p)_m(T_{F_2} - T_0)$.

Simplified Treatment of Combustion-chamber Heat Transmission.—Equation 25 or its equivalent has been used as a basis for deriving various simplified relations, easier to use but restricted in applicability in proportion to the degree of simplification. Several of these will be presented.

Billet-reheating Furnaces.—For continuous billet-reheating furnaces Eq. 25 has been modified as follows: (1) q is heat transferred to the stock, not from the flame; (2) convection terms have been omitted; (3) to compensate therefor and to allow for steadiness of furnace operation, $\mathfrak{F}_{CF}$ is evaluated using $1.2r_f \cdot \epsilon_F$ instead of ϵ_F, where r_f is the ratio of average billet-pushing rate over a period of several hours to pushing rate during periods of steady operation; (4) ϵ_F is flame emissivity due to CO_2 and H_2O only, as discussed under Gas Radiation; (5) $F_{RC} = A_C F_{CR}/A_R = A_C/A_R$; (6) an average value of $(T_F^4 - T_C^4)$ is used, equal to the geometric mean of its value at the two ends of the furnace, and at the hot end T_F is taken as the calculated "theoretical" flame temperature, or adiabatic-combustion temperature. The equation has been tested on reheating furnaces of various types and found satisfactory by Eberhardt and Hottel.[204]

Petroleum Heaters.—For cracking-coil and tube-still furnaces Eq. 25 has been modified by Hottel[319b] as follows: (1) by omitting the last term, q becomes heat transferred to oil instead of heat lost by flame; (2) $h_c A_c'$ has for simplification been assigned an average value equal to $7A_C\mathfrak{F}_{CF}$ (the term is unimportant relative to the radiation term). The relation is then

$$q_C = [\sigma(T_F^4 - T_C^4) + 7(T_F - T_C)]A_C\mathfrak{F}_{CF} \tag{31}$$

Comments on page 79 concerning the proper values of A_C and A_R for the case of tubes mounted on a wall apply. In evaluating $\mathfrak{F}_{CF}$, ϵ_F is calculated allowing for gas radiation only; $\epsilon_C = 0.9$. In applying Eq. 31 to data for 19 furnaces, Lobo and Evans[439] found that F_{RC} was represented closely by $A_C/(A_C + A_R)$ for values of A_R/A_C from 0 to 1, by A_C/A_R for values of A_R/A_C from 3 to 6.5. Since Eq. 31 involves heat received by oil rather than heat lost by the flame, when it is combined with the energy balance represented by Eq. 30, the latter must be modified. The term i is replaced by

$i - q_L$, where q_L is the external heat loss from the combustion chamber. A simplified graphical treatment of the solution of Eqs. 30 and 31 is available (Lobo and Evans[439]) together with a comparison of results with 85 tests on 19 furnaces of widely different types and excess air, burning fuel oil, or refinery gas; the average deviation was 5.3 per cent; excluding tests almost certainly faulty, the average deviation was less than 4 per cent ($q_{exp.}$ *vs.* $q_{calc.}$).

A relation for petroleum heaters, somewhat easier to use than Eq. 31 but not so safe, is obtainable by assuming certain terms in Eq. 25 constant, combining with Eq. 30 to eliminate T_F, and finding an expression different in form but numerically similar over the range of interest. The relation is

$$\eta = \frac{1}{1 + \dfrac{\sqrt{i/A_c \mathfrak{F}_{CF}}}{1.4 \left(\dfrac{i/w_G(c_p)_m}{100}\right)^{1.6}}} \tag{32}$$

where η is the ratio of heat transferred to oil to the enthalpy of the entering air and fuel (net value). Other equations applicable in this field are those of Wilson, Lobo, and Hottel,[770] and of Mekler.[477]

Steam-boiler Furnaces.—For calculating heat transmission in the radiant sections of steam-boiler furnace settings, many empirical relations are available. One of the simplest is the Orrok-Hudson equation

$$\eta = \frac{1}{1 + \dfrac{r_{af} \sqrt{w_A}}{27}} \tag{33}$$

in which r_{af} is the weight ratio of air to fuel; w_A is the firing rate expressed as pounds of equivalent good bituminous coal per hour per square foot of exposed tube area (complete circumference if not buried in wall).

Mullikin[493] assumes that the flame emissivity ϵ_F is unity for large pulverized coal-, oil-, or gas-fired furnaces and that compensation for this somewhat too high value comes from use of the same value for gas temperature in Eqs. 25 and 30. When ϵ_F is unity, the term $A_c \mathfrak{F}_{CF}$ of Eq. 25 becomes simply $A_c \epsilon_c$ (though the remarks on page 79 concerning proper evaluation of A_c apply). Mullikin introduces additional multiplying factors on A_c to allow for resistance of overlying slag or refractory facing on metal-block walls. These are 0.7 for bare-faced metal blocks on tubes and 0.35 for refractory-faced metal blocks on tubes. The simplification suggested is unsafe to use on small furnaces, where ϵ_F is certainly not unity.

Wohlenberg and Mullikin[777] have presented a somewhat more rigorous analysis of the same data.

Wohlenberg[776,777] uses a relation intrinsically similar to Eq. 29, together with a heat balance involving the assumption of equality of flame and exit-gas temperatures; he presents the relation for η in the form of the product of a number of quantities each making separate allowance for one of the variables under control.

Illustration 6.—Natural gas is being burned for steam generation in a combustion chamber of whch the back wall and floor are water-cooled. The gas passes through a tube nest directly above and covering the top of the combustion chamber. The chamber is 16 ft wide by 16 ft long by 20 ft high. The gas, fired at the rate of 130,000 cu ft/hr (measured and fired at 60°F, 30 in. Hg, saturated) with 15 per cent excess air (saturated) has the equivalent composition $C_{1.25}H_{4.5}$ and a net heating value of 1070 Btu/cu ft. The "cold" surfaces of the chamber have an average temperature of 350°F. What is the rate of heat input to the water-cooled walls, floor, and tubes above, exclusive of any convection to the roof tubes as the gas passes up through them? What percentage of the enthalpy of the entering fuel does this represent?

Derived Data.—By stoichiometry,[325,434] the products of combustion contain 8.60 per cent CO_2, 16.36 per cent H_2O, 2.44 per cent O_2, and 72.60 per cent N_2, wet basis; their total is 4910 lb-mols. From specific-heat charts the average molal heat capacity of the products between 2000 and 60°F is 8.25; between 2500 and 60°F it is 8.45.

Assumptions.—The external loss from the refractory walls will be assumed equal to the convection to them on the inside. Convection coefficients inside the chamber = 2.0. Refractory wall conductance $k_w/x_w = 0.9$. The flame completely fills the chamber. To the emissivity of the flame due to nonluminous gases will be added 0.1 to allow for the luminosity due to cracked hydrocarbons in the flame (this varies enormously with burner type). The emissivity of the "cold" surfaces = 0.8, and absorptivity equals emissivity. The mean flame temperature is 100°F above the exit-gas temperature (these approach one another as firing rate increases).

Solution.—Equations 25 and 30 are to be solved for q_F and T_F. $A_C = 16 \times 20 + 16 \times 16 \times 2 = 832$ sq ft. (The effective area of the tube nest, for radiation reception, is that of a plane replacing the tubes.) $A_R = 16 \times 20 \times 3 = 960$ sq ft. $A_C' = 16 \times 20 + 16 \times 16 = 576$ (plane of tube nest is excluded here). Evaluation of $\mathfrak{F}$ involves F_{RC} (or F_{CR}) and ϵ_F. In this problem F_{RC} and F_{CR} are equally tedious to evaluate; F_{RC} shall be chosen. Since the three refractory rectangles do not all "see" the same arrangement of surfaces above them, it is necessary to determine the product $A_R F_{RC}$ for each and to add them, then to divide by the total A_R. Consider first the front wall, 16 by 20 ft, which "sees" three cold faces, one directly opposite, one above, and one below. The fraction of its radiation intercepted by the wall opposite comes from Fig. 25, line 2. By the method of Illustration 2 of this section, $F = \sqrt{0.196 \times 0.26}$

= 0.225, the fraction of the radiation from the front refractory wall intercepted by the rear water-cooled wall. To find the fraction intercepted by the water-cooled floor, reference is made to Fig. 24. From that figure, when $Y = 20/16$ and $Z = 16/16$, $F = 0.17$. Since the imaginary top plane replacing the tubes intercepts the same fraction as the water-cooled floor, the total fraction intercepted by cold surfaces is $0.17 \times 2 + 0.225 = 0.565$; and $A_R F_{RC}$ for the front refractory wall is $16 \times 20 \times 0.565 = 181$ sq ft. A similar procedure leads to the value $(0.17 \times 2 + 0.213)$ or 0.553 as the fraction of the radiation from either refractory side wall which is intercepted by the three cold faces. Then the final value of F_{RC} is

$$F_{RC} = \frac{(16)(20)(0.565) + (16)(20)(0.553)(2)}{(16)(20) + (16)(20)(2)} = 0.56$$

Flame emissivity ϵ_F is next to be evaluated. The equivalent gray-body emissivity of a flame at T_G in interchange with cold surfaces at T_S is given by Eq. 20, the terms of which are the same as in Eq. 19.

One must first make a provisional guess as to the value of t_G and adjust later if necessary. Temporarily assume 2500°F. The effective beam length for gas radiation would be 0.6 times one side if the chamber were cubical (see Table II); 0.6 times an average side of 18 ft, or 10.8 ft, may be used (a considerable error in this assumption will not materially affect the result). Then $P_C L = (0.086)$ $(10.8) = 0.93$, and $P_W L = (0.1636)(10.8) = 1.77$. Because t_S is so low compared to t_G, the approximate method of determining α_G for CO_2 will be used (see page 65). At $t_G = 2500$°F and $t_S = 350°$, using Figs. 28, 29, and 31 and substituting into foregoing Eq. 20, one obtains

$$\epsilon_F = \frac{(0.11 + 0.193 \times 1.08 - 0.05) - \left(\frac{810}{2960}\right)^4 (0.12 + 0.35 \times 1.08 - 0.028)}{1 - (810/2960)^4}$$
$$= 0.27$$

due to gas radiation. (In this particular example ϵ_F could have been taken as the sum of the ϵ_G's with no allowance for the absorption terms.) Adding an allowance for soot luminosity, $\epsilon_F = 0.37$. From Eq. 27,

$$\overline{F}_{CF} = 0.37 \left(1 + \frac{960/832}{1 + \frac{0.37}{0.63} \cdot \frac{1}{0.56}} \right) = 0.578$$

In using Eq. 26 to allow for the effect of receiver-surface emissivity, one should note that the radiation-receiving surfaces are of two kinds, plane surfaces in floor and back wall and a nest of tubes in the roof. The former will have an emissivity (or absorptivity) of 0.8. The tube nest will exhibit an effective absorptivity much higher, because any beams penetrating up between tubes will have many chances for absorption after reflection. In the present example a mean value of 0.9 will be used on the whole of A_C. Then, by Eq. 26,

$$\mathfrak{F}_{CF} = \frac{1}{\frac{1}{0.578} + \frac{1}{0.9} - 1} \cdot 1 = 0.544$$

This amounts to saying that the flame-wall system interchanges 54 per cent as much heat as a system of parallel black planes close together, having an area A_C and temperatures T_F and T_C. The over-all refractory-wall coefficient = U = $1/(\frac{1}{2} + 1/0.9 + \frac{1}{2})$ = 0.47. Substitution into Eq. 25 now gives

$$q_F = 0.173 \left\{ \left(\frac{T_F}{100}\right)^4 - \left(\frac{810}{100}\right)^4 \right\} (832)(0.544) + (2)(576)(T_F - 810)$$
$$+ (0.47)(960)(T_F - 520)$$

An energy balance, Eq. 30 (with the gas-exit temperature assumed 100°F below T_F), gives

$$q_F = (130,000)(1070) - (4911)(8.45)(T_F - 100 - 520)$$

Solution by trial and error of these two simultaneous equations gives T_F = 2780 (2320°F) and q_F = 50,400,000 Btu/hr. If the flame emissivity and heat capacity are adjusted to 2300° instead of 2500° and the solution of equations repeated, one obtains t_F = 2290° and q_F = 51,600,000 Btu/hr, indicating that the final result is insensitive to the temperature at which ϵ_F and Mc_p are evaluated. Not all the heat q_F goes to the water-cooled surfaces; the third term in the heat-transfer equation represents loss through refractory walls. This is $(0.47)(960)$ (2230) or 1,000,000 Btu/hr. Then, finally, the heat received by the water-cooled surfaces, exclusive of convection to the first tube row, is 51,600,000 − 1,000,000 = 50,600,000 Btu/hr, or 50,600,000/(130,000)(1070) = 36.4 per cent of the enthalpy of the entering fuel.

Problems

1. A large plane, perfectly insulated on one face and maintained at a fixed temperature T_1 on the bare face, which has an emissivity of 0.90, loses 200 Btu/(hr)(sq ft) when exposed to surroundings at absolute zero. A second plane having the same size as the first is also perfectly insulated on one face, but its bare face has an emissivity of 0.45. When the bare face of the second plane is maintained at a fixed temperature T_2 and exposed to surroundings at absolute zero, it loses 100 Btu/(hr)(sq ft).

Let these two planes be brought close together, so that the parallel bare faces are only 1 in. apart, and let the heat supply to each be so adjusted that their respective temperatures remain unchanged. What will be the net heat flux between the planes, expressed in Btu/(hr)(sq ft)?

2. A furnace having walls 28.25 in. thick contains a peephole 7 by 7 in. in cross section. If the temperature of the inner walls of the furnace is 2200°F, what would be the heat loss through the peephole to surroundings at 70°F?

3. An electric furnace of rectangular cross section is to be designed for batch heating of a stock from 70 to 1400°F. The hearth, covered with stock, is 6 by 12 ft in area. The refractory side walls are well insulated. Parallel to the plane of the roof, in a plane several inches below it, is a system of round-rod resistors, each 10 ft long and 0.5 in. in diameter, spaced on 2-in. centers. The plane of the resistors is 4 ft above the top of the stock.

What is the heating time for a 6-ton batch of stock having a mean specific heat of 0.16, when the resistor temperature is maintained at 2000°F?

Notes.—Assume that the emissivities of the resistors and stock are 0.6 and 0.9, respectively, and neglect heat losses and heat storage in the walls of the furnace.

4. An annealing furnace 10 ft long has a cross section normal to length, as shown in Fig. 35. The firebox *a* is at a uniform temperature of 2200°F, and the 10- by 6-ft hearth *b* is covered with stock at a temperature of 1400°F. So far as radiant heat transfer is concerned, assume that the firebox acts like a uniformly black plane *c*, 2 ft high over the bridge wall. Neglect the contribution of the combustion products to the radiant heat interchange in the system, and

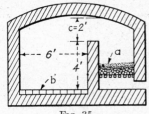

Fig. 35.

neglect convection. Assume no external losses from the furnace, and assume that the refractory surfaces have emissivities of 0.65.

  a. Calculate the direct interchange of heat by radiation between the firebox and the stock, if the latter is a black surface.
  b. Calculate the total net interchange between the two if the stock is a black surface.
  c. Repeat *b*, assuming that the stock has an emissivity of 0.75.
  d. Calculate the average temperature of the working chamber walls and roof for condition *c*.

5. On a clear night, when the effective black-body temperature of space is *minus* 100°F, the air is at 60°F and contains water vapor at a partial pressure equal to that of ice or water at 32°F. A very thin film of water, initially at 60°F, is placed in a very shallow well-insulated pan, placed in a spot sheltered from the wind ($h = 0.46$), with a full view of the sky.

State whether ice will form, and support this with suitable calculations.

6. The convection section of an oil pipe still on which performance data are available is composed of a bank of tubes 24 ft long, 3.5 in. i.d., and 4.0 in. o.d. There are six tubes in each horizontal row; center-to-center spacing of the tubes, arranged on equilateral triangular centers, is 8 in. The minimum free area for gas flow is 53.8 sq ft. Oil enters the bottom row of tubes at 420°F and flows upward through each row in series, leaving the convection section at 730°F. Flue gas at atmospheric pressure from the combustion chamber, flowing transverse to the tubes, enters the top of the bank at 1550°F, with a mass velocity of 810 lb/(hr)(sq ft of minimum free area) and leaves at the bottom of the section at 590°F.

The flue gas contains 7.1 per cent CO_2 (dry basis); the ratio of $H_2O:CO_2$ in the flue gas is 1.38; the molecular weight of the flue gas is 27.5; the mean molal heat capacity between 1550 and 590°F is 7.77.

Calculate the number of rows of tubes required.

Additional Data and Assumptions

1. External heat losses in the section are negligible.

2. The emissivities of all surfaces are 0.9. Because of the high emissivities, radiation received on a surface by reflection may be ignored.

3. Preliminary calculations indicate that the temperature drop through the oil film and tube wall is 30°F.

4. Average length of radiant beams through the gas will differ for the tube surface and for the refractory surface, but the latter will be assumed equal to the former. Likewise, the convection coefficient of heat transfer from gas to refractory will be assumed the same as from gas to tubes.

5. The effect of the refractory end walls, through which the tubes pass, will be neglected.

6. For convection heat transfer from flue gases, simplified Eq. 8a, page 230, is satisfactory.

CHAPTER IV

DIMENSIONAL ANALYSIS

Introduction.—In the following chapter, dimensional analysis is applied to problems in both fluid dynamics and heat transfer. The theory of models is outlined, and the utility of self-consistent units in dimensionless ratios is illustrated. By using more than the necessary minimum number of dimensions and including the corresponding dimensional constants in the analysis, the conversion factors required in any consistent system of units are automatically introduced. This is particularly helpful when the technical system of units is to be employed in evaluating the dimensionless ratios.

Granting that all the factors controlling a physical situation are known, dimensional analysis is a method by which this knowledge may be capitalized and put into a form useful for planning experiments and in interpreting the data obtained. The method is particularly valuable where the mathematical relations are unknown or complex and will indicate the logical grouping of the factors into dimensionless combinations. The latter feature is helpful in interpreting data where two or more factors have been varied in different experiments. Wherever possible, however, correlations should be supported by data where each factor is varied separately.

The dimensional formula for each measured quantity or factor has the form of products of powers of the various dimensions involved. Hence each dimensionless combination of factors must be a product of the factors, each entering with an exponent such that all dimensions cancel. As pointed out by Bridgman,[89]* fundamental equations can be so arranged that the quantities enter the equations through certain combinations that are dimensionless, and the *form of such equations is independent of the size of the units involved* in the various terms in the equation.

DIMENSIONAL ANALYSIS APPLIED TO FLUID DYNAMICS

In applying the method, the first step is to write the dimensions of each of the quantities or factors entering the physical situation.

* See also Blasius,[65] Buckingham,[94] Helmholtz,[299] Lamb,[417] Nusselt,[521] Rayleigh,[580] Reynolds,[585] Stanton and Pannell,[695] Stokes,[702] and Comings.[151]

The dimensions of a given factor or quantity are determined by its definition in terms of dimensions that are arbitrarily selected as fundamental. The choice of dimensions is largely a matter of convenience, and hence there is nothing absolute about the dimensions of any quantity. In problems in fluid dynamics, the ordinary mechanical quantities mass* M, length L, and time θ may conveniently be selected as fundamental dimensions. One can treat force F as a dimension. The basic law of Newton, that force is proportional to the product of mass and acceleration, is

$$F = ma/g_c = ML/\theta^2 g_c \tag{1}$$

where g_c is a conversion factor or a **dimensional constant,** which has a numerical value dependent on the units chosen. If FML and θ are treated as having separate dimensions, the dimensions of g_c are those of ma/F or $ML/F\theta^2$. Alternatively, by calling g_c dimensionless in Eq. 1, the dimension F may be replaced by ML/θ^2 or the dimension M by $F\theta^2/L$; if g_c is thus made dimensionless its

TABLE I.—SOME MECHANICAL QUANTITIES AND THEIR DIMENSIONS

Symbol	Quantity	Net dimensions		
		$FML\theta$	$ML\theta$	$FL\theta$
D	Diameter	L	L	L
L	Length	L	L	L
y	Roughness of pipe surface	L	L	L
V	Velocity, average	L/θ	L/θ	L/θ
g	Acceleration due to gravity	L/θ^2	L/θ^2	L/θ^2
a	Acceleration	L/θ^2	L/θ^2	L/θ^2
m	Mass	M	M	$F\theta^2/L$
F	Force	F	ML/θ^2	F
g_c	Conversion factor, ma/F	$ML/F\theta^2$	None	None
w	Mass rate of flow	M/θ	M/θ	$F\theta/L$
ρ	Density, mass per unit volume	M/L^3	M/L^3	$F\theta^2/L^4$
γ	Specific weight, $\rho g/g_c$	F/L^3	$M/L^2\theta^2$	F/L^3
p	Pressure	F/L^2	$M/L\theta^2$	F/L^2
μ_F	Viscosity, $F\theta/L^2$	$F\theta/L^2$	$M/L\theta$	$F\theta/L^2$
μ_M	Viscosity, $\mu_F g_c = \mu$	$M/L\theta$	$M/L\theta$	$F\theta/L^2$
	$DV\rho/\mu_F$	$ML/F\theta^2$	None	None
	$DV\rho/\mu_M = DV\rho/\mu_F g_c = DV\rho/\mu$	None	None	None

* In this book, mass always denotes the absolute quantity of matter, regardless of the units such as pounds, grams, or tons in which M might be expressed numerically.

numerical value is unity. All these practices are allowable. From these arbitrarily selected fundamental dimensions other quantities may be derived; for example, velocity is expressed as L/θ. Table I lists certain factors or quantities, and the corresponding dimensions in each of three systems $FML\theta$, $ML\theta$, and $FL\theta$.

NOTE: Throughout this book the symbol μ designates the product $\mu_F g_c$; hence the dimensionless Reynolds number is written $DV\rho/\mu$.

In making a dimensional analysis, one may use any of the three sets of dimensions listed in Table I or other appropriate sets, but fundamentally the same result will be obtained regardless of the choice of dimensions. If a system containing more than the minimum necessary number of dimensions, such as the $FML\theta$ system, is selected, the corresponding conversion factor, g_c in this case, should be included. The introduction of g_c, through choice of the $FML\theta$ system, throws no light on whether or not the acceleration due to gravity affects the problem.[151]

The following problems illustrate a procedure for making a dimensional analysis.

Illustration 1.—Consider the pressure drop due to friction for isothermal turbulent flow of an incompressible liquid at constant mass rate through a long, straight, smooth pipe of uniform diameter. From a knowledge of the physical situation it is clear that the controlling factors are L, D, V, ρ, and μ. For flow in long pipes it is reasonable to assume that the pressure drop due to friction is directly proportional to the length of the pipe. For the sake of illustration it is assumed that one does not know the exact way in which D, V, ρ, μ, and g_c enter the equation. Letting ϕ represent **any** function, one writes

$$-dp_F/dL = \phi(D, V, \rho, \mu, g_c) \qquad (2)*$$

which sometimes is called the "pi theorem."
For convenience, the foregoing will be replaced by an infinite series:

$$-dp_F/dL = \alpha D^a V^b \rho^c \mu^e g_c^f + \alpha' D^{a'} V^{b'} \rho^{c'} \mu^{e'} g_c^{f'} + \cdots \qquad (2a)$$

wherein the dimensionless factor α and the dimensionless exponents may have any value required by the situation. Since all terms of the series are alike in form, one may deal with only the first term. Referring to Table I and substituting the dimensions of the factors in the $FML\theta$ system in Eq. 2a, one obtains

$$\frac{F/L^2}{L} = \alpha(L)^a \left(\frac{L}{\theta}\right)^b \left(\frac{M}{L^3}\right)^c \left(\frac{M}{L\theta}\right)^e \left(\frac{ML}{F\theta^2}\right)^f \qquad (2b)$$

Eq. 2b must be dimensionless with respect to each dimension; hence the following condition equations must apply.

* This is equivalent to
$$\phi(dp/dL, D, V, \rho, \mu, g_c) = 0$$

ΣF: $1 = -f$; hence $f = -1$

ΣM: $0 = c + e + f$; hence $c = 1 - e$

$\Sigma\theta$: $0 = -b - e - 2f$; hence $b = 2 - e$

ΣL: $-3 = a + b - 3c - e + f$; hence $a = -1 - e$

Since there are five unknowns (the exponents) and four equations (no two of which gave the same result), one may solve in terms of any one unknown.* Arbitrarily retaining e, substitution of the values of the exponents in Eq. 2a gives

$$-g_c D \; dp_F/\rho V^2 \; dL = \alpha(\mu/DV\rho)^e \qquad (2c)\dagger$$

Since the exponential form was used for convenience, dimensional analysis shows that

$$-g_c D \; dp_F/\rho V^2 \; dL = \phi(DV\rho/\mu) \qquad (2d)$$

The dimensionless term on the left is usually written as $2f$, where f is called the **friction factor**. Experimental study (page 119) shows that for long smooth pipes f is indeed a function of $DV\rho/\mu$ alone. For short pipes f depends also on L/D because of entrance effects; for rough pipes an additional ratio y/D is required.

If the flow had been streamline instead of turbulent, experimental data would show density does not enter, and one would obtain

$$-g_c D^2 \; dp_F/\mu V \; dL = \text{constant} \qquad (2e)$$

This result is of the form of Poiseuille's law (page 120); from theory, confirmed by many experiments, the constant of Eq. 2e is found to be 32.

DIMENSIONAL ANALYSIS APPLIED TO HEAT TRANSFER

In applying dimensional analysis to problems in heat transfer, it is customary to employ at least four dimensions: mass M, length

---

* This case follows the rule: $n_g = n_f - n_d$, which states that the number of dimensionless groups obtained equals the difference between the number of factors involved and the number of dimensions employed. If there were no exceptions, it would be unnecessary to determine the number of groups by algebraic procedure, since by inspection all the factors could be grouped to form the number of dimensionless arrangements predicted by the rule: $n_g = n_f - n_d$. Some writers follow the latter procedure, regardless of the fact that the rule has exceptions not readily foreseen by the novice. Given compatible assumptions, if two of the condition equations obtained by the algebraic procedure give the same information, one more dimensionless group will be obtained than predicted by the rule: $n_g = n_f - n_d$. If some of the original assumptions are incompatible, there is no solution, and hence n_g of zero can be less than $n_f - n_d$. Because of these deviations, the algebraic procedure is recommended.

† Had one retained a, b, or c, instead of e, the results, although differing superficially from the foregoing, would be mutually convertible one into the other. If the same problem were solved, using the $ML\theta$ or $FL\theta$ systems, the same result would be obtained, except that since g_c is dimensionless in the $ML\theta$ and $FL\theta$ systems, g_c would not have appeared in Eq. 2d.

TABLE II

Symbol	Quantity	Net dimensions	
		$FML\theta TH$	$ML\theta T$
A	Area of surface	L^2	L^2
b	Breadth, perimeter	L	L
c	Specific heat, on mass basis	H/MT	$L^2/\theta^2 T$
d	Prefix indicating differential	None	None
D	Diameter	L	L
D_v	Diffusivity, volumetric	L^2/θ	L^2/θ
$-dt/dL$	Temperature gradient	T/L	T/L
	Force	F	ML/θ^2
g	Acceleration due to gravity	L/θ^2	L/θ^2
g_c	Conversion factor	$ML/F\theta^2$	None
G	Mass velocity, w/S	$M/\theta L^2$	$M/\theta L^2$
h, U	Coefficients of heat transfer	$H/\theta L^2 T$	$M/\theta^3 T$
J	Mechanical equivalent of heat	LF/H	None
k	Thermal conductivity	$H/\theta LT$	$ML/\theta^3 T$
$k/\rho c$	Thermal diffusivity	L^2/θ	L^2/θ
K_H	Kinetic-energy equivalent of heat	$ML^2/\theta^2 H$	None
L	Length	L	L
p	Pressure per unit area	F/L^2	$M/L\theta^2$
Q	Quantity of heat	H	ML^2/θ^2
q	Steady rate of heat flow	H/θ	ML^2/θ^3
r	Radius	L	L
R	Thermal resistance	$T\theta/H$	$T\theta^3/ML^2$
S	Cross section	L^2	L^2
t, T	Temperature	T	T
V	Velocity	L/θ	L/θ
w	Mass flow rate	M/θ	M/θ
x, y, z	Distances	L	L
Greek			
α	Proportionality factor	None	None
β	Coefficient of expansion	$1/T$	$1/T$
Γ	w/b	$M/\theta L$	$M/\theta L$
γ	Specific weight, F/L^3	F/L^3	$M/L^2\theta^2$
∂	Prefix, indicating partial derivative	None	None
Δ	Prefix, indicating finite difference	None	None
ϵ	Emissivity	None	None
κ	Specific-heat ratio	None	None
λ	Enthalpy change	H/M	L^2/θ^2
μ	Viscosity, $M/L\theta$	$M/L\theta$	$M/L\theta$
τ	Tractive force per unit area	F/L^2	$M/L\theta^2$
ρ	Density, mass per unit volume	M/L^3	M/L^3
σ	Surface tension	F/L	M/θ^2
ϕ, ψ	Prefixes, indicating functions	None	None

L, time θ, and temperature or temperature difference T. It is allowable to add force F as a dimension, by including the conversion factor g_c in the dimensional analysis, as was done on page 89; similarly the dimension of heat H may be added by including either the mechanical equivalent of heat J (having dimensions LF/H) or the product Jg_c or K_H (the kinetic-energy equivalent of heat), which has the dimensions ML^2/θ^2H.

The symbols and dimensions of a number of quantities are shown in Table II. The net dimensions in the $FML\theta TH$ system are readily obtained by inspection, since they correspond to the technical units in which many engineers evaluate these factors. Table II also shows the net dimensions in the $ML\theta T$ system, in which neither force nor heat is assigned a separate dimension; the dimensions of force are obtained by calling g_c dimensionless, which gives force the dimensions of mass times acceleration, ML/θ^2; the dimensions of heat are obtained by calling Jg_c dimensionless, which gives heat the dimensions of kinetic energy, ML^2/θ^2. The use of either set of dimensions leads to fundamentally the same result; the advantage of using the first set is that the result of the dimensional analysis will automatically contain[151] the necessary conversion factors for use in any system of units, including technical units. If one uses the second set, the unmodified result of the dimensional analysis will be suitable only for systems of units in which the conversion factors ignored in the problem are numerically equal to unity. However, the results of the dimensional analysis, using the $ML\theta T$ system, are sound and can be made applicable to all systems of units by later insertion of the proper conversion factors in the result.[741] Use of the first set of dimensions is recommended.

For example, if one assumes h to depend only on V, reference to Table II shows that this could not be a general relation, since the dimensions of h and V are incompatible.

Illustration 2.—For heating or cooling a fluid flowing without phase change through heated or cooled tubes, it is desired to determine the logical grouping of the factors affecting the film coefficient of heat transfer h, which is defined by the equation

$$h = \frac{dq}{dA \, \Delta t} = \frac{(w \, c \, dt)}{(\pi DL)(\Delta t)} = \frac{(H/\theta)}{(L^2)(T)}$$

The heat is conducted through the liquid film; hence k should be a factor. Because the film thickness depends on the mass velocity G of the fluid, tube diameter D, and viscosity μ, these factors should affect h; and since for a given q, the specific heat affects the bulk temperature of the stream, c also should enter. These same factors appear in the basic energy and hydro-mechanical equations.

Proceeding as on page 89,

$$h = \alpha G^a D^b c^e \mu^f k^i K_H^m \tag{3}$$

The dimensional constant $K_H (= ML^2/\theta^2 H)$ must be introduced since the $ML\theta TH$ system is to be used, and both M and H appear in the factors involved. Substitution of the dimensions in Eq. 3 gives

$$\frac{H}{\theta L^2 T} = \left(\frac{M}{\theta L^2}\right)^a (L)^b \left(\frac{H}{MT}\right)^e \left(\frac{M}{L\theta}\right)^f \left(\frac{H}{\theta LT}\right)^i \left(\frac{ML^2}{H\theta^2}\right)^m \tag{3a}$$

Summation of the exponents of like dimensions gives the condition equations

$$\begin{aligned}
\Sigma H: & \quad 1 = e + i - m \\
\Sigma M: & \quad 0 = a - e + f + m \\
\Sigma L: & \quad -2 = -2a + b - f - i + 2m \\
\Sigma \theta & \quad -1 = -a - f - i - 2m \\
\Sigma T: & \quad -1 = -e - i
\end{aligned}$$

Simultaneous solution* gives $b = a - 1$, $f = e - a$, $i = 1 - e$, and $m = 0$; substitution in Eq. 3 gives

$$\frac{hD}{k} = \alpha \left(\frac{DG}{\mu}\right)^a \left(\frac{c\mu}{k}\right)^e \tag{3b}$$

It is noted that the exponents arbitrarily retained, a and e, were those appearing on G and c, respectively, and hence G and c each appeared only once in Eq. 3b. If different pairs of exponents had been retained, the corresponding factors would have appeared only once, but all the various results would be mutually convertible. For the case under discussion the dimensionless ratios usually retained are DG/μ, $c\mu/k$, and either h/cG or hD/k, the last equaling the product of the other three. The final result is

$$hD/k = \phi[(DG/\mu),(c\mu/k)] \tag{3c}$$

in which the unknown functions may be of any kind and must be experimentally determined.

Illustration 3.—In the literature,† the following equation is given for boiling liquids:

$$\frac{h}{k} \sqrt{\frac{\sigma}{\rho L}} = a \left(\frac{q}{A\rho_v \lambda D_B N_B}\right)^{0.8} \tag{4}$$

* Since two of the condition equations (ΣM and $\Sigma \theta$) gave the same information, three dimensionless groups were obtained from seven factors expressed in terms of five dimensions, and hence the rule $n_f = n_g - n_d$ did not apply. The same situation is found when the problem is solved in terms of $ML\theta T$, and Eq. 3b is again obtained by the algebraic procedure. If it is assumed that h depends on both V and ρ, rather than upon the product $V\rho = G$, Eq. 3b is again obtained.

† Eq. 12 of reference 193, based on reference 347.

where D_B is the most common bubble diameter, N_B is the most common bubble frequency $(1/\theta)$, and the other terms are defined in Table II. It is desired to determine whether or not the equation is dimensionally balanced and, if it is not, what changes should be made so that the constant a would represent a pure number.

Solution.—Substituting the dimensions of the various terms on the left-hand side of Eq. 4, using the $FML\theta TH$ system, one obtains

$$\frac{(H/\theta L^2 T)}{(H/\theta LT)} \sqrt{\frac{F/L}{M/L^3}} = \sqrt{\frac{F}{M}}$$

In order to make the left-hand side dimensionless, the term under the radical must be multiplied by M/F. Since gravity g plays a part in the phenomenon, it is evident that the term under the radical should be multiplied by

$$\frac{g_c}{g} = \frac{ML/F\theta^2}{L/\theta^2} = \frac{M}{F}$$

Since Eq. 4 was given in a paper specifying technical units, wherein g_c/g equals unity, the ratio could be omitted. However, as shown above, to make the left-hand side give the same numerical value in any system of units, it should be written as

$$\frac{h}{k} \sqrt{\frac{\sigma g_c}{\rho_L g}} \text{ or } \frac{h}{k} \sqrt{\frac{\sigma}{\gamma_L}}$$

(In reference 347, the latter form was correctly given.)

Substitution of the dimensions of the various terms in the right-hand side of Eq. 4 shows that the right-hand side is dimensionless.

Had the same problem been solved with the $ML\theta T$ system, Eq. 4 would have been found to be dimensionless when written as $(h/k) \sqrt{\sigma/\rho_L g}$, which does not contain g_c, considered dimensionless in the $ML\theta T$ system. In order to make this form suitable for any consistent system, it would have to be multiplied by $\sqrt{g_c}$.

Based on various sets of assumptions as to the factors involved dimensional analysis gives:
For forced convection:

$$hD/k = \phi[(DV\rho/\mu), (c_p\mu/k)] \tag{5}*$$

For natural convection:

$$hD/k = \phi[(D^3\rho^2 g/\mu^2), (\beta \Delta t), (c_p\mu/k)] \tag{6}$$

For condensing vapor:

$$hD/k = \phi[(D^3\rho^2 g/\mu^2), (\mu\lambda/k \Delta t)] \tag{7}$$

For boiling liquids:

$$hD/k = \phi\left[\left(\frac{D^2\rho^2 \Delta tkJg_c}{\mu^3}\right), \left(\frac{\mu^2}{\rho D\sigma g_c}\right), \left(\frac{c_p\mu}{k}\right)\right] \tag{8}$$

* A rearranged form is $h/c_v V\rho = \phi'[(DV\rho/\mu), (c_p\mu/k)]$ (5a)

In the literature certain dimensionless groups have been named as follows:

TABLE III.—SOME DIMENSIONLESS GROUPS

Group	$(1)^a$	$(2)^b$	Name
hD/k	Nu	N_{Nu}	Nusselt number
$DV\rho/\mu$	Re	N_{Re}	Reynolds number
$c\mu/k$	Pr	N_{Pr}	Prandtl number
$DV\rho c/k$	Pe	N_{Pe}	Peclet number = Re · Pr
wc/kL	Gz	N_{Gz}	Graetz number
$D^3\rho^2 g\beta \ \Delta t/\mu^2$	Gr	N_{Gr}	Grashof number
$h/cV\rho$	St	N_{St}	Stanton number
$(h/k)(\mu^2/\rho^2 g)^{1/3}$	Co	N_{Co}	Condensation number
$(L^3\rho^2 g\lambda/k\mu \ \Delta t)$	Cv	N_{Cv}	Used in equation for condensing vapor
hr_m/k	Bi	N_{Bi}	Biot number
$k\theta/\rho c r_m^2$	Fo	N_{Fo}	Fourier number
$\mu/\rho D_v$	Sc	N_{Sc}	Schmidt number
$2g_c D \ \Delta p_F/4 \ \rho V^2 L$	f	f_F	Fanning friction factor

^{a} Column 1 shows the abbreviations usually employed.

^{b} Column 2 shows the symbols tentatively proposed by Subcommittee Z-10c of the American Standards Association, March, 1941.

LIMITATIONS TO RESULTS OBTAINED BY DIMENSIONAL ANALYSIS

As stated at the beginning of this discussion (page 90) the result obtained by applying dimensional analysis is limited by the validity and completeness of the assumptions made prior to the analysis. Thus, if one assumes that h depends upon a number of factors that happen to be dimensionally compatible, the analysis will show this to be the case but will throw no light on the validity or completeness of the assumptions. Experiment is the only safe basis for determining the correctness and adequacy of the assumptions.[357] However, if the assumptions are known to be correct and complete, then the result of dimensional analysis, *i.e.*, the logical grouping of the factors or variables into dimensionless groups, can be accepted without hesitation.

THEORY OF MODELS

Granting that the assumptions involved are known to be correct and adequate, dimensional analysis would show that the equation is dimensionally sound and would indicate the grouping of the factors in dimensionless moduli. However, in most cases, the relationship between these dimensionless moduli can be determined only by experiment. Resistance to flow of air around airplanes, water around ships, or liquids through a new type of heat exchanger can be determined by experiments with scale models. The data, determined from experiments with scale models, can be plotted in dimensionless groups and used for full-sized equipment. If, as in Illustration 1, Eq. 2d, the term $g_c \, \Delta p_F D / N \rho V^2$ is some unknown function of $DV\rho/\mu$, experiments on the scale model should be run at the *same* values of $DV\rho/\mu$ that will be used with the full-sized equipment. If a scale model one-tenth full size is used and the same fluid and same temperatures are used for both the scale model and the full-sized apparatus, since D will be one-tenth as large, in order to make $DV\rho/\mu$ the same in both cases, V should be ten times as large as on the full scale. If this velocity is excessive, a different fluid or a different temperature can be used, giving a sufficiently large value of μ/ρ for the experiments with the model.

Thus based on dimensional analysis, this "theory of models" has a firm foundation[246] and is of great value in planning experiments. However, the method demands care in the analysis of all controlling factors and thorough familiarity with the technique of allowing for their variations. For example, the effect of roughness and scale deposits should not be overlooked.

CONSISTENT UNITS

It should be clear that the numerical value of any *dimensionless* group is independent of the units employed, provided a consistent set is employed. Thus if the ratio of length to diameter of a given pipe is 48:1, the same result will be obtained regardless of whether the units employed are inches per inch, feet per feet, or meters per meter. The same principle applies to the more complex dimensionless groups. Thus, consider the isothermal flow of a liquid, having a density of 56.0 lb/cu ft and a viscosity of 0.0056 lb/(sec)(ft), at an average velocity of 5.0 ft/sec through a pipe having an inside diameter of 0.0833 ft. Evaluating all terms on the basis of the fps system of units, the Reynolds number would be $(DV\rho/\mu) = (0.0833)$ $(5.0)(56.0)/0.0056 = 4165$ in this set of consistent units. If each of the terms be converted* to the cgs system of units, $DV\rho/\mu = (2.54)(152.5)(0.898)/8.33 = 4165$ in this set of consistent units. **In other words, in any one set of self-consistent units the numerical value of a dimensionless group is the same as in any other set of**

---

* Conversion factors for the Reynolds number are given on p. 88 and for viscosity, on p. 407.

self-consistent units. Hence, if convenient, one may use one set of self-consistent units in one dimensionless group and a different set of self-consistent units in a second dimensionless group appearing in the same equation.

Throughout the book, the preferred primary units are those shown in Table IV.

TABLE IV.—PREFERRED PRIMARY UNITS (TECHNICAL SYSTEM)

Quantity	Dimen- sions	Units
Mass	M	Mass pound of commerce, 454 grams
Force	F	Pound force = 44,400 dynes = 32.2 poundals
Length	L	Feet
Time	θ	Hours (seconds used in flow of fluids)
Temperature	T	Degrees Fahrenheit for t, degrees Fahrenheit absolute for T
Heat	H	Btu
g_c	$ML/F\theta^2$	$\dfrac{32.2 \text{ mass pounds} \times \text{feet}}{\text{pounds force} \times \text{seconds}^2}$ $= \dfrac{4.17 \times 10^8 \text{ mass pounds} \times \text{feet}}{\text{pounds force} \times \text{hours}^2}$
J	LF/H	778 ft × pounds force per Btu

The corresponding units of various secondary quantities are given in the various nomenclature tables in later chapters.

Other Systems of Units.—If it is desired to employ an English absolute system, using force in poundals and mass in pounds matter, all dimensionless equations in the book will give the correct results by taking g_c as unity. Similarly, one can employ a gravitational English system, involving force pounds and slugs (pounds matter/32.2); again g_c equals unity. A similar situation exists with respect to the corresponding systems of metric units.

Problems

1. Calculate the dimensionless Reynolds number for the following conditions: i.d. of 1 in., average velocity of 125 cm/sec, density of 49.9 lb/cu ft, and an absolute viscosity of 0.0053 force lb × seconds per square foot.

2. Experiments have been made on the rate of heat transfer from a metal surface to a number of boiling liquids. Steady conditions and constant temperature difference from metal to liquid were maintained in each run. Based on a study of the data, it is believed that the individual surface coefficient of heat transfer h depends upon the following factors: viscosity μ, pipe diameter D, thermal conductivity k density ρ, and surface tension σ (expressed as force/length).

a. Based on these assumptions, apply dimensional analysis and arrange the variables in the proper number of groups.

b. Repeat, considering the specific heat c also a factor.

3. Making certain assumptions and applying the principles of dimensional analysis to the study of heat transfer by natural convection leads to the conclusion

$$\frac{hL}{k} = \phi\left[(\beta\,\Delta t),\ \left(\frac{L^3\rho^2 g}{\mu^2}\right),\ \left(\frac{c_p\mu}{k}\right)\right]$$

where L is the height of a vertical plate and the other symbols have the customary meaning. Using a vertical plate 2 in. high, at 150°F exposed to dry air at 70°F and 1 atm absolute, it is found that h equals 1.3 Btu/(hr)(sq ft)(deg F).

Assuming that the dimensional analysis is sound and that the values of the physical properties should be evaluated at a film temperature t_f, the arithmetic mean of the temperatures of the wall and the gas, consider the problem of the transfer of heat from a vertical plate in an atmosphere of pure hydrogen at 2 atm absolute.

a. If the plate is at 760°F and the hydrogen is at 600°F, for what height of plate would the one experiment in air be capable of predicting a value for h with hydrogen?

b. What would be the expected value of h under the conditions of a?

Notes.—Assume that $c_p\mu/k$ is the same for all diatomic gases at 1 atm and is independent of temperature.

4. The group $D^2\rho^2 k\,\Delta t/\mu^3$ is dimensionless in the $ML\theta T$ system. For technical units calculate the correct numerical value of the corresponding dimensionless term for the following conditions: D of 0.1 ft, ρ of 50 lb/cu ft, k of 0.08 Btu/(hr)(sq ft)(deg F per ft), μ of 1 lb fluid/(hr)(ft), and Δt of 10°F.

5. A liquid is flowing isothermally at steady mass rate Γ per unit breadth, under the influence of gravity down the outer wall of a tall vertical pipe in the room. Clearly the thickness x of the film may depend on the viscosity μ and density ρ of the liquid.

What dimensionless groups are required?

CHAPTER V

FLOW OF FLUIDS

Introduction.—The following chapter is divided into three sections. The first deals with the mechanism of both streamline and turbulent motion; and, for turbulent motion in pipes, presents the concepts of a laminar-flow layer, a buffer zone, and a turbulent core as are shown by velocity-gradient data. The effect of increased velocity upon film thickness and the effect of roughness of the wall upon velocity distribution are also discussed. The second section presents material and energy balances for steady flow. The third section deals with the laws of friction due to flow inside straight and coiled pipes, through sudden enlargements and contractions in cross section, across tube banks, and in packed tubes. A number of illustrative problems are included.

I. MECHANISM OF ISOTHERMAL FLOW OF FLUIDS

Because of its important relation to heat transfer by conduction and convection between solid and fluid, the mechanism of the flow of fluids is discussed in detail.

ISOTHERMAL STREAMLINE VS. TURBULENT MOTION

As has long been known from the classical researches of Osborne Reynolds[587] and others, the steady isothermal flow of a fluid through a long, straight pipe may occur by one of several mechanisms. When the dimensionless Reynolds number $DV\rho/\mu$* is sufficiently small, the individual particles of fluid flow in straight lines parallel to the axis of the pipe, without appreciable radial component,†

---

* Using the fps system for illustration, D represents i.d. in feet; V = average velocity in feet per second = [cubic feet per second ÷ cross section in square feet]; ρ = density in pounds per cubic foot; and μ = viscosity in lb/(sec) (ft). For flow in conduits, G = weight or mass velocity, expressed as lb/(sec) (sq ft of cross section), is often used instead of the product $V\rho$. In the literature the term $DV\rho/\mu = DG/\mu$ is often abbreviated as Re. Nomenclature is summarized on page 112. Properties of fluids are given in the Appendix.

† Of course, the minute molecules are moving rapidly over the almost infinitesimal mean free paths, but the motion of large groups of molecules (particles) is substantially axial.

as shown in Fig. 36.   This type of motion is variously described as streamline, straight line, viscous, and laminar.   At sufficiently high values of Re, the motion is said to be *turbulent*, because of the presence of innumerable eddies or vortexes present in the central portion of the pipe, as indicated in Fig. 37.   The shapes of the velocity-distribution curves are different for the two types of motion.   Thus, for streamline flow the curve is of parabolic shape:

$$\frac{u}{V} = 2\left(1 - \frac{r^2}{r_0^2}\right) \tag{1}$$

and $V/u_{max} = 0.50$; where as for turbulent flow, the curve rises more sharply near the wall and is flatter in the central section,

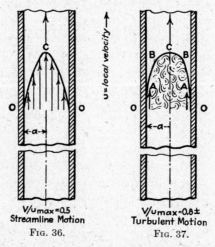

V/u max =0.5
Streamline Motion
Fig. 36.

V/u max =0.8±
Turbulent Motion
Fig. 37.

and V/u_{max} is approximately 0.8.*   Mathematical relations between pressure drop, rate of flow, and other factors are discussed later, and it is shown that the equation for streamline motion is different from the equation for turbulent motion.   As shown below, there is considerable evidence that in the zone OA of Fig. 37, streamline flow exists, in spite of the turbulence in the range BCB.   The critical Reynolds number Re_c is that value of $DV\rho/\mu$ below which streamline motion exists over the entire cross section.   As is well known, Re_c depends upon a number of factors,[630,200] such as the distance of the cross section considered from the entrance to the pipe and the type of entrance.   The following table shows values of Re_c determined by several methods.

* Figure 43, p. 105, shows a plot of V/u_{max} vs. Re.

TABLE I.—CRITICAL REYNOLDS NUMBER FOR CIRCULAR PIPES

Reference	Method	Re_c
a	Pipe friction	Between 2100 and 2300
b	Color band	Above 2000
c	Stethoscope	Between 1890 and 2130
d	Motion of colloidal particles	Between 2000 and 3700

a,b Schiller[630] gives a comprehensive review of data obtained by these two methods.
c Bond.[72]
d Fage and Townend.[217]

For purposes of illustration, the critical value of $DV\rho/\mu$ will be taken as 2100. Between Re of 2100 and, say, 3100, lies a transition zone from streamline to turbulent flow, whereas above a Reynolds number of approximately 3100, the flow will be considered as turbulent, although the upper limit of the transition zone is affected by entrance conditions.[630]*

TURBULENT MOTION

For the usual case, in which the main stream flows in turbulent motion, the work of a number of investigators indicates that the

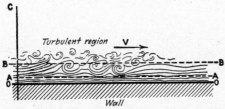

FIG. 38.—Diagram of isothermal turbulent flow of fluid parallel to a surface.

flow conditions resemble those shown diagrammatically in Fig. 38. At the wall OO the velocity is zero; and very near the wall, OA, the fluid is moving in laminar motion. In the buffer layer AB, the motion may be either streamline or turbulent at a given instant. In the zone BC, the motion is always turbulent.

Couch and Herrstrom[157] introduced a color band at the axis of a glass pipe through which water was flowing in turbulent motion and found that the color was quickly dissipated by the turbulence, as

* For flow of liquids in open channels, the type of fluid motion is affected not only by the Reynolds number, but also, as shown by Robertson and Rouse,[600] by the Froude number, $V/\sqrt{gy}$, which characterizes the wave motion which occurs when $V/\sqrt{gy}$ exceeds 1.

was the case in the classical color-band experiments of Reynolds.[587] A second color band, laid down simultaneously near the wall, was not disturbed, thus indicating either that near the wall the flow was streamline in character or that if eddies existed, they were too feeble to dissipate the color band. This experiment showed substantial turbulence at the axis and no noticeable turbulence near the wall.

It is generally believed that the thickness AB of the transition or "buffer" layer varies with time, because of the more or less

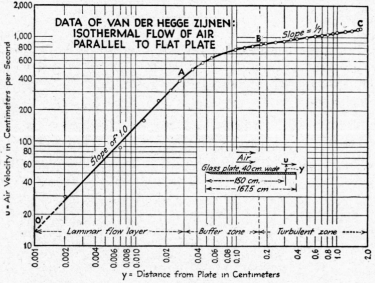

Fig. 39.—Velocity distribution near a flat plate at a point 150 cm from upstream edge.

periodic formation of vortexes, but that, nevertheless, an *average* thickness may be assigned to the buffer zone. Except for flow at Reynolds numbers only slightly above the critical, the thickness OA of the laminar-flow layer is very small, although doubling the velocity of the main stream will make a substantial and important reduction in its thickness.

Flow over Plates.—Figure 39 shows the results of explorations[729]* of the velocity of air flowing parallel to a horizontal plate of glass, using the apparatus indicated diagrammatically in the lower part

* Air velocities were measured by a calibrated hot-wire anemometer, made of wire 0.005 cm in diameter. For locations very close to the wall, the anemometer readings were corrected for abnormal behavior when near solids.

of Fig. 39. Up to a layer thickness of approximately 0.03 cm, the flow is apparently laminar in character, as indicated by the straight line $O'A$ of *unit* slope. In the buffer zone AB, from 0.03 to 0.17 cm from the wall, the velocity increases from 410 to 850 cm/sec, whereas in the turbulent zone BC, from 0.17 to 1.7 cm from the wall, the velocity increases from 850 to 1200 cm/sec. The turbulent zone BC is represented by the straight line having a slope of one-seventh; in the buffer zone AB the slope of the curve gradually changes from unity to one-seventh. Figure 40 shows the same data plotted to rectangular coordinates; the laminar-flow layer is now

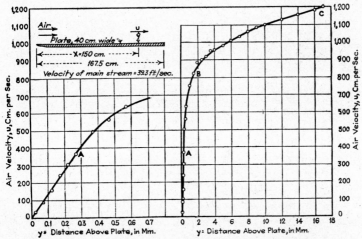

Fig. 40.—Data of Fig. 39, plotted to rectangular coordinates.

represented by the straight line OA, and extrapolation back to the origin would indicate no slip at the wall.

Similar results for the isothermal flow of air over smooth plates have been obtained by a number of workers.* Although air velocities were obtained by Pitot tubes in some cases and by hot-wire anemometers in others, the results support those of Fig. 39. Data are available to show that wide variations in $DV\rho/\mu$ cause some variation in the slope of the curves of u *vs.* y in the turbulent region.

Effect of Increasing Air Velocity.—Figure 41 shows velocity explorations in isothermal runs, using five different air velocities. It is seen that increasing the velocity of the main stream of air from 13.1 to 78.7 ft/sec decreases the thickness of the laminar-flow film (zone where slope is unity) from 0.087 to 0.018 cm.

* Jurges,[361] Hansen,[278] Dryden and Kuethe,[199] and Elias.[209]

Flow through Pipes.—Figure 42 shows the radial distribution of gas velocity for the isothermal turbulent flow of air in smooth pipes, based on the pioneer 1911 data of Stanton.[691] It is seen that, for a Reynolds number of 39,200 "reduced velocities," u/u_{max}, and

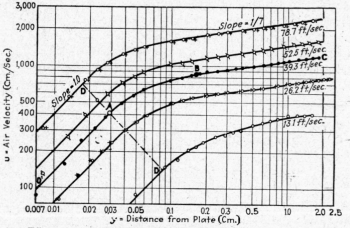

Fig. 41.—Effect of air velocity upon film thickness 150 cm from upstream edge. (*Data of Van der Hegge Zijnen.*[729])

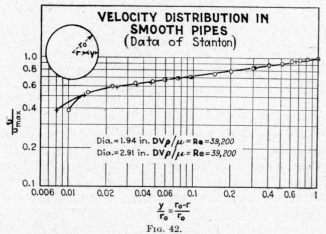

Fig. 42.

"reduced positions" agree well for two sizes of pipe. Further work on the velocity distribution of air flowing in turbulent motion in pipes was published by Stanton, Marshall, and Bryant,[694]* who

* Some of the data are reproduced by Rice[592] and by McAdams.[453] The method of interpreting Pitot-tube readings, obtained very close to the wall, is supported in a later paper by Barker.[44]

made velocity explorations to within 0.005 cm of the wall. These explorations showed the existence of a layer of fluid flowing in laminar motion near the wall and indicated a velocity of zero at the wall.

In ordinary work, *average* velocities V over the entire pipe are used rather than local velocities. In a 1914 paper, Stanton and Pannell[695] presented data on the ratio V/u_{max} as a function of the Reynolds number $DV\rho/u$. The data were obtained for isothermal flow of *air* in smooth pipes of diameters ranging from 0.28 to 2.0 in. and for *water* in smooth pipes having diameters of 0.28 and 1.12 in. The results are shown by curve A of Fig. 43 to logarithmic coordi-

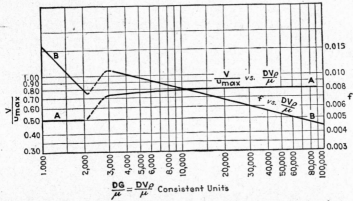

Fig. 43.—Ratio of average to maximum (axial) velocity, and friction factor, for isothermal flow in smooth pipes.

nates with V/u_{max} plotted as ordinates against $DV\rho/\mu$, or Re. Up to Re of 2000, V/u_{max} is 0.5, as called for by theory for isothermal streamline flow in a long, straight pipe, but in the transition range of Re from 2000 to 3000, V/u_{max} rises sharply from 0.5 to 0.726 and, thereafter, more slowly in the range of turbulent motion. For comparison, a curve of the friction factor f^* for long, smooth pipes is plotted on Fig. 43 as curve B, and f is seen to undergo sudden changes at about the same values of Re as were noted for V/u_{max}. Figure 44 shows V/u_{max} plotted *vs.* $Du_{max}\rho/\mu$, for use in prediction of V from measurement of u_{max} at the axis of a long pipe.

Effect of Roughness of Surface.—Photographs have been taken by Simmons and Dewey[670]† of "smoke" in air streams flowing

---

* Based on data of Fig. 51, p. 118.

† The photographs were taken across the mid-section of the plate, which was 3 ft long and 1 ft wide. Exposures of 1/100,000 sec were made by use of

isothermally between parallel flat plates.   The line marked AA in Fig. 45 represents the upper edge of the dense layer of smoke apparently traveling in the laminar motion.   Figure 46 was taken with a wire 0.05 in. in diameter placed across the plate next to the surface. The distributing effect of the wire on the laminar layer is clearly indicated in Fig. 46 and suggests that the presence of thermocouple wires, attached to a heat-transfer surface, may introduce abnormal conditions in the stream of fluid.   These results also arouse interest in the effect of a *marked* roughening of a heat-transfer surface.   Judging the thickness of the laminar layer by the

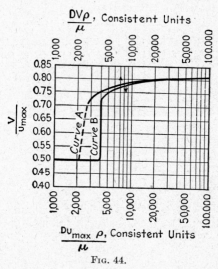

Fig. 44.

known diameter of the wire, one obtains a thickness of the same order of magnitude as found by velocity measurements under comparable conditions.   Since smoke was not introduced into the turbulent zone, these photographs throw no light upon the mechanism of fluid flow in the turbulent zone.

Velocity explorations[730] in a stream of air flowing over an artificially roughened surface (Fromm waffle plate) gave curves similar to those for the smooth plate (Fig. 39, page 102), but in the turbulent zone BC the slope du/dy was 0.25 for the rough plate, compared with 0.14 for the smooth plate.   Thus, the marked

---

a spark coil for illumination.   The smoke was produced by the mingling of the water vapor carried by the air with the vapor emitted by liquid titanium tetrachloride in a narrow longitudinal groove on the plate.

roughness of the plate affected the velocity gradient in the turbulent zone.

Figure 47 shows velocity explorations by Stanton,[691] using two sizes of pipes roughened by cutting a double screw thread in the

Fig. 45.—Laminar flow near the midsection of Plate 1. $V = 20$ ft/sec.

inner walls, the depth of the threads in both pipes being about the same fraction of the diameter. In the turbulent core BC, the slopes du/dy are approximately 0.23 for these three runs.

Fig. 46.—Turbulent flow near the midsection of Plate 1, induced by a circular wire of 0.05-in. diameter placed across the surface 2 in. forward of the midsection, $V = 20$ ft/sec. (*Courtesy of British Aeronautical Research Committee.*)

The velocity distribution for smooth pipes (Fig. 42) shows a flatter curve than for artifically roughened pipes (Fig. 47). In comparing his results for rough and smooth pipes, Stanton[691] made the important discovery, later confirmed and extended by Nikuradse,[514] that the velocity-distribution curves could be correlated by plotting the "velocity-deficiency ratio" $(u_m - u)/u^\star$ vs. the position ratio r/r_0 or $[1 - (y/r_0)]$. The term $u^\star$ is defined as $V \sqrt{f/2}$, and since it involves the average velocity V and the dimensionless friction factor, it is called the **friction velocity.** In obtain-

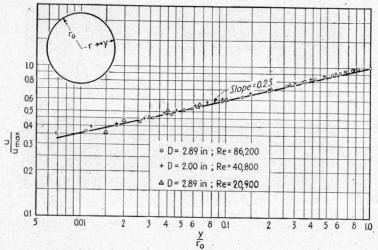

FIG. 47.—Velocity-distribution data of Stanton[691] for flow of air in artificially roughened pipes.

ing equations for velocity-distribution curves in the turbulent core, Prandtl[575] used the form

$$\frac{u_m - u}{u^\star} = \frac{1}{K} \ln_e \frac{r_0}{y} \tag{2}$$

$$\frac{du}{dy} = \frac{u^\star}{Ky} \tag{2a}$$

and von Karman[369] uses

$$\frac{u_m - u}{u^\star} = -\frac{1}{K} \left[\sqrt{\frac{r}{r_0}} + \ln_e \left(1 - \sqrt{\frac{r}{r_0}} \right) \right] \tag{3}$$

$$\frac{du}{dy} = \frac{u^\star}{2Kr_0(1 - \sqrt{r/r_0})} \tag{3a}$$

Figure 48 shows velocity distrbution data of Nikuradse[514] for flow of water at various average velocities in artificially roughened pipes of various sizes. For the turbulent core, curves are shown to represent Eqs. 2 and 3, with K taken as 0.38. Equation 2 is simple in form and fits the data fairly well; Eq. 3, which is more complex than Eq. 2, fits the data quite well. Although both equations call for a finite velocity gradient at the axis, where du/dy is zero, both have been used successfully to predict friction factors from measured velocity distributions.

Figure 49 shows velocity-distribution data of Nikuradse[514] for flow of water at various average velocities in smooth pipes having

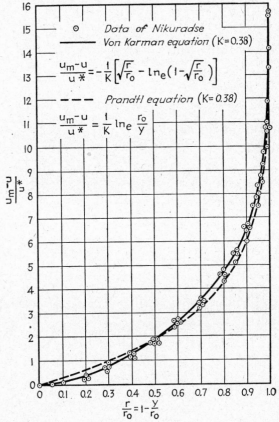

FIG. 48.—Velocity-deficiency ratios *vs.* radius ratios; the "friction velocity" u^* or $u^\star$ equals $V\sqrt{f/2}$.

diameters ranging from 10 to 100 mm. The ratio $u/u^\star$ is designated as u^+, and the ratio $yu^\star\rho/\mu$ is designated by y^+. As for flow of air over flat plates (Fig. 39, page 102), the data fall into three zones:

A **laminar flow layer** near the wall, extending from y^+ of 0 to y^+ of 5, wherein $u^+ = y^+$.

A **buffer layer** extending from y^+ of 5 to y^+ of 30, for which von Karman[369] writes $u^+ = -3.05 + 5.0 \ln y^+$.

A **turbulent core,** for which various writers give $u^+ = 5.5 + 2.5$ ln y^+, based on Eq. 2. This "universal" velocity-distribution

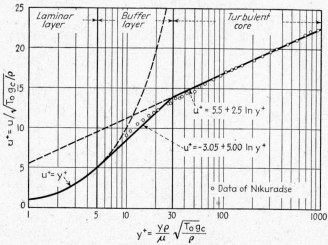

Fig. 49.—Generalized velocity-distribution diagram for isothermal flow of water[514] in artificially roughened pipes. The ordinate u^+ is a velocity ratio $u/u^\star$, the abscissa y^+ is a Reynolds number $y\rho u^\star/\mu$, and the friction velocity $u^\star$ equals $V\sqrt{f/2}$. This method of plotting correlates the velocity distribution u *vs.* y for a number of runs at various average velocities in pipes having various diameters and various degrees of roughness at the wall. (*von Karman.*[369])

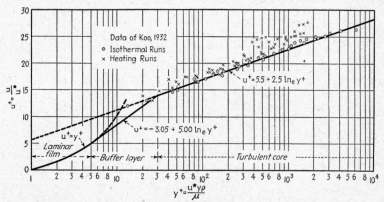

Fig. 50.—Data of Koo[403] for upward and downward turbulent flow of water in a copper tube having an inside diameter of 1.95 in., DG/μ ranging from 15,000 to 75,000. Radial traverses of local velocity and temperature were made with a micrometer impact tube and fine-wire thermocouple.

diagram for turbulent flow in pipes has been used in deriving analogies between heat transfer and friction and analogies between mass transfer and friction (Chap. VII).

Figure 50 shows data of Koo[403] for flow of water in turbulent motion in vertical pipes, plotted as in Fig. 49, and it is seen that the data for isothermal flow agree well with the curves which are based on the data of Nikuradse, shown in Fig. 49. In the runs in which the water was heated, shown by the symbol x in Fig. 50, μ corresponds to the measured temperature at the position y, and the friction factor (involved in both coordinates as $u^\star = V\sqrt{f/2}$) was taken from Fig. 51 at $DV\rho/\mu_f$, with μ_f evaluated at $t_f = 0.5\ (t_s + t)$. When predicting f on this basis, the data for the heating runs lie to the left of the curve for isothermal flow. The points could be brought closer to the curve by evaluating f at the bulk temperature of the stream. As shown in Chap. VII, several writers, in deriving analogies between heat transfer and friction, erroneously assume that heating and cooling runs would lie on the curve for isothermal flow.

II. ENERGY BALANCES

The solution of every problem in fluid dynamics is based on the law of conservation of energy. For the usual case of the steady state, where the mass rate of flow of fluid is independent of both time and location of the cross section chosen, assume the apparatus to be cut by any two sections, each taken at right angles to the direction of flow of fluid.

Material Balance.—For steady mass rate of flow, the law of conservation of matter may be written

$$w = \frac{V_1 S_1}{v_1} = \frac{V_2 S_2}{v_2} \tag{4}$$

This is sometimes called the *equation of continuity*. The ratio w/S appears so often in heat-transfer calculations that it is herein designated by a single symbol G and is called *mass velocity:*

$$G = w/S = V/v = V\rho \tag{4a}$$

It is noted that G is independent of temperature, pressure, and state of aggregation.

Balance of Mechanical and Heat Energy.—Where only mechanical and heat energies are involved, the law of conservation of energy requires that the sum of the mechanical and heat energies possessed by the fluid at the first section, plus the mechanical and heat energy added between sections, equals the sum of the mechanical and heat energies possessed by the fluid at the second section. Considering a time interval such that unit weight of fluid enters section 1 and

TABLE II.—NOMENCLATURE FOR FLUID FLOW

In the dimensionless equations in this book, any consistent units may be employed; the units shown in the table are from the technical system: linear dimensions in feet, time in **seconds,** mass or weight of fluid in pounds (1 lb equals 454 gm), forces in pounds force (as for pressure gauges and calculation of work in foot-pounds), heat in Btu, and temperatures in degrees Fahrenheit.

B　　Ratio of L_e to L, dimensionless.

b　　Breadth, wetted perimeter, feet.

c_p　　Specific heat at constant pressure, Btu/(lb of fluid)(deg F).

c_v　　Specific heat at constant volume, Btu/(lb of fluid)(deg F).

d　　Prefix, indicating differential, dimensionless.

D　　Diameter (inside) of conduit, feet.

D_H　　Diameter of helical coil of pipe, feet.

D_0　　Diameter (outside) of tube, feet.

D_p　　Diameter of packing, average, feet.

E　　Internal energy, Btu per pound of fluid.

f　　Friction factor, dimensionless, in Fanning equation; f', f'', f''', and f'''' are factors in Eqs. 17 to 20, inclusive.

F_c　　Friction due to sudden contraction, feet × force pounds per pound of fluid.

F_e　　Friction due to sudden enlargement, feet × force pounds per pound of fluid.

ΣF　　Friction, total, feet × pounds force per pound of fluid.

g　　Gravitational acceleration, local, usually taken as standard value, 32.2 ft/(sec)(sec).

g_c　　Conversion factor in Newton's law of motion, equals 32.2 ft × pounds matter/(sec)(sec)(pounds force).

G　　Mass velocity, equals w/S, lb of fluid/(sec)(sq ft of cross section); G equals $V\rho$.

h　　Individual coefficient of heat transfer, Btu/(hr)(sq ft)(deg F).

i　　Enthalpy, $E + (pv/J)$, Btu/per pound of fluid.

J　　Mechanical equivalent of heat, 778 ft × force pounds per Btu.

K_c　　Dimensionless factor in contraction-loss equation.

K　　Dimensionless factor in Eqs. 2 and 3.

L　　Length of straight pipe, feet.

L_e　　Equivalent length, feet; length of fictive length of straight pipe having same resistance as that caused by fittings, valves, end losses, etc.

L'　　Depth of tube bank in direction of flow, feet.

M　　Average molecular weight of a gas. For a perfect gas, M equals pounds matter in 359 cu ft at 32°F and normal barometric pressure.

N　　Number of rows of tubes over which fluid flows.

P　　Power, foot pounds per second, theoretically required.

p　　Absolute pressure (intensity of), pounds force per square foot.

Q'　　Heat added (net) from surroundings, Btu per pound of fluid.

TABLE II.—NOMENCLATURE FOR FLUID FLOW.—(*Continued*)

R_G Gas constant equals pv/T, equals $1544/M$, feet $\times$ force pounds per degree Fahrenheit absolute.

r Local radius, feet.

r_0 Total radius, feet.

r_h Hydraulic radius, feet; r_h equals cross section of stream, divided by wetted perimeter $r_h \doteq S/b$.

S Cross section normal to fluid flow, square feet.

t Bulk temperature, degrees Fahrenheit; t' equals $t + 0.25(t_s - t)$.

t_f Equals "film" temperature, degrees Fahrenheit; $t_f = t + 0.5(t_s - t)$.

t_s Surface temperature, degrees Fahrenheit.

T Absolute temperature, degrees Fahrenheit absolute (degrees Fahrenheit $+$ 460); T_m for mean of terminal temperatures.

u Local velocity, feet per second.

$u^\star$ Friction velocity, feet per second; $u^\star = V\sqrt{f/2}$.

u^+ A dimensionless ratio; $u^+ = u/u^\star$.

V Average velocity, feet per second, equals cu ft of fluid/(sec)(sq ft of cross section).

v Specific volume, cubic feet per pound of fluid, equals $1/\rho$.

w Mass rate of flow, pounds of fluid per second.

W_e Work (net) added from surroundings, feet $\times$ force pounds per pound of fluid.

x Ratio of pitch to outside diameter of tubes, dimensionless; x_l is longitudinal value in direction of fluid flow, and x_t is transverse to direction of fluid flow.

y Distance from wall, feet; clearance, feet; y_l is longitudinal clearance and y_t is transverse clearance.

y^+ A dimensionless ratio; $y^+ = yu^\star\rho/\mu$.

z Vertical distance above any arbitrarily chosen datum plane, feet.

Greek

α Dimensionless ratio in Eq. 5d.

β Dimensionless drag coefficient in Eq. 7d; $\beta = f/2 = g_c\tau_0/\rho V^2$.

Γ Mass rate of flow per unit perimeter, lbs of fluid/(sec)(ft), equals w/b.

θ Time, seconds.

μ Absolute viscosity of fluid, lb/(sec)(ft) equals $\mu_F g_c$, where μ_F is expressed in pounds force $\times$ seconds per square foot; μ equals $0.000672 \times$ viscosity in centipoises.

μ/ρ Kinematic viscosity, square feet per second.

π $3.1416 \cdots$.

ρ Density, pounds fluid per cubic foot ($\rho_w = 62.3$ for liquid water at room temperature); $\rho' = \rho/\rho_w$; also, ρ' is used for density in grams per cubic centimeter.

τ_0 Tractive force at wall due to fluid friction, pounds force per square foot of wall; $\tau' = \tau_o A$, pounds force.

ϕ Dimensionless term defined on page 121.

leaves at section 2 and expressing all energy terms as heat per unit weight of fluid, one obtains the over-all balance of mechanical and heat energy

$$\frac{1}{J}\left(z_1\frac{g}{g_c} + \frac{V_1^2}{2g_c} + p_1v_1\right) + E_1 + \frac{W_e}{J} + Q'$$
$$= \frac{1}{J}\left(z_2\frac{g}{g_c} + \frac{V_2^2}{2g_c} + p_2v_2\right) + E_2 \quad (5)*$$

wherein the symbols have the significance shown in Table II, page 112. Q' represents the *net* heat input from the surroundings, *i.e.*, the gross heat input less losses to the surroundings. V represents the average velocity of the fluid over the entire cross section and is defined as the volumetric rate of flow divided by the cross section S available for fluid flow. The term $E + (pv/J) = i$ is defined as the **enthalpy** of the fluid, Btu per pound, and values of $i - i_{32°F}$ are given by the usual tables for fluids such as water (see page 397), ammonia, sulphur dioxide, carbon dioxide, etc. The term E, intrinsic energy per unit mass, is best defined by the difference term $i - (pv/J)$. Since the ratio g/g_c, in technical units, is usually substantially equal to unity, Eq. 5 may be written

$$Q' = i_2 - i_1 + \frac{1}{J}\left[(z_2 - z_1) + \left(\frac{V_2^2 - V_1^2}{2g_c}\right) - W_e\right] \quad (5b)\dagger$$

* The corresponding differential form is

$$\frac{dW_e}{J} + dQ' = \frac{dz}{J} + dE + \frac{d(pv)}{J} + \frac{2V\,dV}{2g_cJ} = \frac{dz}{J}\frac{g}{g_c} + di + \frac{V\,dV}{g_cJ} \quad (5a)$$

In the latter equality the term $di = dE + d(pv)/J$ represents the change in enthalpy.

† The corresponding equation for a differential length, containing no pump, is

$$dQ' = di + \frac{1}{J}\left(dz + \frac{2V\,dV}{2g_c}\right) \quad (5c)$$

Strictly, the kinetic-energy term $V^2/2g_cJ$ should be replaced by the integral

$$KE_H = \frac{1}{w}\int\frac{dM\cdot u^2}{2g_cJ} = \frac{V^2}{2\alpha g_cJ} \quad (5d)$$

where u is the local velocity at a given point in the cross section. Thus, for isothermal streamline flow in a long straight circular pipe, where the velocity distribution is parabolic, by combining Eqs. 5d and 1, the kinetic terms can be shown to be V^2/g_cJ instead of the usual $V^2/2g_cJ$; *i.e.*, α equals ½. For flow, well in the turbulent range, the velocity gradient is less steep than for streamline flow, and as an approximation α is taken as unity. Since in Eq. 5b only *differences* in the kinetic-energy terms are involved, the use of the square of the

Since for perfect gases $pv = 1544T/M$, E equals c_vT, and $c_p - c_v$ equals $1544/778\ M$ or $1.985/M$, the enthalpy change for perfect gases becomes

$$i_2 - i_1 = \int_1^2 c_p\, dT = (c_p)_m(T_2 - T_1) \tag{6}$$

Illustration 1.—Air is flowing at constant mass rate through a horizontally arranged air heater and is heated by some form of heating surface from a temperature of 70°F at section 1 to 170°F at section 2, the cross section being equal at both sections. The absolute pressure is normal barometric at the first section and less by 1 in. water at the second section. The average air velocity at section 1 is 20 ft/sec. Calculate the net heat input Q', assuming that $(c_p)_m$ is 0.24.

Solution.—The absolute pressure at the second section $29.92 - (1/13.6) = 29.85$ in. mercury, and the velocity, assuming the perfect gas law, is

$$V_2 = (20)\left(\frac{460 + 170}{460 + 70}\right)\left(\frac{29.92}{29.85}\right) = 23.8 \text{ ft/sec}$$

Expressing all terms in Btu per pound of air (Eqs. 5b and 6),

$$Q' = 0.24(630 - 530) + \frac{(23.8)^2 - (20)^2}{(64.4)(778)} = 24 + 0.0033$$

Illustration 2.—If in the preceding illustration the heater had been vertical, the air leaving the apparatus at a level 10 ft above the air inlet, would the net heat input have been materially different than for the horizontal heater?

Solution.—Per pound of air, the term $(z_2 - z_1)/J = 10/778 = 0.0129$ Btu, which is negligible compared to the 24 Btu necessary to increase the enthalpy.

For the conditions of Illustrations 1 and 2, the change in kinetic energies amounted to only 0.014 per cent of the increase in enthalpy, and the change in potential energies was only 0.054 per cent of the change in enthalpy. Under ordinary conditions, such as those of Illustrations 1 and 2, the changes in both potential and kinetic energies are usually neglected, giving what might be termed the "usual heat balance": $Q' = i_2 - i_1$. Under conditions involving the heating or cooling of fluids flowing at very high velocities, the change in kinetic energies may be important compared to changes in enthalpy.

Illustration 3.—Water is being evaporated in a vertical tube apparatus having tubes 15 ft long. If the water enters the tubes as liquid at a temperature of 212°F and at an absolute pressure of 15 lb/sq in and an average velocity

average velocity, in place of the integral expression, ordinarily introduces little error. Where kinetic-energy terms are important relative to other terms in Eq. 5b, and the flow is streamline at one section and turbulent at the other, it is worth while to compute kinetic-energy terms from Eq. 5d.

of 3 ft/sec and the mixture of water and steam leaves at 209.6°F and 14 lb/sq in. abs, with 3 per cent of the original water as steam, what would be the heat input expressed as Btu per pound of entering water?

Solution.—Writing Eq. 5b, with all terms expressed as Btu per pound of entering water,

$$Q' = \frac{z_2 - z_1}{J} + \frac{V_2^2 - V_1^2}{2g_c J} + i_2 - i_1$$

Using the steam tables[372] (page 397), $v_1 = 0.01672$ cu ft/lb. At 14 lb/sq in. abs, 1 lb of liquid occupies 0.01672 cu ft, and 1 lb of dry-saturated vapor occupies 28.04 cu ft; on the average, $v_2 = 0.97(0.01672) + 0.03(28.04) = 0.858$ cu ft. Then $V_2 = 3(0.858/0.01672) = 154$ ft/sec.

$$
\begin{aligned}
& & & \text{Btu/lb} \\
i_2 - i_1 &= [0.97(177.61) + 0.03(1149.5)] - 180.07 &=& 26.70 \\
(V_2^2 - V_1^2)/2g_c J &= [(154)^2 - (3)^2]/(64.4)(778) &=& 0.47 \\
(z_2 - z_1)/J &= {}^{15}\!/_{778} &=& 0.02 \\
Q' & & =& 27.19
\end{aligned}
$$

For the conditions of Illustration 3 the changes in kinetic and potential energies represented 1.8 per cent of the heat input.

CALCULATION OF FRICTION LOSSES

Balance of Mechanical Energy, Corrected for Transformation of Mechanical and Heat Energy.—This form of the energy balance is the one familiar in hydraulics and applies to the flow of any fluid at constant mass rate, even with simultaneous heat transmission. Because of friction, some mechanical energy is lost as such through irreversible changes. Because of changes in volume due to changes in pressure and temperature, a compressible fluid (such as a gas or a vapor) expands and develops a work of expansion $\int p\, dv$ at the expense of change in internal energy or externally supplied heat. By the law of conservation of energy, the sum of the various forms of mechanical energy present at the first section, plus the mechanical energy received between sections from the surroundings, plus the mechanical energy created at the expense of heat energy, equals the sum of the various forms of mechanical energy present at the second section, plus the friction. Indeed, ΣF is best defined as the term necessary to balance Eq. 7. Over an interval of time such that 1 lb of fluid enters the first section and leaves the second, this equation becomes, expressing all terms in foot-pounds per pound of fluid,

$$z_1 \frac{g}{g_c} + \frac{V_1^2}{2g_c} + p_1 v_1 + W_e + \int_1^2 p\, dv = z_2 \frac{g}{g_c} + \frac{V_2^2}{2g_c} + p_2 v_2 + \Sigma F \quad (7)$$

This is generally called *Bernoulli's theorem.* Since the kinetic energy has been taken as $V^2/2g_c$, this equation is more nearly correct for turbulent flow, as shown in the footnote on page 114. ΣF includes all forms of friction loss occurring between sections, including losses F_c due to contractions in cross section, pipe friction F, and losses F_e due to enlargements in cross section. Since $p_1v_1 + \int_1^2 p\, dv - p_2v_2$ always equals $-\int_1^2 v\, dp$, the equation may be written more compactly as

$$W_e - \int_1^2 v\, dp = (z_2 - z_1)\frac{g}{g_c} + \frac{V_2^2 - V_1^2}{2g_c} + \Sigma F \qquad (7a)$$

The corresponding equation for a differential length, containing no pump, is

$$-v\, dp = \frac{g}{g_c}\, dz + \frac{V\, dV}{g_c} + dF \qquad (7b)$$

III. FRICTION

The significance of the friction term in Eq. 7b is emphasized by the following derivation.

Friction.—Consider steady mass rate of flow of a fluid through a horizontal pipe of uniform diameter. Focus attention on a differential length dL of the pipe. Because of friction there exists a retarding force or drag at the wall, equal to $\tau_0 b\, dL$. The force acting on the upstream end of the element of volume $S\, dL$ is pS and that on the downstream end is $(p + dp)(S)$. Newton's law of motion (force is proportion to mass times acceleration) gives

$$S[p - (p + dp)] - \tau_0 b\, dL = \frac{1}{g_c}\left(\frac{S\, dL}{v}\right)\left(\frac{dV}{\alpha\, d\theta}\right)$$

Multiplying through by v/S and replacing $dL/d\theta$ by V, one obtains

$$-v\, dp = V\, dV/\alpha g_c + v\tau_0 b\, dL/S \qquad (7c)$$

By definition $v\tau_0 b\, dL/S$ is the energy transmitted to the wall due to friction and is represented by the symbol dF. A similar derivation, for an inclined conduit, of any cross section, gives Eq. 7b above. From experiments with turbulent flow, it is found that the drag τ_0 is approximately directly proportional to the density and to the square of the average velocity:

$$\tau_0 = \beta\rho V^2/g_c \qquad (7d)$$

where β is a dimensionless factor, usually replaced by $f/2$, giving a form of the friction equation used by some writers

$$\tau_0 = f\rho V^2/2g_c \qquad (7e)$$

Since dF equals $v\tau_0 b\, dL/S$, this may be written

$$\frac{dF}{dL} = \frac{fV^2}{2g_cS/b} = \frac{fV^2}{2g_cr_h} \qquad (7f)$$

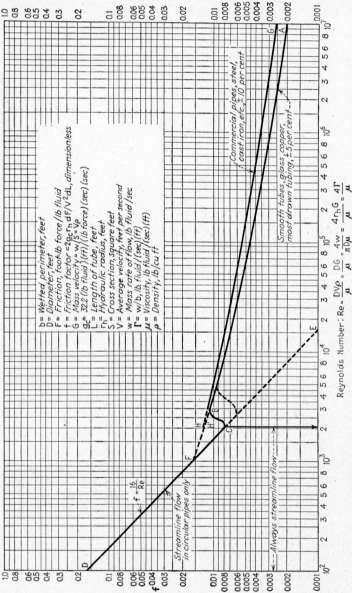

FIG. 51.—Friction factors for isothermal flow of Newtonian fluids in pipes having two degrees of roughness. The dimensionless Reynolds number $DV\rho/\mu$ is numerically equal to 7730 $D'V\rho'/\mu'$ where D' is in inches, V in fps, ρ' is specific gravity relative to water, and μ' is in centipoises.

wherein the hydraulic radius r_h is defined equal to the ratio of cross section to wetted perimeter: $r_h = S/b$.

FLUID FRICTION INSIDE PIPES

Fanning Equation.—For isothermal turbulent flow in straight pipes it is found experimentally that the friction follows the so-called "Fanning equation"

$$dF/dL = fV^2/2g_c r_h \qquad (8)*$$

For a circular pipe, where the hydraulic radius r_h equals $D/4$, the Fanning equation is

$$\frac{dF}{dL} = \frac{4fV^2}{2g_c D} = \frac{4fG^2}{2g_c\rho^2 D} = \frac{6.49fw^2}{2g_c\rho^2 D^5} \qquad (8a)$$

wherein any consistent system of units may be employed. (The recommended set of units is shown in Table II, page 112.)

Smooth Pipes.—The friction factor f of Eqs. 8 and 8a is based on test data, and, as shown by Stanton and Pannell, Blasius, and others, is found to depend upon two dimensionless groups: the Reynolds number $Re = DV\rho/\mu = DG/\mu$ and "relative roughness," *i.e.*, the actual average roughness divided by the diameter. Based on the data of a number of investigators on the flow of air, water, and oils in clean, smooth pipes of brass, copper, lead, and glass, with diameters ranging from 0.5 to 5.0 in., it is found that the values of f, when plotted *vs.* the Reynolds number, lie in a relatively narrow band, giving the recommended curve[194,191] for smooth pipes, Curve *BC* of Fig. 51. Based on the correlation of 1380 experimental points, lying in the range of $Re = 3000$ to 3,000,000, the empirical equation of Koo[403] for long smooth pipes is

$$f = 0.00140 + 0.125/(Re)^{0.32} \qquad (9)$$

Over the limited range of Re from 5000 to 200,000

$$f = 0.046/(Re)^{0.2} \qquad (9a)$$

Using the equations for velocity distribution (page 110), von Karman predicts the following relation between f and Re for smooth pipes:

$$1/\sqrt{f} = 4.0 \log_{10} (Re \sqrt{f}) - 0.40 \qquad (9b)$$

---

* Some writers multiply the right-hand side of Eq. 8 by factors of 2 or 4 and thus change the definition and consequently the numerical value of the friction factor; throughout this book the symbol f is used consistently as the factor defined in Eq. 8.

which fits the data for friction in smooth pipes and is recommended for extrapolation to high values of Re.

Rough Pipes.—Data of a number of observers[*] for clean pipes of steel and cast iron are represented (within a deviation of ± 10 per cent in f) by Curve HG[194,191] of Fig. 51. Curve HG may be represented by the equation[191]

$$1/\sqrt{f} = 3.2 \log_{10} (Re \sqrt{f}) + 1.2 \qquad (9c)$$

For badly corroded or tuberculated pipes, due especially to a decrease in diameter, the value of f, based on the observed friction drop and the original diameter, may rise to very high values, depending primarily on the average actual diameter of the opening in the tuberculated pipe.[376,562]

For isothermal *streamline* flow in a straight circular pipe, the pressure drop due to friction is given by Poiseuille's law, which is derived from the definition of absolute viscosity of the fluid, assuming no slip at the wall and constant viscosity.[†] This equation has been verified for the flow of hydrocarbon oils in pipe sizes ranging from capillary tubes up to 12-in. steel pipe.[770a]

$$\frac{dF}{dL} = \frac{32\mu V}{g_c D^2 \rho} = \frac{32\mu G}{g_c D^2 \rho^2} = \frac{40.75\mu w}{g D^4 \rho^2} \qquad (10)$$

wherein any consistent units are employed. Apparently for clean pipes, the nature of the wall has little influence upon the pressure drop. Equation 10 may be used for flow in the streamline region, but it is generally customary to equate Eq. 10 to Eq. 8a, thus determining the value of f in Eq. 8a to be used for streamline flow in circular pipe:

$$f = 16\mu/DV\rho = 16\mu/DG = 16/Re \qquad (11)$$

By this procedure it is possible to employ the Fanning equation to *both* streamline and turbulent flow, reading the appropriate value of f from a plot of f vs. DG/μ, as shown in Fig. 51 (page 118).

Effect of Heat Transfer upon Friction for Flow inside Pipes.— Few data are available on the friction factors for nonisothermal flow. Data[‡] for heating or cooling inside pipes may be correlated with

---

[*] Data for flow of fluids at acoustic velocities[237,371] are in reasonably good agreement with the data of Fig. 51.

[†] By definition, $g_c \, d\tau/dA = \mu \, du/dy$; the effect of pressure on μ and the consequent modification of Eq. 10 are discussed by Hersey and Snyder.[302]

[‡] References 373, 375, 761, 127.

those for isothermal flow either [454a] by evaluating at a special temperature [$t' = t + (t_s - t)/4$ for DG/μ below 2100, and $t_f = t + (t_s - t)/2$ for DG/μ above 2100] and using Fig. 51, or[668] by considering the ordinate of Fig. 51 to be the product of the nonisothermal f and a factor ϕ [where $\phi = 1.1 (\mu/\mu_s)^{0.25}$ for DG/μ below 2100 and $\phi = 1.0 (\mu/\mu_s)^{0.14}$ for DG/μ above 2100], interpreting the abscissa as DG/μ based on mean bulk temperature. Either of these approximate methods is satisfactory. In the turbulent region, at a given DG/μ, the effect of heat transfer upon f is usually small. A complex but sound method for streamline flow is available.[428,472a]

Resistance of Fittings.—These are allowed for by assigning a fictitious or equivalent length L_e of straight pipe to the existing straight pipe and using the sum $L_e + L$, in Eq. 8 for turbulent flow. For DG/μ above 2100 to 3000, the dimensionless ratio L_e/D for the fitting apparently varies but little with DG/μ, and values are taken from Table III.

TABLE III.—L_e/D RATIOS FOR SCREWED FITTINGS, VALVES, ETC., TURBULENT FLOW ONLY[a]

Fitting	L_e/D	Fitting	L_e/D
45-deg elbows..............	15	Tee (used as elbow entering branch).................	90
90-deg elbows, standard radius....................	32	Couplings, unions.........	Negligible
90-deg elbows, medium radius....................	26	Gate valves, open............	7[b]
90-deg elbows, long sweep...	20	Gate valves, one-fourth closed..................	40[b]
90-deg square elbows.......	75	Gate valves, one-half closed	200[b]
180-deg close return bends...	75	Gate valves, three-fourths closed..................	800[b]
180-deg medium-radius return bends....................	50	Globe valves, open........	300[b]
Tee (used as elbow, entering run)....................	60	Angle valves, open........	170[b]

[a] Drew and Genereaux, p. 825 of reference 557.

[b] Rough estimate; values depend on construction of valve.

Enlargement Losses.—Friction occurs because of sudden enlargements and contractions in the cross-sectional area of a duct.

The frictional loss on sudden enlargement of a cross section is usually calculated from the equation

$$F_e = (V_1 - V_2)^2/2g_c \tag{12}$$

where V_1 is the average velocity of the fluid in the upstream section of pipe and V_2 is the average velocity in the downstream section. This formula has been shown by Schutt[649] to be exact for liquids flowing in turbulent motion and may be used safely for gases flowing at moderate velocities. Where the enlargement is gradual (total angle of divergence not greater than 7 deg), the friction loss may be calculated by integrating Eq. 8. When the angle of divergence is greater than 7 deg, no simple treatment will apply.[*]

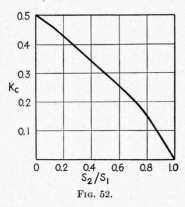

FIG. 52.

Contraction Losses.—The friction caused by a sudden contraction of the cross-sectional area of a pipe, or that at a sharp-edged entrance to a pipe, may be calculated from the formula

$$F_c = K_c V_2^2 / 2g_c \qquad (13)$$

F_c is the friction due to sudden contraction, foot-pound per pound of fluid; V_2 is the average linear velocity downstream, feet per second; and K_c is a function of S_2/S_1, the ratio of the smaller cross-sectional area to the larger, as is given in Fig. 52.[†]

For rounded or conical entrances, there is little entrance loss ($K = 0.05$) if the flow in the smaller pipe be turbulent. Other cases are treated on p. 821 of reference 557.

Effect of Curvature of Pipe upon Friction.—For the isothermal flow of fluids in curved pipes, the friction loss may be considerably more than in straight pipes, conditions being otherwise the same. For isothermal *streamline* flow in curved pipes, sufficient data are available[‡] to show the mechanism of the flow and to allow calculation of the pressure drop. Color-band work showed that the particles of fluid follow tortuous paths, traveling from the center of the pipe toward the outside wall and then crossing back toward the inside wall. Near the wall, therefore, the particles of fluid travel faster in a curved section of pipe than in a straight section, because of their spiral path. Because of this increased velocity near the wall and the longer path traveled per foot of pipe length by the individual fluid particles, a higher friction drop in curved pipes is to be expected. Color-band and pressure-drop experiments also show that streamline flow can exist at much higher Reynolds number in curved pipe than in

* Donch,[180] Gibson,[248] Kroner,[412] and Nikuradse.[511]
† From Hughes and Safford, "Hydraulics," p. 330, Macmillan, New York, 1911.
‡ Eustice,[213] White,[760] and Taylor.[710]

straight pipe. The following table, prepared by Drew,[183] shows some experimental values of the critical Reynolds number for flow in pipe coils.

TABLE IV.—EFFECT OF CURVATURE ON CRITICAL VALUES OF Re_c

Diameter of pipe to diameter of coil D/D_H	Re_c	
	White (friction)	Taylor (color band)
1/15.15	7590	....
1/18.7	....	7100
1/31.9	....	6350
1/50	6020	
1/2050	2270	

To evaluate the friction factor for fluids flowing in *streamline motion* through pipe coils, use Fig. 53, prepared by Drew.[183] If the friction factor for curved pipes, so calculated, is less than 0.009, the flow is turbulent, not viscous, and the foregoing rule fails.

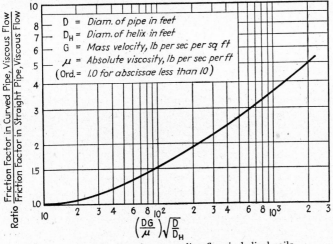

FIG. 53.—Drew chart for streamline flow in helical coils.

The data on *turbulent flow in smooth curved pipes* indicate substantially the same friction factor as for straight pipes, if D/D_H is not greater than 1/500. For sharper curves, the data available indicate a considerable increase of the friction factor in the lower turbulent region.

Flow inside Rectangular and Annular Sections.—For *turbulent* flow, the pressure drop in rectangular ducts and annular spaces may be calculated as for circular pipes, using an "equivalent diameter" equal to $4r_h$. The available data*

* Atherton,[19] Cornish,[156] Drew,[186] Fromm,[238] Kratz, Macintire and Gould,[407] Lea,[427] Mikrjukov,[480] and Nikuradse.[512]

on oil, water, and air support this procedure. If the core is not concentric with the larger pipe, substantial deviations may occur.

For *isothermal streamline* flow inside straight ducts of various shapes, theoretical equations have been derived by many writers.* The friction for isothermal streamline flow through a *rectangular* duct of sides y and b is given by the theoretical equation:

$$\frac{dF}{dL} = \frac{4V\mu}{ybg_c n\rho} = \frac{4G\mu}{ybg_c\rho^2 n} = \frac{4w\mu}{y^2b^2\rho^2 g_c n}. \tag{14}$$

Since the hydraulic radius r_h equals $yb/2(y + b)$, the corresponding friction factor f in Eq. 8 is

$$f = 4\mu/G(y + b)n \tag{15}$$

In Eqs. 14 and 15, n is a function of the aspect ratio b/y, given by Fig. 54. For broad parallel plates, having a clearance y,

$$dF/dL = 12\mu G/y^2 g_c\rho^2 \tag{15a}$$

The pressure drop through an *annular space* of inner diameter D_1 and outer diameter D_2 is given by the equation

$$\frac{dF}{dL} = \frac{32G\mu}{\rho^2 g_c \left(D_2^2 + D_1^2 - \dfrac{D_2^2 - D_1^2}{2.3 \log_{10} (D_2/D_1)} \right)}. \tag{16}$$

which can be approximated by Eq. 15a.

The equations for streamline flow in straight ducts of various shapes do not coincide with that for straight circular pipes, even when expressed in terms of the hydraulic radius. Data† on streamline flow in rectangular sections and annular spaces agree with the theoretical equations. The data of Trahey and Smith[720] for rectangular ducts and a comparison with the data of Fromm, Lea, and Cornish for rectangular ducts are given by Drew.[186] The ratio of sides y/b varied from 0.05 to 1.

The available data for flow in long rectangular ducts and annular spaces indicate that the transition from streamline to turbulent flow occurs at a Reynolds number $4r_h G/\mu$ of about the same values as for straight circular pipes, *i.e.*, 2100 to 2300, wherein r_h, the hydraulic radius, is the cross-sectional area divided by the wetted perimeter. Flow in short ducts is treated elsewhere.[557]

Packed Tubes.—Figure 55[116] shows the "modified friction factor" f' for flow of gases through beds of *dry* packed solids plotted *vs.* $D_p V_0\rho/\mu$ and defined by the dimensionless equation

$$dF/dL = 4f'f''V_0^2/2g_c D_p \tag{17}$$

V_0 is the superficial linear velocity, feet per second, based on the cross section of the empty tower of diameter D, feet; D_p is the average diameter of the packing, feet; and f'' is the "wall-effect factor," taken from the work of Furnas.[240]

---

* Boussinesq,[79] Graetz,[256] Greenhill,[259] and Lamb.[418]

† Cornish,[156] Davies and White,[165] Drew,[186] Lea,[427] Nikuradse,[512] and Trahey and Smith.[720] According to Lea, Eq. 16 gives pressure drops much higher than the experimental values when D_2/D_1 is very great.

The dimensionless value f'' is plotted *vs.* the ratio of diameters of packing and tower, D_p/D. Figure 55 includes data for isothermal conditions and for runs where heat was being transferred by externally heating with steam. Data

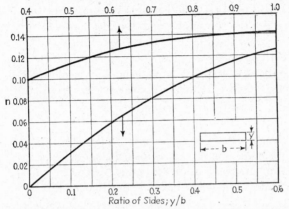

Fig. 54.—Values of n, for Eq. 14, for streamline flow in rectangular ducts.

such as those in Fig. 55 are useful in calculating the pressure drop for the flow of gases through catalyst heat exchangers. When liquid is flowing down through the packing, the value of f' is increased over that for the dry packing.[557]

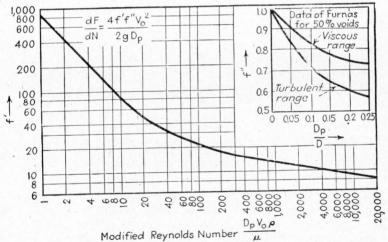

$$\frac{dF}{dN} = \frac{4 f' f'' V_o^2}{2 g D_p}$$

Fig. 55.—Friction factors for flow through packed tubes. (*Chilton and Colburn.*)

Colburn and King[150] give data for the pressure drop due to friction in cooling air flowing through a horizontal tube containing different types of turbulence promoters. They also showed an interesting plot relating heat-transfer coefficient and pressure drop due to friction. Data for water are given by Nagaoka and Watanabe.[497]

Friction Loss for Flow outside Tubes

Flow Parallel to Axis.—For turbulent flow outside and parallel to the axis of the tubes, as in certain types of heat exchangers, data are available for both gases and liquids, and the recommended treatment is given on Fig. 51, page 118.

Flow Normal to Axis.—The friction for turbulent flow of fluid normal to a bank of tubes, N rows deep, may be considered as due to N contractions and enlargements, which leads to the dimensionless equation[121]

$$F = 4f'''NV_{max}^2/2g_c \tag{18}$$

For turbulent flow of air across banks of staggered pipes, of various diameters, with a wide range of transverse and longitudinal spacings, Andreas[7] and Grimison[269] find that in Eq. 18 f''' depends on arrangement and a Reynolds number. Grimison gives the functions for a large number of arrangements both for staggered and in-line positions of the tubes; the data are approximated by the dimensionless equations of Jakob:[339a]

For tubes in line:

$$f''' = \left(0.044 + \frac{0.08x_l}{(x_t - 1)^n}\right)\left(\frac{D_0 G_{max}}{\mu_f}\right)^{-0.15} \tag{19}*$$

in which $n = 0.43 + (1.13/x_l)$

For staggered tubes

$$f''' = \left(0.23 + \frac{0.11}{(x_t - 1)^{1.08}}\right)\left(\frac{D_0 G_{max}}{\mu_f}\right)^{-0.15} \tag{19a}$$

in which x_l is the ratio of the longitudinal pitch to tube diameter, x_t is the ratio of the transverse pitch to tube diameter, and pitch is center-to-center distance. Thus for tubes in line, with x_l of 2 and x_t of 2, Eq. 19 gives $f''' = 0.20 \ (D_0 G_{max}/\mu_f)^{-0.15}$; for staggered tubes, with x_t of 2, Eq. 19a reduces to $f''' = 0.34 \ (D_0 G_{max}/\mu_f)^{-0.15}$. These equations are based on the data of Grimison[269], which cover values of $D_0 G_{max}/\mu_f$ ranging from 2000 to 40,000. In all cases G_{max} is based on the minimum free area, either in the transverse or diagonal opening. These equations are applied quantitatively in Chap. XI, where diagrams of tube layouts are also shown.

---

* Below $D_0 G_{max}/\mu_f$ of 10,000, f''' should be taken constant at the value given by Eq. 19 at $D_0 G_{max}/\mu_f$ of 10,000.

Below values of $y\rho V_{max}/\mu$ of 40, streamline flow develops, and the available data are correlated by the equation[121]

$$F = \frac{53\mu L' V_{max}}{g_c \rho D_e^2} \tag{20}$$

where $D_e = 4r_h = (4s_T s_L/\pi D) - D$; s_T and s_L are defined on page 218.

Calculation of Pressure Drop in Tubes

It should be emphasized that the calculation of pressure drop for steady flow involves combining the energy balance with the appropriate equation for friction. For steady flow in tubes, combination of Eqs. 7b and 8a gives

$$-v\,dp = \frac{g}{g_c}\,dz + \frac{V\,dV}{\alpha g_c} + \frac{4fV^2\,dL}{2g_c D} \tag{21}$$

Liquids.—For incompressible fluids, such as liquids at moderate pressures, the specific volumes, and consequently the velocities in a pipe of uniform diameter, are constant, and integration gives

$$v(p_1 - p_2) = \frac{g}{g_c}(z_2 - z_1) + \frac{4fV^2 L}{2g_c D} \tag{21a}*$$

The friction factor depends on DG/μ; if the temperature varies, μ and consequently f will vary; f_m designates the length-mean value $f_m = 1/L \int_0^L f\,dL$ (see page 118).

Gases and Vapors.—For compressible fluids, changes in specific volume may be such that allowance for this variation may be necessary. For example, consider steady mass flow of a compressible fluid through a horizontal duct of constant hydraulic radius. Over the range in pressures involved, the constant R_G in the gas law will be called constant, $v = R_G T/p$. Upon dividing Eq. 21 by v^2 and noting that V equals Gv, one obtains

$$-\frac{1}{R_G}\int \frac{p\,dp}{T} = \frac{G^2}{g_c}\int \frac{dv}{v} + \frac{G^2}{2g_c r_h}\int f\,dL \tag{22}$$

Since in most cases the absolute temperature of the fluid will not vary greatly, a mean value T_m is used as an approximation. As explained above, f varies but little with temperature, especially for turbulent flow, and integration gives

$$\frac{p_1^2 - p_2^2}{2R_G T_m} = \frac{G^2}{g_c}\ln\frac{v_2}{v_1} + \frac{f_m L G^2}{2g_c r_h} \tag{22a}$$

* If changes in cross section are involved, F_c and F_e of p. 121 are added to the right-hand side of this equation.

The left-hand side is equal to $(p_1 - p_2)(\rho_a)$, wherein ρ_a equals $(p_1 + p_2)/2R_G T_m$. Division of Eq. 22a by ρ_a gives

$$p_1 - p_2 = \frac{G^2}{\rho_a g_c} \ln \frac{v_2}{v_1} + \frac{f_m G^2 L}{2g_c r_h \rho_a} \qquad (22b)$$

Where v_2/v_1 is less than 2:1, little error is introduced by writing Eq. 22b as follows:

$$p_1 - p_2 = \frac{G^2}{g_c} (v_2 - v_1) + \frac{f_m L G^2}{2g_c r_h \rho_a} \qquad (22c)$$

End Losses.—Combination of the energy balance (Eq. 7b) with the equation for friction due to a sudden contraction (Eq. 13) gives

$$v_a(p_0 - p_1) = \frac{V_1^2 - V_0^2}{2g_c} + \frac{K_c V_1^2}{2g_c} \qquad (23)$$

Similarly, for a sudden enlargement between sections 2 and 3, combination of Eqs. 7b and 12 gives

$$v_a(p_2 - p_3) = \frac{V_3^2 - V_2^2}{2g_c} + \frac{(V_2 - V_3)^2}{2g_c} \qquad (24)$$

The ratio of the total friction, including end losses, to that in the tubes alone, neglecting change in density, is obtained by combining Eqs. 8a, 12, and 13.

$$B = \frac{\Sigma F}{F_t} = 1 + \frac{K_c + \left(1 - \dfrac{S}{S_H}\right)^2}{4fL/D} \qquad (25)$$

in which S/S_H is the ratio of the combined internal cross section of the tubes to that of the header compartments. If desired an additional term may be included for reversals in direction of flow; by including a term for the overall change in kinetic energy, B becomes the ratio of total pressure drop to that in the tubes alone.

The friction drag, per unit area of surface, is

$$\tau_0 = \Delta p_f S/A = BfG^2/2g_c \rho \qquad (26)$$

and the power necessary to overcome friction, per unit area of surface, is

$$P/A = \tau_0 V = BfG^3/2g_c \rho^2 \qquad (26a)$$

For flow across a bank of tubes the friction drag, per unit area of surface, is

$$\tau_0 = 4f'''G_{max}^2 y_t/2g_c \rho \pi D_0 \qquad (27)$$

and the corresponding necessary power is

$$P/A = \tau_0 V_{max} = 4f'''G_{max}^3 y_t/2g_c\rho^2\pi D_0 \tag{27a}$$

Illustration 4.—A hydrocarbon oil is flowing at constant weight rate inside the straight tubes of a vertically arranged heater, making three single passes, entering at the bottom and leaving at the top at a level 10.5 ft above the oil inlet. The tubes have an actual i.d. of $\frac{3}{4}$ in. and a length of 10 ft between tube sheets. The effective cross section of each header box is twice the internal cross section of the tubes entering each header box. The tubes are heated by dry, saturated steam condensing at 350°F. The average mass velocity in the tubes is 300 lb of oil/(sec)(sq ft of cross section), and the oil enters the first pass at 60° and leaves the last pass at 210°F. The viscosity is 5 centipoises at 60°, 1.25 at 205°, 1.2 at 210°, and 0.8 at 280°F. The specific gravity of the oil is 0.841 at 60° and 0.785 at 210°F, relative to water at 60°F. Calculate the pressure drop from the first to the last header box, using curve AB of Fig. 51.

Solution.—To convert centipoises to lb/(sec)(ft), multiply by 0.000672. The corresponding values of μ are then 0.00336 lb./(sec)(ft) at 60°, 0.000841 at 205°, 0.000806 at 210°, and 0.000538 at 280°F. To determine whether the motion is turbulent, *i.e.*, if DG/μ exceeds 2100, DG/μ will be evaluated at the terminal oil temperatures. $Re = DG/\mu = 0.0625 (300)/0.00336 = 5580$ at 60° and 23,300 at 210°F. Since the flow is turbulent, the value of the friction factor will be evaluated at (DG/μ_f), corresponding to $t_f = 0.5(t_s + t)$. At the entrance, $t_{f1} = 0.5(350 + 60) = 205°F$, $DG/\mu_{f1} = 22,300$, and, from Fig. 51 page 118, $f_1 = 0.0062$; at the oil exit, $t_{f2} = 0.5(350 + 210) = 280$, $DG/\mu_{f2} = 34,900$, and $f_2 = 0.0058$. Then $f_m = 0.5(0.0062 + 0.0058) = 0.0060$. Since the average density is $62.3(0.813) = 50.6$ lb/cu ft, $V = 300/50.6 = 5.93$ ft/sec. The estimated friction loss in the straight tubes by Eq. 8a, page 119, is

$$F = \frac{4f_m L V^2}{2g_c D} = \frac{(4)(0.0060)(30)(5.93)^2}{(2)(32.2)(0.0625)} = \frac{6.3 \text{ ft} \times \text{force pounds}}{\text{mass pounds}}$$

Since the details of construction of the header boxes are not available, the losses due to sudden contraction (page 122), reversal of direction, and sudden enlargement (page 121) will be evaluated, assuming $1.0V^2/2g_c$ for each reversal in direction. The total losses for the three sets is then $3(0.3 + 1.0 + 0.25)(5.93)^2/64.4 = 2.54$. Summarizing the losses:

	Ft × force lb
	Lb fluid
Friction in three passes of straight pipe =	6.30
End losses =	2.54
Total friction =	8.84
Lift =	10.50
Loss in total head =	19.34

This is equivalent to a pressure drop of $19.34(50.6)/144 = 6.8$ force lb/sq in. The same result would have been obtained by basing total friction loss on an effective frictional length $8.84/6.30 = 1.40$ times the actual length of straight pipe.

The following example illustrates the application of Eqs. 22c, 23, and 24.

Illustration 5.—Air is flowing at constant weight rate inside the straight horizontal tubes of a cooler at a mass velocity of 2 lb/(sec)(sq ft of cross section). The air enters the tubes at 500°F and normal barometric pressure and leaves at 180°F. The tubes have an actual i.d. of 2.00 in. and are 19 ft long. Calculate (a) the pressure drop in the tubes, expressed as inches of water, and (b) the over-all pressure drop between upstream and downstream chambers, if these have cross sections twice those of the steel tubes.

Solution—a. From Fig. 204, page 411, the viscosity of air, expressed as pounds per second per foot, is 0.0000195 at 500° and 0.0000141 at 180°F. Since DG is $(2/12)2$, the values of $Re = DG/\mu$ are 17,100 and 23,600, and, from Fig. 51, page 118, the corresponding values of f are 0.0077 and 0.0072, with $f_m = (0.0077 + 0.0072)/2 = 0.0075$. The hydraulic radius $r_h = D/4 = \frac{1}{24}$ ft. The average molecular weight of air is 29.0, *i.e.*, 29 lb of air occupy 359 cu ft at 32°F and normal atmospheric pressure.

$$v_1 = \frac{359}{29}\left(\frac{500 + 460}{492}\right) = 24.1 \text{ cu ft/lb}$$

Assuming that the final absolute pressure is substantially normal barometric pressure,

$$v_2 = \frac{359}{29}\left(\frac{640}{492}\right) = 16.1 \text{ cu ft/lb}$$

As an approximation $T_m = (960 + 640)/2 = 800$;

$$\rho_\mu = \frac{(\rho_1 + \rho_2)}{2RT_m} = \frac{2(14.69)(144)}{2(1544/29)(800)} = 0.0497$$

The values of v, V, and G are illustrated by Fig. 56.

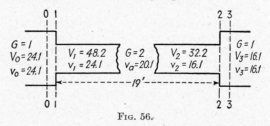

Fig. 56.

By Eq. 22c,*

$$p_1 - p_2 = \frac{(2)^2}{32.2}(16.1 - 24.1) + \frac{(0.0075)(19)(2)^2}{64.4(1/24)(0.0497)}$$
$$= -0.993 + 4.27 = 3.28 \text{ lb/sq ft}$$

or

$$(3.28)\left(\frac{12}{62.3}\right) = 0.63 \text{ in. of water}$$

* Assuming heat transmission has negligible effect on velocity distributions. See note on p. 114.

In this case the pressure increase due to change in kinetic energy in the tube was roughly 23 per cent of the pressure drop due to friction, or approximately 30 per cent of the net drop in pressure. However, the change in kinetic energy is only 0.033 per cent of the net heat input (Eqs. 5b and 6).

$$Q' = 0.24(500 - 180) + \frac{(32.2)^2 - (48.2)^2}{778(64.4)} = 76.8 - 0.0257 \text{ Btu/lb}$$

b. The entrance loss $F_c = K_c V_1^2 / 2g_c$ and from the plot (page 122), $K_c = 0.3$, whence by Eq. 23 (page 128),

$$p_0 - p_1 = \frac{V_1^2 - V_0^2}{2g_c v_{\text{av.}}} + \frac{K_c V_1^2}{2g_c v_{\text{av.}}} = \frac{(48.2)^2 - (24.1)^2}{(64.4)(24.1)}$$
$$+ \frac{0.3(48.2)^2}{(64.4)(24.1)} = 1.12 + 0.45 = 1.57 \text{ lb/sq ft}$$

By Eq. 24 (page 128),

$$p_2 - p_3 = \frac{V_3^2 - V_2^2}{2g_c v_{\text{av.}}} + \frac{(V_2 - V_3)^2}{2g_c v_{\text{av.}}} = \frac{(16.1)^2 - (32.2)^2}{64.4(16.1)}$$
$$+ \frac{(32.2 - 16.1)^2}{64.4(16.1)} = -0.75 + 0.25 = -0.5 \text{ lb/sq ft}$$

SUMMARY

Differences	Lb/sq ft	In. of water
$p_0 - p_1 = 1.12 + 0.45$..........	+1.57	+0.301
$p_1 - p_2 = -0.99 + 4.27$.........	+3.28	+0.630
$p_2 - p_3 = -0.75 + 0.25$........	−0.50	−0.096
$p_0 - p_3$........	4.35	0.835

Since 1 atm is equivalent to a pressure of $14.69(144) = 2115$ lb/sq ft, little error was made in neglecting the change in p in calculating v_2. Assuming 500 air tubes, the volumetric rate of flow at the exit would be $500(3.14)1/144(32.2) = 351$ cu ft/sec at normal pressure. With the fan at the exit, the power theoretically required would be $351 (4.35)/550 = 2.77$ hp.

Problems

1. Water, at a gauge pressure of 94 lb/sq in., enters a tube having an actual i.d. of 2.00 in., at a rate of 13.6 lb/sec. After flowing through a fixed length of this tube, the water flows through additional tubing having an actual i.d. of 1.00 in. and leaves section 2 at a gauge pressure of 47 lb/sq in. at an elevation 20 ft above the inlet to the larger tube. There is no pump between the sections described. The net heat input from the surroundings is 0.35 Btu/sec. It is agreed to neglect variations in density, which is to be considered constant at 62.3 lb/cu ft.

a. Calculate the total friction expressed in foot pounds per pound of water.

b. Assuming that c_v is 1.00 Btu/(lb)(deg F), calculate the temperature rise ·f the water, expressed in degrees Fahrenheit.

2. Dry air is flowing through a horizontal drawn copper tube, 1 in. o.d. and No. 18 BWG, at a rate of 808 lb/hr. The central section, 18 ft long, is steam-jacketed. At the entrance to the jacketed section, the air is at 70°F, and the absolute pressure is 2 atm. At the exit from the jacketed section, the air is at 170°F, and the absolute pressure is 1 atm.

a. Calculate the Btu transferred hourly through the copper wall of the jacketed section.

b. Estimate the friction F from the test data.

c. Calculate the predicted pressure drop, and compare it with the observed value.

3. It is desired to design a pipe line of inside diameter D ft to transport water at a rate of Q cu ft/hr, for θ hr per year, to serve condensers and coolers located z ft above a lake, and at a distance of L ft away. There is no charge for taking water from the lake, but power costs C_e dollars per foot-pound of work delivered to the fluid. The first cost of the pipe line will be $K_{10}D$ dollars per foot, the first cost of the pump and motor is C_1 dollars for each 1000 cu ft/hr capacity, and the fraction F_a of the first costs of pump, motor, and line is to be charged off annually to cover fixed charges on the investment. The gauge pressure of the water at the condensers and coolers is to be P lb/sq in.

a. Derive the general equation for the optimum velocity in the pipe line.

b. Derive a general equation for the optimum total cost of cooling water, expressed as C cents per 1000 cu ft.

c. Calculate the value of C for a case in which L is 10,000 ft, z is 30 ft, P is 60 lb per sq in., power at the switchboard costs 0.80 cent per kwh, the expected over-all efficiency of the pump and motor is 50 per cent, C_1 is 100, θ is 8640, K_{10} is 2.3, annual fixed charges are 15 per cent, and the water rate is 22,300 cu ft per hr.

CHAPTER VI

INTRODUCTION TO HEAT TRANSFER BETWEEN FLUIDS AND SOLIDS

Introduction.—Over-all and individual coefficients of heat transfer are defined, and the resistance concept is applied to the important problem of transmission of heat through a series of resistances. The effect of deposits of scale on the heating surface is discussed, and a table of coefficients of heat transfer through scale deposits is given. Mean temperature difference is treated in detail, several illustrative problems are solved, and measurement of tube temperature is considered. Correlation and prediction of

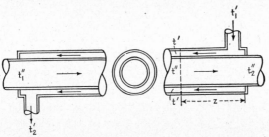

Fig. 57.—Diagram of counterflow heat exchanger; drawings of typical exchangers are shown in Chap. XI.

heat-transfer coefficients and application to design are reserved for subsequent chapters.

Local Over-all Coefficient of Heat Transfer.—In the majority of heat-transfer cases met in industrial practice, heat is being transferred from one fluid through a solid wall to another fluid.

In an apparatus such as shown diagrammatically in Fig. 57, hot fluid flows through the jacket, and a cold fluid flows through the tube. All mass-flow rates are constant, and the steady state has been attained; hence the temperature at each point in the apparatus is independent of time. Consider any cross section located at a distance z from the point of entry of the hot fluid. If the hot stream were drawn off at this section and mixed, it would have a temperature t', called the *bulk temperature;* t'' is the corresponding bulk temperature of the colder fluid at z. For such

133

conditions Newton found that the rate dq of heat transfer was directly proportional to the over-all difference between the temperatures of the warmer and colder fluids $t' - t''$ or Δt, and to the heat transfer surface dA:

$$dq = U \, dA \, \Delta t \tag{1}$$

and the proportionality factor U is called the *local over-all coefficient* of heat transfer or merely the *local over-all coefficient*. In computing U, one may use the area of heating surface dA', the area of the cooling surface dA'', or the logarithmic mean surface dA_w (see page 12). Since in a given case $dq/\Delta t$ is fixed, one can obtain three values of local over-all coefficients U', U_w, U'', which are related by means of area ratios:

$$U' \, dA' = U_w \, dA_w = U'' \, dA'' \tag{1a}$$

It is immaterial which heat transfer surface is chosen so long as it is specified. The subscripts o for outside, w for wall, and i for inside are often used on U to indicate which area was used in the equation $U = dq/dA \, \Delta t$.

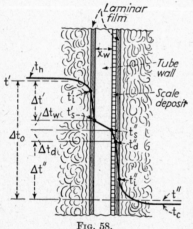

Fig. 58.

As will be shown later, the numerical value of U in a given set of units may vary ten thousandfold, depending on the nature of the fluids, their velocities, and other factors to be discussed elsewhere. Equation 1 [*] is the basic relation for heat transfer between fluids separated by a retaining wall, and the remaining chapters deal with means of predicting the over-all coefficient of heat transfer. This requires consideration of the nature of the thermal resistances met as the heat flows from the warmer fluids through the retaining wall to the other fluid.

Diagram of Temperature Gradients at a Section of a Heat Exchanger.—Continuing the discussion of the conditions at position z of Fig. 57, temperatures will be plotted as ordinates against distance from the hottest point in the warmer fluid, as in Fig. 58. It is noted that the highest temperature of the hot fluid t_h is slightly above the bulk temperature t' of the hot fluid and that the outer surface is at a lower temperature t'_s.

Local Individual Coefficient of Heat Transfer.—As a result of the difference in temperature between the hot fluid and wall, $t' - t'_s$ or $\Delta t'$, the heat flow rate dq is proportional to $\Delta t'$ and to the heat transfer surface dA':

$$dq = h'\, dA'\, \Delta t' \tag{2}$$

The proportionality factor h' is called the *local individual coefficient of heat transfer* or merely *local individual coefficient* and, depending on the fluid, its velocity, and other factors, could have a numerical value ranging from, say, 0.5 to 50,000 Btu/(hr)(sq ft) (deg F). In flowing from the hot fluid to the heating surface, heat was transferred both by mechanical mixing or convection and by conduction in the moving fluid.

Heat Transfer through Solid Conductors.—As shown in Chap. I, the rate of conduction through the retaining wall of thickness x_w having the logarithmic mean area dA_w is given by the equation

$$dq = \frac{k_w\, dA_w\, \Delta t_w}{x_w} \tag{3}$$

The heat flows by conduction at the same rate dq through the deposit of dirt or scale having thickness x_d on the cooling surface dA'':

$$dq = \frac{k_d\, dA''\, \Delta t_d}{x_d} = h_d\, dA''\, \Delta t_d \tag{4}$$

The thickness of the dirt deposit is usually quite small, and for convenience the area of the heat-transfer surface is used. In many cases there are deposits of foreign materials on both heat-transfer surfaces. The ratio of the thermal conductivity to the thickness of the deposit k_d/x_d is usually designated as h_d.

The heat now flows at a rate dq by conduction from the point where the temperature is t''_d to the point where the temperature is t''_i and thence by mechanical mixing and convection, and also by conduction in the moving fluid, to the cold fluid at t''.

As a result of the difference between the temperature of the outer surface of the deposit and the bulk temperature of the cold fluid, $t''_d - t''$ or $\Delta t''$, the local individual coefficient to the cold fluid is defined by the Newton relation

$$dq = h''\, dA''\, \Delta t'' \tag{5}$$

Relation between Local Over-all and Local Individual Coefficients.—This relation is readily obtained by solving Eqs. 2, 3, 4, and 5 for the local individual temperature drops:

$$\Delta t' = dq/h' \, dA'$$
$$\Delta t_w = dq \, x_w/k_w \, dA_w$$
$$\Delta t_d = dq/h_d \, dA$$
$$\Delta t'' = dq/h'' \, dA''$$

Since the rate dq of heat flow is constant and the sum of the individual drops $\Delta t'$, Δt_w, Δt_d, and $\Delta t''$ is the over-all temperature difference Δt, addition gives

$$\Delta t = dq \left(\frac{1}{h' \, dA'} + \frac{x_w}{k_w \, dA_w} + \frac{1}{h_d \, dA''} + \frac{1}{h'' \, dA''} \right) \tag{6}$$

Comparison of Eq. 6 with Eq. 1, $\Delta t = dq/U \, dA$, gives

$$\frac{\Delta t}{dq} = \frac{1}{U \, dA} = \frac{1}{h' \, dA'} + \frac{x_w}{k_w \, dA_w} + \frac{1}{h_d \, dA''} + \frac{1}{h'' \, dA''} \tag{7}$$

wherein $U \, dA$ may be written as $U' \, dA'$, $U_w \, dA_w$, or $U'' \, dA''$. Equation 7 is often solved for a particular U, giving

$$\frac{1}{U} = \frac{dA}{h' \, dA} + \frac{x_w \, dA}{k_w \, dA_w} + \frac{dA}{h_d \, dA''} + \frac{dA}{h'' \, dA''} \tag{7a}$$

Where the thickness of the wall is small compared with the diameter of the tube, as an approximation one may use the equation for series flow through a plane wall, with scale deposits on both sides

$$\frac{1}{U} = \frac{1}{h'} + \frac{1}{h_d'} + \frac{x_w}{k_w} + \frac{1}{h_d''} + \frac{1}{h''} \tag{7b}$$

Illustration 1.—What would be the over-all coefficient for a surface condenser made from 18-gauge Admiralty metal 1-in. tubes (page 417), if the steam-side coefficient is 2000, the deposit factors are 2000 on each side, and the water-side coefficient is 1800? What would U_0 be if the tubes were cleaned on both sides, and only on the inside?

Solution.—As shown by the table on page 417, the tube has a wall thickness of 0.049 in. and an i.d. of 0.902 in.; the mean tube diameter is 0.951 in. From page 381, k is 63. If it is noted that the area ratios of Eq. 7a can be replaced by diameter ratios, on a basis of 1 sq ft of outer surface, one obtains

$$\frac{1}{U_0} = \frac{1}{2000} + \frac{1}{2000} + \frac{0.049/12}{63(0.951/1.00)} + \frac{1}{2000(0.902/1.00)} + \frac{1}{1800(0.902/1.00)}$$
$$= 0.0005 + 0.0005 + 0.000068 + 0.000554 + 0.000615 = 0.00224$$

Hence $U_0 = 1/0.00224 = 446$ Btu/(hr)(sq ft of outside surface)(deg F).

If the scale deposits were removed from both sides, the other coefficients remaining unchanged, U_0 would rise to $1/(0.0005 + 0.000068 + 0.000615) = 845$. With tubes clean inside and fouled outside, U_0 would be 595.

Because of the fact that the individual coefficients h' and h'' depend upon fewer variables than the over-all coefficient U, it simplifies correlation of data to study, wherever possible, individual rather than over-all coefficients.* With methods available for predicting values of h, values of U are readily calculated from Eqs. 7a or 7b.

Resistance Concept.—By defining an over-all resistance R_t for unit area dA as $1/U$ and corresponding individual resistances R' as $dA/h'\,dA'$, R_w as $x_w\,dA/k_w\,dA_w$, R_d as $dA/h_d\,dA''$ and R'' as $dA/h''\,dA''$, Eq. 7a becomes

$$R_t = R' + R_w + R_d + R'' \tag{8}$$

showing that the individual thermal resistances are additive for flow of heat through a series of resistances.

Summarizing,

$$dq = \frac{\Delta t}{\dfrac{1}{U\,dA}} = \frac{\Delta t}{\dfrac{1}{h'\,dA'} + \dfrac{x_w}{k_w\,dA_w} + \dfrac{1}{h_d\,dA''} + \dfrac{1}{h''\,dA''}} \tag{9}$$

It is noted that Eq. 9 is analogous to Eq. 26a of page 23, for series conduction of heat through several solids.

Coefficients for Scale Deposits.—The resistance of a scale deposit is usually obtained from the relation

$$\frac{1}{h_d} = \frac{1}{U_d} - \frac{1}{U_c} \tag{10}$$

wherein U_d is the over-all coefficient for the apparatus with the deposit present, and U_c is the over-all coefficient after cleaning. Apparent thermal conductivities of various boiler scale deposits are given by Partridge[550] and by Biskamp.[63b]† The following table shows that values of h_d for water depend on the kind of water, the temperatures of water and heating medium, and the water velocity.

---

* As brought out on p. 271, when tests have been run under suitable conditions, it is possible by the use of a graphical method to resolve the over-all thermal resistance for unit area $1/U$ into the component thermal resistances. This method does not involve measurement of surface temperatures in collecting test data and is, therefore, particularly helpful in the analysis of heat-transfer data from plant equipment.

† Biskamp shows the effect of increased porosity in decreasing the apparent thermal conductivity of boiler scale.

TABLE I.—HEAT-TRANSFER COEFFICIENTS h_d FOR SCALE DEPOSITS FROM WATER,[a] FOR USE IN EQ. 9

Temperature of heating medium.......	Up to 240°F		240–400°F	
Temperature of water................	125°F or less		Above 125°F	
Water velocity, feet per second........	3 and less	Over 3	3 and less	Over 3
Distilled............................	2000	2000	2000	2000
Sea water...........................	2000	2000	1000	1000
Treated boiler feed water.............	1000	2000	500	1000
Treated make-up for cooling tower.....	1000	1000	500	500
City, well, Great Lakes...............	1000	1000	500	500
Brackish, clean river water...........	500	1000	330	500
River water, muddy, silty[b]...........	330	500	250	330
Hard (over 15 g/gal).................	330	330	200	200
Chicago Sanitary Canal..............	130	170	100	130

[a] From "Standards of Tubular Exchanger Manufacturers Association, 1941," 366 Madison Ave., New York City.

[b] Delaware, East River (New York), Mississippi, Schuylkill, and New York Bay.

TABLE II.[a]—h_d FOR MISCELLANEOUS CASES

Organic vapors, liquid gasoline......................... 2000

Refined petroleum fractions (liquid), organic liquids, refrigerating liquids, brine, oil-bearing steam........... 1000

Distillate bottoms (above 25° API), gas oil or liquid naphtha below 500°F, scrubbing oil, refrigerant vapors, air (dust)... 500

Gas oil above 500°F, vegetable oil...................... 330

Liquid naphtha above 500°F, quenching oils............. 250

Topped crude below 25°API, fuel oil.................... 200

Cracked residuum, coke-oven gas, illuminating gas....... 100

[a] From "Standards of Tubular Exchanger Manufacturers Association," 1941, 366 Madison Ave., New York City.

Values of h_d are also given on pages 175, 273, 274, and 279.

Figure 59 is a photograph of slag deposits on the rear-wall tubes of a stoker-fired boiler, taken through the side observation door during operation. The thickness of the deposit varies with time, building up to a certain extent and then falling off, later to be replaced by new deposits.

Figure 60* shows a photograph of the tube bundles in an exchanger after operation with cracked hydrocarbon-oil vapors

* Courtesy of C. H. Leach Company, New York, N. Y.

and gases at 780°F outside the tubes and oil at 730°F inside the tubes. The upper half of the tubes have been cleaned by a sand blast, whereas the lower section have not yet been cleaned, and the cokelike deposit on the tubes is seen. It is possible to unbolt and hoist the shell, sand-blast the tubes, bolt up, and apply a cold-oil test in only 6 hr, while other portions of the cracking plant are

FIG. 59.—Slag deposits on wall tubes in a stoker-fired boiler.

undergoing cleaning. Improper operation of the cracking plant, involving undue entrainment of tar particles in the vapors entering the exchanger, can aggravate the condition shown in Fig. 60. Through the provision of "lanes" in the tube bundle and adequate clearance between shell and tube, cleaning is facilitated.

Optimum Operating Conditions.—In heating or cooling a liquid or a gas flowing without change in phase, an increase in the mass velocity of the fluid past the surface is accompanied by a decrease in the thickness of the effective film through which the heat must be conducted, thus increasing the individual coefficient. If corresponding individual resistance $1/h$ is a substantial fraction of the

FIG. 60.—Photograph of a tube bundle showing "coke" deposits of portion of tubes not yet sand-blasted.   (*Courtesy of C. H. Leach Company.*)

total resistance $1/U$, the over-all coefficient will increase, and the total surface required for a given heat-transfer rate q will decrease, thus reducing fixed charges on the investment. However, the use of higher velocity increases the pressure drop and power cost. The optimum velocity, at which total costs are a minimum, is treated in Chap. XI.

Where cooling water is purchased at sufficient pressure to force it through the cooler at any desired velocity, power costs for the water need not be considered, and it is possible to calculate the optimum ratio of water to hot fluid or the corresponding over-all temperature difference at the hot end of the cooler, Chap. XI.

In recovering waste heat with an exchanger, as the amount of heat-transfer surface is increased the amount of heat recovered increases, but the fixed charges on the exchanger also increase. There is hence an optimum mean temperature for the particular operation, as shown in detail in Chap. XI.

MEAN TEMPERATURE DIFFERENCE

In a steadily operated heat exchanger the temperatures of both fluids are fixed at a given position, but usually the temperature of one or both of the fluids changes as the fluid flows through the apparatus, and consequently it is necessary to integrate the basic equation

$$dq = U \, dA \, \Delta t \tag{11}$$

which holds at any point. If the cross section is constant the velocities are fixed, and each individual coefficient and consequently the over-all coefficient U depend on physical properties of the fluids, which, in turn, depend on temperature. Since both temperature and temperature difference are related to q by means of energy and material balances, U and Δt depend on q, and hence the variables are separated by writing the equation in the form

$$\int \frac{dq}{U \cdot \Delta t} = \int dA \tag{12}$$

If necessary, this equation may be integrated graphically, but in many cases the integration may be made algebraically, as illustrated below.

Case I. *Constant U, Parallel or Counterflow Operation.*—First consider steady heat exchange between two fluids flowing either in a countercurrent (Fig. 57) or parallel-flow apparatus. Neglecting kinetic-energy changes relative to changes in enthalpy (page 114)

and assuming no heat losses, the energy balance gives

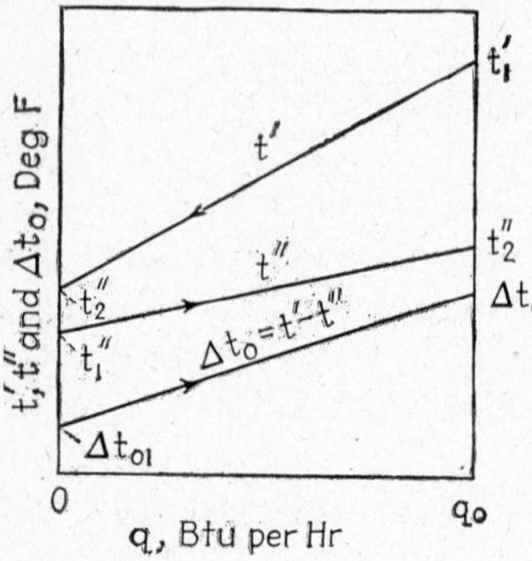

$$dq = w'c' \, dt' = \pm w''c'' \, dt'' \quad (13)*$$

where w is the mass rate of flow, c is the specific heat, and t is the bulk temperature. As before, single primes designate the hotter fluid and double primes the colder. If the specific heats are substantially constant, as is often the case, integration of the heat balance shows that q is linear in each temperature (see Fig. 61). Consequently the over-all difference in temperature ($\Delta t = t'' - t'$) is also linear in q. The slope of the plot of Δt vs. q is

$$\frac{d(\Delta t)}{dq} = \frac{(\Delta t)_2 - (\Delta t)_1}{q_o} \quad (14)$$

Eliminating dq from Eqs. 11 and 14, one obtains

$$\frac{d(\Delta t)}{U \, \Delta t} = \frac{(\Delta t_2 - \Delta t_1) \, dA}{q_o} \quad (14a)$$

If, as when a gas-side resistance is controlling, U is substantially constant, integration, from O to A and from Δt_1 to Δt_2, gives

$$\frac{1}{U} \ln \frac{\Delta t_2}{\Delta t_1} = \frac{(\Delta t_2 - \Delta t_1)A}{q_o} \quad (15)$$

Upon comparing this with the arbitrarily written equation

$$q_o = UA \, \Delta t_m \quad (16)$$

one finds that in this case

$$\Delta t_m = \frac{\Delta t_2 - \Delta t_1}{\ln \dfrac{\Delta t_2}{\Delta t_1}} \quad (17)$$

* The plus sign applies to counterflow and the minus sign to parallel flow. If one of the temperatures remains constant, because of change in phase, this is equivalent to an infinite value of the specific heat; in such a case the direction of fluid flow is immaterial. If $w'c'$ equals $w''c''$, the temperature difference is constant, and hence $q_o = UA \, \Delta t$.

Figure caption (Fig. 61): axes labeled t', t'' and Δt_o, Deg F (vertical); q, Btu per Hr (horizontal); curves t', t''; points t'_1, t''_2, t''_1, Δt_{o2}, $\Delta t_o = t' - t''$, Δt_{o1}, q_o.

Fig. 61.

which is the so-called logarithmic-mean over-all temperature difference." It is strictly correct for constant U, steady operation, constant specific heats, and parallel or counterflow adiabatic operation. If the temperature of one of the fluids is constant, direction of fluid flow is immaterial. Equation 17 is often used as an approximation where the percentage variation in U is moderate.

Case II. *Variable U, Parallel or Counterflow Operation.*—If U varies substantially with temperature, one can consider the exchanger to consist of a number of exchangers in series, in each of which U is linear in temperature, and hence in Δt: $U = a + b \Delta t$. Eliminating U from Eqs. 11 and 14, integrating and rearranging, one obtains[513]

$$q_o = A \left[\frac{U_1 \Delta t_2 - U_2 \Delta t_1}{\ln_e \dfrac{U_1 \Delta t_2}{U_2 \Delta t_1}} \right] \tag{18}$$

which involves the logarithmic mean of the $U \Delta t$ products. It is important to note that each product contains Δt at one end and the U at the other. If U_1 equals U_2 this reduces to Eq. 15.

Illustration 2.—Dry saturated steam, condensing at $227°F$, is to be used to heat $13,400$ lb/hr of a hydrocarbon oil from 80 to $217°F$ while flowing inside straight tubes. The specific heat of the oil is substantially constant at 0.47 Btu/(lb) (deg F); the over-all coefficient U_i from steam to oil varies with the bulk temperature of the oil as shown below.

Calculate the square feet of inside heat-transfer surface required.

t, deg F	80	95	110	130	160	190	217
U_i	29.5	38	47	51	70	81.5	91.7

Solution.—Since heat loss to the surroundings does not affect the temperature of the condensing steam, Eq. 18 is not vitiated by heat loss. Upon plotting U *vs.* t, three straight lines are drawn from 80 to $110°$, 110 to $160°$, and 160 to $217°F$. Equation 18 is then applied separately to each of the three zones. For example, for the zone in which t rises from 80 to $110°F$, Eq. 18 gives

$$A = \frac{13,400(0.47)(110 - 80) \ln [(29.5)(227 - 110)/(47)(227 - 80)]}{29.5(227 - 110) - 47(227 - 80)} = 37.9 \text{ sq ft}$$

Similar calculations give 59.8 and 143 sq ft for the other two zones, giving a total inside surface of 241 sq ft for all three zones. An alternative method would have been to plot $1/U \Delta t$ as ordinates against t and to obtain the area under the curve, which would equal A/wc.

Even in cases in which the percentage change in U is substantial it is sometimes customary to report U on the basis on the logarithmic mean over-all temperature difference (Eq. 17), giving

$$U_x = q/A \, \Delta t_l \qquad\qquad (18a)$$

If U is linear in t or Δt, this practice is allowable if U_x is associated with the temperature t_x obtained[140] by eliminating q/A from Eqs. 18 and 18a, noting that U equals $U_0 (1 + bt)$; the value of t_x is readily obtained from Fig. 62.

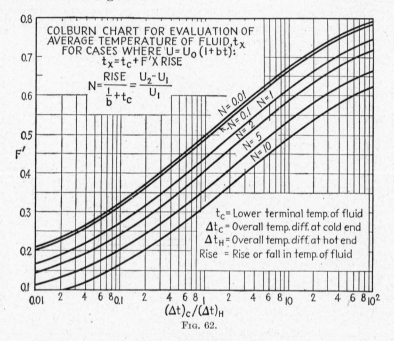

COLBURN CHART FOR EVALUATION OF AVERAGE TEMPERATURE OF FLUID, t_x FOR CASES WHERE $U = U_0 (1 + bt)$:

$$t_x = t_c + F' \times RISE$$

$$N = \frac{RISE}{\frac{1}{b} + t_c} = \frac{U_2 - U_1}{U_1}$$

t_c = Lower terminal temp. of fluid
Δt_c = Overall temp. diff. at cold end
Δt_H = Overall temp. diff. at hot end
Rise = Rise or fall in temp. of fluid

FIG. 62.

Illustration 3. Given a counterflow exchanger in which the warmer fluid is cooled from 300 to 105°F and the colder fluid is heated from 100 to 250°F. Estimates of U at the terminals give U_h of 120 and U_c of 60, and U of 90 at the section at which the colder stream is at 175°F. Since U is linear in the temperature of the colder stream, Eq. 18 gives the correct flux

$$\frac{q}{A} = \frac{60(50) - 120(5)}{2.3 \log_{10} \dfrac{60(50)}{120(5)}} = \frac{2400}{2.3(0.699)} = 1490 \frac{Btu}{(hr)(sq\ ft)}$$

Alternately t_x may be found from Fig. 62 as follows: $N = (120 - 60)/60 = 1$, $\Delta t_c/\Delta t_h = 5/50 = 0.10$, $F' = 0.274$, and $t_x = 100 + 0.274(250 - 100) = 141°F$; $U_x = 60 + (141 - 100)(120 - 60)/(250 - 100) = 76.4$. Since the logarithmic mean difference Δt_l is $(50 - 5)/\ln_e 10 = 19.5°F$, the flux is $q/A = U_x \Delta t_l = 76.4(19.5) = 1490$ Btu/(hr)(sq ft), checking the value given by Eq. 18. It is noted that $F' = (t_x - t_c)/(t_2 - t_c)$ is 0.274. Had one arbitrarily evaluted U_m

as $(120 + 60)/2 = 90$, and multiplied this by Δt_l, the flux so calculated would have been 18 per cent higher than the correct value. The error would have been further increased by arbitrarily using an arithmetic mean Δt.

Case III. *Constant U, Multipass Flow.*—Many exchangers consist of a bundle of tubes inside a suitable shell. To obtain the economic velocities and corresponding heat-transfer coefficients it is often necessary to arrange the flow paths so that either or both fluids must reverse directions one or more time in passing through the exchanger. In such cases there results a combination of

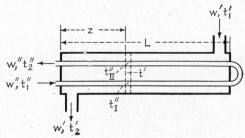

FIG. 63.—Diagram of 1-2 exchanger.

parallel and counterflow, called *reversed flow*. A simple case is shown diagrammatically in Fig. 63; this is called a 1–2 *exchanger*, since it contains one shell pass and two tube passes.

Cold fluid at t_1'', having constant specific heat c'', enters the first pass at the steady mass rate w'' and leaves the second pass at t_2''. Warmer fluid at t_1', having constant specific heat c', enters at a steady mass rate w' at either end of the shell and leaves the other end of the shell at t_2'. At any distance z from the inlet to the first pass the tube-side fluid has bulk temperatures t_I'' in the first pass and t_{II}'' in the second pass. Assuming no losses to the surroundings, the heat balance is

$$\pm w'c'\,dt' = w''c''(dt_I'' - dt_{II}'')$$

the sign depending on the direction of flow of the shell-side fluid. Designating the heat-transfer area per unit length as a', the rate equations are

$$w''c''\,dt_I'' = U(a'\,dx)(t' - t_I'')$$
$$-w''c''\,dt_{II}'' = U(a'\,dx)(t' - t_{II}'')$$

Upon assuming U constant, integration[727] gives the value of Δt_m defined by the equation $q_o = w'c'(t_1' - t_2') = Ua'2L\,\Delta t_m = UA\,\Delta t_m$

$$\Delta t_m = \frac{\sqrt{(t_1' - t_2')^2 + (t_2'' - t_1'')^2}}{\ln\dfrac{t_1' + t_2' - t_1'' - t_2'' + \sqrt{(t_1' - t_2')^2 + (t_2'' - t_1'')^2}}{t_1' + t_2' - t_1'' - t_2'' - \sqrt{(t_1' - t_2')^2 + (t_2'' - t_1'')^2}}} \tag{19}$$

Equation 19 also applies to cases in which the cold fluid flows through the shell.

Instead of using this cumbersome equation, one defines a dimensionless correction factor Y in the relation $Y = \Delta t_m / \Delta t_l$, where Δt_l is the logarithmic mean difference calculated for counterflow

$$\Delta t_l = \frac{(t_1' - t_2'') - (t_2' - t_1'')}{\ln_e \dfrac{t_1' - t_2''}{t_2' - t_1''}} \tag{20}$$

The correction factor may then be plotted in terms of two dimensionless parameters:

$$X = (t_2'' - t_1'')/(t_1' - t_1'') \tag{21}$$
$$Z = (t_1' - t_2')/(t_2'' - t_1'') = w''c''/w'c' \tag{22}$$

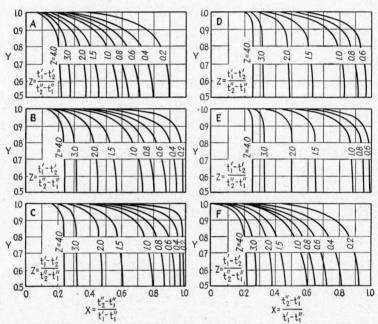

Fig. 64.—Mean temperature difference in reversed-current exchangers. (Shell side well mixed at a given cross section.) (*A*) 1 shell pass and 2, 4, 6, etc., tube passes. (*B*) 2 shell passes, and 4, 8, 12, etc., tube passes. (*C*) 3 shell passes, and 6, 12, 18, etc., tube passes. (*D*) 4 shell passes, and 8, 16, 24, etc., tube passes. (*E*) 6 shell passes, and 12, 24, 36, etc., tube passes. (*F*) 1 shell pass, and 3, 6, 9, etc., tube passes. (*Courtesy of Bowman, Mueller, and Nagle, Trans. A.S.M.E.*)

Figures 64 and 65 show graphs of Y *vs.* X for various values of Z for each of a number of types of exchangers, from the comprehensive paper of Bowman, Mueller, and Nagle.[32] In the derivations that led to most of the charts the shell-side fluid was assumed to be

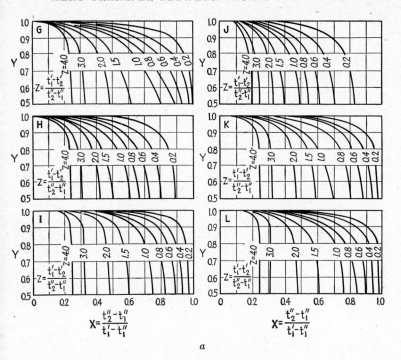

a

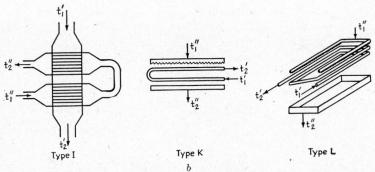

b

FIG. 65.—Mean temperature difference in cross flow exchangers. (*G*) Cross flow, both fluids unmixed, 1 tube pass. (*H*) Cross flow, shell fluid mixed, 1 tube pass. (*I*) Cross flow, shell fluid mixed, 2 tube passes, shell fluid flows across second and first passes in series. (*J*) Cross flow, shell fluid mixed, 2 tube passes, shell fluid flows over first and second passes in series. (*K*) Cross flow (drip type), 2 horizontal passes with U-bend connections (trombone type). (*L*) Cross flow (drip type), helical coils with 2 turns. (*Courtesy of Bowman, Mueller, and Nagle, Trans. A.S.M.E.*)

mixed at a given cross section.   This requires a substantial number of cross baffles on the shell side, as shown in Fig. 66.   The drop in temperature of the shell fluid in any one of the baffled compartments is neglected in the derivation.

If the shell contains longitudinal baffles, to prevent mixing of the shell-side fluid (as in Chart G, Fig. 65), this may be allowed for in the derivations and in some cases* the corresponding values of Y would be somewhat higher than with the shell-side fluid mixed.

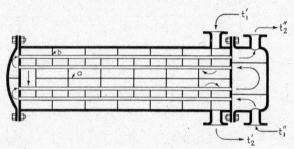

Fig. 66.—Diagram of a 2-4 exchanger (shell fluid mixed), with two passes in the shell (containing one longitudinal baffle a, and a number of cross baffles) and four tube passes.   Several types of exchangers are shown in Chap. XI.

The assumption that introduces the largest error is that of constancy of the over-all coefficient, which may vary substantially with temperature in the case of viscous fluids such as the less volatile fractions of petroleum.   It is sometimes possible to arrange several multipass exchangers in series with counterflow through the various units.

Illustration 4.—Given an exchanger in which the shell-side fluid enters at 400° and leaves at 200° and the tube-side fluid enters at 100° and leaves at 200°. Assuming that U, w', c', w'', and c'' are constant and that heat losses are negligible, determine the mean over-all temperature difference from hot to cold fluid (a) for a counterflow apparatus and (b) for a reversed-current exchanger with one well-baffled pass in the shell and two passes in the tube.

Solution.—(a) With counterflow, the terminal differences are $400 - 200°$ or 200° at the hot end and $200 - 100°$ or 100° at the cold end.   The logarithmic mean difference for counterflow, Δt_l, is then $100/(2.3)(0.301)$ or 144°.

(b) $X = (200 - 100)/(400 - 100) = \frac{1}{3}$; $Z = (400 - 200)/(200 - 100) = 2$; from Curve A of Fig. 64, $Y = 0.80 = \Delta t_m/144$; $\Delta t_m = 115°$.   As noted previously, if the temperature of either of the fluids remains constant, direction of fluid flow is immaterial, and Y equals 1; *i.e.*, the logarithmic mean tempera-

---

* Comparisons of Y for flow with the shell-side fluid, mixed and not mixed, are given in reference 242; values of Y are available[241] for exchangers having unequal numbers of tubes per pass.

ture difference applies for adiabatic operation with constant U, w', w'', c' and c''.

Measurement of Surface Temperature. *—Where it is desired to obtain individual coefficients of heat transfer between fluid and surface by direct measurement, the problem of determination of the true temperature of the solid surface arises. Reviews of the literature of measurement of surface temperature are given by Othmer and Coates[542] and by Colburn and Hougen.[147] As suggested by a study of Fig. 46, page 107, the presence of a thermocouple wire on a surface tends to disturb the flow of the fluid in the zone near the surface, and even if the correct surface temperature were measured, the nature of the fluid flow would be abnormal and the results misleading. For this reason, where the thermocouple leads are brought out through the fluid stream it is desirable, whenever possible, to attach the leads to that side of the surface whose individual coefficient is not under investigation. Where thermocouple leads are brought out through the fluid stream, heat transfer between the fluid and the wire causes a flow of heat along the wire to or from the junction, tending to introduce error.

Bailey[36] gives a good discussion of the effects of temperature gradients in thermojunctions on the error introduced in the measurement of surface temperature, the effects of heat capacity upon lag with varying temperature, and methods for predicting the performance of cylindrical couples. In order to minimize the error due to heat conduction by the leads, it is advisable to submerge the leads from the thermal junction in an isothermal zone† in the tube wall. This matter is discussed by Elias[209] who employed a number of types of thermocouples. In research work, it is possible to bring the leads out axially through the metal wall itself rather than radially through the fluid stream,[401] although this method has not been used often.[335]

The mean temperature of a tube wall may be determined by using the tube as a resistance thermometer;[104] the change in tube length with change in temperature may also be used;[690,708] these methods are suitable only for research work. Optical methods are also available.[17a]

The following methods of installing thermocouples in tube walls are satisfactory.

* Fundamentals of pyrometry are given in references 17a and 227a.

† References 674, 401, and 607.

(1) A groove is cut in that part of the outer surface later to be located in a substantially isothermal zone,[147,553] the bare junction is placed in direct contact with the metal wall of the tube, the electrically insulated leads are installed in the grooves so that at least 1 in. of each lead is in the groove,* and the grooves are filled with suitable material. If surface conditions are important, as in boiling or condensing, it is advisable to plate the assembly with a suitable coating of metal.

(2) The junction is threaded through a chordal hole,[292,293] each lead is submerged in a circumferential groove for at least 1 in., and the groove is filled as described above. This method does not disturb the surface of the metal near the junction. A modification[40] of this method involves placing the junction in a hole drilled at an angle to the axis of the tube.

(3) A traveling thermocouple, adapted to use with short tubes, has been described recently.[335]

Kambara and Matsui[363] compare lags of thermometers and thermocouples. Roeser[605] discusses the errors introduced by the diffusion of gases through the walls of pyrometer protection tubes. Spear and Purdy[683] discuss the difficulties involved in making temperature measurements in rubber and insulating materials by means of thermocouples.

At a given cross section taken at right angles to the direction of the fluid stream, it will be clear that under certain conditions the temperature of the wall will tend to be nonuniform at various points around the perimeter.† This condition is likely to arise with the flow of liquid or gas in the streamline or early turbulent regions through a *horizontal* pipe externally heated or cooled, since differences in fluid density at different temperatures may bring about nonuniformity in temperature of the *fluid* at a given radius, as shown in Fig. 70, page 160. Furthermore, when a fluid flows at right angles to a heated or cooled pipe, from a study of Figs. 100 to 110 on pages 211 to 216, it is clear that the velocity varies with position around the perimeter, tending to develop nonuniformity in temperature at various points on the perimeter of the wall. Because of the high thermal conductivity of the metal, however, these inequalities tend to be of little importance except at substantial values of q/A.

---

* The length of leads submerged in the tube wall should be as large as convenient; this is particularly important if the wire diameter is relatively large.

† References 675, 40, 41, and 553.

As shown above, there are complications in correctly determining surface temperature at a given point and in observing and averaging surface temperatures at various points on the perimeter. When the temperature difference between wall and fluid is small, an error of a given number of degrees in measuring the tube-wall

TABLE III.—NOMENCLATURE

A Area of heat transfer surface, square feet; A' on warmer side, A'' on colder side.

a' Area of heat-transfer surface per unit length of tube, square feet per foot.

b Temperature coefficient in the relation $U/U_0 = 1 + bt$, 1/deg. F.

c Specific heat, Btu/(lb fluid)(deg F); c' for warmer fluid; c'' for colder fluid.

d Prefix, indicating differential, dimensionless.

F' Dimensionless ratio in Fig. 62, $F' = (t_x - t_c)/(t_h - t_c)$.

h Individual coefficient between fluid and surface, Btu/(hr)(sq ft)(deg F); h' is based on A' and $\Delta t'$; h'' is based on A'' and $\Delta t''$; h_d is for scale deposit.

k Thermal conductivity, Btu/(hr)(sq ft)(deg F/ft); k_d for dirt deposit; k_w for tube wall.

L Tube length, feet.

q Rate of heat transfer, Btu per hour; q_0 for entire apparatus.

R Thermal resistance, deg F/(Btu)(hr); R' for warmer side; R'' for colder side; R_d for dirt deposit; R_t for total, $R_t = \Sigma R$; R_w for tube wall.

t Bulk temperature, degrees Fahrenheit; t' of warmer fluid; t'' of colder fluid, t''_I and t''_{II} for colder fluid in first and second passes, respectively.

t_s Surface temperature, degrees Fahrenheit; t'_s for warmer surface; t''_s for colder surface.

U Over-all coefficient of heat transfer, Btu/(hr)(sq ft)(deg F); U' based on A'; U'' based on A''; U_c for clean; U_d for dirty or fouled apparatus.

w Mass rate of flow of fluid, pounds per hour; w' for warmer fluid; w'' for colder fluid.

x Thickness, feet; x_d for dirt deposit; x_w for tube wall.

X Dimensionless ratio, $X = (t''_2 - t''_1)/(t'_1 - t''_1)$.

Y Dimensionless ratio, $\Delta t_m / \Delta t_l$.

Z Dimensionless ratio, $Z = (t'_1 - t'_2)/(t''_2 - t''_1) = w''c''/w'c'$.

z Distance, feet.

Δt Temperature drop through an individual resistance, degrees Fahrenheit; $\Delta t'$ and $\Delta t''$ for warmer and colder sides, respectively; Δt_d for dirt deposit; Δt_w for wall.

Δt Over-all temperature difference between bulk temperatures of warmer and colder fluids, degrees Fahrenheit; Δt_1 and Δt_2 at terminals; Δt_m is true mean value; Δt_l is logarithmic mean value for counterflow.

temperature will introduce a large percentage error in the temperature difference, whereas when the temperature difference is large the effect will not be serious. For example, for oil flowing through a steam-heated pipe, most of the temperature drop is on the oil side, and although measurements of the pipe-wall temperature are of little value in computing the steam-side resistance, the same measurements will be satisfactory for measuring the thermal resistance from wall to oil.

Temperature Stresses in Tubes.—The high pressures, temperatures, and heat inputs of modern cracking plants and water-tube boilers present added difficulties in the design of the tubes. This question of temperature stresses has been discussed by Lorenz,[447] Dahl,[162] Orrok,[540] and DeBaufre.[173] A mathematical and experimental investigation with special reference to tubes for cracking plants is given by Luster.[452]

Problems

1. A simple gas to gas heat exchanger built of concentric pipes has a total length of 100 ft. The hot gas flows through the inside pipe at a steady mass rate and is cooled from 230 to 150°F. The cold gas, flowing at a steady mass rate through the jacket, is heated from 70 to 150°F. After having traveled 50 ft, the hot gas has an average temperature of 190°F.

It is proposed to lengthen the exchanger in order to heat the cold gas from 70 to 170°F instead of from 70 to 150°F. As before, the hot gas will enter at 230°F. The mass-flow rates of hot and cold gas remain unchanged, and heat losses may be neglected.

a. Calculate the necessary length of the enlarged exchanger.
b. In the enlarged unit, how many feet will the cold gas flow from its point of entry in order to reach a temperature of 150°F?
c. In the enlarged exchanger, what will be the temperature of the cold gas after it has traveled 100 ft?

2. 10,000 lb/hr of sulphuric acid (specific heat of 0.36) is to be cooled in a two-stage countercurrent cooler of the following type: Hot acid at 174°C is fed to a tank, where it is stirred in contact with cooling coils; the continuous discharge from this tank at 88°C flows to a second stirred tank and leaves the second tank at 45°C. Cooling water at 20°C flows into the cooling coil of the second tank and from there to the cooling coil of the first tank. The water is at 80°C as it leaves the coil in the hot-acid tank.

Calculate the total area of cooling surface necessary, assuming U of 200 and 130 for the hot and cold tanks, respectively, and neglecting heat losses. (Answer is 165 sq ft.)

3. It is desired to design an adiabatic heat exchanger to cool continuously 100,000 lb/hr of water from 200 to 153°F by means of an equal weight of cold water entering at 100°F. The water velocities will be such that the over-all coefficient of heat transfer U will be 400. Calculate the square feet of heat-exchange surface needed for each of the following proposals:

a. Parallel flow.
b. Counterflow.
c. Reversed current in an apparatus like that of Fig. 63, page 145, with the hot water flowing through the shell and the cold water through the tubes.
d. Cross flow, with one tube pass and one shell pass.

4. A stock is being continuously melted in a vertical kiln. The stock enters the top at 100°F, melts at 2100°F, and the molten stock leaves at the bottom at 2100°F. The hot burner gases enter the bottom of the kiln at 2500°F, in direct contact with the stock, and leave at the top. The average specific heat of the stock and gases, considered constant, are 0.20 and 0.28, respectively. The stock has a heat of fusion of 200 Btu/lb.

Per ton of stock fed, calculate the theoretically minimum pounds of burner gas necessary and the corresponding outlet temperature of the burner gas. What would be the corresponding height of kiln?

5. For the conditions of Illustration 1, Chap. VI, assume that the tubes are 10 ft long and that each tube handles 9770 lb of water hourly. Calculate the heat-transfer rate per tube in Btu/hour, for t' of 120°F and t_1 of 80°F.

6. For a differential length of tube in the condenser of Illustration 1, Chap. VI, at a section where the steam temperature is 120°F and the water temperature is 80°F, calculate:

    a. The average temperature of the effective film of condensate and the temperature drop through this film.

    b. The average temperature of the effective film of water and the temperature drop through this resistance.

Note: Physical properties are given in the Appendix.

7. A steam-heated oil preheater consists of standard 1-in. condenser tubes heated externally by steam condensing at a gauge pressure of 15 lb/sq in. The oil enters the tubes at a gauge pressure of 10 lb/sq in. The volatility of the oil is such that there is no substantial vapor generation in the preheater.

The unit was recently by-passed and shut down for cleaning the inside of the tubes. When the preheater was again returned to operation, the capacity was at first appreciably greater than that which existed before cleaning but within a few hours was far below that which existed just prior to cleaning. The preheater was again shut down, and inspection revealed that the tubes were still clean. What do these facts mean to you?

CHAPTER VII

HEATING AND COOLING FLUIDS INSIDE TUBES

Abstract.—The chapter is divided into four sections. The first treats the mechanism of fluid flow, analogies between transfer of heat and momentum, and the quantitative relations between the heat-transfer coefficient and factors such as mass velocity, diameter, and physical properties. Recommended relations, design charts, and illustrative problems are included. The second deals likewise with streamline flow and the third with the transition region. The fourth treats flow in rectangular sections and annular spaces, gravity flow of liquids in layer form, and flow parallel to plane surfaces.

For DG/μ exceeding 10,000, heat-transfer coefficients for gases and liquids of low viscosity are correlated within an average deviation of ± 20 per cent by Eq. 4c (page 168), as shown in Figs. 76, 80, 81, and 84. For common gases Eq. 4c can be simplified to Eq. 4k, which is the basis of the design chart (Fig. 79); for water Eq. 4c reduces to Eq. 9c (Fig. 85) and a design relation (Eq. 10a). For streamline flow $(DG/\mu < 2100)$ Eq. 19 is recommended, which correlates the available values of h_a within an average deviation of ± 15 per cent and yields the design relation, Eq. 19a; Eq. 20 is used as an approximation to allow for the effect of natural convection. In the transition region $(2100 < DG/\mu < 10,000)$ Eq. 4c is used for gases unless G is less than $1200 P^{2/3}$, and Eq. 4c and Fig. 86 are used for liquids of low viscosity; for viscous liquids Fig. 92 is recommended $(\pm 25$ per cent). Coefficients for turbulent flow of air or water in rectangular sections are plotted in Fig. 93 and average 20 per cent below those predicted from Eq. 4c with D replaced by four times the hydraulic radius based on total wetted perimeter; Fig. 94 gives the relation for streamline flow in rectangular sections. Equation 25 is based on the turbulent flow of air or water through the annular spaces between concentric tubes; coefficients for flow of air parallel to a single plane are correlated in Fig. 99. Coefficients for gravity flow of water in layer form are correlated within an average deviation of ± 15 per cent by Eq. 28 based on Fig. 95 for

154

turbulent flow, and ± 20 per cent by the curves of Fig. 98 for stream-line flow; data for streamline flow of oils in layer form are given in Fig. 97 and Eq. 30.

Introduction.—Many types of industrial heat-transfer equipment involve heat transfer between a surface, usually metallic or refractory, and a fluid that is heated or cooled without evaporation or condensation. In the power-plant field illustrations include fire-tube boilers, superheaters, economizers, preheaters, and condensers. In addition to fluids such as air, flue gases, water, and steam, the petroleum industry involves a variety of products ranging from fixed hydrocarbon gases to the very viscous liquids such as lubricating oils and asphalts. Other chemical industries involve heat transfer to molten metals and slags, broken solids, acids, and organic solvents.

There is a distinct difference between the mechanism of heat transfer for fluids flowing in turbulent motion on the one hand and streamline motion on the other. Consequently, certain factors, notably average velocity of the fluid past the heat-transfer surface, in general have a more marked effect upon the rate of heat transmission for fluids flowing in turbulent motion than in streamline motion. Other factors, such as tube length, often have greater importance for streamline motion than for turbulent flow. Hence these two cases are treated separately, first consideration being given to the more common turbulent flow.

In many cases, the pipes are smooth, such as drawn tubes of steel, copper, brass, nickel, lead, aluminum, special alloys, and glass, or of only moderate roughness, as cast iron, cast steel, wrought iron, etc., and this section deals largely with heat transfer for turbulent flow of fluids in relatively clean smooth metal tubes. The importance of deposits of slag, scale, and like encrustations on the heat-transfer surface depends upon the thickness and nature of the deposits and also upon the other thermal resistances involved. Such matters are treated on pages 138 and 197. The effect of roughness is treated on pages 106 and 175. In the following section, it is assumed that heat transfer by radiation is absent or has been allowed for by the methods of Chap. III. In other words, this section deals with heat transfer by the combined mechanisms of conduction and convection for fluids flowing inside tubes.

Heat-transfer problems ordinarily fall into one of two classes:

1. The use of quantitative relations to design apparatus for proposed installations.

TABLE I.—NOMENCLATURE

A	Area of heat-transfer surface, square feet.
a, a_1, a_2	Constants.
B	Thickness of layer of coolant, feet.
b	Wetted perimeter, feet.
b_1, b_2, b_3	Constants.
c	Specific heat, Btu/(lb fluid)(deg F); c_p at constant pressure, c_v at constant volume.
D	Inside diameter, feet; D', *inches*.
D	Diameter, feet; D_e equivalent diameter equals $4r_h$; D_H of helix; D_i, inside diameter of pipe; D_p, of packing; D_1 and D_2 for sides of rectangular section and for diameters of annulus.
d	Prefix, indicating differential, dimensionless.
$\mathfrak{F}$	Dimensionless factor in calculation of radiation, allowing for emissivities and geometrical arrangement.
f	Friction factor, dimensionless; for values, see Chap. V.
G	Mass velocity, lb/(hr)(sq ft of cross section) equals w/S; G_t is value at transition point.
g	Acceleration due to gravity, 4.17×10^8 ft/(hr)(hr).
g_c	Conversion factor, 4.17×10^8 (lb of fluid)(ft)/(hr)(hr)(pounds force).
h	Coefficient of heat transfer between fluid and surface, Btu/(hr)(sq ft)(deg F); h_a is based on arithmetic mean Δt; h_m is based on length mean Δt; h_{m1} is based on initial Δt; h_A and h_I are defined on page 178.
j	A product of dimensionless terms; $j = (h/cG)(c\mu_f/k)^{2/3}$; $j' = (h/cG)(c\mu/k)^{2/3}(\mu_s/\mu)^{0.14}$.
k	Thermal conductivity of fluid, Btu/(hr)(sq ft)(deg F per ft); k_f is ordinarily evaluated at $t_f = (t + t_s)/2$.
K	Dimensionless constant.
L	Heated length of a straight tube, feet; L' is unheated length of calming section.
$\ln_e$	Natural logarithm $= 2.303 \times \log_{10}$.
m, n, p	Exponents.
P	Total pressure, atmospheres.
q	Rate of heat transfer, Btu per hour; q_c by conduction and convection in fluid; q_r by radiation between surfaces.
r	Radius, feet; r is local value, r_0 is total radius.
r_h	Hydraulic radius, feet; r_h equals S/b.
r_v	Ratio of velocities, dimensionless; r_v equals u_i/V.
S	Cross section of stream, square feet.
t	Bulk temperature, degrees Fahrenheit, t_s of surface, t_{sv} of saturated vapor, t_y at local distance y from surface, t_1 at inlet, t_2 at outlet, t_∞ at substantial distance from surface.
U	Over-all coefficient of heat transfer between two streams, Btu/(hr)(sq ft)(deg F).
u	Local velocity, feet per hour; u_{max} is maximum value.
V	Average velocity, feet per hour; $V = G/\rho$; V_∞ at substantial distance from surface; V' ft/sec.
w	Mass rate of flow, pounds fluid per hour.

TABLE I.—NOMENCLATURE.—(*Continued*)

X	Abscissa of graph.
Y	Ordinate of graph.
y	Normal distance from wall, feet; y_1 is thickness of laminar-flow layer near wall.
y_1^+	A dimensionless number used in empirically correlating h by means of Eq. 3; for isothermal flow, $y_1^+ = (y_1 V \rho / \mu_1)(\sqrt{f}/2)$, where y_1 is the thickness of the laminar film.
Z	Grashof number, dimensionless, equal to $(D^3 \rho^2 g / \mu^2)(\beta \, \Delta t)$.

Greek

α	Thermal diffusivity, square feet per hour, equals $k/\rho c$.
β	Coefficient of volumetric expansion, reciprocal degrees Fahrenheit.
Γ	Mass flow rate per unit breadth, pounds fluid/(hour)(ft); for a vertical tube, Γ equals $w/\pi D$; for a horizontal tube, Γ_H equals $w/2L$.
Δt	Temperature difference between bulk temperature of fluid and temperature of the surface, degrees Fahrenheit; Δt_a is arithmetic mean, Δt_m is length mean, Δt_y is local value at point y; Δt_{max} is maximum local value.
Δt_m	Mean value of over-all difference in temperature between hot and cold streams, degrees Fahrenheit (see Chap. VI).
ϵ	Eddy viscosity, square feet per hour; ϵ_ν is for momentum transfer; ϵ_α, for heat transfer.
μ	Absolute viscosity, lb/(hr)(ft); ordinarily, μ is evaluated at bulk temperature of the stream, μ_f at t_f, and μ_s at t_s; $\mu_f' = \dfrac{1}{y} \displaystyle\int_0^{y_1} \mu \, dy$
ν	Kinematic viscosity of fluid, square feet per hour; $\nu = \mu/\rho$.
π	$3.1416 \cdots$.
ρ	Density, pounds of fluid per cubic foot; ρ_f at t_f, ρ_∞ at substantial distance from surface; ρ' is in grams per cubic centimeter.
τ	Tractive force per unit surface of wall, pounds force per square foot.
ϕ	Prefix, designating function, dimensionless.

2. The prediction of the effect of changes in operating conditions upon the performance of existing equipment.

As pointed out in Chap. VI, such problems are simplified by resolving the over-all thermal resistance into the various individual resistances: from the warmer fluid to the tube, through the tube wall and scale deposits, and from solid to colder fluid. Consequently the following section deals largely with the quantitative relations between the individual coefficient of heat transfer h between fluid and solid and the various factors influencing the magnitude of the coefficient.

I. TURBULENT FLOW

Mechanism.—Data relative to the isothermal flow of fluids have been presented in Chap. V, and it was shown that, for isothermal turbulent motion, velocity explorations taken from the wall

out into the main body of fluid indicate a thin layer near the wall
where the flow is streamline, a buffer zone beyond the film, and
finally a turbulent zone in the main body of the fluid.   Explorations
of velocity and temperature in a fluid stream are of considerable
interest, both in studying the mechanisms by which the heat is
transferred from wall to fluid and in investigating the assumptions
made in deriving theoretical relations involving rates of heat
transmission from tube to fluid.

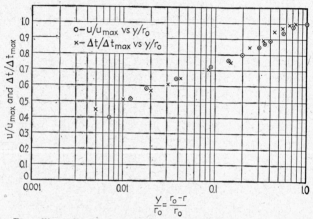

Fig. 67.—Pannell's explorations of velocity and temperature for air flowing upward
in a heated brass pipe, $D' = 1.92$ in., $u_{max} = 87.4$ ft./sec.

Gases.—In a pioneer investigation in 1916, Pannell[545]* made
velocity and temperature explorations across an *air* stream flowing
upward in turbulent motion in an electrically heated *vertical* brass
pipe having an inside diameter of 1.92 in.   Figure 67 shows the
results of a run made with the wall at 109.4°F and the air at the axis
at 75.9°F.   The ratio of local to maximum velocity u/u_{max} is
plotted *vs.* the position ratio y/r_0, where u is the local velocity at
distance y from the wall and r_0 is the radius of the tube.   Although
heat was being transferred, the velocity-distribution curve resembles
those for isothermal runs with air (see Fig. 42, page 104).   Figure
67 also shows the ratio of local to maximum temperature difference
$(t_s - t_y)/(t_s - t_0)$ plotted *vs.* y/r_0, and it is noted that the distribution of temperature difference is similar to that of velocity.   The
data of Fig. 67 are replotted on logarithmic paper in Fig. 68, and
the slopes of both curves are roughly one-seventh.

* Explorations were made across the stream at the middle of the heated
section, 46.1 in. long, which was preceded by 197 in. of unheated section.

Figure 69 shows data[209]* for the horizontal flow of air past a vertical heated copper plate, and in the turbulent zone *BC*, the slopes of the curves of both velocity and temperature difference are 0.15.

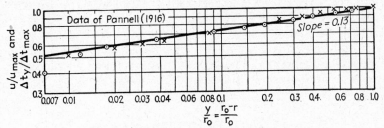

Fig. 68.—Data of Fig. 67, plotted on logarithmic paper.

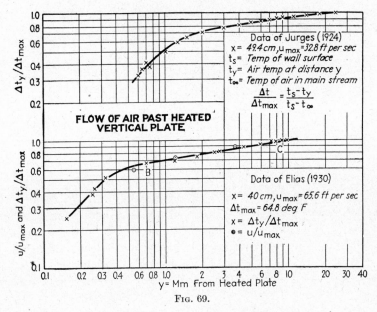

Fig. 69.

Similarity in shapes of the curves of velocity and temperature distribution were found for main-stream velocities ranging from 49 to 115 ft/sec. The curves of velocity distribution in the presence of heat transfer are similar in *shape* to those for isothermal runs on air (see Figs. 39 to 41, pages 102 to 104). Figure 69 also includes

*Considerable attention was given to the choice of thermocouples, most of the tests being made with a wire 0.01 cm thick. Explorations were made 40 cm from the entrance to the heated section in a plane at right angles to the air stream.

temperature explorations of Jurges,[361] who did not include velocity explorations except in isothermal runs (page 103). The various data for temperature distribution for the flow of *air* past heated surfaces give curves of the same shape as those for velocity distribution.

Liquids.—Woolfenden[720]* measured local temperatures t_y in a vertical plane across a stream of water flowing in turbulent motion in a long *horizontal* copper pipe, 2.06-in. inside diameter, heated by condensing steam. In Fig. 70 the ratios of local to maximum temperature difference from the pipe to water are plotted *vs.* the positions expressed as fractions of the radius r/r_o. The run made

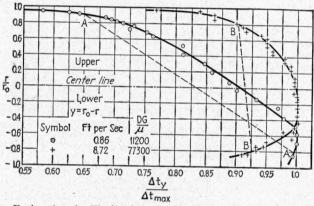

Fig. 70.—Explorations by Woolfenden,[780] of temperature of water flowing inside a horizontal steam-heated pipe, $D' = 2.06$ in.

at a Reynolds number DG/μ of 11,200, represented by curve AA of Fig. 70, brings out the important point that *the temperature distribution* was not symmetrical with respect to the axis. Because of its reduced density, the heated water rose to the upper portion of the horizontal pipe. Certain theoretical equations (pages 162 to 164) ignore this lack of symmetry in the temperature distribution.

For Curve BB, where the Reynolds number is nearly seven times that for Curve AA, the dotted tie-line is nearly vertical, and the temperature distribution is more nearly symmetrical for the higher water rate. For DG/μ of 77,000–80,000, Fig. 71 shows the velocity and temperature distribution ratios plotted *vs.* y/r_0, using

* Explorations were made in a vertical plane at the end of a steam-heated length of 12 ft, preceded by an unheated length of 18 ft. The temperature of the top side of the heated pipe was measured by thermocouples. Immediately upon leaving the heated length, the water was mixed and its bulk temperature determined.

logarithmic coordinates.   It is noted that the distribution of temperature and velocity are not the same, since the slope of the curve of $\Delta t_y/\Delta t_{max}$ *vs.* y/r_0 is 0.06, whereas that for u/u_{max} is 0.15.   A similar discrepancy was found in slopes for runs at lower values of DG/μ.   The Prandtl number $c_p\mu/k$ ranged from 1.8 to 7.0. For air ($c_p\mu/k$ of 0.74) the temperature and velocity fields are substantially identical (Fig. 69).

Referring to the two water runs compared in Fig. 70, the value of Δt_{av}, which is the difference between the temperature of the

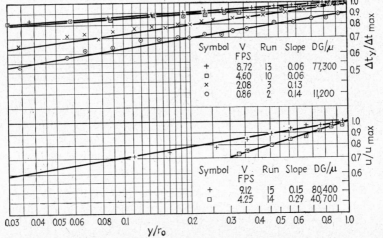

Fig. 71.—Data of Woolfenden for the upper portion of the pipe.

surface and the bulk temperature obtained by mixing all the fluid leaving the section, is 86 to 89 per cent of Δt_{max} from surface to axis. In measuring bulk temperature, it is clear that the omission of a mixing device would introduce a substantial error in the calculation of the coefficient of heat transfer.

METHODS OF ATTACK

1. Mathematical.—As shown on pages 157 to 161, the mechanism of heat transfer by conduction and convection is complicated in the usual case of turbulent motion.   Thus the velocity gradient across the stream does not follow any one simple relation but apparently involves three zones: film, buffer layer, and turbulent core.   The heat leaving the wall is conducted through the film and delivered to the buffer layer.*   In the latter, part of the heat is

* A fraction of the heat is consumed in warming the film flowing along the

transferred by convection, *i.e.*, by mechanical mixing due to eddies; the remainder of the heat is transferred by conduction under the influence of the radial gradient in temperature.   The heat is then transferred to the turbulent core, where the mixing is apparently more thorough, as indicated by temperature gradients smaller than in the portions nearer the wall.   As the fluid passes through the pipe, the radial temperature gradients are continually changing. From the foregoing, it is evident why so little success follows attempts* to apply mathematical analysis in the prediction of heat transfer from the fundamental equation for heat conduction in moving fluids, unless empirical corrections are introduced.[249]† Furthermore, as brought out on page 160, for turbulent flow of water at an average velocity five times the critical, the radial distribution of temperature was far from symmetrical in a horizontal pipe, and apparently natural convection factors were involved, which are ignored in the theoretical treatments.

Analogies between Heat Transfer and Friction.—Many writers have assumed analogies between the equations for the transfer of heat and momentum.   The following section reviews this method of attack and could be omitted by those interested only in the recommended correlations of heat-transfer coefficients.

The first of these analogies was proposed by Reynolds[584] in 1874, long before many heat-transfer data were available.   Assuming that all the thermal resistance is in the turbulent core, this analogy leads to the simple dimensionless equation

$$h/c_p G = f/2 \tag{1}$$

for which symbols are defined in Table I, page 156.   In the derivation it is

---

wall, and this portion does not reach the buffer layer.   However, since the cross section of the film is negligible compared with that of the entire tube, the fraction of the heat carried away by the film, and similarly for the buffer layer, is negligible.

* Reynolds[586] lays the hydrodynamical foundation of the concepts of "*mean mixing lengths* and *eddy* or *fictive viscosity.*"   Latzko[425] derives a theoretical equation for the heat transfer and reviews the literature.   In the derivation, the thermal resistance of the film is neglected compared to that of the turbulent core; consequently the resulting equation, although applicable to gases, does not apply to liquids such as water and the viscous hydrocarbon oils.   Von Karman[366] reviews the Prandtl theory on mixing length.   Nikuradse[513] employs data for distribution of velocity for isothermal flow of water to compute mean mixing lengths of Prandtl.   Dryden, Murnaghan, and Bateman[200] discuss in detail the *eddy viscosity* and Prandtl's mixing-length theory.

† Murphree[496] deduces that hD/k should depend on both DG/μ and $c_p\mu/k$ and compares the derived relation with data of several observers.

assumed that the kinematic viscosity μ/ρ is equal to the thermal diffusivity $\alpha = k/\rho c_p$; *i.e.*, the dimensionless group $c_p\mu/k$ equals unity;* since for gases this assumption is not in large error, Eq. 1 is a rough approximation to actual heat-transfer and friction data for gases, as shown on page 171.

The deviation of Eq. 1 from experimental data increases as $c_p\mu/k$ increases beyond unity.

Prandtl,[572] and later Taylor,[709] extended the Reynolds theory to include a laminar flow layer near the wall and obtained the dimensionless relation

$$\frac{h}{c_p G} = \frac{f/2}{1 - r_v + r_v(c_p\mu/k)_{f'}} = \frac{f/2}{1 + r_v[(c_p\mu/k)_{f'} - 1]} \tag{2}$$

which involves r_v, the ratio of the velocity u_i (at the interface between the film and core) to the average velocity V. The expression $1 - r_v$ may be termed the *relative thermal resistance* of the core and r_v $(c_p\mu/k)_{f'}$ that of the film.

Prandtl[574] modified Eq. 2 by relating r_v to DG/μ and obtained

$$\frac{h}{c_p G} = \frac{f/2}{1 + b_1 (DG/\mu)^{-1/8}[(c_p\mu/k)_{f'} - 1]} \tag{2a}$$

Since $f/2 = b_2/(DG/\mu)^{1/4}$, r_v in Eq. 2 may be replaced by

$$\frac{b_1}{\sqrt{b_2}} \sqrt{\frac{f}{2}}.$$

By replacing the term r_v of Eq. 2 by $1.5 (DG/\mu)^{-1/8}(c_p\mu/k)^{-1/6}$, and $f/2$ by the Blausius relation $0.0395 Re^{-1/4}$, Hoffman[308] correlated roughly the data for a number of fluids having values of $c_p\mu/k$ ranging from 0.74 to 300. Eagle and Ferguson[203] pointed out that Eq. 2 contained no allowance for the buffer layer.

Karman[368,369] further extended the theory to include the buffer layer. Figure 49,[369] page 110, shows von Karman's generalized diagram based on velocity explorations by Nikuradse,[514] plotted on semilogarithmic paper. The equations for the velocity distribution for each of the three zones is shown in Fig. 49. As an approximation, the physical properties of the fluid are treated as constant. Use of the three zones and further assumptions leads to the Karman equation

* The equations for the transfer of momentum and heat are written

$$g_c\tau = \mu \frac{\partial u}{\partial y} + \rho\epsilon_\nu \frac{\partial u}{\partial y} = \rho(\nu + \epsilon_\nu) \frac{du}{dy} \tag{1a}$$

$$\frac{q}{A_s} = -k \frac{\partial t}{\partial y} - c_p\rho\epsilon_\alpha \frac{\partial t}{\partial y} = -\rho c_p(\alpha + \epsilon_\alpha) \frac{\partial t}{\partial y} \tag{1b}$$

In Eq. 1a the eddy viscosity ϵ_ν allows for momentum transfer due to eddy motion, and in Eq. 1b the eddy diffusivity ϵ_α allows for heat transfer due to eddy motion. The numerical values of ϵ_ν and ϵ_α are assumed equal.

In a recent paper reviewing analogies between the transfer of momentum and heat, von Karman[369] points out that Eq. 1 could be obtained from Eqs. 1a and 1b by two alternate procedures: (1) ν and α are assumed negligible compared with ϵ, which is satisfactory for the turbulent core, or (2) ν is assumed equal to α, which is nearly true for gases, since $c_p\mu/k$ is fairly close to unity. In either case, upon assuming that both τ and q are the same function of y, Eq. 1 is obtained, noting that τ_0 equals $f\rho V^2/2g_c$.

$$\frac{h}{c_p G} = \frac{f/2}{1 + 5\sqrt{f/2}\left\{\frac{c_p\mu}{k} - 1 + \ln_e\left[1 + \frac{5}{6}\left(\frac{c_p\mu}{k} - 1\right)\right]\right\}} \quad \cdots \quad (3)$$

For $c_p\mu/k$ of 1, this reduces to Eq. 1, and for moderate values of $c_p\mu/k$, Eq. 3 reduces to the form of Eq. 2. For water and several organic liquids of low viscosity, for which $c_p\mu/k$ ranged from 2 to 30, Lorenz[444]* showed that Eq. 3 fits the data more closely than Eqs. 1 and 2 but that the deviation between Eq. 3 and experimental data continues to increase progressively as $c_p\mu/k$ increases above 30. However, it is remarkable that these theoretical equations fit the data as well as they do in view of the assumptions involved.

Matlioli[473] modified Eq. 3 and obtained better agreement with data for high values of $c_p\mu/k$ than is found with Eq. 3.

Hoffman[309] modifies Karman's equation by using an empirical relation for the velocity distribution that will give a maximum velocity at the axis of the pipe (instead of a discontinuity), and the resulting complex equation was found to fit experimental data more satisfactorily than Eq. 3 for $c_p\mu/k$ ranging from 30 to 300.

Boelter et al.[70] review analogies and employ y_1^+ as a dimensionless parameter defining the unknown thickness y_1 of the laminar layer, instead of using the value of y_1^+ of 5 based on isothermal conditions. By using one set[490] of heat-transfer data involving high $c\mu/k$ to relate empirically y_1^+ to DG/μ and μ_s/μ_1, they are able to predict h/cG for other sets of data† within ±20 per cent, using their complex dimensionless equation‡

$$\frac{h}{c_p G} = \frac{(\sqrt{f/2})\,(\Delta t_{\max}/\Delta t_m)}{y_1^+\left\{\left(\frac{c_p\mu}{k}\right)_1 + \ln_e\left[1 + \left(\frac{c_p\mu}{k}\right)_m\left(\frac{30}{y_1^+} - 1\right)\right] + \frac{2.5}{y_1^+}\ln_e\frac{(DG/\mu)_m(\sqrt{f/2})}{60}\right\}}$$

$$(3a)$$

The same data, expressed as $h/c_p G$, deviated -60 to $+20$ per cent from the simple wholly empirical equation of reference.[176]

2. Dimensional Analysis.—Assuming that the coefficient h of heat transfer by conduction and convection between solid and fluid is controlled by the factors entering the differential equations for both hydrodynamics and heat conduction, dimensional analysis[521] (Chap. V) gives

$$\frac{hD}{k} = \phi\left(\frac{DG}{\mu}, \frac{c_p\mu}{k}\right) \tag{4}$$

wherein the symbols have the significance shown in Table I, page

* The Karman paper shows the graph comparing Eqs. 2 and 3 with the experimental data.

† Smith[676] for oils, Eagle and Ferguson[203] for water, and Colburn and Coghlan[145] for gases.

‡ Reference 70 gives the plots for predicting $\Delta t_{\max}/\Delta t_m$, y_1^+, and μ_f/μ_1; f is obtained from a plot of isothermal values, at DG/μ_1.

156, and the functions relating the first group with each of the other two are to be determined experimentally. Equation 4 is dimensionally sound, and if each of the five factors assumed to affect h were actually involved and no other factors were of importance for clean pipes,* Eq. 4 could be accepted without hesitation.

For a given gas, such as air, the $c_p\mu/k$ or Prandtl number varies but little with moderate change in temperature (page 415), and the same is true of k. For such conditions Eq. 4 becomes, assuming a power function,

$$h = aG^n/D^m \qquad (4a)$$

where m should be equal to $1 - n$, and a depends upon the fluid and temperature involved.

STUDY OF EXPERIMENTAL DATA

Effect of Mass Velocity.—The use of mass velocity was suggested by Reynolds[584] in 1874. Figure 72 shows a plot of h *vs.* G to logarith-

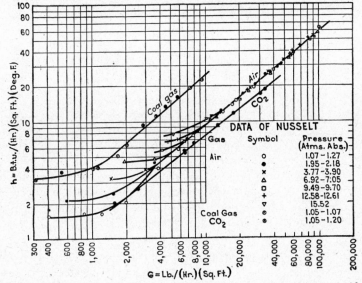

FIG. 72.—Effect of mass velocity upon heat-transfer coefficient, gases inside a horizontal pipe.

mic coordinates, based on Nusselt's[521] data for three different gases flowing in a tube having an inside diameter of 0.868 in. Except

* If tube length affected h, Eq. 4 should also include[521] the ratio D/L; available data show length has no important effect except for streamline flow and in the transition region (pp. 192 to 196).

at the lower values of G, where natural convection increases h (page 170) the slope n is 0.8. In the range where h varied as $G^{0.8}$, mass velocity was controlling, regardless of pressure. In other words, G had the same effect, regardless of whether in the product $G = V\rho$, average linear velocity V was high and density ρ low, or the reverse occurred. The use of G, rather than $V\rho$, simplifies calculations, since by definition

$$G = \frac{w}{S} = \frac{\text{pounds of fluid per hour}}{\text{cross section in square feet}}$$

and is independent of changes in temperature and pressure. Data of Rietschel[598] for air flowing in six sizes of pipes gave values of n ranging from 0.78 to 0.82, averaging 0.79; values of n of 0.8 are indicated by various data.*

As shown later, experiments with water and organic liquids lead to the same result.

Effect of Diameter.—Plots of $h/G^{0.8}$ *vs.* inside diameter, using logarithmic coordinates, give the results shown in Table II. A large

TABLE II.—EXPONENTS ON D, FROM VARIOUS DATA (SEE EQ. 4a)

Observer	Reference	Fluid	Range of D', inches	Exponent m
Rietschel.............	598	Air	0.847–4.68	0.16
Schulze...............	648	Air	0.985–5.90	0.33–0.40
Holmboe.............	314	Steam	0.786–3.94	0.26
Eagle and Ferguson....	203	Water	0.500–1.50	0.20

per cent change in m produces a relatively small per cent change in the value of D^m and in the corresponding predicted value of h. Since from theory m equals $1 - n$, and the value of 0.8 for n is well established by heat-transfer data, it recommended that m be taken as 0.2.

Effect of Physical Properties.—With gases (page 415) the Prandtl number $c_p\mu/k$ varies but little, and hence data for gases throw little light on the effect of physical properties.† A number of writers‡ have compared data for various fluids at a given value of DG/μ and have found that hD/k varied inversely as $c_p\mu/k$ raised

---

* References 107, 270, 272, 314, 359, 565, 601, 612.

† A decrease in $(c_p\mu/k)$ obtained by adding hydrogen to nitrogen[145] caused hD/k to decrease for a given DG/μ.

‡ References 490, 158, 306, 373, 176, 663, 142, 668.

to exponents ranging from 0.4 to 0.3, as shown by Table III. The physical property of the liquid that varies most rapidly with temperature is viscosity, and the constants a_1 and p in the equation

$$\frac{hD}{k} = a_1 \left(\frac{DG}{\mu}\right)^{0.8} \left(\frac{c_p\mu}{k}\right)^p \tag{4b}$$

depend on whether μ is evaluated at the temperature of the surface, the film, or the main body of the fluid.

TABLE III.—VALUES OF a_1 AND p IN EQ. 4b

Author	Date	a_1	p	μ or μ_f	Heating, H Cooling, C
Morris and Whitman[490]...	1928	Note 1	0.37	μ	H and C
Hinton[306]...............	1928	0.0281	0.355	μ	H and C
Dittus and Boelter[176].....	1930	0.0243	0.4	μ	H
Dittus and Boelter[176].....	1930	0.0265	0.3	μ	C
Sherwood and Petrie[663]...	1932	0.024	0.4	μ	H, Note 2
Colburn[142]..............	1933	0.023	0.333	μ_f	H and C
Sieder and Tate[668]........	1936	$0.027(\mu/\mu_s)^{0.14}$	0.333	μ, μ_s	H and C

NOTE 1.—The term $[(hD/k) \div (c_p\mu/k)^{0.37}]$ was shown as a graphical function of DG/μ; for cooling, $0.75h$ for heating was recommended. Morris and Whitman found that their data for heating and cooling could be brought together by using μ_f instead of μ, although the data for heating were spread by this procedure.

NOTE 2.—Sherwood and Petrie found that use of μ_f spread the data more than μ, and preferred μ.

The effect of $c_p\mu/k$ upon hD/k, at a fixed value of DG/μ, is shown by Figs. 73 and 74 for seven different fluids. In Fig. 73, μ in both DG/μ and in $c_p\mu/k$, is evaluated at the bulk temperature, and it is seen that the slope of the curve is 0.4.*

Smoothed data of the same observers are replotted in Fig. 74, with viscosity evaluated throughout at the film temperature, t_f taken as equal to $t + 0.5(t_s - t)$. The data are fairly well correlated by a line having a slope of one-third.

Comparison of Figs. 73 and 74 show that the former, which evaluates physical properties at the convenient bulk temperature,

* Had the values of hD/k been compared at any one value of DG/μ in the range 2100 to 100,000, the exponent on the $c_p\mu/k$ group would still have been substantially 0.4, except for the data for the oils that lie in the "dip region" (p. 192) where the exponent n on DG/μ has not yet fallen to the value of 0.8.

correlates these data slightly better than Fig. 74 and is consequently ordinarily used for fluids having viscosities not more than twice that of water, for Reynolds numbers exceeding 2100:

$$\frac{hD}{k} = 0.023 \left(\frac{DG}{\mu}\right)^{0.8} \left(\frac{c_p\mu}{k}\right)^{0.4} \tag{4c}*$$

In the preceding pages data for a number of fluids were compared at a Reynolds number of 10,000. In the following section repre-

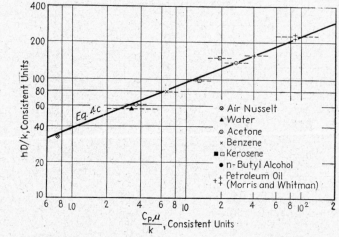

Fig. 73.—Effect of Prandtl number $c_p\mu/k$ upon Nusselt number hD/k for DG/μ of 10,000; μ at bulk temperature. (*Sherwood and Petrie.*)

sentative data for gases and liquids of low viscosity (water, kerosene, benzene, acetone, and butanol) at all Reynolds numbers exceeding 2100 will be examined and the deviations from Eq. 4c determined.

Gases in Straight Tubes. *Data.*—Experimental results of a number of investigators, heating or cooling gases flowing in tubes,

---

* For liquids of high viscosity and Reynolds numbers exceeding 10,000, instead of following the old procedure[454a] of using Eq. 4c with an exponent on $c_p\mu/k$ of 0.3 for cooling and 0.4 for heating, it is more logical to use either the Colburn equation[142] shown on Fig. 74

$$\frac{hD}{k} = 0.023 \left(\frac{DG}{\mu_f}\right)^{0.8} \left(\frac{c_p\mu_f}{k}\right)^{1/3} \tag{4d}$$

or the somewhat more convenient equation of Sieder and Tate[668]

$$\frac{hD}{k} = 0.027 \left(\frac{\mu}{\mu_s}\right)^{0.14} \left(\frac{DG}{\mu}\right)^{0.8} \left(\frac{c_p\mu}{k}\right)^{1/3} \tag{4e}$$

Data for viscous fluids are discussed fully on p. 192.

have been selected for illustration (see Table IV); additional literature references* are available.

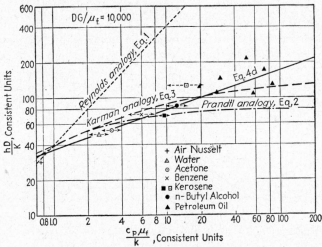

Fig. 74.—Data of Fig. 73, for DG/μ_f of 10,000; μ_f at film temperature, $t_f = 0.5(t + t_s)$.

TABLE IV.—HEAT TRANSFER TO GASES FLOWING INSIDE TUBES

Observer	Gas	Heating or cooling	D', inches	Tube metal	$\dfrac{t + t_s}{2}$, deg F t_f	Pressure, atm P	Measured h or U
Josse[358]	Air	H	0.907	....	160–180	0.1–1.0	U
Holmboe[314]	Steam	C	0.787	Copper	....	1–5	h
Nusselt[521]	Air	H	0.868	Brass	147–194	1.1–16.0	h
Nusselt[521]	CO₂	H	0.868	Brass	Ca. 170	1	h
Nusselt[521]	Coal gas	H	0.868	Brass	Ca. 170	1	h
Rietschel[538]	Air	H	1.32	Steel	Ca. 200	....	U
Royds and Campbell[612]	Air	C	0.994	Steel	180–280	....	U
Grober[270,272]	Air	C	2.44	Steel	160–540	....	h
Poensgen[565]	Steam	C	1.55	"Sm." metal	260–510	1–9	h
Poensgen[565]	Steam	C	3.76	"Sm." metal	230–390	1–7	h
Robinson[601]	Air	H	0.625	Copper	Ca. 240	1	
Robinson[601]	Air	H	1.168	Copper	Ca. 210	1	
Carrier[107]	Air	H	3.73			1	
Guchmann et al.[273]	Air	..	0.983				
Colburn and Coghlan[145]	Note 1	H	0.50	Stainless	Ca. 170	 1	h

NOTE 1.—Gas ranged from 9 to 98 per cent H_2; rest was N_2; $c_p\mu/k$ ranged from 0.73 to 0.45·

The data of Nusselt have already been shown in Fig. 72, page 165, with h plotted *vs.* G. Referring to the data for air at 7 atm

* Bell,[57] Babcock and Wilcox,[23] Bichowsky,[60] Fessenden,[219] Fessenden and Haney,[220] Jordan,[356] Kreisenger and Ray,[411] Nicolson,[510] Pannell,[546] Parsons and Harper,[549] Royds,[610] Schulze,[648] and Sneeden.[679]

pressure, the experimental points lie on a straight line having a slope of 0.8 for mass velocities ranging from 5040 to 99,000 lb/(hr) (sq ft of cross section), but at velocities less than 5040, the points lie above the line having a slope of 0.8. This increase in h at the low velocities, over and above what would be predicted by extrapolating the line of 0.8 slope to the low-velocity range, is believed to be due to additional convection caused by a group of natural-convection factors that includes the density of the gas. As shown on page 242 from data on natural convection, h is affected by a power function

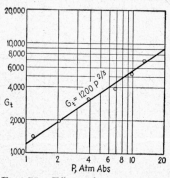

FIG. 75.—Effect of gas pressure upon transitional velocity G_t.

of the density or pressure. Hence it would be expected[136] that the "transitional velocity" G_t at which the values of h begin to be higher than indicated by an exponent of 0.8 upon the G term should be a power function of pressure. Figure 75 shows the values of G_t of Fig. 72 plotted *vs.* pressure in atmospheres, to logarithmic coordinates, and the empirical relation $G_t = 1200P^{2/3}$ is obtained, wherein the dimensional constant of 1200 would involve other factors, which in this case were substantially constant, pressure being the main variable. At the high velocities the turbulence indicated by the Reynolds number is controlling.

The data of Fig. 72 for G greater than G_t are replotted to logarithmic coordinates in Fig. 76 with the dimensionless group hD/k plotted *vs.* the Reynolds number. The data for the three gases, which fell on separate curves in Fig. 72, are now brought together to form a single curve. Figure 76 shows data of other observers for air in pipes. These are in fair accord with the data of Nusselt, the maximum deviation being 30 per cent. The line AA represents Eq. 4c, which for $c_p\mu/k$ of 0.74 reduces to

$$hD/k = 0.02(DG/\mu)^{0.8} \qquad (4f)$$

Since $c_p\mu/k$ varied so little, these data fail to show whether or not the $c_p\mu/k$ term is involved.

Curve BB of Fig. 76 shows the relation predicted by the Reynolds analogy ($h/c_pG = f/2$) for air or other gas having $c_p\mu/k$ of 0.74, based on the values of $f = 0.049(\mu/DG)^{0.2}$ ref. 403. Line AA also represents the prediction from the Prandtl analogy (Eq. 2, page 163) using $c_p\mu/k = 0.74$ and $r_v = 0.3$. For a given value of DG/μ, the values of hD/k predicted from the Prandtl relation are 1.09 times those of the Reynolds analogy.

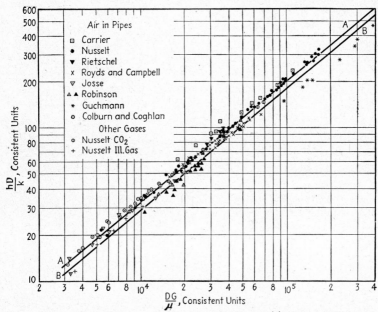

Fig. 76.—Data for gases inside tubes compared with recommended line AA (Eq. 4c); line BB is obtained from the Reynolds analogy (Eq. 1) taking

$$f = 0.049(DG/\mu)^{-0.2}$$

and $c_p\mu/k = 0.74$; line BB also represents the Prandtl analogy (Eq. 2) for r_v of 0.3.

Since, for the gases involved, $c_p\mu/k$ is approximately 0.74, one could eliminate the viscosity term from Eq. 4c by substituting $\mu = 0.74k/c_p$, giving

$$hD/k = 0.026(DGc_p/k)^{0.8} \cdots \qquad (4g)$$

which compares fairly closely with Nusselt's 1909 empirical equation for gases:

$$hD/k = 0.0255(DGc_p/k)^{0.786} \cdots \qquad (4h)$$

Equations of this form, expressing hD/k in terms of the Peclet number DGc_p/k have been used by many writers. Although Eq. 4h contains one less physical property than Eq. 4c, which involves DG/μ, this is of little advantage, since the Reynolds number would normally be calculated to evaluate the pressure drop due to friction (page 118).   As shown below, the Peclet number alone does not satisfactorily correlate the values of hD/k for *liquids*, especially for the viscous oils.   For turbulent flow, a correlation in terms of the Reynolds number, which is satisfactory for both liquids and gases, is preferred to the Peclet number.

Figure 77 shows the data on the cooling of **superheated steam,** without condensation, flowing inside horizontal pipes, without applying a deduction for heat transferred by gas radiation (page

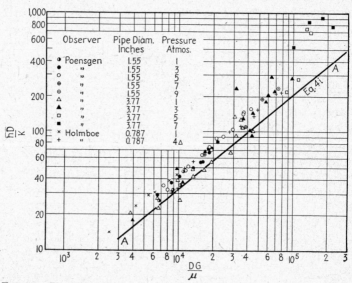

FIG. 77.—Data on cooling of superheated steam (without condensation), not corrected for gas radiation, compared with Eq. 4*i*, obtained by substituting $c_p\mu/k$ of 0.78 in Eq. 4*c*.

64).   The line AA on Fig. 77 is obtained from Eq. 4*c* by substitution of $c_p\mu/k = 0.78$ for steam, giving

$$hD/k = 0.021(DG/\mu)^{0.8} \tag{4i}$$

wherein the units are defined in Table I, page 156.   Equation 4*c* is in fair agreement with the results of Kerr,[385] who worked with superheated steam at pressures up to 3300 lb/sq in. and temperatures up to 800°F, see Prob. 4 at end of Chap. VII.

The exact effect of tube length upon the heat-transfer coefficient for gases in turbulent flow is still in dispute but is apparently of little importance for tubes of the length-diameter ratio ordinarily employed.   Data for the turbulent flow of water (page 179) and hydrocarbon oils (page 195) show a negligible effect upon h of variations in L/D from 59 to 235. For short tubes, where L/D is only 15 to 25, as in the cases of "radiators" for internal-combustion engines, the data of Parsons and Harper[549] are available. The values of G ranged from 7000 to 70,000 lb/(hr)(sq ft of cross section of the tubes), which had an internal diameter of approximately 0.3 in. The values of h, reported in terms of initial rather than average temperature difference, were not greatly different from those for long tubes.

The effect of temperature upon h is still subject to some dispute. The data of Babcock and Wilcox,[23] Fessenden and Haney,[220] and Jordan[356] agree in showing that h increases with increase in the temperature of the gas in cooling runs but disagree as to the exact effect of temperature. The only other pertinent data are those of Schulze,[647]* which were interpreted by Schulze and Schack[627] to show a negligible effect of temperature within the precision of the data, estimated as 10 per cent. Various empirical relations as to the quantitative effect of temperature upon h have been suggested, as indicated by Table V.

TABLE V

Date	Note	Author	h varies as
1919	a	Weber[747]	$(c_p)_g T_g{}^{1/2}$
1924	..	Fessenden[219]	$(c_p)_g T_g / T_f$
1927	b	Dixon[178]	$(c_p)_g T_f{}^{2/3}$
1929	c	Sherwood[659]	$(c_p)_g (1 + 0.0008 T_f)$
1930	d	Nusselt[531]	$(c_p)_s (T_g / T_s)^{1/3}$
1931	e	Reynolds analogy	$(c_p)_g \mu_g{}^{0.2}$

NOTE.—Absolute temperature is represented by T, with subscript s for surface, g for gas, and f for film: $T_f = (T_g + T_s)/2$.

a The Weber equation is compared[433] with data of Nusselt, Josse, Robinson, Fessenden and Haney, and Babcock and Wilcox.

b Based on data of Nusselt,[521] Josse,[358] Robinson,[601] Fessenden and Haney,[220] and Babcock and Wilcox.[23]

c Based on the data mentioned in reference [747] and expressed in terms of the units of Table I, p. 156, Sherwood obtained
$$h = 0.00956(1 + 0.0008 T_f) c_p G^{0.8} / D^{0.2}$$

d Based on data of Jordan[356] and Babcock and Wilcox.[23]

e See Eq. 1, p. 162.

For the data of references 23 and 220, on the cooling of hot flue gases, most of the increase in the apparent h with increase in gas temperature can be attributed to gas radiation (pages 64 to 73).

* See also Nusselt.[531]

Equation 4c calls for a moderate increase in h with increase in gas temperature. Substituting $c_p\mu/k$ of 0.78 as an average for a number of gases (page 415), Eq. 4c becomes

$$h = 0.027 \frac{c_p G^{0.8} \mu^{0.2}}{D^{0.2}} \qquad (4j)$$

wherein the symbols are defined in Table I, page 156.

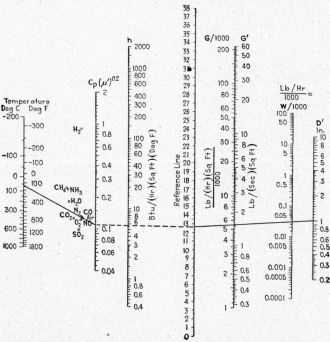

FIG. 78.—Alignment chart* based on Eq. 4j (obtained by substituting $c_p\mu/k$ of 0.78 in Eq. 4c) for turbulent flow of gases in tubes; not to be used if G is less than $1200P^{2/3}$ where h will be higher than shown, owing to natural convection.

Since the viscosities of common gases do not vary widely, and since viscosity enters only as $\mu^{0.2}$, a *simplified* equation, not containing a temperature term, is obtained by substituting μ of 0.0435 lb/(hr)(ft) into Eq. 4j, giving the dimensional equation

$$h = 0.0144 \frac{c_p G^{0.8}}{D^{0.2}} \qquad (4k)$$

wherein the symbols have the units shown in Table I, page 156.

* Figure 78 was prepared by Chilton *et al.*[118]

Equation $4k$ represents the data of Fig. 76, based on the heating of several gases by steam, using pipes ranging from 0.868 to 3.77 in. in diameter. At values of G, expressed in lb/(hr)(sq ft) below $1200P^{2/3}$, Eq. $4k$ may give too conservative results, as brought out on page 170.

In a recent paper, Cope[155a] studied the cooling of air in tubes with three degrees of artificial roughness, in which the height of pyramid ranged from one forty-fifth to one-seventh of the radius of the pipe. Although in the turbulent region the friction ran as high as six times that for smooth tubes, the heat transfer ran only 100 to 20 per cent greater than for smooth tubes. It was concluded that, for the same power loss or pressure drop, greater heat transfer was obtained from a smooth than a rough tube. Incidentally these results show that the Reynolds analogy (Eq. 1) breaks down for tubes as rough as those used by Cope.

The effect of a given scale deposit is usually far less serious for a gas than for water because of the higher thermal resistance of the gas film compared with that of water film. However, layers of dust or of materials that sublime, such as sulphur, may seriously reduce heat transfer between gas and solid. Thus, because of thick deposits of dust in the flues of blast-furnace stoves, Weber[748] found over-all coefficients of heat transfer reduced approximately 40 per cent; for clean surfaces the values of U were roughly double those computed from the Weber equation (page 173) for gases in clean pipes.

Design Chart for Gas Heaters or Coolers.—The heat transferred can be equated to that absorbed by the gas:

$$\frac{\pi}{4} D^2 G c_p (t_2 - t_1) = U_m \pi D L \, \Delta t_m \tag{5}$$

or

$$\frac{t_2 - t_1}{\Delta t_m} = \left(\frac{4L}{D}\right)\left(\frac{U_m}{c_p G}\right) \tag{5a}$$

Usually the gas-side resistance is controlling, *i.e.*, $U_m = h_m$. For design purposes, h may conservatively be predicted from Eq. $4k$. By combining Eqs. $4k$ and $5a$, there results

$$\frac{t_2 - t_1}{\Delta t_m} = \frac{(0.0576)(L/D)}{(DG)^{0.2}}, \tag{5b}$$

and it is noted that the ratio of rise to mean temperature difference depends mainly upon L/D and slightly upon DG.

The convenient alignment chart shown in Fig. 79 is based on Eq. 5b.

Illustration 1.—It is desired to heat 600 lb/hr of a gas from 70 to 190°F, with steam condensing at 220°F outside tubes, which have an i.d. of 0.902 in. It is agreed to use a gas velocity near the optimum value. Calculate the number of tubes in parallel and the length of each tube.

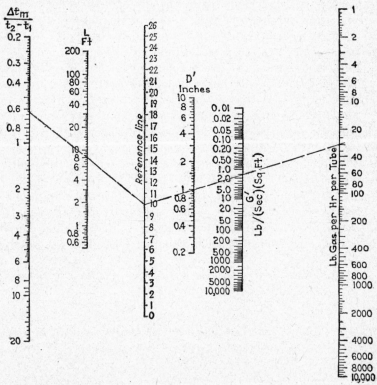

Fig. 79.—Design chart for tubular gas heaters or coolers, which gives conservative results for cases where G is less than $1200P^{2/3}$, where P is absolute pressure in atmospheres. (*Chilton, Colburn, Genereaux, and Vernon.*[118])

Solution.—Using suitable cost data and Eq. 27b (page 368) the optimum value of G' is 1.88 lb/(sec)(sq ft of cross section). Figure 79 shows that the corresponding gas rate per tube is 30 lb/hr; hence $^{600}\!/_{30}$ or 20 tubes in parallel are required.

Since the thermal resistance on the gas side is controlling, U_m is equal to h_m, based on the inside surface. The ratio of the logarithmic mean temperature difference (page 142) to the temperature rise is

$$\frac{(t_{sv} - t_1) - (t_{sv} - t_2)}{(t_2 - t_1)\left[\ln_e \dfrac{(t_{sv} - t_1)}{(t_{sv} - t_2)}\right]} = \frac{1}{\ln_e \dfrac{t_{sv} - t_1}{t_{sv} - t_2}} = \frac{1}{2.3 \log_{10} 15\%_0} = 0.621*$$

A straight line is now drawn on Fig. 79, passing through D' of 0.902 and G' of 1.88 (also through w of 30), and intersects the reference line. Alignment of this intersection with 0.621 on the left-hand line marked $\Delta t_m/(t_2 - t_1)$ gives a reading of 7.3 ft on the L scale. To introduce a factor of safety, each tube should be made 9 ft long.

It is seen that the tube length is independent of the specific heat of the gas.

Illustration 2.—It is desired to heat 5940 lb/hr of a gas from 70 to 190°F, with steam condensing at 220°F outside the pipes. There are available in stock, pipes 18.5 ft long and 2.07 in. in diameter. How many pipes should be used in parallel?

Solution.—The ratio of $\Delta t_m/(t_2 - t_1)$ is 0.621, as in Illustration 1. Aligning 0.621 and 18.5 on the two left-hand scales of Fig. 79, draw a straight line intersecting the reference line. From this point, align with $D' = 2.07$, and read 110 lb/(hr)(tube) on the right-hand scale. Hence, 54 tubes, each 18.5 ft long with 2.07-in. diameter, would serve. If it had been desired to introduce a factor of safety, the first alignment should have been drawn through a value of less than 18.5, say 16 ft, giving 54 lb/(hr)(pipe) and 110 pipes in parallel, each 18.5 ft long. These equations and charts may be employed in the design of gas coolers, where the gas is not being dehumidified. If vapors are condensing during the cooling of the gas-vapor mixture, see Chap. IX.

Gases in Coiled Pipes.—Jeschke[352] cooled air in two helical coils of $1\frac{1}{4}$-in. seamless steel tubing, one having a diameter of 24.8 in. and two turns, and the other having a diameter of 8.27 in. and six turns. The flow, always turbulent, ranged up to DG/μ of 150,000. From the two sets of data obtained, Jeschke proposed the equation

$$\frac{hD}{k} = \left(0.039 + \frac{0.138D}{D_H}\right)\left(\frac{DGc_p}{k}\right)^{0.76} \tag{6}$$

where D/D_H is the ratio of the diameters of pipe and helix, the other units being given in Table I, page 156. For ordinary use, it is sufficient to multiply h from Eq. 4c for long, straight pipes by the term $[1 + 3.5(D/D_H)]$. It is seen that, for a given Reynolds number, h is higher for coiled pipes than for straight pipes. As discussed on page 123, the pressure drop due to fluid friction is also higher, apparently because of greater turbulence in the coiled pipes. It will be recalled that the various analogies between heat transfer and fluid friction predict that h should increase with increase in fluid friction.

---

* It is noted that the only factor affecting this term is the ratio of the terminal temperature differences.

Miscellaneous Shapes.—Flow in rectangular sections and in annular spaces is treated on pages 197 to 202.

Gases in Packed Tubes.[137]—Apparent coefficients of heat transfer (based on the inside surface of the tube) for air flowing through $1\frac{1}{4}$- and 3-in. vertical tubes packed with $\frac{1}{8}$- to 1-in. granular solids, involve apparent mass velocities ranging from 900 to 14,400 lb of air/(hr)(sq ft of cross section of tube). The ratio of the observed apparent coefficient h_A for the packed tube of diameter D_i to h_I for a 1-in. inside diameter empty tube, both having the same mass velocity based on the gross cross section, depends on the ratio D_p/D_i, where D_p is the diameter of the packing.

TABLE VI.—(COLBURN)

D_p/D_i	0.05	0.10	0.15	0.20	0.25	0.30
h_A/h_I	5.5	7.0	7.8	7.5	7.0	6.6

Turbulence Promoters.—The effect of inserting cores, retarders, or other turbulence promoters in tubes is to increase both h (based

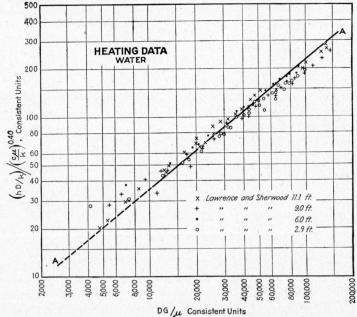

FIG. 80.—Heating of water in tubes ranging in length from 59 to 224 diameters.

on the inside surface of the tube) and the pressure drop. Data for gases[150] and water[497] are available. The best of the retarders described in reference 497 was a coil of wire fitting tightly against the inner surface of the tube; it showed the greatest advantage at the lower Reynolds numbers, where for the same heat transfer the retarder is reported to require only one-fourth the power loss for the empty tube. Internally ribbed tubes with swirlers are available, and a double-pipe exchanger, with radial fins projecting from the smaller tube into the annular space, is described in Chap. VIII.

Liquids of Low Viscosity.—Figure 80[426] shows that the ratio of heated length L to inside diameter D has no effect upon h for

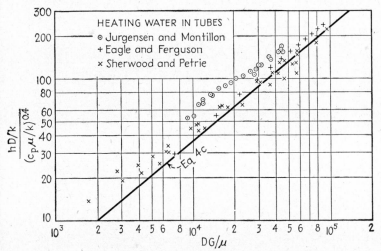

Fig. 81.—Additional data for water (see also Fig. 80).

heating water flowing inside horizontal tubes having lengths ranging from 59 to 224 diameters; to simulate conditions in a commercial condenser, no calming sections were used. A study[426] of data of various observers* for the heating or cooling of water flowing inside horizontal or vertical tubes showed that h was independent of L/D in the range of L/D from 32 to 196. The data of Fig. 80 call for a slope slightly less than 0.8, but the deviations of the data from Eq. 4c are not serious.† The other data mentioned above agree with Eq. 4c as well as those plotted in Fig. 80.

* Reference 426 analyzed the data of references 43, 490, 681, 690, 692, and 696. The data of Burbach[96] are omitted because the temperature of the tube was measured at only one point; those of Webster[750] are omitted because of his method of attaching thermocouples is considered unsatisfactory.

† The correlation could be improved slightly by reducing the exponent on DG/μ to 0.73 and increasing the exponent on $c_p\mu/k$ to 0.49.

Figure 81 shows a comparison of Eq. 4c, based on bulk temperature, with data of several observers.* Figure 82 shows the same

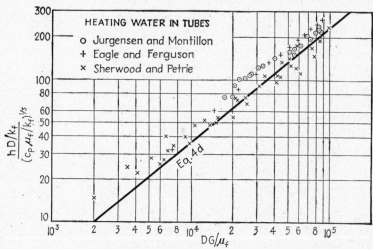

Fig. 82.—Data of Fig. 81, compared with Eq. 4d.

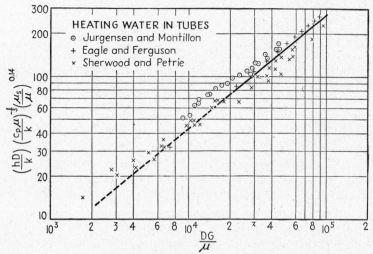

Fig. 83.—Data of Fig. 81, compared with Eq. 4e.

data plotted for comparison with Eq. 4d, page 168, wherein physical properties are evaluated at the film temperature. Figure 83 shows

* Jurgensen and Montillon,[360] Eagle and Ferguson,[203] and Sherwood and Petrie.[663]

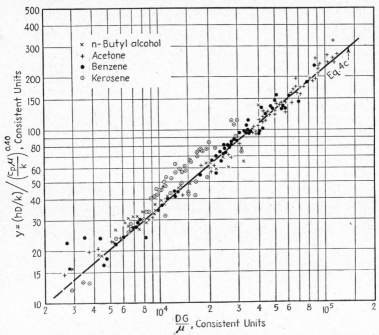

Fig. 84.—Data of Sherwood and Petrie, compared with recommended Eq. 4c; for a given DG/μ exceeding 4,000, maximum variation in Y is ± 30 per cent.

TABLE VII.—PHYSICAL PROPERTIES OF LIQUIDS USED IN REFERENCE 663

Liquid	Boiling point, deg F	μ at 68°F	μ at 122°F	μ at 158°F	c_p	k	ρ	Range of $c_p\mu/k$	$\dfrac{DG/\mu}{1000}$
Acetone...	133	0.78	0.59	....	0.519	0.102	49.4	3.1– 4.1	2.6–120
Benzene ..	177	1.57	1.06	0.85	0.424	0.0883	54.8	5.3– 7.8	2.7–87
n-butanol .	242	7.1	3.42	2.25	0.583	0.0970	50.5	12.3–33.0	2.9–35
Kerosene..	*a*	3.82	2.30	1.73	0.502	0.0875	50.1	10.4–24.2	10.0–32

   k = Btu/(hr)(sq ft)(deg F/ft); assumed constant.
   c_p = Btu/(lb)(deg F); assumed constant.
   ρ = Pounds per cubic foot.
   μ = Viscosity in lb/(hr)(ft) = 2.42 times centipoises.
   $c_p\mu/k$ = Dimensionless quantity, expressed in consistent units.
   a ASTM distillation of original and used material gave (IBP): 320–333°F; 10 per cent off at 357–371°F; 30 per cent off at 389–394°F; 50 per cent off at 416–424°F; 70 per cent off at 445–452°F; 90 per cent off at 490–498°F.

the same data plotted for comparison with the Eq. 4e:

$$\frac{hD}{k} = 0.027 \left(\frac{\mu}{\mu_s}\right)^{0.14} \left(\frac{DG}{\mu}\right)^{0.8} \left(\frac{c_p\mu}{k}\right)^{1/3}$$

Figure 84 shows the data of Sherwood and Petrie[663] for the heating of the liquids listed in Table VII; the straight line is based on Eq. 4c, page 168.

Data for petroleum oils are discussed on pages 192 to 196.

In comparing data, instead of plotting

$$Y = \frac{h\,D/k}{(c_p\mu/k)^m}$$

as ordinates *vs.* DG/μ as abscissas sometimes the ordinates are divided by DG/μ, giving

$$j = \frac{Y}{DG/\mu} = \frac{hD}{k}\left(\frac{c_p\mu}{k}\right)^{-m}\left(\frac{\mu c_p}{DGc_p}\right) = \frac{h}{c_pG}\left(\frac{c_p\mu}{k}\right)^{1-m}$$

Thus if $Y = a_2(DG/\mu)^n$, the corresponding $j = a_2(DG/\mu)^{n-1}$. Thus Colburn[142] writes* Eq. 4d (page 168) as

$$\left(\frac{h}{cG}\right)\left(\frac{c\mu}{k}\right)^{2/3} = \frac{0.023}{(DG/\mu_f)^{0.2}} \qquad (7)$$

or simply as $j_f = 0.023(DG/\mu_f)^{-0.2}$.

The friction factor f (page 119) decreases as DG/μ increases, and the same is true of j; in 1933 this led to an empirical analogy between heat transfer and friction,[142] $j_f = f/2$, which does not correlate heat-transfer data as well as Eq. 4d: $j_f = 0.023(DG/\mu_f)^{-0.2}$.

Simplified Equations.—The use of Eq. 4c, based on bulk temperature, can be simplified by writing it in the form

$$h = [\phi(t)](G')^{0.8}/(D')^{0.2} \qquad (8)$$

wherein

$$\phi(t) = 0.023(3600)^{0.8}(12)^{0.2}k^{0.6}c_p^{0.4}/\mu^{0.4} = 26.4k^{0.6}c_p^{0.4}/\mu^{0.4} \quad (8a)$$

Since at moderate pressures k, c_p, and μ are unique functions of t,

---

* In the turbulent region, where n is 0.8, this rearrangement causes the plot of j *vs.* DG/μ_f to be a flat curve, whereas the slope of the curve of Y *vs.* Reynolds number is a steep curve; furthermore the dimensionless group involving h contains c_p rather than k. It is interesting to note that, for heating or cooling without phase change, the definition of h is $(\pi/4)(D^2)(G)(c_p)(t_2 - t_1)/(\pi DL_H)$ $(\Delta t)_m$, and hence the term h/c_pG is numerically equal to $(D/4L_H)(t_2 - t_1)/(\Delta t_m)$, whereas hD/k equals $(DGc_p/k)(D/4L_H)(t_2 - t_1)/(\Delta t)_m$.

the numerical value of $\phi(t)$ can be evaluated and plotted *vs.* temperature. In using Eq. 8 it is necessary to express the actual inside diameter D' in inches and G' in lb of fluid/(sec)(sq ft of cross section).

Over the range from 40 to 220°F for water $\phi(t)$ equals $5.55(1 + 0.011t)$, where t is expressed in degrees Fahrenheit. Hence, for water

$$h = 5.6(1 + 0.011t)(G')^{0.8}/(D')^{0.2} \qquad (9)*$$

or in terms of water velocity V' ft/sec, based on ρ of 62.3 lb/cu ft, one obtains

$$h = 150(1 + 0.011t)(V')^{0.8}/(D')^{0.2} \qquad (9c)$$

which is of the same form as that of Hinton[306]

$$h = 160(1 + 0.012t)(V')^{0.8}/(D')^{0.2} \qquad (9d)$$

Equation 9 may be combined with the definition of h, $wc_p(t_2 - t_1) = h_m A \, \Delta t_{im}$:

$$\frac{\pi}{4}\left(\frac{D'}{12}\right)^2 (3600\,G')(c_p)(t_2 - t_1) = \frac{\phi(t_m)(G')^{0.8}}{(D')^{0.2}}\left(\frac{\pi D'L}{12}\right)(\Delta t)_{im} \qquad (10)$$

giving a design equation

$$\frac{L}{D'} = 75\,\frac{c_p}{\phi(t_m)}\,(D'G')^{0.2}\,\frac{(t_2 - t_1)}{(\Delta t)_{im}} \qquad (10a)$$

Equation 10a shows that the required ratio of tube length L to diameter D' depends upon the ratio of temperature rise to temperature difference, the temperature level, and the product $(D'G')^{0.2}$.†

---

* Over the range from 40 to 220°F, a plot of $k^{0.6}c^{0.4}/\mu^{0.4}$ for water, *vs.* t in degrees Fahrenheit, gives the straight line

$$k^{0.6}c_p^{0.4}/\mu^{0.4} = 0.21(1 + 0.0108t) = hD^{0.2}/0.023G^{0.8} \qquad (9a)$$

The percentage of variation of h with temperature, indicated by the foregoing relation, is well supported by the data of Eagle and Ferguson.[203] If Eq. 4d were the basis, one would find for water having film temperatures ranging from 40 to 220°F,

$$k_f^{2/3}c_p^{1/3}/\mu_f^{0.467} = 0.17(1 + 0.0133t_f) = hD^{0.2}/0.023G^{0.8} \qquad (9b)$$

When the temperature of the water film is 17.6°F higher than the bulk temperature, *i.e.*, in a water-heating run with Δt_i of 35°F, Eqs. 4c and 4d predict the same value of h.

† Alternately, since in Eq. 9, h is linear in t, one can use Eq. 18 (p. 143) with the terminal values of U and Δt replaced by terminal values of h and Δt_i.

Figure 85 shows a plot of $h \pi D = h \pi D'/12$ based on Eq. 9c, for use in Eq. 9, Chap. VI. The term $h \pi D$ is read from Fig. 85, to correspond with the bulk temperature t and w/D'; w is readily related to D' and V' by Table XXVIII, page 417.

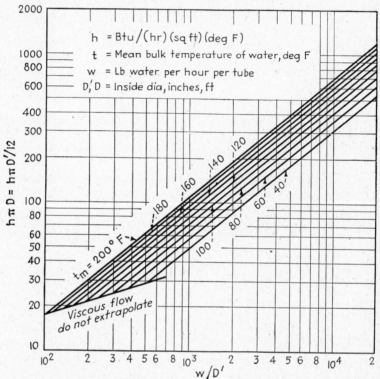

Fig. 85.—Values of h for heating or cooling water (without change in phase) flowing in turbulent motion inside tubes. If the logarithmic mean Δt_i is used, $t_m = t_x$ of Fig. 62, with h and Δt_i replacing U and Δt.

Scale Deposits.—Values of h for scale deposits are given in Table I of Chap. VI.

Liquids in Coiled Pipes.—In the absence of heat-transfer data for liquids in coiled pipes, it is suggested that the procedure given for gases in coiled pipes (page 177) be followed. Richter[596] gives over-all coefficients and pressure drops for a helically coiled double-pipe water-to-water exchanger. With water velocities of 6 and 8 ft/sec, U was 20 per cent higher than in an exchanger made from straight pipe.

Water in Vertical Pipes.—As mentioned on page 179, for values of DG/μ above 2100, Eq. 4c is satisfactory but may be conservative.*

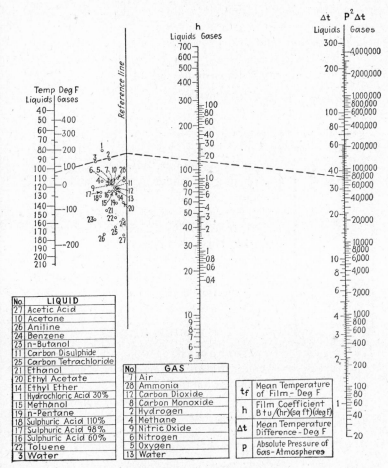

FIG. 86.—Heating fluids flowing upward at low velocities inside vertical tubes, natural convection controlling, based on data for air and water only. (*Chilton et al.*[118])

However, at velocities below the critical,† and sometimes slightly above, free-convection factors may determine h. Colburn and Hougen[147] give the following equations to represent their data for heating water flowing at low velocities, up to 6 lb/(sec)(sq ft) or approximately 0.1 ft/sec, in a 3-in. diameter vertical pipe:

* References 426 and 698.
† For DG/μ below 2100, see also Eq. 20.

$$h = 0.42t(\Delta t)^{1/3} \text{ for } \textit{upward} \text{ flow} \tag{11}$$
$$h = 0.49t(\Delta t)^{1/3} \text{ for } \textit{downward} \text{ flow} \tag{11a}$$

where h is Btu/(hr)(sq ft)(deg F), t is the average water temperature in degrees Fahrenheit, and Δt is the average temperature difference between wall and fluid in degrees Fahrenheit. Using the data for upward flow, they evaluated the constants in the following Nusselt-type natural-convection dimensionless equation:

$$h = 0.128(k_f^2 \rho_f^2 c_p \beta_f \, g(\Delta t)/\mu_f)^{1/3} \tag{12}$$

Since the constants in Eq. 12 compare closely with those in an equation for the natural-convection heat loss from the external surface of a vertical cylinder (page 248), Eq. 12 is recommended as the best estimate now available for the upward flow of fluids having values of $c_p \mu/k$ ranging from 0.73 to 7, at low velocities past vertical surfaces. Figure 86 is an alignment chart, based on Eq. 12, and shows the predicted relation between the liquid involved, the temperature of the film, the temperature difference, and h. For use with gases, a pressure term appears on the chart. Natural-convection data are discussed more fully on pages 237 to 249.

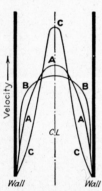

Fig. 87.—Effect of heat transmission on velocity distribution in streamline motion. Curve A, isothermal flow; Curve B, heating of liquid or cooling of gas; Curve C, cooling of liquid or heating of gas.

II. STREAMLINE FLOW

Mechanism.—As mentioned previously, when a fluid is flowing in *isothermal* streamline or laminar motion at constant rate through a long pipe, there is a parabolic velocity gradient over any cross section, with the maximum velocity at the axis and zero velocity at the wall (Fig. 87, Curve A). There is no appreciable mixing of the various layers of fluid, and the motion may be visualized as a series of concentric shells slipping past each other.

Consider a long *vertical* pipe with a liquid at room temperature flowing at low velocity through it, the first section being bare and the second surrounded by a jacket in which steam is condensing at constant temperature. In the unheated section the velocity distribution will be parabolic, but shortly after the liquid enters the heated section a temperature gradient will be established in the liquid, with a high temperature at the wall and a low temperature at the axis. Since the viscosity of a liquid falls as the temperature rises, there will be a viscosity gradient, with a low viscosity at the wall and a high viscosity at the axis. As a result, the layers of liquid near the wall will flow at a greater velocity than in the unheated section. Since the total flow through both sections is the same, it is clear that some of the liquid from the center of the pipe must flow toward the wall in order to maintain the increased velocity near the wall. Thus, the heating of the liquid develops a *radial* component of the velocity, distorting the parabola (Curve B, Fig. 87). If the liquid were cooled, radial flow would again develop, but in this case the flow would be toward the center, changing the velocity distribution as shown diagrammatically by Curve C, Fig. 87. Where change in density with temperature is appreciable, there may occur additional disturbances as in turbulent flow (page 160). For liquids the viscosity decreases as the temperature rises, but for gases the viscosity increases as the temperature rises. Therefore, Curve B, Fig. 87, for the heating of a liquid, applies also to the cooling of a gas and Curve C, to the cooling of a liquid and the heating of a gas. However, since, in general, the rate of change of viscosity with temperature is much less for a gas than for a liquid, it is expected that the effect of heat transmission on velocity distribution in laminar flow probably would be correspondingly less for a gas than for a liquid.

Since in the presence of heat transmission the velocity distribution of isothermal laminar motion is distorted, the term *modified laminar motion* is sometimes used to describe the nonisothermal type of streamline flow. Data are not available to demonstrate the diagram presented, but the qualitative conclusions seem inescapable. Consequently theoretical equations, which ignore the distortion of the parabola, would be expected to apply only when the temperature differences are small, or for fluids whose physical properties varied but little with temperature. The mathematical theory is outlined briefly below.

Theory.—One of the earliest applications of the equation for unsteady-state conduction was given in 1885 by Graetz[256]* for the heating or cooling (without change in phase) of a fluid flowing at constant mass rate in undistorted laminar motion *inside* a pipe having a heated (or cooled) length L.

The fluid of specific heat c_p and thermal conductivity k enters at t_1. The temperature of the inner surface of the heated length is assumed uniform at t_s.

* See also Nusselt,[521,522] Grober,[272] and Leveque.[431] An excellent digest of the literature on the mathematics of conduction in moving fluids is given by Drew.[184]

The flow is assumed laminar in character, so that the distribution of local mass velocity over any cross section is parabolic, with zero velocity at the wall and a maximum velocity at the center line; see Curve A of Fig. 87, page 186. This is the only way that viscosity is assumed to enter the problem. Heat is assumed to be transferred by radial conduction only; the thermal conductivity of the fluid is assumed uniform. With these assumptions, Graetz integrated the Fourier-Poisson equation[566] for radial conduction in a moving fluid and obtained the relation

$$\frac{t_2 - t_1}{t_s - t_1} = 1 - 8\phi(n_1) \tag{13}$$

In Eq. 13, $\phi(n_1)$ represents the convergent infinite series

$$\phi(n_1) = 0.10238e^{-14.6272n_1} + 0.01220e^{-89.22n_1} + 0.00237e^{-212n_1} + \cdots \tag{13a}*$$

n_1 represents the dimensionless term $\pi kL/4wc_p$. It is noted that a coefficient of heat transfer is not involved in Eq. 13.

From the definition of the individual average coefficient of heat transfer h_m and the usual heat balance, h_mD/k becomes

$$\frac{h_mD}{k} = \frac{1}{\pi}\left(\frac{wc_p}{kL}\right)\frac{(t_2 - t_1)}{(t_s - t)_m} \tag{14}$$

Hence equations of the type of Eq. 13 can be rearranged to involve h_m, and the average h may be based upon *any* type of mean temperature difference desired.† For design purposes the arithmetic mean of the terminal values

$$(t_s - t)_a = \frac{(t_s - t_1) + (t_s - t_2)}{2} \tag{15}$$

is convenient. Equations 13, 14, and 15 may be combined to give

$$\frac{h_aD}{k} = \frac{2}{\pi}\left(\frac{wc_p}{kL}\right)\left(\frac{1 - 8\phi(n_1)}{1 + 8\phi(n_1)}\right) \tag{16}$$

Curve AB of Fig. 88 represents the theoretical relation based on parabolic distribution of mass velocity and is plotted from Eq. 16 and extended above wc_p/kL of 400 by an equation of Léveque.[431] Inspection of Fig. 88 shows that, for values of wc_p/kL greater than 10, the the theoretical curve is closely approximated by the empirical equation[193]‡

$$\frac{h_aD}{k} = 1.75\left(\frac{wc_p}{kL}\right)^{1/3} = 1.62\left(\frac{4}{\pi}\frac{wc_p}{kL}\right)^{1/3} \tag{17}$$

* Drew[184] tabulates n_1 and $\phi(n_1)$.

† Norris and Streid[516] tabulate the theoretical values of hD/k vs. $4wc/\pi kL$, with h based on initial Δt, arithmetic mean Δt, and logarithmic mean Δt.

‡ In references 142 and 668 the constants of 1.75 and 1.62 were incorrectly given as 1.65 and 1.5.

For the special limiting case where the fluid is heated nearly to the constant temperature of the wall, $t_2 = t_s$, it is clear that $(t_s - t)_m = (t_s - t_1)/2 = (t_2 - t_1)/2$, and from the definition of $h_a D/k$, one obtains

$$\frac{h_a D}{k} = \frac{2Wc_p}{\pi k L} \tag{18}$$

which is the equation of the asymptote AE at the lower left-hand corner of Fig. 88. With constant surface temperature, it is clear that no reliably observed value of $h_a D/k$ could lie above this asymptote.*

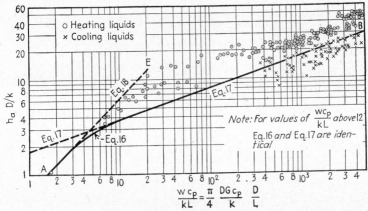

Fig. 88.—Poor correlation is due to omission of a term to allow for effect of radial variation in viscosity.

Viscous Liquids.—Experimental data for heating oils and glycerine, flowing in horizontal or vertical pipes, run considerably above Eq. 17, and most of the data for cooling run below (Fig. 88). As outlined previously, Eq. 17 takes no account of disturbance due to variation of physical properties with temperature and the consequent natural convection effects. For runs wherein DG/μ is less than 2100, Sieder and Tate[668] have correlated the available data† for heating and cooling viscous liquids by plotting $y = [(h_a D/k) \div$

---

* Papers by Blackett, Henry, and Rideal[64] and by Henry[300] describe a method for the experimental determination of the specific heat of gases. The gas is passed through an electrically heated tube at very low velocities, as in the zone AE of Fig. 88. Under these conditions the thermal conductivity of the gas is not involved, and the specific heat of the gas is deduced from the measured temperature gradient in the heated wall.

† References 127, 192, 373, 395, 409, 662, 185, 676, 668.

$(4wc_p/\pi kL)^{1/3}]$ *vs.* the dimensionless ratio μ/μ_s, where μ is the viscosity at the average bulk temperature and μ_s is the viscosity at the average temperature of the inside surface of the tube (Fig. 89). The equation of the straight line through the points* is $y = 1.86$ $(\mu/\mu_s)^{0.14}$, and hence

$$\frac{h_a D}{k}\left(\frac{\mu_s}{\mu}\right)^{0.14} = 1.86\left(\frac{4wc_p}{\pi kL}\right)^{1/3} = 1.86\left[\left(\frac{DG}{\mu}\right)\left(\frac{c_p\mu}{k}\right)\left(\frac{D}{L}\right)\right]^{1/3} \quad (19)$$

is the **recommended equation** for heating or cooling viscous liquids flowing in streamline motion (DG/μ less than 2100) inside horizontal or vertical tubes. At values of $4wc_p/\pi kL$ below 13, the outlet

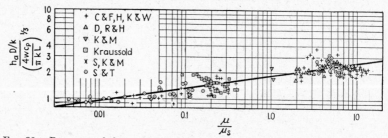

Fig. 89.—Recommended correlation[668] of data for heating and cooling liquids flowing in nonisothermal streamline motion inside tubes.

temperature closely approaches the constant temperature of the inner surface, and Eq. 18 applies. At a negligible value of Δt, $(\mu/\mu_s)^{0.14}$ approaches unity, and the constant (1.86) in Eq. 19 is 15 per cent higher than the constant of 1.62 in the theoretical equation. This discrepancy may be due to lack of attainment of the parabolic distribution of mass velocity, owing to inadequate length of calming section† and to errors in the values of k. By eliminating $h_a D/k$ from Eqs. 19, 14 and 15, the design equation is obtained:

$$\left(\frac{wc_p}{kL}\right)^{2/3}\left(\frac{t_2 - t_1}{\Delta t_a}\right)\left(\frac{\mu_s}{\mu}\right)^{0.14} = 6.33 \quad (19a)$$

* Equation 19 is based on data for tubes having diameters ranging from 0.39 to 1.57 in. and heated lengths ranging from 3 to 11.6 ft; μ/μ_s ranged from 0.004 to 14.

† Even for isothermal streamline motion the parabolic distribution of fluid velocity is apparently not established, because of entrance effects, until the fluid passes through an adequate calming section. According to the theory advanced by Boussinesq,[78] the minimum ratio of length to diameter in the calming section, even with a rounded entrance to the pipe, is $L/D = 0.065$ (DG/μ).

Data[485] for heating asphalt at 307 to 395°F, flowing in stream-line motion inside a horizontal 1-in. steel tube, give values of h ranging from 30 to 55 at velocities ranging from 2 to 13 ft/sec.

Water and Gases.—In order to allow for the effects of natural convection for streamline flow of any fluid in tubes of various sizes, it is necessary to introduce the Grashof number:

$$Z = [(\beta \, \Delta t)(D^3 \rho_f^2 g / \mu_f^2)]$$

the significance of which is discussed on page 242. Colburn[142] has correlated the data for water,[148] air,[521] and petroleum oil[373] by the complex equation

$$\frac{h_a D}{k} = 1.62 \left[\left(\frac{\mu}{\mu_f}\right)^{\frac{1}{3}} (1 + 0.015 Z^{\frac{1}{3}}) \right] \left(\frac{4 w c_p}{\pi k L}\right)^{\frac{1}{3}} \qquad (20)*$$

Equation 19, for viscous liquids in tubes of ordinary size, is a special case of Eq. 20, since the Grashof number is small and the term $1.62 \ (\mu/\mu_f)^{\frac{1}{3}}(1 + 0.015 Z^{\frac{1}{3}})$ reduces to $1.86 \ (\mu/\mu_s)^{0.14}$ It is rarely necessary to use Eq. 20, since at the optimum velocity (page 365) liquids of low viscosity or gases would involve DG/μ above 2100, in which case Eq. 4c (page 168) would apply. In a recent paper Martinelli *et al.*[472a] find that the data of Watzinger and Johnson[746] for the cooling of water flowing downward in a vertical tube (L/D of 20) average 10 per cent above Eq. 20 and their own data for heating water flowing upward in a vertical tube (L/D of 126) averaged 20 per cent above Eq. 20. The data[472a] for heating petroleum oil flowing upward (L/D from 126 to 602) averaged 40 per cent above Eq. 20. By using a complex equation Martinelli *et al.* correlate their data, and those of reference 746, with a maximum deviation of ± 30 per cent, and an average deviation of ± 10 to 15 per cent.

Illustration 3.—It is desired to heat oil from 68 to 140°F while it is flowing through horizontal ⅝-in. o.d. steel tubes, No. 16 BWG (page 417), each 8 ft long, in a multipass preheater, jacketed by steam condensing at 220°F. It is agreed that each tube shall handle 600 lb/hr of oil.

Calculate the number of passes necessary.

Data and Notes.—The thermal conductivity of the oil may be assumed constant at 0.080, and the specific heat is constant at 0.50; however, the viscosity varies with temperature as shown below.

t, deg F..........	68	80	90	100	110	120	130	140	220
μ', centipoises.....	23	20	18	16.2	15	13.5	12	11	3.6

---

* In reference 142 the constant was accidentally given as 1.5 instead of the proper value of 1.62, based on the theory.

Solution.—The largest value of DG/μ will correspond to the highest bulk temperature, 140°F, where $\mu = 2.42(11) = 26.6 \, \text{lb}/(\text{hr})(\text{ft})$; since $D = 0.495/12 = 0.0412$ ft, $DG/\mu = 4w/\pi D\mu = 4(600)/(3.14)(0.0412)(26.6) = 694$; since DG/μ is less than 2100, Eq. 19 applies to all passes. The dimensionless term $4wc/\pi kL$ is $4(600)(0.5)/\pi(0.08)(8) = 597$, which is larger than the asymptotic value, below which Eq. 19 does not apply.

Equation 19 must be applied to each pass in turn. If the oil leaves the first pass at 88°F, $t_a = (68 + 88)/2 = 78$, μ' is 20.5 centipoises. If t_s is 215°F, a little colder than the outer surface at 220°F, μ'_s is 4.25 centipoises, and $(\mu'/\mu'_s)^{0.14}$ is 1.25. From Eq. 19

$$h = \frac{1.86k}{D}\left(\frac{\mu}{\mu_s}\right)^{0.14}\left(\frac{4wc}{\pi kL}\right)^{\frac{1}{3}} = \frac{1.86(0.08)(1.25)(597)^{\frac{1}{3}}}{(0.0412)} = 38.$$

$$\Delta t_a = (t_s - t)_a = 215 - 78 = 137°F$$

and hence

$$t_2 - t_1 = \frac{h_a A_i (\Delta t)_a}{wc}$$

$t_2 - t_1 = (38)(\pi \times 0.0412 \times 8)(137)/(600)(0.5) = 18°F$, which is sufficiently close to the assumed value.

The resistance of the steam side and scale deposit, based on h of 1000, equals $1/(1000)(10 \times \pi \times 0.625/12) = 0.00061$, and that of the tube wall is $(0.065/12)/(26)(10 \times \pi \times 0.56/12) = 0.00014$, giving a total resistance, excluding that on the oil side, of 0.00075; hence $220 - t_s = q\Sigma R = (600 \times 0.5 \times 18)(0.00075) = 4.1°F$ *vs.* 5° assumed. The oil enters the second pass at 86°F and leaves at a new value of t_2, which is calculated as shown above. The procedure is repeated until the outlet temperature from the last pass equals or exceeds 140°F.

III. TRANSITION REGION

At DG/μ below 2100, hD/k is directly proportional to the cube root of DG/μ and inversely proportional to the cube root of L/D, whereas at DG/μ greater than 10,000, hD/k is directly proportional to the eight-tenths power of DG/μ and is independent of L/D. Hence in the transition range (DG/μ of 2100 to *ca.* 10,000) hD/k will depend on DG/μ and L/D to varying degrees, depending on the magnitude of DG/μ.

For the viscous liquids, Eq. 19 applies at DG/μ below 2100 and Eq. 4e, at DG/μ above 10,000. For L/D of 182, Fig. 90 shows straight lines AB and CD, based on these two equations: $Y' = 0.328(DG/\mu)^{\frac{1}{3}}$, and $Y' = 0.027(DG/\mu)^{0.8}$. At DG/μ of 2100, the equation for streamline flow has an ordinate of 4.2; the equation for turbulent flow, if extrapolated to DG/μ of 2100, would call for 12.3. Hence, as DG/μ increases beyond 2100, the curve must rise rapidly in order to reach the line CD. In fact, in this range, the exponent $n(h = a_3 G^n)$ can exceed unity, which means that h increases faster than G increases. Hence, in an oil heater of moderate length, an increase in oil-feed rate may be accompanied by an *increase*

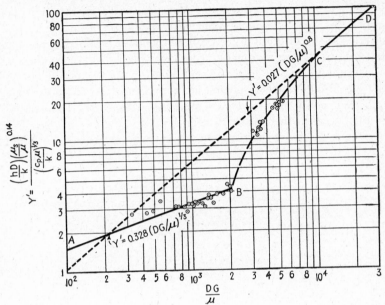

FIG. 90.—Data[662] for oils flowing inside tubes; *BC* is transition or "dip" region.

TABLE VIII.—HEATING AND COOLING HYDROCARBON OILS INSIDE STRAIGHT TUBES[a]

References	D', inches	L/D	L'/D	Tube metal	Tube (horizontal or vertical)	Liquid (heated or cooled)	Notes
312, 761, 127	0.494	119–100	50–109	Copper	H	H and C	1, 2
490	0.620	196	20	Steel	H	H and C	2
373	0.494	110–105	100	Copper	H	H and C	1, 2
662	0.593	235–61	0	Copper	H	H	3, 4
663	0.494	95	110	Copper	H	H	1, 4
409	1.58–0.394	305–76	......	Brass	V	C	
676	0.822	149	50	Copper	H	H and C	
668	0.620	99	39	Copper	H	H and C	
723	0.745	188	0	Nickel	V	H	

NOTE 1.—Heat balances checked within 10 per cent.

NOTE 2.—Tube cleaned frequently by a rag.

NOTE 3.—Heat balances checked within 10 per cent in over half the runs.

NOTE 4.—Tube cleaned frequently by a stiff brush; reported U only.

[a] Over-all coefficients from condensing steam to diphenyl oxide have been determined[258] for DG/μ ranging from 900 to 12,000.

in temperature rise for given inlet and surface temperatures. However, when DG/μ becomes sufficiently large, n becomes 0.8, and, as a result, an increase in feed rate is then accompanied by a small but definite *decrease* in temperature rise.

Figure 90 shows experimental points[662] for a petroleum oil flowing through a steam-heated horizontal tube having L/D of 182, and such points are used in empirically determining the location of the curves in the transition region.

Figure 91 shows the recommended curves for heating or cooling various liquids, based on the data described in Tables VIII and IX.*

TABLE IX.—HEATING AND COOLING HYDROCARBON OILS INSIDE STRAIGHT TUBES

References	Name of oil	Viscosity centipoises			Density, lb/cu ft		Molecular weight, ref. 228	Measured[675] k		Notes
		68°F	140°F	212°F	60°F	212°F		86°F	212°F	
312, 761, 127	Velocite B	73.0	11.0	4.2	55.9	52.7	333	0.0825	0.0800	
490	Gas oil	4.0	2.0	1.5	52.5					1
490	Straw oil	23.0	5.3	2.5	54.8					1
490	Light motor	100	15.0	5.0	57.2					1
373	Spindle	24.5	5.7	2.37	54.2	50.8	303	0.0825	0.0805	
373	Red oil	......	44.0	9.9	57.8	54.6	418	0.0815	0.0796	
662	Light HT oil	60.0	9.5	3.2	57.5		284	0.0765	0.0748	
663	Kerosene	1.58	0.82							2
409	Machine oil	......	29.0	5.5	57.9					3
409	Transformer oil	......	6.7	3.4	54.4					4
676	Petroleum oil	39.5	7.0	2.62	56.6	53.2		0.0784	0.0765	5
668	A, 16° API									6
668	C, 21° API									6
668	B, 24.5° API									6
723	Petroleum oil	2300	160	30	57.3	54.1				7

NOTE 1.—k was taken as 0.078.

NOTE 2.—Reference 663 used $k = 0.0875$, $\rho = 50.1$, $c = 0.502$ (see also page 181).

NOTE 3.—Reference 409 used $k = 0.0861 - 0.00028 \times$ degrees Fahrenheit.

NOTE 4.—Reference 409 used $k = 0.0821 - 0.00028 \times$ degrees Fahrenheit.

NOTE 5.—$c = 0.394 + 0.00054 \times$ degrees Fahrenheit; k from reference 159.

NOTE 6.—c was taken from reference 230; k from reference 159.

$$k = \frac{(0.0677)[1 - 0.0003\,(t - 32)]}{\rho'_{60°F}}$$

NOTE 7.—c was taken from reference 230; k was taken at the exceptionally low value of 0.0178 ± 0.0005.

* Additional data for oils, for Reynolds numbers ranging from 5000 to 30,000, are given in the form of curves by Buhne.[95] Similar data for water are given by Watzinger and Johnson.[746]

It is noted that good agreement is found among the data of White, Clapp and FitzSimons, and Keevil (Fig. 91). The data of Morris and Whitman and of Petrie are somewhat higher, whereas the data of Kiley and Mangsen are lower. The effect of the length-diameter ratio L/D is small for oils, at DG/μ of 2100 to 3000, as shown by the data of Kiley and Mangsen.

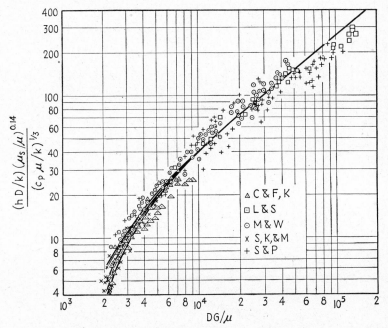

Fig. 91.—Data for heating and cooling petroleum fractions or water (L & S) flowing in turbulent motion inside tubes; for DG/μ exceeding 10,000, the curve is based on Eq. 4e (page 168). In the transition region ($2100 < DG/\mu < 10,000$) the points depend on L/D, because of the proximity to the region of streamline flow. This effect is shown in Fig. 92.

Data[723] for the heating of petroleum oil flowing at DG/μ from 4600 to 42000 (4.2 to 7.8 ft/sec) inside vertical nickel tubes 11.7 ft long, 0.745-in. inside diameter show h ranging from 68 at 350°F to 173 at 530°F. Taking k as 0.08, the coefficients run 60 per cent below those predicted from Eq. 4c. Data[723] are also reported for linseed oil.

Figure 91 also shows several sets of data for cooling. The data of a given observer, for both heating and cooling, are well correlated by this method of plotting, especially those of Morris and

Whitman. For hydrocarbons at a given DG/μ the deviation in hD/k does not exceed ± 30 per cent.

Where temperatures of 300 to 1000°F are desired, one may use a molten salt mixture (40 per cent $NaNO_2$, 7 per cent $NaNO_3$, and 53 per cent KNO_3 by weight). Physical properties (c, μ, and ρ) are available.[399] Values of h, for flow inside a 6-ft length of standard ⅜-in. iron pipe, range from 133 to 2660 as V' varied from 0.8 to 6 ft/sec; bulk temperatures ranged from 580 to 960°F.

The height of the chart shown in Fig. 91 can be reduced by dividing the ordinates by $DGc_p/\mu c_p$, giving a new ordinate

$$j' = \left(\frac{hD}{k}\right)\left(\frac{\mu_s}{\mu}\right)^{0.14}\left(\frac{k}{c_p\mu}\right)^{\frac{1}{3}}\left(\frac{\mu c_p}{DGc_p}\right) = \left(\frac{h}{c_p G}\right)\left(\frac{c_p\mu}{k}\right)^{\frac{2}{3}}\left(\frac{\mu_s}{\mu}\right)^{0.14} \quad (21)$$

Thus, for streamline flow, Eq. 19 could be written

$$j' = 1.86\left(\frac{D}{L}\right)^{\frac{1}{3}}\left(\frac{DG}{\mu}\right)^{-\frac{2}{3}} \quad (21a)$$

and for turbulent flow, Eq. 4e would become

$$j' = 0.027(DG/\mu)^{-0.2} \quad (21b)$$

The corresponding plot of j' vs. DG/μ is shown in Fig. 92.

With liquids of low viscosity and with compressed gases, natural-convection effects further complicate the situation, with

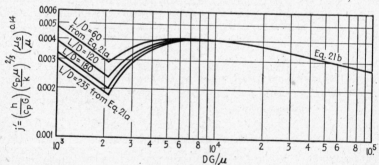

Fig. 92.—Recommended curves for warming or cooling liquids flowing (without phase change) inside tubes.

the result that the coefficients of heat transfer are higher than shown in Figs. 89 to 92. The tentative procedure[142] involves interpolation between the results of Eqs. 4d and 20, by connecting curves characterized by values of μ/μ_f. Figure 92 is a special case, for viscous liquids, of the general procedure.

Low Values of Prandtl Number.—In dealing with a very small value of $c_p\mu/k$ such as that for liquid mercury (0.026), it is recommended that $(c_p\mu/k)^{2/3}$ of Eq. 7 be changed[141] to $[0.05 + (c_p\mu/k)^{2/3}]$. This change does not affect the agreement between Eq. 7 and experimental data except at very low Prandtl numbers, in which case the modified form seems better for extrapolation and fits data for H_2 slightly better than Eq. 7. For mercury, the Grashof number would be quite high, because of exceptionally small values of μ/ρ, and consequently the effect of natural convection, in increasing h, would not fade out until a Reynolds number of approximately 20,000 was reached; in such cases it is important to follow the procedure outlined on page 196.

Scale Deposits.—Certain crudes and residual stocks may foul the tubes, thus reducing the over-all coefficient of heat transfer; scale deposit coefficients are given in Chap. VI. Figure 60, page 140 shows a photograph of a cokelike deposit on the tubes of a heat exchanger in an oil-cracking plant. When the primary heating coils in such plants are operated at high rates of heat transfer, a deposit is quite likely to be found in the tubes at the end of a long run, and this is usually removed by a mechanical cleaner. However, the over-all coefficient from gas to oil is not reduced unduly, because of the high thermal resistances on the gas side. With certain hydrocarbon oils, at low temperatures the deposit of a waxlike layer on the cooling surface will give a lower heat-transfer coefficient than predicted for a clean surface.

IV. MISCELLANEOUS SHAPES

Rectangular Cross Sections.—Table X summarizes the conditions used by several observers who heated or cooled fluids flowing in horizontal ducts of copper or brass. For turbulent flow, Fig. 93 shows $y = h_m D_e/k \div (c_p\mu/k)^{0.4}$ plotted *vs.* $D_e G/\mu$ with D_e taken as four times the hydraulic radius r_h.

$$D_e = 4r_h = \frac{4S}{b} = \frac{4(D_1 D_2)}{2D_1 + 2D_2} = \frac{2D_1 D_2}{D_1 + D_2} \qquad (22)$$

Line AA represents Eq. 4c (page 168) with D_e replacing D. The extensive data of Cope[37] for heating and cooling water in sections with aspect ratios ranging from 1 to 7.9 and for his circular pipe are well correlated by the use of D_e. A mean line through the data has a slope slightly more than 0.8 and is some 20 per cent below Eq. 4c at the lower values of $D_e G/\mu$. The temperature differences were small (5 to 10°F), and the results for heating agreed with those for cooling. The heat-transfer data for the artificially roughened tube agreed with those for the smooth tubes, but the friction factors were as much as 20 per cent higher.

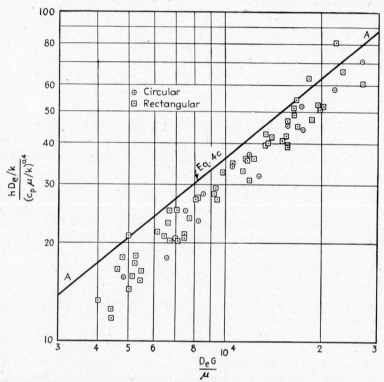

Fig. 93.—Data of Cope[37] for heating and cooling of water flowing inside rectangular and circular ducts.

The data of Washington and Marks[745] for heating air in ducts with aspect ratios ranging from 8.9 to 40.0 are correlated by D_e when $D_e G/\mu$ exceeds 15,000. At values of $D_e G/\mu$ less than 15,000, the data for the widest duct check Eq. 4c, but those for the narrower ducts lie substantially below Eq. 4c.

The friction factors of reference 37 ran from 5 to 30 per cent higher than expected; those of reference 745 agreed with the expected values within ± 20 per cent.

The data for $D_e G/\mu$ below 3500 are plotted in Fig. 94, with $h_a D_e/k$ vs. $4wc_p/\pi kL = D_e^2 Gc_p/kL$.

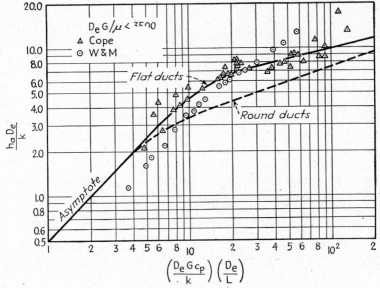

Fig. 94.—Data for flow of air or water at D_eG/μ below 3500, in rectangular or circular ducts. The curves are based on heat transfer by radial conduction only, with undistorted streamline flow.

TABLE X.—FLOW IN RECTANGULAR AND CIRCULAR SECTIONS

Reference	Fluid	N', feet	Width, inches	Height, inches	Aspect ratio	D_e, feet	L/D_e
37	Water	3	0.126	0.995	7.9	0.0187	322
	Water	3	0.248	0.873	3.52	0.0322	187
	Water	3	0.354	0.748	2.12	0.0400	150
	Water	3	0.551	0.551	1.00	0.046	130
	Water	3	0.674[a]	.....	.....	0.056	107
	Water	3	1.00[b]	.....	.....	0.0833	72
	Water	3	1.00[b]	.....	.....	0.0833	72
745	Air	0	0.125	5.00	40.0	0.0203	197
		0	0.250	5.00	20.0	0.0397	101
		0	0.562	5.00	8.9	0.0842	47.5
516	Air	c	0.311	2.00	6.44	0.045	11.1
516	Air		0.250	3.00	.....	......	50
			......	3.00	.....	......	26
			0.0156	3.00	.....	......	8.7

[a] Circular cross section.

[b] The inside walls of all ducts and tubes were smooth except for this circular tube, which had been grooved to a depth of 0.01 in by a Whitworth thread tool that cut one complete spiral per inch of length; there were 20 right-handed and 20 left-handed such grooves per inch of length.

[c] The length of the calming section was not given, but "well-rounded approaches" were used.

The data of any one observer are again well correlated by the use of D_e. The solid curve is the theoretical relation of Nusselt for streamline flow between broad parallel plates[516] obtained similarly to the curve for round ducts (shown by the dashed line) and discussed on page 188. The data of Cope for water lie closer to the theoretical curve than those of Washington and Marks for air.

Annular Spaces.—The usual procedure involves substituting an equivalent diameter D_e, equal to four times the hydraulic radius, in the heat-transfer equation for fluids flowing inside pipes. However, there are two methods of evaluating the hydraulic radius. If heat flows through only one of the two wetted surfaces, the hydraulic radius based on the perimeter of the surface through which heat flows is given by either

$$D'_e = 4r_h = \frac{(\pi)(D_2^2 - D_1^2)}{\pi D_1} = \frac{(D_2^2 - D_1^2)}{D_1} \tag{23}$$

or

$$D'_e = 4r_h = \frac{(\pi)(D_2^2 - D_1^2)}{\pi D_2} = \frac{(D_2^2 - D_1^2)}{D_2} \tag{23a}$$

which is the conservative procedure recommended by Nusselt.[523,526] A second procedure involves evaluation of the hydraulic radius from the total wetted surface, as is customary in calculation of fluid friction:

$$D_e = 4r_h = \frac{(\pi)(D_2^2 - D_1^2)}{\pi(D_2 + D_1)} = (D_2 - D_1) \tag{24}$$

It is clear that the first procedure gives a larger equivalent diameter than the second. Since for turbulent flow of fluid inside pipes, h is usually taken as inversely proportional to the 0.2 power of diameter, the Nusselt procedure will predict smaller values of h than those based on total wetted surface; Eq. 24 is recommended. Where heat is flowing through both surfaces, these two methods lead to the same result, that of Eq. 24.

Consider the flow of hot air through an annular space between concentric pipes, with cooling water inside the smaller pipe and insulation outside the larger pipe. Heat will be transferred by convection to both the smaller and larger pipes. The heat received by the larger pipe will in part be lost through the insulation, and the remainder will be radiated to the smaller pipe. The latter may be substantial compared to that received directly by convection, as shown in the following example.

Illustration 4.—Assume that the air is at 520°F, the outer surface of the smaller pipe is at 100°F and the value of h from gas to metal is 5 Btu/(hr) (sq ft)(deg F). For illustration, assume that the i.d. of the larger pipe is 2.07 in. and that the o.d. of the smaller is 1.66 in. Calculate the heat radiated to the smaller pipe expressed as a per cent of that received directly by convection, neglecting heat losses through the insulation. To simplify the problem, it is agreed to ignore the effects of axial gradients in temperature.

Solution.—The area ratio A_2/A_1 is $2.07/1.66 = 1.246$. The rate of heat transfer by convection q_{c2} from gas to the larger pipe having absolute temperature T_2 is

$$q_{c2} = hA_2(T_g - T_2) = 5(1.246A_1)(980 - T_2) = \text{Btu/hr}$$

The heat radiated from A_2 to A_1 is given by Eq. 14, page 59,

$$q_r = 0.173\mathfrak{F}_E \left[\left(\frac{T_2}{100} \right)^4 - \left(\frac{T_1}{100} \right)^4 \right]$$

Assuming that the emissivities are 0.9,

$$q_r = \frac{0.173A_1[(T_2/100)^4 - (560/100)^4]}{\dfrac{1}{0.9} + \left(\dfrac{1}{1.246} \right) \left(\dfrac{1}{0.9} - 1 \right)} = \text{Btu/hr}$$

By a heat balance on the larger surface, $q_{c2} = q_r$, whence $T_2 = 871$°F abs, $t_2 = 411$°F, and $q_{c2} = q_r = 686 \times A_1$ Btu/hr. The heat transferred directly by convection from gas to the smaller pipe is

$$q_{c1} = hA_1(T_g - T_1) = 5(A_1)(980 - 560) = 2100 \times A_1 \text{ Btu/hr}$$

Hence

$$q_{c2}/q_{c1} = q_r/q_{c1} = 686/2100 = 0.327$$

The total heat received by the smaller pipe by radiation is then 32.7 per cent of that transferred directly by convection. If allowance be made for heat loss through the insulation ($k = 0.04$) having i.d. and o.d. of 6.37 and 2.37 in., respectively, and an outer surface temperature of 105°F, $t_2 = 401$°F, $q_r = 640$ and the ratio q_r/q_{c1} is 0.304 instead of 0.327.

Heat-transfer data for the cooling of air both in pipes and in annular spaces between concentric pipes are given by Jordan.[356]

Liquids in Annular Spaces.—One type of heat exchanger having considerable use in the refrigerating industry for low-temperature work is the double-pipe exchanger. In this type there are two concentric pipes with one fluid flowing inside the smaller pipe and the other in the annular space.

Monrad and Pelton[484a] have obtained coefficients for water or air flowing in annular spaces between concentric tubes, with Reynolds numbers ranging from 12,000 to 220,000, for values of D_2/D_1 of 1.65, 2.45 and 17. The coefficient h_1, from the inner tube to the fluid in the annulus, could be correlated by an equation similar to Eqs. 4c or 4d, giving

$$\left(\frac{h_1}{c_p G}\right)\left(\frac{c_p \mu}{k}\right)^{2/3} = \frac{0.020\,(D_2/D_1)^{0.53}}{(D_e G/\mu)^{0.2}} \tag{25}$$

in which D_e is based on Eq. 24. The coefficients h_2, from the outer tube to the fluid in an annulus in which D_2/D_1 was 1.85, agreed satisfactorily with those predicted from Eqs. 4c and 4d, with D replaced by D_e defined by Eq. 24.

Using a modification of the graphical method of interpreting $1/U$ from steam condensing inside tubes to water flowing in turbulent motion through 10 horizontal annuli having values of D_e ranging from 0.0145 to 0.0995 ft, it was found[233] that the coefficients h_m for the annuli were correlated by the dimensionless equation

$$\frac{h D_e}{k} = 0.032 \frac{D_2}{D_1}\left(\frac{D_e G}{\mu}\right)^{0.8}\left(\frac{c_p \mu}{k}\right)^{0.4} \tag{25a}$$

wherein D_e is defined by Eq. 24.* Equation 4c is preferred.

Streamline flow in annuli is treated in reference 349.

Heinrich and Stückle[298] give over-all coefficients for oil flowing in a vertical double-pipe exchanger and on oil flowing through the shell of a tube-and-shell exchanger without baffles. In these cases, the oil flows strictly parallel to the tubes. Over-all coefficients on experimental tube-and-shell heat exchangers are available.[666,667]

Gravity Flow of Liquid in Layer Form.—In heating or cooling water flowing downward inside vertical tubes, the economical water rate may be such that the tube will not be filled and a layer of water will flow down the vertical wall. By using upward flow, the water will fill the tube. It is interesting to predict which type of flow would give the larger coefficient for a given water rate, tube diameter, and temperature. Equation 4c will be used for both cases, with D replaced by D_e, equal to four times the hydraulic radius r_h, where r_h is the cross section S filled by the fluid, divided by the perimeter b wetted by the fluid. Since by definition

$$\frac{D_e G}{\mu} = \frac{4 r_h G}{\mu} = \frac{4}{\mu}\frac{S}{b}\frac{w}{S} = \frac{4w}{\mu b} = \frac{4\Gamma}{\mu} \tag{26}$$

it is seen that S disappears, and hence $D_e G/\mu$ will be the same whether the fluid partially or completely fills the tube. Since the physical properties are the same, h should vary inversely as D_e for each type of flow. For flow of a layer of thickness B, S equals

---

* The same data could also be correlated by using D_e' of Eq. 23, if the constant in Eq. 25 be increased to 0.04.

$\pi(D - B)(B)$, b equals πD, and D_e equals $4S/b$ equals $4B(D - B)/D$; for the full tube, D_e equals D.

Hence

$$\frac{h \text{ for layer flow}}{h \text{ for the full tube}} = \frac{D^2}{4B(D - B)} \tag{27}$$

Since layer flow inside a tube can be obtained only under conditions in which B is less than $D/2$, it can be seen from Eq. 27 that h for layer flow should exceed that for the full tube.

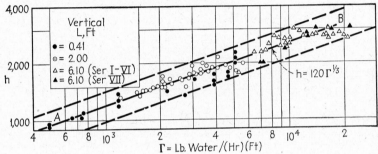

Fig. 95.—Coefficients[456] for gravity flow of water in layer form inside vertical tubes.

The extensive data of Bays[53] and coworkers for heating water flowing in layer form down the inside walls of vertical tubes* having inside diameters of 1.5 and 2.5 in. and heights ranging from 0.407 to 6.08 ft are plotted in Fig. 95 and are correlated within ±18 per cent by the dimensional equation[456]

$$h_m = 120\Gamma^{1/3} = 120\left(\frac{w}{\pi D_i}\right)^{1/3} \tag{28}$$

Figure 96 shows the over-all coefficients U from steam to water, and the vertical falling-film heater (Curve AB) gives over-all coefficients 2.2 times those for the same pipe (Curve EF) running full with upward flow of water. Curve CD shows data for a falling-film heater 0.41 ft high, having an inside diameter of 0.125 ft.

Although data for other liquids are not available, the following dimensionless equation[188] may be used for estimating h:

$$\frac{h}{\sqrt[3]{k^3\rho^2g/\mu_f^2}} = 0.01\left(\frac{c\mu}{k}\right)^{1/3}\left(\frac{4\Gamma}{\mu_f}\right)^{1/3} \tag{29}$$

This equation reduces to Eq. 28 at a film temperature of approximately 190°F.

* To minimize disturbances a rounded inlet was used.

Using the same apparatus described above, heating data were obtained [55] for two petroleum oils flowing in layer form down the

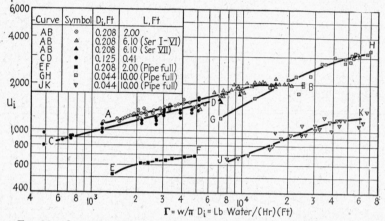

Fig. 96.—Over-all coefficients[456] from steam to water for three vertical falling-film heaters, compared with data for two vertical tubes, running full. The vertical falling-film heater *AB* gives over-all coefficients 2.2 times those *EF* for the same pipe running full; dropwise condensation on chrome plate, promoted with oleic acid, was used in both cases. For the 10-ft length of standard ⅝-in. copper pipe running full (reference 226), the use of dropwise condensation on chrome plate, promoted with oleic acid *GH* gave over-all coefficients over twice those obtained *JK* without the promoter. For curves *GH* and *JK*, a value of Γ of 10,000 corresponds to a velocity of 4.06 ft per sec.

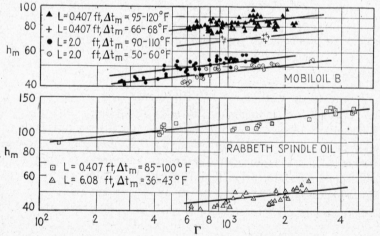

Fig. 97.—Data[55] for gravity flow of oils in layer form in streamline motion in vertical tubes.

inner walls of vertical tubes. Figure 97 shows the data for stream-line flow, $4\Gamma/\mu$ less than 2000. It was found that h_a varied directly as $\Gamma^{1/6}$ and inversely as $L^{1/3}$. The data may be correlated by the dimensionless equation

$$\frac{h_a}{\sqrt[3]{k^3 \rho^2 g / \mu_f^2}} = 0.67 \left(\frac{c\mu_f^{5/3}}{kL\rho^{2/3}g^{1/3}}\right)^{1/3} \left(\frac{4\Gamma}{\mu_f}\right)^{1/9} \tag{30}$$

which is of the form of the theoretical equation of Nusselt[528]* but involves a constant (0.67) 20 per cent lower.

In industrial work, various liquids are cooled while they flow through horizontal pipes by allowing a layer of water to trickle over the outer surfaces in the so-called "trickle" or "trombone" coolers. The published data[3,716] were obtained with slightly inclined pipes that caused ripples in the water film, and as a result h_a varied as $(\Gamma_H)^{1/3}$ instead of $(\Gamma_H)^{1/9}$. The symbol Γ_H represents $w/2L$, where w is the water rate over each straight tube of length L. For values of $4\Gamma_H/\mu$ less than 2100, the data are correlated within ± 25 per cent by the dimensional equation[456]

$$h_a = 65(\Gamma_H/D_o)^{1/3} \tag{31}†$$

The corresponding data are shown in Fig. 98. If the pipe diameter were very large or w were very small, the water would leave the bottom of the tube at substantially the temperature of the outer wall of the pipe. For this limiting case, the definition of h_a gives, for negligible evaporation,

$$h_a = \frac{(2\Gamma_H L)(c)(t_s - t_1)}{(\pi D_o L)\left(t_s - \dfrac{t_1 + t_s}{2}\right)} = \frac{4c}{\pi}\frac{\Gamma_H}{D_o} \tag{32}$$

which is the equation of the asymptote AB of Fig. 98. At low water rates the occurrence of points to the left of AB is due to evaporation.

Gas Flow Parallel to a Single Plane.—Both the heat-transfer coefficient and the friction factor should depend upon a Reynolds number $LV_\infty\rho_\infty/\mu$ based on the length L over which the gas flows. In fact, an analogy between heat transfer and friction gives the dimensionless equation[142]

$$\left(\frac{h_{m1}}{c_p V_\infty \rho_\infty}\right)\left(\frac{c_p\mu}{k}\right)^{2/3} = a\left(\frac{LV_\infty\rho_\infty}{\mu}\right)^{-n} \tag{33}$$

---

* This theoretical equation is applied to streamline flow between broad parallel plates on p. 199.

† For D_o of 0.159 ft, Eq. 31 is identical with Eq. 28 for turbulent flow of water down vertical surfaces.

where V_∞ and ρ_∞ are the linear velocity and density of the main stream measured at a substantial distance from the plane where

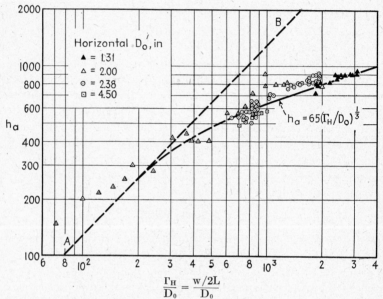

Fig. 98.—Coefficients for gravity flow of water in layer form over nearly horizontal pipes.

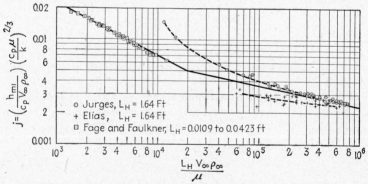

Fig. 99.—Data for gas flowing parallel to a single plane; solid curves are from Colburn; note that $h_{m1} = q/(A)(t_s - t_\infty)$.

velocity, density, and temperature are uniform; the average coefficient h_{m1} is based on $q/A = h_{m1}(t_s - t_\infty)$. The supporting data are shown[142] in Fig. 99.

The data of Jurges[361] for flow of air at room temperature parallel to a vertical copper plate 1.64 feet square may be represented by Eq. 34 and Table XI:

$$h_{m1} = a_4 + b_4(V')^n \tag{34}$$

TABLE XI.—FACTORS IN EQ. 34

Nature of surface	Velocity less than 16 ft/sec			Velocity between 16 and 100 ft/sec		
	a_4	b_4	n	a_4	b_4	n
Smooth.............	0.99	0.21	1.0	0	0.50	0.78
Rough..............	1.09	0.23	1.0	0	0.53	0.78

where h is expressed in Btu/(hr)(sq ft)(deg F), and V' is in feet per second. These tests of Jurges were made with air at room temperature and pressure.* Since mass velocity rather than linear velocity is the fundamental variable in forced-convection equations, Schack[627] recommends that V' of Eq. 34 be multiplied by $(460 + 70)/(460 + t)$ when the temperature t of the air differs materially from 70°F. For very low velocities the heat transfer is largely by natural convection, in which case the heat-transfer coefficient for natural convection should also be calculated from the procedure given on page 240 and the larger of the two values used.

Liquids Flowing over Plates.—The Stamsvik heat exchanger[688] involves heat transfer between plates and thin layers of liquids. For the flow of certain viscous oils, the apparatus is said to give higher values of h for a given pressure drop than a shell-and-tube exchanger. The various leaves of the apparatus are held together by pressure applied by a worm, as in a conventional filter press; upon dismantling the apparatus, it is easy to clean the heat-transfer surfaces.

Problems

1. A tubular air heater has been accurately designed to heat a given quantity of air per hour to 170°F. The air passes inside 120 tubes, arranged in parallel, with steam condensing on the outside. From Eq. 5b, it is calculated that the tubes should be 16 ft long.

Because of deviation of data from Eq. 5b, it is agreed to build the apparatus with a 20 per cent factor of safety so that it will be surely able to heat the given flow of air to 170°F. One engineer proposes to obtain this factor of safety by

* Experimental data are also given by Frank,[235] Haucke;[287] Nusselt;[527] Rowley, Algren, and Blackshaw;[609] Taylor and Rehbock;[712] and Wagener.[739]

using 20 per cent more tubes in parallel, 16 ft long. Another argues that a 20 per cent factor of safety should be obtained by making the tube diameters 20 per cent greater than the accurate design requires.

Discuss the advantages and disadvantages of the foregoing methods. How would you build the heater to have a 20 per cent factor of safety?

2. In a semiworks scale plant, it is desired to cool 6,000 lb/hr of straw oil from 240 to 80°F in a countercurrent standard 2- by 3-in. concentric pipe cooler. The cooling water will flow in the annular space between the two pipes and the oil through the central 2-in. pipe. It is proposed to use a water rate of 8,000 lb/hr entering the cooler at 70°F.

Calculate the number of 18.5-ft lengths of concentric pipe sections needed.

Data and Notes.—The oil has a specific heat of 0.50 Btu/(lb)(deg F). Its thermal conductivity may be taken as 0.08 Btu/(hr)(sq ft)(deg F per ft), independent of temperature. The following table gives the viscosity of the oil (in centipoises) as a function of temperature.

t, deg F..........	70	80	95	110	130	160	200	240
μ'..............	22	18	13.5	10.8	8.1	5.7	3.8	2.7

It is agreed to neglect heat losses.

3. An oil is flowing at constant mass rate through a horizontal cylindrical metal tube electrically heated for a length of 4 ft by passing direct current longitudinally through the tube. At the entrance to the heated length, the inside surface of the tube wall is at 150°F, and the oil is at 100°F; the corresponding temperatures at the exit from the heated section are 205°F and 200°F. Heat loss from the outer surface and longitudinal conduction of heat may be neglected. The fluid does not change phase on heating, and the specific heat may be considered constant, although the viscosity varies substantially with change in temperature. The electrical resistance of the tube is constant, and the coefficient of heat transfer from tube to fluid may be assumed to increase linearly with increase in temperature of the fluid.

a. Plot oil temperature *vs.* heated length, showing the correct shape of curve, and explain briefly but clearly what determines the shape.

b. Would it be possible for the inner surface of the tube wall at an intermediate cross section to have a temperature as low as 137°F? Explain.

4. The following data were obtained[385]* with an experimental heat exchanger that consisted of a horizontal steel tube 0.503 in. i.d. and 1.002 in. o.d., surrounded by a concentrically arranged steel tube 1.263 in. i.d., well insulated externally. 2400 lb/hr of high-pressure steam at an absolute pressure of 1643 lb/sq in and at 821°F entered the inner tube and left with an absolute pressure of 1523 lb/sq in and a temperature of 722°F; 953 lb/hr of low-pressure steam at an absolute pressure of 189 lb/sq in, at 424°F, entered the annular space and left at an absolute pressure of 122 lb/sq in with a temperature of 744°F. Values of the physical properties of the steam are given in the Appendix, page 397.

Predict the tube length theoretically required, and compare it with the observed length of 20 ft.

* These data were not published in reference 385 but were made available through the courtesy of H. J. Kerr.

5. It is desired to cool 14,000 lb./hr of a solution containing 80 per cent ethanol and 20 per cent water by weight from 172 to 104°F by counterflow of 1100 U.S. gal/hr of water at 68°, in an uninsulated concentric-pipe exchanger made of standard 2- and 3-in. steel pipe (page 416), with the water flowing inside the 2-in. pipe. The temperature of the surroundings will be 68°F.

How many standard lengths, each 18.5 ft long, must be connected in series?

6. It is proposed to superheat steam while it is flowing under pressure in alloy tubes ($k = 15$) having outside diameter of 2.00 in. and wall thicknesses of 0.25 in. The tubes are to be placed in that part of the furnace where the effective black-body temperature of the surroundings is 2040°F. In order to avoid frequent replacements of the tubes, it is specified that the maximum temperature on the outside walls of the tubes shall not exceed 1400°F.

At a cross section of the tubes where the steam has a bulk temperature of 540°F and c_p of 0.8, what must be the minimum steam rate expressed in pounds per hour per tube?

Notes.—It is agreed to neglect gas radiation between the inner wall and the steam, to employ Eq. 4k as an approximation, and to assume ϵ of 0.9.

CHAPTER VIII

HEATING AND COOLING FLUIDS OUTSIDE TUBES

Abstract.—The following chapter deals with the individual coefficients of heat transfer for warming or cooling of fluids flowing across tubes and certain miscellaneous shapes by both forced and natural convection. The first section illustrates the mechanism of heat transfer and fluid flow by a number of photographs. The second deals with the flow of liquids and gases across plain tubes, finned tubes, streamlined shapes, and spheres. The data for tube banks are correlated by dimensionless relations involving h_cD/k_f, $c_p\mu_f/k_f$, $D_oG_{\max}/\mu_f$, and dimension ratios. In contrast to flow inside tubes, there is no abrupt change in type of fluid motion, and corresponding change in heat transfer, at a critical value of the Reynolds number. Data for the flow of gas normal to a single cylinder are employed to illustrate the method of computing the true temperature of a gas from the apparent temperature indicated by a thermometer or thermocouple and from the temperature of the surrounding surfaces. The third section treats natural convection of heat from horizontal and vertical tubes, plates, and miscellaneous shapes. A general correlation involves the Nusselt, Grashof, and Prandtl numbers; use of these relations is facilitated by alignment charts. Simplified relations are also given, and tables of over-all coefficients for coils and jacketed vessels are included.

Data for heating and cooling gases flowing at $D_oG_{\max}/\mu_f$ from 0.1 to 250,000 are correlated with an average deviation of ± 20 per cent in Fig. 111; data for heating liquids (Fig. 113) cover a much smaller range of the Reynolds number but involve $c_p\mu_f/k$ from 6 to 1200 and show that, for a given $D_oG_{\max}/\mu_f$, hD/k is proportional to the 0.3 power of the Prandtl number. Data for heating gases by tube banks (Fig. 114) are available for $D_oG_{\max}/\mu_f$ from 2000 to 40,000, and the recommended general procedure is given in Fig. 115. Data for finned surfaces are correlated in Figs. 119 and 120, and those for spheres in Fig. 122. Heat-transfer data for natural convection from horizontal cylinders are correlated in Fig. 126 and are readily

210

evaluated from the alignment chart, Fig. 128; values of h_c for vertical planes are correlated in Fig. 129. Simplified equations for h_c are given in Eqs. 14–19, values of h_r are plotted in Fig. 27 of Chap.

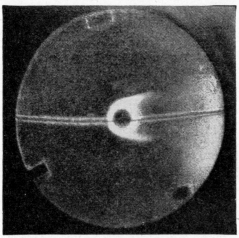

Fig. 100.—Photograph of air flowing horizontally at a velocity of 0.3 ft/sec at right angles to a heated cylinder. (*Photograph from Ray, Proc. Ind. Assoc. Cultivation Sci.*)

III, and the total heat transfer is evaluated by Eq. 13. Values of $h_c + h_r$ for horizontal oxidized steel tubes are shown in Table VIII, over-all coefficients for coils and jacketed vessels are summarized in Tables IX and X, and practice problems are given at the end of the chapter.

MECHANISM OF HEAT TRANS- FER AND FLUID FLOW

Figure 100 shows a photograph by Ray[579] taken with air flowing from left to right past a horizontal internally heated hot cylinder. Because of the change of refractive index with change in temperature, the heated air appears brighter than the cold air. Additional data for wires of

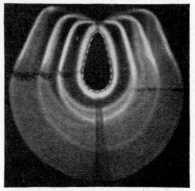

Fig. 101.—Schlieren photograph. (*Schmidt,*[636] *Forsch. Gebiete Ingenieurw.*)

several diameters are given by Praminik.[571]

Figure 101 shows shadow (*schlieren*) photographs of a heated streamline shape suspended in still air, using the technique described by Schmidt,[636] which involves the use of a screen and shows more detail than obtained with an ordinary shadow photograph taken without a screen (Fig. 102).

Kennard[378] describes a method for measuring temperature distribution around heated bodies exposed to colder air, which

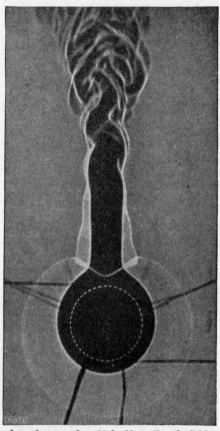

Fig. 102.—Shadow photograph. (*Schmidt*,[636] *Forsch. Gebiete Ingenieurw.*)

depends on the change of the index of refraction of air with change in temperature. By the use of a suitable interferometer, the interference fringes are measured, and from the resulting photographs it is possible to compute the temperature gradients without using any material thermometer.*

---

* A similar method has been described by Hansen,[279] Kennard,[377] and Ramdas and Paranzpe.[577]

Figure 103 shows a photograph of the fringes in front of a vertical plate, 29.4°C warmer than the ambient air. Figure 104 shows the corresponding temperature distribution calculated from the results,

FIG. 103.—Interference fringes due to natural convection from a heated plate to air. (*Photograph by Kennard.*[378]   *Courtesy of Reinhold, New York City.*)

and it is seen that the temperature field is similar to those (such as Fig. 123 page 238) obtained by other workers who made explorations with thermocouples. Temperature fields around a horizontal heated cylinder, based on the measurement of interference fringes,[375] are similar to those shown in Fig. 125, page 239.

Experiments made under isothermal conditions throw light upon the nature of the flow of fluid past cylindrical models. Figure 105, by Rubach,[613] shows conditions at an instant when the eddies in the rear of the cylinder were growing in size. Eventually these eddies become too large to be protected by the cylinder and are swept downstream. Similar photographs are shown in papers by Prandtl.[573] Reiher[583] and Lorisch[448] have published photographs of "smoke" in air currents flowing isothermally past models of various shapes. The models were

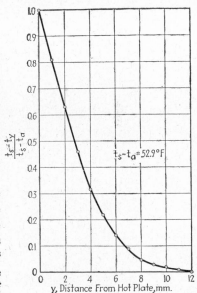

$\frac{t_s - t_y}{t_s - t_a}$

$t_s - t_a = 52.9°F$

y, Distance From Hot Plate, mm.

FIG. 104.—Temperature gradients calculated by Kennard,[378] from results shown in Fig. 103.

covered with filter paper wetted with aqueous hydrochloric acid, and the smoke was produced by interaction of ammonia vapor in the air stream with the acid vapor diffusing from the wetted surface. Hence the photographs show the flow con-

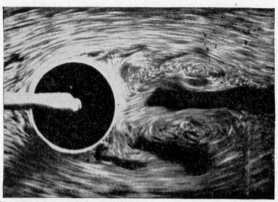

Fig. 105.—Isothermal flow of liquid normal to the axis of a cylinder. (*Photograph from Rubach,*[613] *Forschungsarb.*)

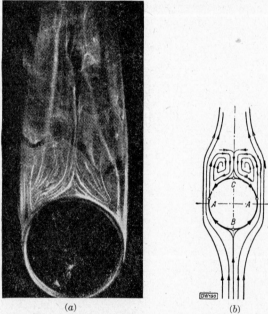

(*a*)   (*b*)

Fig. 106.—(*a*) Photograph of eddies at the rear of a cylinder by air flowing at a Reynolds number of approximately 2700. (*b*) Idealized drawing from the photograph. (*From Lorisch, Forschungsarb.*)

ditions of air that has been in close proximity to the model. Figure 106 shows the eddies in the rear of the cylinder.

Figures 107 and 108 show the flow of air, at a velocity of approximately 5 ft/sec, through a bank of tubes 0.67 in. diameter, "staggered" in Fig. 107 and "in-line" in Fig. 108. For the same air velocity, Reiher found that the staggered arrangement, similar to

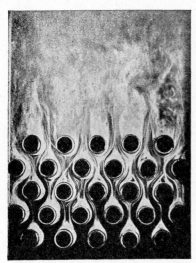

FIG. 107.—Air flowing normal to a bank of *staggered* pipes. (*Photograph from Lorisch, Handbuch der Experimental-Physik.*)

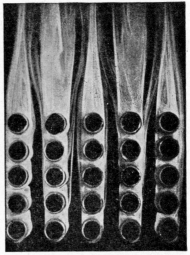

FIG. 108.—Air flowing normal to a bank of pipes in line. (*Photograph from Lorisch, Handbuch der Experimental-Physik.*)

Fig. 107, gave substantially higher coefficients of heat transfer than an arrangement similar to Fig. 108. Morris,[489] Dryden and Keuthe,[199] and Fage[215] have used hot-wire anemometers or Pitot

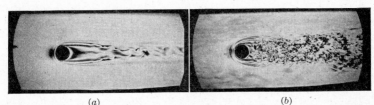

(a)   (b)

FIG. 109.—Shear patterns for isothermal flow of a dilute suspension of bentonite past a cylinder, photographed by Hauser and Dewey.[291]

tubes to explore the air velocity in the zone near an unheated cylinder and have found nonuniformities in velocity, as would be expected. Figure 109 shows photographs[291] of isothermal flow of water past a cylindrical model in a closed glass channel. The flow pattern is made visible by the addition of a small concentration of specially prepared colloidal bentonite and is photographed between crossed polarizing plates with transmitted light showing variation in the double refraction of this suspension with velocity gradient.[291]

From the foregoing discussion of the mechanism of heat transfer for gases flowing at right angles to tubes and of the nature of fluid flow over such surfaces, it can be inferred that the coefficient of heat transfer between fluid and pipe will not be uniform around the perimeter. Drew and Ryan[197] have reported measurements of the variation in local rate of heat flow at various positions around a vertical steam-heated pipe and have found results similar to those based on the work of Lorisch[448]* for absorption. The

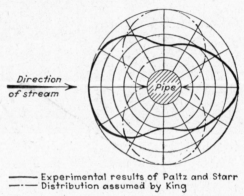

——— Experimental results of Paltz and Starr
—·— Distribution assumed by King

Fig. 110.—Distribution of heat flow per unit area around a cylinder, the fluid flowing normal to the axis. (*Drew and Ryan.*[197])

results of a run by Paltz and Starr[544] are shown plotted in Fig. 110, with local rates of heat flow plotted radially at various positions around a single steam-heated cylinder. The solid curve shows the actual distribution of the heat flux, and it is noted that the maximum local rate of heat flow occurred at the front and back, and the minimum rate, approximately 40 per cent of the maximum, was found at the sides.† The dotted curve of Fig. 110 indicates the distribution assumed by King[386] in obtaining his theoretical equation for heat transfer for a gas flowing at right angles to a tube. Although King's assumed curve is displaced 90 deg from the experimental curve, it has roughly the same shape, which may be

* See also Thoma[715] and Nusselt.[533]

† Similar results are given by Klein,[400] Fage and Falkner,[216] Small,[672] Krujilin and Schwab,[415] and Krujilin.[414]

why King's theoretical equation predicts results of the right order of magnitude for gases.[114]

For practical purposes it is advisable to deal with the average coefficient of heat transfer for a tube, or bank of tubes, rather than a local coefficient at a given point on the perimeter, and the following discussion applies to such average coefficients. The net rate of heat exchange (Σq) between a body and its surroundings is evaluated by adding the rates of heat flow due to convection and radiation

$$\Sigma q = q_c + q_r$$

Chapter III gives details of the evaluation of q_r due to radiation between solids and solids and radiation between solids and certain gases such as carbon dioxide, water vapor, sulphur dioxide, and ammonia. The present chapter deals largely with the evaluation of the rate of heat transfer due to the combined mechanisms of conduction and convection in fluids, ordinarily referred to as *convection*. However, the effects of simultaneous transfer by radiation and convection are treated in the present chapter on pages 245 and 247. At low velocities, the effect of natural convection may increase the heat transfer beyond what would be predicted from the equations for forced convection. Under such conditions the heat transfer should also be predicted from the equations for natural convection (pages 240 to 250), the higher of the two values being then employed.

Dimensionless Equations.—When the movement of the fluid past the surface is due to mechanical means, the convection is said to be forced. For such conditions it is shown that the data are satisfactorily correlated by means of the dimensionless equation of the Nusselt type

$$\frac{hD_o}{k_f} = \phi\left(\frac{D_o G}{\mu_f}, \frac{c_p \mu_f}{k_f}\right) \tag{1}$$

Expressed in terms of power functions, Eq. 1 becomes

$$\frac{hD_o}{k_f} = b_1 \left(\frac{D_o G}{\mu_f}\right)^n \left(\frac{c_p \mu_f}{k_f}\right)^m \tag{2}$$

It is recalled that Eq. 2 is similar to that used in Chap. VII for the correlation of the data on heat transmission for fluids flowing inside tubes.

TABLE I.—NOMENCLATURE

A Area of heat-transfer surface, square feet; A_m for mean area of conductor, A_o for outside surface, A_p for surface of pyrometer at t_p, A_s for surface at temperature t_s.

a Dimensional factor, equal to $(hb/kS)^{0.5}$, reciprocal feet.

B Thickness of effective film, feet.

b Breadth, perimeter of heat-transfer surface, feet.

b_1 Constant, to be determined experimentally.

c_p Specific heat of fluid at constant pressure, Btu/(lb)(deg F).

D_e Effective diameter (page 236), feet.

D_f Mean diameter of fictive film, feet.

D_o Outside diameter of cylinder, feet.

d Prefix, indicative derivative, dimensionless.

e Base of natural logarithms, 2.718.

G Mass velocity, of fluid, lb/(hr)(sq ft of cross section).

G_{max} Mass velocity based on minimum free cross section (either transverse to stream or on diagonal clearances, whichever is less), lb/(hr)(sq ft of cross section).

g Acceleration due to gravity, ordinarily taken as 4.17×10^8 ft/(hr)(hr).

h Surface coefficient of heat transfer, Btu/(hr)(sq ft)(deg F); h_c for natural convection; h_r for radiation.

k Thermal conductivity, (Btu)(ft)/(hr)(sq ft)(deg F); k_f for the fluid is evaluated at the film temperature $t_f = t_s - 0.5(t_s - t)_m$; k_w is k for the retaining wall.

L Height of vertical plate or cylinder, feet.

m, n Exponents, dimensionless.

N Number of rows over which fluid flows, dimensionless.

P Absolute pressure, atmospheres.

q Rate of heat flow, Btu per hour; q in general, q_c by natural convection, q_{gr} by gas radiation, q_k by conduction through solid, q_r by radiation between two surfaces.

r_h Hydraulic radius, feet.

s Spacing between centers of tubes, feet; s_L, longitudinal; s_T, transverse to stream.

S Cross section available for flow, square feet.

T Absolute temperature, degrees Fahrenheit absolute $= t + 460$.

t Thermometric temperature, degrees Fahrenheit; bulk temperature for a fluid; t_a for air; t_e for surface of enclosure; t_f for film temperature, $t_f = t_s - 0.5(t_s - t)_m$; t_g for gas (true temperature); t_p for pyrometer; t_s for surface.

U Over-all coefficient of heat transfer, Btu/(hr)(sq ft)(deg F temperature difference from fluid to fluid).

V Linear velocity, feet per hour.

V_{max} G_{max}/ρ, feet per hour; V'_{max} feet per second.

x Thickness of conductor, length along fin, feet; x_f is total length of bar fin; distance along vertical plane, feet.

y Distance from wall, feet.

z Vertical distance, feet.

Table I —Nomenclature.—(*Continued*)

Z Grashof number, dimensionless, $L^3\rho^2 g\beta\ \Delta t/\mu^2$; Z_f at film temperature, Z_s at surface temperature; for vertical places, L = height; for horizontal pipes, $L = D_o$.

Greek

β Coefficient of volumetric expansion, reciprocal temperature; for perfect gases, β equals $1/T$.

Δt Temperature difference, degrees Fahrenheit; Δt, between surface and ambient fluid; Δt_m, length-mean value; Δt_o, at base of fin; Δt_x at any point on fin.

ϵ Emissivity, dimensionless.

μ Absolute viscosity of fluid, lb/(hr)(ft), equal to $2.42 \times$ centipoises; μ_f at t_f; μ' in centipoises.

π 3.1416.

ρ Density, pounds per cubic foot; ρ_f at t_f.

ϕ, ψ Functions to be determined experimentally.

Fluid Flow at Right Angles to Single Cylinders

Gases.—In a pioneer paper, A. Davis[167] plotted hD_o/k_f as ordinates *vs.* log $D_o V\rho_f c_p/k_f$, based on several sets of data for gases

Table II.*—Data on Forced Convection of Heat between Air and Single Cylinders

Reference	Observer	Cylinder diameter, inches	Air temperature deg F	Tube temperature, deg F	Velocity, ft/sec	Absolute pressure, atm
380	Kennelly *et al.*	0.0004–0.0008	70	Up to 1076	0–60	1
379	Kennelly and Sanborn	0.00045	60	770–1035	0–62	0.4–4
386	King	0.0011–0.006	60	440–1840	0.5–25	1
329	Hughes	0.17–1.99	60	212	0–50	1
247	Gibson	3.75	50	190	8.9–51	1
583	Reiher	0.6–1.1	500	70–95	9–19	1
544	Paltz and Starr	3.25	70	212	23–40	1
737	Vornehm	0.95–1.2	390	80–105	4–25	1
305	Hilpert	0.00075–5.9	70	200–230	6–97	1
266, 267	Griffiths and Awbery	1.25–3.25	65	83–120	2.5–20	1
273	Goukman *et al.*	1.38				
672	Small	4.5	70	171–198	5–40	1
58	Benke	0.276–0.354	70	532–916	4–32	1

* Data are also given by Van Bylevelt.[103]

flowing at right angles to single pipes and wires, obtaining a curve concave upward but giving no equation, although a good correlation was apparently obtained over a wide range in the variables. Using one or more sets of data, other writers* have evaluated the functions in Eq. 1, or in the following simplified form:

$$hD_o/k_f = \phi(D_oG/\mu_f) \tag{3}$$

often employing power functions. Table II summarizes the ranges of experimental conditions for a number of sets of data selected for determining the equation to be recommended for the flow of gases at right angles to single cylinders. These data have been corrected for radiation from solid to solid; this correction is not particularly large for the data on pipes and is almost negligible for the data on wires.

In correlating data on air $c_p\mu_f/k_f$ was taken as 0.74. Figure 111 shows the data of Table II on logarithmic paper with the dimensionless group hD/k_f as ordinates *vs.* the dimensionless Reynolds number DG/μ_f as abscissas. It is noted that the data lie reasonably close to the smooth curve AA drawn through the points. The range of variables involved in the data cover the extreme ranges tabulated below.

TABLE III.—RANGE OF DATA FOR AIR FLOWING NORMAL TO SINGLE CYLINDERS

Diameter, inches	0.0004–5.9
Air velocity, feet per second	0–62
Air temperature, degrees Fahrenheit	60–500
Cylinder temperature, degrees Fahrenheit	70–1840
Pressure, atmosphere absolute	0.4–4
DG/μ_f, consistent units	0.2–235,000
hD/k_f, consistent units	0.5–500

The dimensionless relation recommended for the flow of gases at right angles to single cylinders, based on data for both wires and pipes, is shown by the curve AA in Fig. 111. The following equation may be used for D_oG/μ_f from 0.1 to 1000:

$$hD_o/k_f = 0.32 + 0.43(D_oG/\mu_f)^{0.52} \tag{4}$$

Figure 111 shows data only for air, but since, as shown in Fig. 113, Eq. 4 also correlates data for liquids where $c_p\mu/k$ ranges from

* Nusselt,[527] Rice,[590] Gibson,[247] Reiher,[583] Ulsamer,[725] and King.[389]

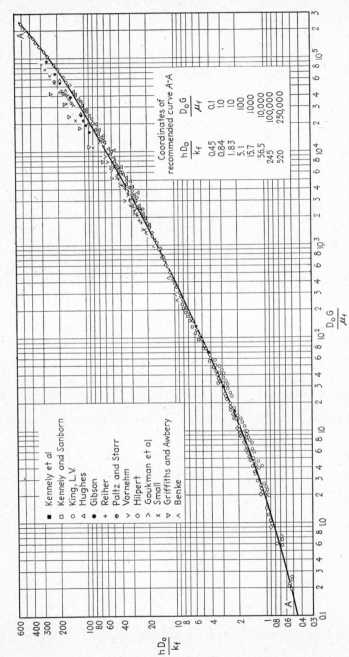

FIG. 111.—Data for heating and cooling air flowing normal to single cylinders, corrected for radiation to surroundings. These results may be applied to heating and cooling liquids by multiplying the values of h for gases by the term $1.1(c_p\mu_f/k)^{0.3}$.

6 to 1240, Eq. 4a is recommended for estimating the heat transfer by forced convection to any gas, for D_oG/μ_f from 0.1 to 1000:

$$\frac{hD_o/k_f}{(c_p\mu_f/k_f)^{0.3}} = 0.35 + 0.47\left(\frac{D_oG}{\mu_f}\right)^{0.52} \tag{4a}$$

For single pipes in the range of D_oG/μ_f from 1000 to 50,000 the dimensionless equation

$$\frac{hD_o/k_f}{(c_p\mu_f/k_f)^{0.3}} = 0.26\left(\frac{D_oG}{\mu_f}\right)^{0.6} \tag{4b}$$

represents the data within ±20 per cent. For air and diatomic gases ($c_p\mu_f/k_f$ of 0.74), this reduces to

$$hD_o/k_f = 0.24(D_oG/\mu_f)^{0.6} \tag{4c}$$

By integration of the equation for thermal conduction in a moving fluid, King[386]* obtained the theoretical relation

$$\frac{hD_o}{k} = \frac{1}{\pi} + \left[\frac{2}{\pi}\left(\frac{D_oG}{\mu}\right)\left(\frac{c_p\mu}{k}\right)\right]^{0.5}$$

which is a refinement of the previous equations of Boussinesq[79] and Russell.[618] A curve based on this equation, taking $c_p\mu_f/k_f$ for air of 0.74, would lie as much as 40 per cent above the data of Fig. 111. In view of the assumptions made, this disagreement is not surprising; it is of considerable interest that a wholly theoretical equation, based on a number of assumptions made to permit integration, comes so close to the data.

If the heat transfer by conduction and convection were computed as due only to conduction through an effective circular film† of thickness B and mean diameter D_f, one would obtain

$$q = h\pi D_oL\ \Delta t = k_f\pi D_fL\ \Delta t/B$$

which reduces to $hD_o/k_f = D_f/B$. As shown on page 12, D_f is the logarithmic mean

$$D_f = \frac{D_o + 2B - D_o}{\ln_e\left(\dfrac{D_o + 2B}{D_o}\right)} = \frac{2B}{\ln_e\left(1 + \dfrac{2B}{D_o}\right)}$$

The curvature of the line on Fig. 111 can be eliminated by plotting hD_o/k_f vs. D_fG/μ_f. For pipes D_fG/μ_f is substantially equal to D_oG/μ_f, but for small wires, D_fG/μ_f is much greater than D_oG/μ_f and hence the abscissas of the left-hand points in Fig. 111 are moved to the right, thus substantially eliminating the curvature. However, since the introduction of D_f leads to a trial-and-error procedure, this correlation is not recommended.

* The derivation of this equation is discussed by Drew.[184]
† As postulated by Langmuir,[420] Rice,[591,592,594] and others.

It is noted that Eqs. 4*b* and 4*c* contain the physical properties μ_f and k_f, which could be expressed in terms of t_f for any given gas such as air. Since in certain types of problems, trial-and-error work is occasioned by the use of film temperature, some writers have proposed empirical equations relating h, D_o, G and gas temperature[114] or in some cases have eliminated the temperature term as illustrated by the equation of Gibson.[247] A simplified equation for pipes, containing no temperature term, is shown below

$$h = 0.026 G^{0.6}/D_o^{0.4} \qquad (4d)$$

and is suitable for problems where the temperature of the film is in the range from 100 to 300°F. Equation 4*d* is obtained from Eq. 4*c* by substituting the values of μ_f and k_f for air at 200°F.

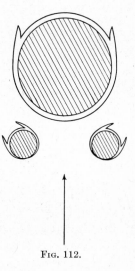

The effect of increasing the turbulence of the air in increasing the heat-transfer coefficient was studied by Reiher, who obtained as much as 50 per cent increase in h by passing the air through a grid to increase turbulence in the air flowing over the single pipe.

Goukhman *et al.*[255] found that h for a 35-mm cylinder could be increased 23 to 30 per cent by placing a pair of 12-mm cylinders ahead of the large cylinder, as shown in Fig. 112, and explained the increase as due to changes in the measured local drag coefficients.

Fig. 112.

Calculation of True Temperature of a Gas.—For computing the true temperature of a gas from the reading of a thermocouple or pyrometer placed in a gas stream and in sight of surrounding walls that may be at various temperatures, a heat balance for the pyrometer is used:

$$q_{gr} + q_c = q_r + q_k \qquad (5)$$

wherein q_{gr} is the rate of heat flow between gas and pyrometer by the mechanism of *gas radiation* (see pages 64 to 73), q_c is the rate of heat flow between gas and pyrometer by *convection* (see Fig. 111, page 221, and Eq. 4*c*, page 222), q_r is the sum of the various terms representing the radiant heat interchange between the pyrometer and the various surfaces that it "sees," evaluated by the methods of pages 55 to 64, and q_k is the heat **conducted** from the thermocouple to the walls confining the gas stream.   In the simple case of a gas stream having true temperature T_g and flowing through a duct of a diameter large compared to that of the pyrometer at temperature T_p, the inner surfaces of the walls having approximately constant temperature T_s, a heat balance on the pyrometer gives the equation

$$q_{gr} + h_c A_p (T_g - T_p) = (0.173)(\epsilon A_p)\left[\left(\frac{T_p}{100}\right)^4 - \left(\frac{T_s}{100}\right)^4\right] + q_k \quad (5a)$$

Values of ϵ, the emissivity of the surface of the pyrometer, are obtained from Table XIII, page 393; and T_p and T_s represent, respectively, the temperatures of the pyrometer and walls, expressed in degrees Fahrenheit absolute.   Instead of using Eq. 5a, which involves the fourth power of the absolute temperature, it is possible to employ temperature in degrees Fahrenheit, as shown in the following alternate procedure.   By definition, $q_r = h_r A(t_p - t_s)$, where h_r is the appropriate "radiation coefficient of heat transfer" from solid to solid, plotted in Fig. 27, page 63, as a function of temperatures expressed in degrees Fahrenheit.   Hence, Eq. 5a may be written

$$q_{gr} + h_c A_p(t_g - t_p) = h_r A_p(t_p - t_s) + q_k \quad (5b)$$

Under the conditions in which q_{gr} and q_k are negligible compared to q_c and q_r, Eq. 5b simplifies to

$$t_g - t_p = (t_p - t_s)(h_r/h_c) \quad (5c)$$

From Eq. 5c it is clear that the difference between the true and apparent temperatures of the gas, $t_g - t_p$, increases with (1) increase in the temperature difference between the pyrometer and the walls, $t_p - t_s$, (2) with increase in the simplified radiation coefficient h_r, and (3) with decrease in the convection coefficient h_c, between gas and pyrometer.   Since h_r increases with temperature level far faster than does h_c, the error in measuring gas temperature increases with increase in temperature.   In order to reduce the error and to avoid a calculation, several procedures are used.

The true gas temperature is sometimes estimated by measuring the apparent gas temperature by several thermocouples of different diameters, and extrapolating to zero diameter.[410]   Or, a sample of the gas stream, flowing at low velocity, is caused to flow at high velocity through an insulated tube past a thermocouple, giving the "high-velocity" thermocouple.[495]* These two schemes reduce the error by increasing h_c. The temperature difference between walls and couple can be reduced by the use of radiation screens, so that the couple "sees" the warmer screens bathed in hot gas rather than the colder walls. The radiation correction also can be reduced by covering the surface of the pyrometer with a tightly fitting surface[754] of polished metal (see page 393), such as aluminum foil. It is interesting to note that the effect of radiation on thermometers was recognized by Wells[754] in 1818. A summary of 26 methods of reducing error in measuring gas temperatures is given by Mullikin.[494]

Illustration 1.—Air is flowing steadily through a duct whose inner walls are at 500°F. A thermocouple, housed in a rusted steel well, inserted at right angles to the air stream, indicates a temperature of 300°F. The mass velocity of the air is 3600 lb/(hr)(sq ft), and the o.d. of the well is 1 in. Estimate the true temperature of the air, neglecting q_k.

Solution.—From Eq. 4d, $h_c = 9.6$, and from Fig. 27, page 63, $h_r = 4.44$ for a black body. The emissivity will be taken as 0.9; hence h_r is 0.9×4.44 equals 4.0. From Eq. 5c,

$$t_p - t_g = \frac{(t_s - t_p)(h_r)}{h_c} = \frac{(500 - 300)(40)}{9.6} = 83°F.$$

Hence

$$t_g = 300 - 83 = 217°F.$$

Liquids Flowing at Right Angles to Single Cylinders.—The

most comprehensive available data are those of Davis[169] on the transfer of heat by forced convection from several sizes of wires to water and to four hydrocarbon oils having a wide range of viscosities. Values of c_p, μ, k, and ρ were determined for each of these oils. Meager data were obtained by Worthington and Malone[782] for heat transfer from a wire to water. Davis correlated these data but obtained a complex relation involving six empirical constants. A less involved correlation of the data of Davis on liquids, and of several other investigators on air, was made both by Ulsamer[725] and by King,[389] using an equation of the form of Eq. 2, page 217, with m of 0.3.

The data of Davis on water, paraffin oil, and three transformer oils are plotted in Fig. 113. Davis used single wires of diameters 0.00803, 0.00598, and 0.00401 in., moved through the liquid at room temperature at velocities of 0.36 to 2.3 ft/sec. The points for a large temperature difference lie, in general, above points for a

---

* Assman[18] devised the high-velocity thermocouple in 1892 and called it an *aspiration pyrometer*.

small temperature difference, probably because of natural convection effects. Nevertheless, the data of Davis may be expressed within approximately 5 to 15 per cent by the line *BB* of Fig. 113, represented by the equation

$$\frac{(hD_o/k_f)}{(c_p\mu_f/k_f)^{0.3}} = 0.86 \left(\frac{DV\rho_f}{\mu_f}\right)^{0.43} \tag{6}$$

It is recommended that Eq. 6 be used for estimating heat-transfer coefficients for forced convection from single wires to liquids when

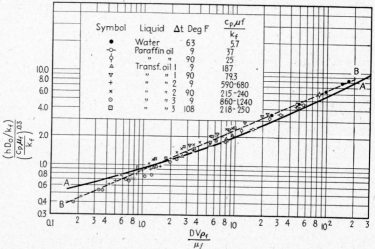

Fig. 113.—Data of Davis[169] for flow of liquid normal to a single cylinder. Curve *BB* represents the data for liquids, and Curve *AA* corresponds to Curve *AA* of Fig. 111, for gases.

$D_oV\rho_f/\mu_f$ lies between 0.1 and 200. For values of $D_oV\rho_f/\mu_f$ above 200, Eq. 4a is recommended.

BANKS OF TUBES

The case of forced convection outside banks of tubes is of considerable importance, especially in air heaters and heat exchangers.

Gases.—Many data are available for the flow of air at right angles to banks of tubes as shown in Table IV, page 227. Since the term $c_p\mu_f/k_f$ was constant at 0.74, the data are usually correlated by an equation of the type used for air flowing across single tubes:

$$hD_o/k_f = b_2(D_oG_{max}/\mu_f)^n \tag{7}$$

wherein G_{max} is based on the minimum free area available for fluid flow, regardless of whether the minimum area occurs in the trans-

TABLE IV.[a]—FLOW OF AIR OVER BANKS OF TUBES, STAGGERED S AND IN LINE I

Reference No.	Observer	O.d., inch D_o'	Transverse spacing, center to center, s_T/D_o	Longitudinal spacing, center to center, s_L/D_o	No. rows deep	S or I	Tube temp., °F	Air temp., °F
598	Rietschel	1.3	1.15	1.00	4	S	220	60
108, 100	Carrier and Busey	1.32	2.00	1.42	32	S	227, 298	20
682	Soule		2.08					
6	Allen	1.32	2.08		4–20	S	225	32–60
583	Reiher	0.591	1.49, 1.93	1.20, 1.93	4, 5	S, I	68–95	490
114	"Radiator"	0.275	1.85	1.27	9	S	200	70
437	Lindmark		1.4, 1.76	1.22, 1.55	5	S		
175	Dehn		5.0					
266, 267	Griffiths and Awbery	1.9	1.67, 2.36	1.67, 1.18	3	I, S		
84	Brandt							
327	Huge	0.5–2.0	1.25–3.0	1.25–3.0	10	S, I		
561	Pierson	0.31	1.25–3.0	1.25–3.0	1–10	S, I		
58	Benke	0.28–0.35	2.0–22.0	3.9–5.0	2–10	S, I		
771	Winding	1.5	1.33	1.33	8	S	212	76–91

[a] Gibson[247] gives data for a helical coil of pipe.   Data on pipe heaters and on cast-iron Vento heaters are given by Soule.[682]

verse or diagonal openings.[269]   Tucker[722b] determined the heat-transfer coefficients to air flowing normal to a single vertical 1-in. tube placed at the center of the third row of a bank of staggered unheated tubes 5 rows deep.   In each of the 15 bundles used, the tubes were arranged at the apexes of isosceles triangles.   Three ratios of longitudinal to transverse spacing were used: s_L/s_T of $0.5\sqrt{3}$, 1.0, and 1.5; with each of these, transverse pitches of 1.25, 1.5, 2, 3, and 4 tube diameters were employed.   It was found that the large changes in the transverse and longitudinal clearances had a negligible effect on the value of h at a given mass velocity through the minimum free area, which in all cases involved the transverse clearance, $s_T - D_o$; the data are plotted in Fig. 114 and are correlated by Eq. 7, with b_2 of 0.30 and n of 0.6, with an average deviation of ± 5 per cent.   In a bank five rows deep, h in a given row increased as the test pipe was moved toward the rear of the bank; Tucker recommended that the mean h for N rows deep be taken as $[N/(N + 0.54)]$ times that for the third row; upon comparing his own data with those from the literature,* he noted a slight decrease in b_2 as D_o increased:

* **Chappell and McAdams,**[114] Reiher,[583] Rietschel,[598] and Carrier and Busey.[108]

D_o', inches	0.28	0.59	1.0	1.3
b_2	0.35	0.31	0.30	0.28

Table V shows the values of b_2 and n obtained by Grimison[269] from the extensive data of Huge[327] and of Pierson[561] for banks 10 rows deep.* The data for flow of air across a bank of staggered tubes show somewhat higher heat-transfer coefficients than across a single tube for corresponding tube sizes and air velocities. The increase for the rows in the rear of the bank over those in the front row is due to increased turbulence (see Fig. 107, page 215). This effect is shown by the data of a number of investigators.† Table VI shows the ratio of the mean coefficient for N rows to that for a bank 10 rows deep.[561]

TABLE V.—GRIMISON'S VALUES OF b_2 AND n IN EQ. 7
$$hD_o/k_f = b_2(D_oG_{max}/\mu_f)^n; \quad t_f = t_s - (t_s - t)_m/2.$$

Transverse spacing = S_T/D_o	$s_L/D_o = 1.25$		$s_L/D_o = 1.5$		$s_L/D_o = 2$		$s_L/D_o = 3$	
	b_2	n	b_2	n	b_2	n	b_2	n
Staggered								
0.600	.....	.....	.....	.....	.....	.....	0.213	0.636
0.900	.....	.....	.....	.....	0.446	0.571	0.401	0.581
1.000	.....	.....	0.497	0.558				
1.125	.....	.....	.....	.....	0.478	0.565	0.518	0.560
1.250	0.518	0.556	0.505	0.554	0.519	0.556	0.522	0.562
1.500	0.451	0.568	0.460	0.562	0.452	0.568	0.488	0.568
2.000	0.404	0.572	0.416	0.568	0.482	0.556	0.449	0.570
3.000	0.310	0.592	0.356	0.580	0.440	0.562	0.421	0.574
In line								
1.250	0.348	0.592	0.275	0.608	0.100	0.704	0.0633	0.752
1.500	0.367	0.586	0.250	0.620	0.101	0.702	0.0678	0.744
2.000	0.418	0.570	0.299	0.602	0.229	0.632	0.198	0.648
3.000	0.290	0.601	0.357	0.584	0.374	0.581	0.286	0.608

TABLE VI.—RATIO OF h_m FOR 10 ROWS DEEP TO THAT FOR N ROWS DEEP

N	1	2	3	4	5	6	7	8	9	10
Ratio for staggered tubes	.....	0.70	0.82	0.87	0.92	0.94	0.96	0.97	0.99	1.0
Ratio for in-line tubes	0.64	0.76	0.83	0.87	0.92	0.94	0.96	0.97	0.99	1.0

* The values of b_2 and n of Table IV are in fair agreement [269] with the data of references 108, 114, 437, 583, 598, and 266.

† References 583, 598, 771, and 561.

In the Grimison paper,[269] the same correlation is rearranged to give

$$hD_o/k_f = 0.28F_a(D_oG_{max}/\mu_f)^{0.61} \tag{7a}$$

wherein the dimensionless arrangement factor F_a depends on D_oG_{max}/μ_f and the dimension ratios s_T/D_o and s_L/D_o. For a wide variety of arrangements of tubes, for D_oG_{max}/μ_f ranging from 1000 to 40,000, F_a varies from 0.9 to 1.27 for staggered banks and from 0.67 to 1.1 for in-line banks.

The data on heat transfer for air flowing normal to nonbaffled banks of tubes ran 27 per cent above those for single tubes. Figure

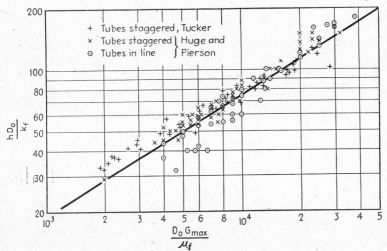

Fig. 114.—Data for heating air, compared with Eq. 8; at low values of D_oG_{max}/μ_f, in line banks give low results.

114 shows data of Huge[327] and Pierson[561] compared with Eq. 8, which was proposed by Colburn[142] before these data were available. The following dimensionless equation, for N of 10,

$$\frac{h_mD_o}{k_f} = 0.33\left(\frac{c_p\mu_f}{k_f}\right)^{1/3}\left(\frac{D_oG_{max}}{\mu_f}\right)^{0.6} \tag{8}$$

is recommended for both liquids and gases flowing normal to banks of staggered tubes, not baffled, for D_oG_{max}/μ_f exceeding 2000. At values of D_oG_{max}/μ_f below 2000, use of Fig. 115 is suggested. For banks of tubes in line (not staggered) it is recommended that Eq. 8 be used, with the constant reduced to 0.26, which amounts to using Eq. 4b for single tubes with G_{max} replacing G.

A simplified dimensional equation for gases flowing normal to staggered tubes is

$$h = 0.133 c_p G_{max}^{0.6}/D^{0.4} \qquad (8a)$$

Flow of Liquids over Banks of Pipes.—In the petroleum industry, shell-and-tube heat exchangers are widely used. The usual type consists of a bundle of long tubes with one liquid flowing inside the tubes and the other outside the tubes. Cross baffles of various types are inserted at right angles to the tubes to increase velocity and give more cross flow in long heat exchangers. In this

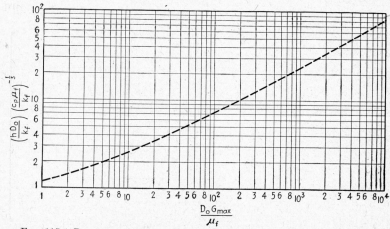

Fig. 115.—Recommended curve for estimating h for heating or cooling fluids flowing normal to staggered banks of tubes 10 rows deep; for $D_o G_{max}/\mu_f$ above 2000 the curve is based on Eq. 8, and for lower values is drawn parallel to the curve for single tubes (Fig. 111) and is supported by unpublished data for liquids. For values of N less than 10, multiply h by the factors given in Table VI. For in-line banks, use 0.8 times the values of h given above.

design, the flow of the liquid outside the tubes is partly parallel to and partly across the tubes. In short-tube exchangers the liquid in the shell flows across the tubes; baffles are not used. This design is similar to that for air flowing at right angles to banks of tubes, except that the cross section varies where a cylindrical shell is used.

To allow for the effect of the leakage that ordinarily occurs around the baffles in cross-baffled exchangers, one assumes no leakage, computes the corresponding coefficient h from Eq. 8, and multiplies h by 0.6.[120]

For water Eq. 8 reduces to the dimensional equation

$$h_m = 370(1 + 0.0067 t_f)(V'_{max})^{0.6}/(D'_0)^{0.4} \qquad (9)$$

wherein t_f is in degrees Fahrenheit, V'_{max} is in feet per second, and D'_o is inches. For tubes in line, one deducts 20 per cent; for flow across baffled exchangers, h is taken as 0.6 times the value calculated for no leakage (see also page 357).

Short[666] reports shell-side coefficients of heat transfer and pressure drop for oils and water flowing through an experimental heat exchanger in which a wide variety of cross baffles were used.

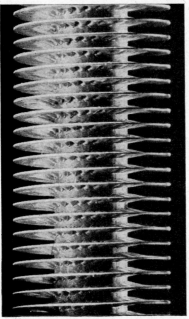

Fig. 116.—Crimped-finned tube Type K. (*Courtesy Fedders Mfg. Co., Inc., Buffalo, N.Y.*)

Mean Temperature Difference in Multipass and in Cross-flow Exchangers.—It should be remembered that the logarithmic-mean temperature difference does not apply in multipass and cross-flow heat exchangers, unless the temperature of one of the fluids is constant (see page 145).

Extended Surfaces (Fins).—When the thermal resistance on the inside of a metal tube is much lower than that on the outside, as when steam condensing in a pipe is being used to heat air, externally finned surfaces, or extended heating surfaces, are of value in increasing substantially the rate of heat transfer per unit length of tube. For the finned pipes used in ordinary air-heating practice, the temperature of the tip of the fin is nearly that of the pipe.

FIG. 117.—Concentric-tube apparatus with longitudinal fins on smaller

The temperature drop through bar fins may be predicted from equations* obtained by integration of the conduction equation, page 7. Thus, for finite fins of constant cross section S and perimeter b, having surface temperature t_x, exposed to a fluid at t_a, a heat balance gives $-k\,S(d^2t_x/dx^2)dx = hb\,dx(t_x - t_a)$, neglecting radial gradient in temperature. Integration gives

$$\frac{(\Delta t)_x}{(\Delta t)_o} = \frac{\cosh a(x_f - x)}{\cosh ax_f} \tag{10}$$

$$\frac{(\Delta t)_m}{(\Delta t)_o} = \frac{\tanh ax_f}{ax_f} \tag{10a}$$

wherein cosh and tanh represent the hyperbolic cosines and tangents, respectively:

$$\cosh y = \frac{e^y + e^{-y}}{2}; \qquad \tanh y = \frac{e^y - e^{-y}}{e^y + e^{-y}}$$

and e is 2.718. In Eqs. 10 and 10a, a equals $(hb/kS)^{0.5}$, where b is the exposed perimeter, x is the length from the base of the fin of length x_f, and Δt is the temperature difference between fin and air; $(\Delta t)_0$ at the base, $(\Delta t)_x$ at distance x, and $(\Delta t)_m$ for the entire fin.

Figure 118[459] shows the experimental data of Stewart,[699] who measured temperatures along metal bars heated at one end and exposed to the air in a room. The theoretical curves, based on Eq. 10, are seen to agree closely with the observed data.

Heat-transfer data from finned plates are given by Wagener,[739] Taylor and Rehbock,[712] and Doetsch.[179] A satisfactory correlation

* Parsons and Harper,[549] Harper and Brown,[282] and Griffiths.[264] End effects are treated by Jakob.[340]

of h/cG, $L_H G/\mu$ and a dimensionless ratio involving a shape factor are given by Doetsch for fins of various cross sections.

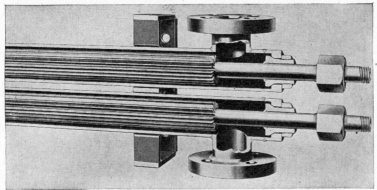

tube; Twin G-Fin Section. (*Courtesy Griscom-Russell Co., New York City.*)

For a given mass velocity of the air, Norris and Spofford[515] find the highest coefficients for flow normal to cylindrical fins, intermediate values for flow parallel to discontinuous strip fins,

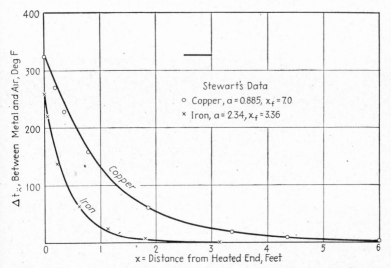

Fig. 118.—Comparison[459] of theoretical and actual temperature gradients in bar fins based on data of Stewart;[699] formerly thermal conductivities of metals were determined from such data.

and the lowest coefficients for flow between parallel continuous fins. The data are correlated by the dimensionless equation[515]

$$\frac{h}{cG}\left(\frac{c_p\mu_f}{k}\right)^{2/3} = 1.0\left(\frac{z_pG}{\mu_f}\right)^{-1/2} \tag{11}$$

The values of z_pG/μ_f ranged from 260 to 12,000, and for air, the left-hand side of the equation equals $3.3\,h/G$. The gas-film coeffi-

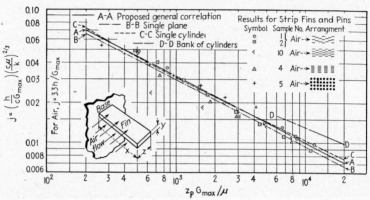

FIG. 119.—Correlation by Norris and Spofford[515] of their data for heating air by *short* fins consisting of strips or pins; $z_p = 2(z + y)$; z_p is twice the heated length L_H over which the air travels. In the range of z_pG_{max}/μ involved, this method of plotting also correlates data for air flow normal to smooth single cylinders (Fig. 111) and parallel to short planes (Fig. 99). The pin fins had diameters ranging from 0.02 to 0.125 in., and the strip fins were 0.125 in. long. The viscosity is evaluated at t_f.

cients h were computed from the measured over-all coefficients U by the resistance equation

$$\frac{1}{h\Delta t_m/\Delta t_o} = \frac{1}{U} - \frac{A}{h_sA_s} - \frac{x_wA}{k_wA_w} \tag{11b}$$

The "effectiveness" $\Delta t_m/\Delta t_o$ was calculated from Eq. 10a and the vapor-side coefficient was evaluated by assuming film-type condensation (Chap. IX). Friction factors were also reported.

TABLE VII.—CRIMPED-FINNED STEEL TUBES USED BY GRIFFITHS AND AWBERY

Tube	Tube diameter, inches	Fin length, inches	Fin thickness, inches	Fin pitch, inches	$2L_H = z_p$, inches
B	1.00	0.485	0.028	0.50	3.89
A	1.34	0.955	0.037	0.62	6.64
C	2.00	0.960	0.038	0.63	7.44
D	2.39	0.970	0.038	0.62	7.88

Griffiths and Awbery[267] report coefficients from *single* steel-finned steel tubes having the dimensions shown in Table VII. Other data for single finned tubes are available.*

Figure 120 shows the data of Griffiths and Awbery for (1) the second row in a staggered bank of finned tubes (Tube A of Table VII) having a transverse pitch of 3.38 in. and a longitudinal pitch of 2.4 in., and (2) the single finned tubes (A, B, C, and D of Table

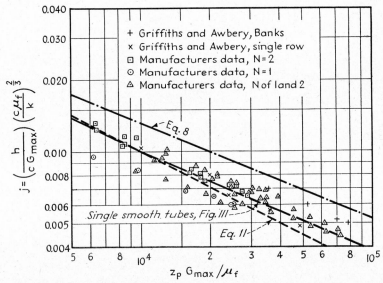

Fig. 120.—Data for air flowing normal to spiral-finned tubes, compared with Eq. 11 for short strip and pin fins, and with the curves for staggered banks of plain tubes (Eq. 8) and the curve for single plain tubes (Fig. 111).

VII). Data† for banks of spiral-finned tubes, one or two rows deep, with crimped or noncrimped fins, are also plotted in Fig. 120, arbitrarily taking z_p as twice the heated length of the equivalent square fin:

$$z_p = 2L_H = 2\sqrt{\frac{\pi(D_0 + 2x_p)(N)(2x_p) + (\pi D_0)(1)}{2N}}$$

* Stanton, Booth, and Marshall,[693] Gibson,[245] Wagener,[739] and Biermann and Pinkel.[62] Data for flow of air normal to a finned pipe (4.5 in. in diameter) enclosed in a cylindrical jacket (7.1 in. in diameter) are given by Schey and Ellerbrock.[629]

† Courtesy of York Heating and Ventilating Co., 1929, and of Aerofin Corporation (*Aerofin Bulletin* 32, 1935); N is the number of turns per foot.

For noncrimped fins, z_p is taken as

$$2L_H = 2 \sqrt{\frac{(\pi/4)[(D_o + 2z)^2 - D_0^2]2N + \pi D_o + \pi y(2z)(N)}{2N}}$$

Streamline Shapes.—Hughes[329] tested in a wind tunnel a steam-heated copper model having a streamlined contour similar to that

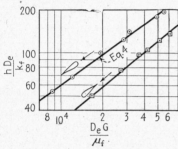

FIG. 121.—Data of Hughes.[329]

of a teardrop. When the air approached the rounded end of the model, higher values of h were obtained than when the air approached the pointed end.

For air approaching the rounded end, the data can be brought into close agreement with those for single cylinders (Fig. 111) by plotting hD_e/k_f vs. D_eG/μ_f, where D_e is the effective diameter, equal to the total perimeter divided by π, Fig. 121. When the angle of incidence is changed, the exponent relating h and G

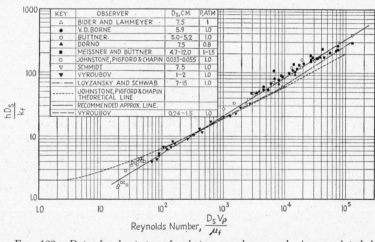

KEY	OBSERVER	D_s,CM	P,ATM
△	BIDER AND LAHMEYER	7.5	1
●	V. D. BORNE	5.9	1.0
○	BÜTTNER	5.0 - 5.2	1.0
▲	DORNO	7.5	0.8
■	MEISSNER AND BÜTTNER	4.7 - 12.0	1 - 1.5
□	JOHNSTONE, PIGFORD & CHAPIN	0.033-0.055	1.0
▽	SCHMIDT	7.5	1.0
▼	VYROUBOV	1 - 2	1.0
— · —	LOYZANSKY AND SCHWAB	7 - 15	1.0
- - - -	JOHNSTONE,PIGFORD & CHAPIN THEORETICAL LINE		
———	RECOMMENDED APPROX. LINE.		
	VYROUBOV	0.24 - 1.5	1.0

FIG. 122.—Data for heat transfer between spheres and air, correlated by Williams;[767] data of Vyroubov[738] are based on mass transfer. For conduction to a stagnant medium the theoretically minimum value of hD/k is 2 (as shown by Table II of Chap. I) unless the spheres have diameters of the order of the mean free paths of the ambient fluid.

changes.[93,714] Coefficients for the leading end of a model of an airfoil are available.[283]

At a given mass velocity of the air, Winding[771] finds that a bank of staggered steel tubes eight rows deep gives substantially the same results whether the tubes are circular, oval, or streamline in shape; all three tubes had a perimeter of 4.7 in. Hence the data can be correlated in terms of z_p.

Spheres.—Figure 122 shows data* for heat transfer between spheres and air, correlated by Williams.[767] In the range of DG/μ_f from 20 to 150,000 the straight line has the dimensionless equation

$$hD/k_f = 0.33(DG/\mu_f)^{0.6} \tag{12}$$

Hixson and Baum[307] report coefficients of heat transfer from water to lumps of ice, in agitated vessels.

NATURAL CONVECTION

Mechanism.—Visualize a heated vertical surface exposed to the colder air in a room. Since the density of the air near the heated surface is less than that of the main body of the air, the difference in gravitational forces causes an upward flow of air near the plate. This is the so-called "chimney effect." If the plate were colder than the air, because of greater density and pressure near the plate, the air would flow downward. In either case heat is conducted through the gas layers and is carried away by bulk motion or convection. Although both conduction and convection are involved, the process is called "natural" or "free" convection. Although measurements of heat-transfer coefficients from surfaces dates back many years, most of the experimental work on the mechanism has been done in the twentieth century.

The mechanism of heat loss by conduction and convection from vertical surfaces has been studied by Griffiths and Davis,[268] Nusselt and Jurges,[534] Schmidt,[633] and Schmidt and Beckmann.[640]

Figure 123 shows the velocity and temperature fields near a vertical heated plate, 1 ft high, measured by Schmidt.[633] At a given distance z from the bottom, the local upward air velocity increases with increases in distance y from the wall, goes through a

---

* In plotting data for irregular particles, where total surface had been estimated from rates of settling, D was taken as the diameter of a spherical particle having the same surface as the irregular particle. The data of Compan[153] and Hartmann[284] would fall roughly 80 and 50 per cent, respectively, below the curve in Fig. 122. Part of the data of Vyroubov,[738] plotted in Fig. 122, are based on mass-transfer measurements.

maximum at a distance of from 2 to 3 mm from the plate, and then decreases with further increase in y. Results for taller plates

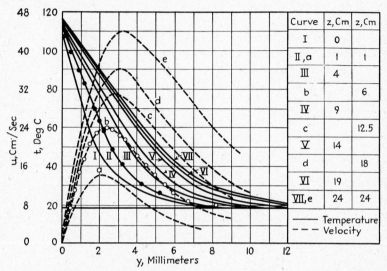

Curve	z,Cm	z,Cm
I	0	
II,a	1	1
III	4	
b		6
IV	9	
c		12.5
V	14	
d		18
VI	19	
VII,e	24	24

——— Temperature
– – – Velocity

FIG. 123.—Velocity and temperature explorations by Schmidt at various distances from a heated vertical plate exposed to air.

show that the local air velocity ultimately approaches an asymptotic value, depending on the height of the plate and the Δt employed. The air streams approach the plate laterally at the bottom and diagonally further up the plate.

The temperature gradients are steepest near the bottom of the plate, where the air is the coldest, and decrease as the air flows up the plate, also approaching an asymptotic value.

The average coefficient for the plate is an inverse function of height for small heights and is substantially independent of height for tall plates. Similar results for plates of various heights are given in the other references cited above. The results of Koch[402] for tall vertical cylinders are similar to those for vertical plates.

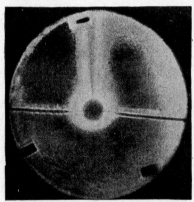

FIG. 124.—Natural convection from a horizontal cylinder to air. (*Photograph from Ray,[579] Proc. Ind. Assoc. Cultivation Sci.*)

Ray[579] used a photographic procedure* whereby heated air near a hot horizontal cylinder appeared brighter in color than the colder air. Figure 124 shows such a photograph, indicating two horn-shaped currents of rising air. In another natural-convection run, the temperature field was mapped by the use of a very small thermocouple, and, although the uncorrected temperatures so obtained are probably inaccurate, the results (Fig. 125) show a

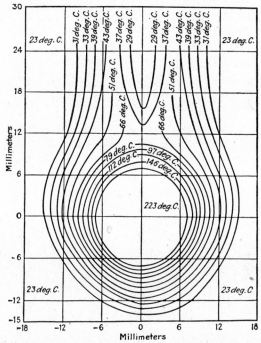

Fig. 125.—Temperature explorations around a hot horizontal cylinder in air. (*From Ray, Proc. Ind. Assoc. Cultivation Sci.*)

striking resemblance to Fig. 124. Additional data of a similar nature were published by Praminik[571] who used wires of several diameters. The data on temperature and velocity distribution emphasize the complexity of natural-convection phenomena.

Saunders[623] and coworkers[644] employ an ingenious optical method to study the mechanism of heat transfer by natural convection to water or air from a bottom-heated horizontal plate. Light beams are passed horizontally through the fluid, and photo-

---

* A small, hollow copper cylinder 0.72 cm in diameter, enclosing a heating coil, was housed in a wooden box for protection against stray currents of air.

graphs are taken at right angles. Because of deflections of the beams, the photographs show a cell-like pattern under certain conditions. When the product of the Grashof and Prandtl numbers ranges from 2000 to 45,000, alternate portions of the fluid circulate upward and downward in streams of substantial width, and the term **cellular motion** is used to describe the phenomenon. As this characteristic product increases, the rate of fluid circulation increases, and the width of the cells decreases, until a "well-defined turbulence" ensues at 45,000. The slope of the curve of flux vs. Δt increases sharply at this critical point.[623]

In order to correlate natural-convection data on liquids and gases over a wide range of conditions, it is necessary to use a large number of variables combined in dimensionless groups, as shown on page 242. However, for air at atmospheric pressure, the heat-transfer coefficients for natural convection may be correlated with sufficient precision by means of two variables: Δt and a dimension characteristic of the shape and orientation of the heat-transfer surface.

The additional heat transferred by radiation is usually substantial, compared with that by convection, and the total loss is calculated by the following equation

$$q = h_c A_s(t_s - t_a) + h_r A_s(t_s - t_e) \tag{13}$$

where t_s, t_a, and t_e are the temperatures of the surface of the body, the air, and the enclosing walls, respectively, and h_r is obtained from Fig. 27, page 63. Where t_s and t_a are the same, the equation becomes

$$q = (h_c + h_r)(A_s)(t_s - t_a) \tag{13a}$$

Simplified Equations.—The following simplified equations are recommended:

Horizontal plates, facing upward:

$$h_c = 0.38(\Delta t)^{0.25} \tag{14}*$$

Horizontal plates, facing downward:

$$h_c = 0.2(\Delta t)^{0.25} \tag{15}*$$

Vertical plates more than 1 ft high:

$$h_c = 0.27 \,\Delta t^{0.25} \tag{16}*$$

* Based on data of Griffiths and Davis for plates for 3 to 4 ft square. Wilkes[766] gives data for inclined plates.

Vertical plates less than 1 ft high:

$$h_c = 0.28(\Delta t/L)^{0.25} \tag{17}*$$

Vertical pipes more than 1 ft high:

$$h_c = 0.27(\Delta t/D_o)^{0.25} \tag{18}†$$

Horizontal pipes:

$$h_c = 0.27(\Delta t/D_o)^{0.25} \tag{19}‡$$

The experiments of Griffiths and Davis, of Schmidt, and of Mull and Reiher[492] show that h_c for a vertical plate is not affected by the presence of a parallel plate more than 20 mm away. Griffiths and Davis also determined heat transfer between a hot and a cold vertical plate separated by a completely enclosed air space, which was varied from $\frac{1}{2}$ to 2 in. in thickness and from 24.8 to 49.6 in. in height. Over this range, the heat transfer by convection was found to depend only on the temperature difference and to be approximately 60 per cent of that found for a single vertical plate not enclosed. A good summary of data for heat transfer in enclosed air spaces is given by King.[388]

Natural Convection to Various Fluids.—A correlation of data on various fluids under a wide variety of conditions involves relationships between dimensionless groups obtained by the use of dimensional analysis.

The factors involved in the natural convection of heat between solids and fluids were disclosed in 1881 in a pioneer paper by Lorenz,[445] who considered the upward movement of air along a *vertical* heated plane, the motion being attributed to differences in air density due to differences in temperature. Employing the differential equation for thermal conduction in a moving fluid, he obtained, upon integration, the dimensionally compatible equation

---

* Based on Fig. 129, p. 248, for an air-film temperature of 150°F; supported by data of King,[388] Heilman,[297] Langmuir,[421] Schmidt,[633] Schmidt and Beckmann,[640] and Griffiths and Davis.[268]

† Based on a rough correlation of data of Griffiths and Davis,[268] Koch[402] and Carne.[106] The data of Griffiths and Davis on vertical pipes 6.87 in. in diameter, ranging in height from 0.153 to 0.94 ft run higher than called for by Eq. 18 but are discounted[388] because of probable end effects due to the use of 0.25-ft lengths of unheated refractory on the ends.

‡ Obtained from Eq. 23, p. 244, by substituting the properties of air at a film temperature of 150°F; the supporting data are plotted in Fig. 126, p. 243.

$$\frac{h_c L}{k} = 0.548 \left[\left(\frac{c_p \mu}{k} \right) \left(\frac{L^3 \rho^2 \beta g (\Delta t)}{\mu^2} \right) \right]^{\frac{1}{4}} \qquad (20)$$

wherein the symbols are defined on page 218. According to the treatment of Lorenz, the coefficient of heat transfer h_c by natural convection depends upon the height L of the plane,* the difference in temperature Δt between solid and ambient gas, the acceleration g due to gravity, and the following physical properties of the gas: thermal conductivity k, specific heat c_p, absolute viscosity μ, density ρ, and coefficient of expansion β. For ideal gases, $\beta = 1/T$. In correlating data on heat transfer by natural convection, a number of writers[†] employ the dimensionless groups of Eq. 20; for horizontal cylinders the outside diameter D_o replaces height L of the vertical wall.

Temperature and velocity fields near a heated horizontal cylinder have been measured by Jodlbauer.[353] These results have been closely predicted from theoretical considerations by Hermann[301]; for Grashof numbers Z_s exceeding 10,000, Hermann predicts $hD/k_s = 0.37(Z)_s^{0.25}$ for natural convection from single horizontal cylinders to diatomic gases ($c_p \mu / k = 0.74$). If this equation for gases were generalized by adding $(c_p \mu / k)^{0.25}$, one would obtain

$$\frac{h_c D}{k_s} = 0.4 \left(Z_s \cdot \frac{c_p \mu_s}{k_s} \right)^{0.25} \qquad (20a)$$

For small Δt, Eq. 20a averages 15 to 25 per cent lower than the data for gases and liquids.

The heat-transfer coefficient from an internally heated 0.75-in. horizontal tube 1 ft long, immersed in a water bath, was increased[472] up to fivefold by vibrating the pipe sinusoidally in a vertical direction, but when the vibration was less than a certain critical value no increase was obtained.

Horizontal Cylinders.—Data on heat transfer by natural convection from single horizontal cylinders are available on air, hydrogen, carbon dioxide, oxygen, water, aniline, carbon tetrachloride, glycerine, toluene, and olive oil, covering a 7300-fold range of diameters, a 10,000-fold range of pressures, an 11,000-fold range in the value of $c_p \mu / k$, and a range of Δt from a few degrees to 2850°F. Figure 126 shows the excellent correlation obtained. The physical

---

* It has been shown (p. 238) that h_c is practically independent of the height of the wall, except for short vertical walls.

† Nusselt,[524,530] Davis,[166-169] Rice,[590] Koch,[402] King,[388] and Hermann.[301]

properties c_p, k, ρ, μ, and β were evaluated at a temperature halfway between the temperature of the surface of the cylinder and the temperature of the ambient fluid.*

The correlation of Rice[590] differs in principle from that of Davis.[168]   Instead of correlating $(h_c D_o)/k_f$ as a function of $(D_o^3 \rho_f^2 \beta g \, \Delta t)/\mu_f^2$ and $(c_p \mu_f)/k_f$, Rice followed the Langmuir[419,422] concept of a fictive film of uniform thickness B, having an i.d. D_o, an o.d. $D_o + 2B$, and a logarithmic-mean diameter D_f.   The

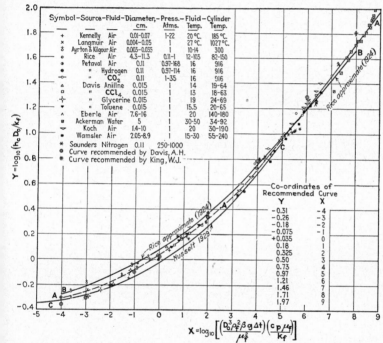

Fig. 126.—Natural convection from horizontal cylinders to gases and liquids; see also Fig. 127.

thickness of the film is taken arbitrarily to be that necessary to account for the observed heat loss by natural convection as due wholly to thermal conduction. Rice determined the constants in the dimensionless exponential relation

$$\frac{D_o}{B} = a \left[\frac{D_o^3 \rho_f^2 \beta g \, \Delta t}{\mu_f^2} \right]^n \left[\frac{c_p \mu_f}{k_f} \right]^m \tag{21}$$

* Saunders[621] found that the heat loss from a wire to nitrogen at pressures ranging from 1 to 1000 atm could be correlated with data of other observers only by assuming $c_p \mu / k$ independent of pressure; since $c_p \mu$ increases with increase in pressure, k must do likewise.   Vargaftik[733] reports the effect of pressure on k for steam and for nitrogen.

as shown on p. 222,

$$\frac{h_c D_o}{k_f} = \frac{2}{\ln_e \left[1 + \dfrac{2B}{D_o} \right]} \tag{22}$$

Upon eliminating B/D_o from Eqs. 21 and 22, the curved line of Rice is obtained, Fig. 126.

Employing the same data on gases and liquids used by Davis in 1922, plus additional data of his own on heating air outside single horizontal pipes, Rice[590] gave the constants of Eq. 21 for cylinders of any diameter, $n = 0.25$, and $m = 0.25$. The approximate equation of Rice, solved for hD_o/k_f, is shown on Fig. 126.

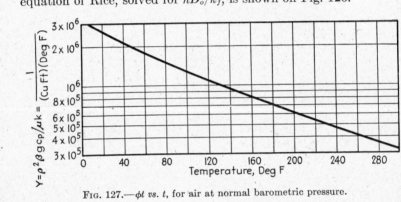

FIG. 127.—ϕt *vs.* t, for air at normal barometric pressure.

Recommended General Procedure: Single Horizontal Cylinders.*— For estimation of heat-transfer coefficients from single horizontal wires or pipes to any fluid, the use of AA,† Fig. 126, is recommended. The data on heat transfer from horizontal *pipes* to air (Eberle, Wamsler, Rice, and Koch) and to water (Ackerman), at X exceeding 3, are represented by the dimensionless equation

$$\frac{h_c D_o}{k_f} = 0.53 \left[\left(\frac{D_o^3 \rho_f^2 \beta g \ \Delta t}{\mu_f^2} \right) \left(\frac{c_p \mu_f}{k_f} \right) \right]^{0.25} \tag{23}$$

To facilitate the use of Eq. 23, Fig. 126, and subsequent relations involving the products of the Grashof and Prandtl numbers for air at normal barometric pressure, Fig. 127 shows a plot of the dimensional term

* As noted on p. 210, latent-heat changes have been excluded here but are treated in Chaps. IX and X.

† This curve differs approximately 10 per cent from that developed by Davis[168] from a portion of the data used in Fig. 126.

$$\phi(t_f) = \left(\frac{\rho^2 g \beta}{\mu^2}\right)\left(\frac{c_p \mu}{k}\right) \ vs. \ \text{film temperature}$$

Hence Eq. 23 may be written

$$hD_o/k_f = 0.53[D_o^3 \ \Delta t \phi(t_f)]^{\frac{1}{4}} \tag{23a}$$

However, for estimating h_c from single horizontal pipes to air at room temperature and atmospheric pressure, Eq. 19, page 241, is simpler to use and is equally accurate.

For heat transfer from *large* horizontal pipes, where D_f is substantially equal to D_o, Rice's approximate equation becomes

$$\frac{h_c D_o}{k_f} = 0.47\left[\left(\frac{D_o^3 \rho_f^2 \beta g \ \Delta t}{\mu_f^2}\right)\left(\frac{c_p \mu_f}{k_f}\right)\right]^{0.25} \tag{24}$$

since the diameter of the film approaches the diameter of the pipe. Figure 128 is an alignment chart,* based on Eq. 24, for the rapid estimation of heat-transfer coefficients for natural convection from a single horizontal pipe to various gases and liquids. This chart gives conservative values for h_c, about 10 per cent lower than Eq. 23. In the case of liquids, only the film temperature, *i.e.*, the arithmetic mean of the temperature of fluid and pipe, the pipe diameter, and the temperature difference are needed for the estimation of h_c. In the case of gases, a pressure term is included.

Illustration 2.—It is desired to estimate the value of h_c between ammonia gas at 10 atm pressure and 200°C (392°F) to a 2-in. cylinder at 100°C (212°F).

Solution.—Using Fig. 128, page 246, align $t_f = 150$°C. (302°F) on the left-hand scale with point 9. Since $p^2(\Delta t)/D = (10)^2(180)/2 = 9000$, locate this point on the right-hand scale marked $p^2 \ \Delta t/D'$, join this point by a straight line with the previously determined point on the reference line, and read $h_c = 4.3$ Btu/(hr)(sq ft)(deg F) on the scale for gases.

Simultaneous Loss by Radiation.—Radiation (pages 45 to 84) is an important factor in the loss of heat from surfaces where the gas movement is due to natural convection, except for small wires, where the values of h_c for the wires are normally so very large that substantially the entire heat loss is due to natural convection, even with large differences in temperature between the wires and the surrounding solids. The heat radiated from the warmer solid to the surrounding walls may be expressed in terms of the coefficient

* Prepared by Chilton, Colburn, Genereaux, and Vernon.[118]

of heat transfer by radiation h_r and is obtained by multiplying the ordinate from Fig. 27, page 63, by the emissivity from Table XIII, page 393. Table VIII shows values of $h_c + h_r$ from single horizontal

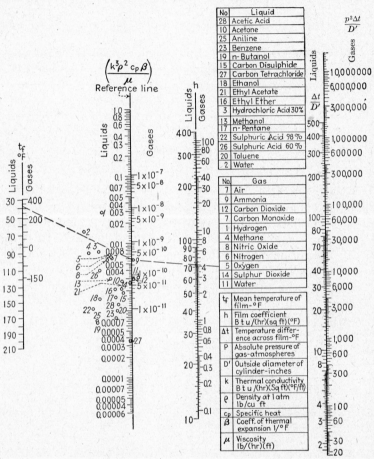

Fig. 128.—Alignment chart for estimation of natural-convection coefficient h_c between single cylinders and gases and liquids, based on Eq. 24; since Eq. 23 best correlates the data, the values of h from the chart should be multiplied by 1.1.

pipes of steel, with oxidized surfaces, based on data of Heilman[296] and McMillan.[464]

The data of Table VIII for bare horizontal pipes may be used in predicting the heat loss from an insulated horizontal steam pipe by employing Eq. 13a, page 240, as shown in the following calculation.

Illustration 3.—A standard horizontal 2-in. steel steam pipe (o.d. = 2.38 in.) is insulated with a 2-in. layer of pipe covering, $k = 0.04$ Btu/(hr)(sq ft) (deg F/ft). The steam is condensing at 370°F, and the room is at 80°F. Required, the heat loss in Btu/(hr)(100 ft length), insulated as described above, and if bare.

TABLE VIII.*—VALUES OF $(h_c + h_r)$, BTU/(HR)(SQ FT)(DEG F) FROM PIPE TO ROOM

For Horizontal Bare Standard Steel Pipe of Various Sizes in a Room at 80°F

Pipe nominal diameter, inches	Temperature difference, degrees Fahrenheit													
	50°	100°	150°	200°	250°	300°	350°	400°	450°	500°	550°	600°	650°	700°
1	2.26	2.50	2.73	3.00	3.29	3.60	3.95	4.34	4.73	5.16	5.60	6.05	6.51	6.98
3	2.05	2.25	2.47	2.73	3.00	3.31	3.69	4.03	4.43	4.85	5.26	5.71	6.19	6.66
5	1.95	2.15	2.36	2.61	2.90	3.20	3.54	3.90	4.30					
10	1.87	2.07	2.29	2.54	2.82	3.12	3.47	3.84						

*Values of $h_c + h_r$ for Δt up to 1000°F are given by Bailey and Lyell.[38]

For the bare pipes the controlling resistance is that on the outer surface. From Table VIII, by interpolation for standard 2-in. pipe and Δt of 290°F, $h_c + h_r$ is 3.4. Since q equals $(h_c + h_r)(A)_o(\Delta t)$,

$$q = (3.4) \left(\pi \times \frac{2.38}{12} \times 100 \right) (290) = 61,300 \text{ Btu/hr}$$

For the insulated pipe, x/kA_m and $1/(h_c + h_r) A_0$ are the important resistances. By Eq. 11, p. 12, the logarithmic-mean area A_m is

$$\frac{100\pi}{12} \left[\frac{6.38 - 2.38}{2.3 \log_{10} \dfrac{6.38}{2.38}} \right] = 105.5 \text{ sq ft}$$

and the outer surface is $100 \, \pi \, 6.38/12 = 166.8$ sq ft. Assuming $h_c + h_r$ of 1.8, Eq. 13a, page 240, gives

$$q = \frac{370 - 80}{\dfrac{2/12}{0.04(105.5)} + \dfrac{1}{(1.8)(166.8)}} = \frac{290}{0.0395 + 0.00333}$$

= 6780 Btu/hr. Assuming $h_c + h_r = 1.8$ for an o.d. of 6.38 in. gives a surface resistance 0.00333, which is 7.8 per cent of the total resistance, 0.0428; hence the corresponding difference from outer surface to air would be 0.078(290) = 23°F, and from Table VIII it is seen that $h_c + h_r$ would be approximately 1.8 for this condition. Since the surface resistance was such a small fraction of the total resistance, no closer approximation is warranted. Methods for calculating the most economical thickness of insulation are given in Chap. XI.

Vertical Planes.—King correlated[388] his own data and six sets of data* for short vertical planes and obtained a curve nearly the same as that shown in Fig. 129. The extensive data of Saunders[621] and of Weise[753] are shown in Fig. 129. The solid line is the recommended curve through the data; the dashed line shows the theoretical equation of Lorenz, which agrees well with the data in range

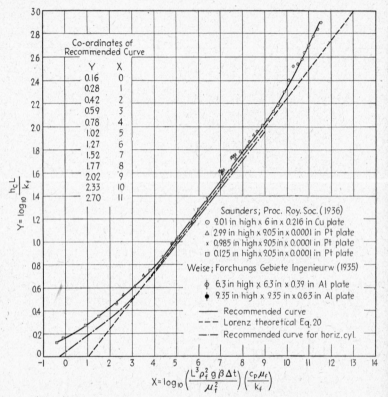

FIG. 129.—Natural convection from short vertical plates to air; see also Fig. 127.

of log X from 4 to 9; the same is true for the dot-and-dash curve for horizontal cylinders (from Fig. 126).

Over the range of log X from 4 to 9 the recommended curve has the equation

$$\frac{h_c L}{k_f} = 0.59 \left[\frac{L^3 \rho_f^2 g \beta \, \Delta t}{\mu_f^2} \cdot \frac{c_p \mu_f}{k_f} \right]^{0.25} \tag{25}$$

* Griffiths and Davis,[268] Montsinger and Cooney,[486] Nusselt and Jurges,[534] Heilman,[297] Schack,[628] and Schmidt and Beckmann.[640]

The constant of 0.59 is 8 per cent higher than the theoretical value calculated by Lorenz, page 242; and 16 per cent higher than the theoretical value computed by Hermann.[301] For air at room temperature and atmospheric pressure, Eq. 25 reduces to

$$h_c = 0.28(\Delta t/L)^{0.25} \qquad (25a)^*$$

which approximates the data of King[388] for vertical plates 3 ft wide ranging in height from $\frac{1}{24}$ to 1 ft. The data of Hilpert,[304] for vertical plates 3.84 in. square and 2.32 in. square give h 25 per cent lower than Eq. 25a. Additional supporting data† are available.

TABLE IX.—COILS IMMERSED IN LIQUIDS[139,557]
Over-all Coefficients U Expressed as Btu/(Hr)(Sq Ft)(Deg F)

Substance inside coil	Substance outside coil	Coil material	Agitation	U	Reference
Steam	Water	Lead	Agitated	70	581
Steam	Sugar and molasses solutions	Copper	None	50–240	705
Steam	Boiling aqueous solution	....	....	600	113
Cold water	Dilute organic dye intermediate	Lead	Turbo-agitator at 95 rpm	300	113
Cold water	Warm water	Wrought iron	Air bubbled into water surrounding coil	150–300	115
Cold water	Hot water	Lead	0.40 rpm paddle stirrer	90–360	560
Brine	Amino acids	....	30 rpm	100	113
Cold water	25 per cent oleum at 60°C	Wrought iron	Agitated	20	71
Water	Aqueous solution	Lead	Sleeve propeller at 500 rpm	250	581
Water	8% NaOH	....	22 rpm	155	113
Steam	Fatty acid	Copper (pan cake)	None	96–100	481
Milk	Water	....	Agitated	300	218

Miscellaneous Shapes.—King[388] reports that the data of Montsinger and Milner on natural convection from a heated copper block, 11 in. long, $\frac{1}{2}$ in. thick and $2\frac{1}{2}$ in. high, submerged in several grades of transformer oils, are correlated by the dimen-

* This is the same as Eq. 17, p. 241.
† Nusselt,[520] Langmuir,[420] and Kirkpitscheff.[396]

sional equation

$$h_c = 17 \, \Delta t^{0.25}/(\mu'_f)^{0.4} \tag{26}$$

Data for heat loss from finned convectors and cast-iron sections are available.[405]

Coils and Liquids.—As noted on page 246, Fig. 128 may be used to predict values of h_c from a *single* horizontal cylinder to a liquid. However, where steam coils of various designs are submerged in tanks of liquids, the results will differ with the design and location

TABLE X.—JACKETED VESSELS*
Over-all Coefficients U Expressed in Btu/(Hr)(Sq Ft)(Deg F)

Fluid inside jacket	Fluid in vessel	Wall material	Agitation	U	Reference
Steam	Water	Enameled CI	0–400 rpm	96–120	570
Steam	Milk	Enameled CI	None	200	80
Steam	Milk	Enameled CI	Stirring	300	80
Steam	Boiling milk	Enameled CI	None	500	80
Steam	Milk	Enameled CI	200 rpm	86	570
Steam	Fruit slurry	Enameled CI	None	33–90	570
Steam	Fruit slurry	Enameled CI	Stirring	154	570
Steam	Water	CI with loose lead lining	Agitated	4–9	581
Steam	Water	CI with loose lead lining	None	3	581
Steam	Boiling SO₂	Steel	. . . .	60	581
Steam	Boiling water	Steel	. . . .	187	581
Hot water	Warm water	Enameled CI	None	70	570
Cold water	Cold water	Enameled CI	None	43	570
Ice water	Cold water	Stoneware	Agitated	7	581
Ice water	Cold water	Stoneware	None	5	581
Brine, low velocity	Nitration slurry	Stoneware	35–38 rpm	32–60	113
Water	Sodium alcohol-ate solution	Frederking (cast in coil)	Agitated, baffled	80	113
Steam	Evaporating water	Copper	. . . .	381	604a
Steam	Evaporating water	Enamelware	. . . .	37	604a
Steam	Water	Copper	None	148	14
Steam	Water	Copper	Simple stirring	244	14
Steam	Boiling water	Copper	None	250	14
Steam	Paraffin wax	Copper	None	27	328
Steam	Paraffin wax	Cast iron	Scraper	107	328
Water	Paraffin wax	Copper	None	24	328
Water	Paraffin wax	Cast iron	Scraper	72	328

of the coil and obviously will be affected by the use of stirrers, scrapers, the deposition of scale, etc. (see page 138). Over-all coefficients are given in Tables IX and X.*

* Colburn, references 139 and 557.

TABLE XI.—ORDINARY RANGES OF U*
(Under special conditions higher or lower values may be realized)
Over-all Coefficients U Expressed in Btu/(Hr)(Sq Ft)(Deg F)

Type of heat exchanger	State of controlling resistance		Typical fluid	Typical apparatus
	Free convection, U	Forced convection, U		
Liquid to liquid................	25– 60	150–300	Water	Liquid-to-liquid heat exchangers
Liquid to liquid................	5– 10	20– 50	Oil	
Liquid to gas...................	1– 3	2– 10	....	Hot-water radiators
Liquid to boiling liquid...........	20– 60	50–150	Water	Brine coolers
Liquid to boiling liquid...........	5– 20	25– 60	Oil	
Gas to liquid...................	1– 3	2– 10	....	Air coolers, economizers
Gas to gas.....................	0.6– 2	2– 6	....	Steam superheaters
Gas to boiling liquid.............	1– 3	2– 10	....	Steam boilers
Condensing vapor to liquid........	50–200	150–800	Steam to water	Liquid heaters and condensers
Condensing vapor to liquid........	10– 30	20– 60	Steam to oil	
Condensing vapor to liquid........	40– 80	60–150	Organic vapor to water	
Condensing vapor to liquid........	....	15–300	Steam-gas mixture	
Condensing vapor to gas..........	1– 2	2– 10	....	Steam pipes in air, air heaters
Condensing vapor to boiling liquid..	40–100	......	....	Scale-forming evaporators
Condensing vapor to boiling liquid..	300–800	......	Steam to water	
Condensing vapor to boiling liquid..	50–150	......	Steam to oil	

* Colburn, references 139 and 557.

Problems

1. It is desired to preheat 31,600 lb of air per hour from 70 to 200°F by means of dry saturated steam condensing at 220°F inside vertical standard 1-in. steel pipes (see page 416). The heater consists of a staggered bank of vertical pipes, each 4 ft long, spaced on 2⅝-in. equilateral-triangular centers. It is agreed that the heater is to be 40 rows wide.

Calculate the necessary number of rows of pipe and the total feet of pipe required.

2. By brazing a helical ribbon of metal to the outside of the pipes, the total area per foot of pipe will be eight times that for the plain pipe. If it is assumed that the average value of h is 0.8 times that for the plain pipe, how many rows of this finned pipe would be required for the conditions and duty of Problem 1?

3. An electrically heated wire having an emissivity of 0.70 is maintained at 140°F in a room that is maintained at 40°F, and the steady heat loss is 500 Btu/

(hr)(sq ft of wire surface). It is proposed to increase the temperature of the surface of the wire to 440°F.

Calculate the heat loss expressed in Btu/(hr)(sq ft) when the steady state is obtained, the room being maintained at 40°F.

4. Producer gas under 5-lb gauge pressure is flowing at a steady rate of 5440 lb/hr through a horizontal bare steel main having an i.d. of 16 in. and an o.d. of 16.5 in. The surroundings are at 100°F.

a. Calculate the local heat loss as Btu/(hr)(sq ft of outer surface) of this pipe at a cross section where the true gas temperature is 1700°F.

b. Outline the method that you would use to obtain the heat loss from a substantial length L of the producer-gas main, if it is assumed that the temperature of the gas entering the main is known, giving one complete sample calculation.

Data and Notes.—The Orsat analysis of the dry producer gas shows 8.3 mol per cent CO_2 and 91.7 mol per cent CO, H_2, N_2, and hydrocarbons. The molal ratio CO_2:H_2O is 2.67.

Assume the following physical properties for the producer gas: c_p of 0.29 Btu/(lb)(deg F), μ of 0.11 lb/(hr)(ft), and k of 0.043 Btu/(hr)(sq ft)(deg F per ft).

5. A glass thermometer (ϵ of 0.96) is inserted in a large duct of circular cross section at right angles to the walls; the thermometer bulb, $\frac{1}{4}$ in. in diameter, is at the center of the duct. Air flows through the duct at the rate of 4000 lb/(hr)(sq ft of duct cross section). The temperature of the walls of the duct is 786°F, and the thermometer reads 300°F.

a. Calculate the true temperature of the gas.

b. If a thin silver shield (ϵ of 0.03) is placed around the thermometer bulb, what will be the new reading of the thermometer?

c. Calculate the temperature that would be indicated if the thermometer were replaced by a thermocouple having a cylindrical junction $\frac{1}{16}$-in. in diameter placed so that the gas flow is normal to the longitudinal axis of the cylindrical junction (ϵ of 0.90).

6. An air heater involves condensation of steam inside horizontal tubes and flow of air at right angles to the tubes in a shell containing a number of vertical segmental baffles. When using exhaust steam condensing at a gauge pressure of 5 lb/sq in. and G_{max} of 2000 lb air/(hr)(sq ft), the apparatus will heat air from 80 to 180°F.

What G_{max} should be used to make the apparatus heat hydrogen (molecular weight of 2.02) from 80 to 180°F, using the same steam pressure?

7. A high-velocity thermocouple assembly consists of a standard $\frac{3}{4}$-in. steel pipe with a calibrated unshielded thermocouple (0.024 in. o.d.) inserted at the axis of the tube at such a large distance from the open end that radiation from the surroundings has a negligible effect on the temperature of the thermocouple. Furnace gases are aspirated through the tube to give a mass velocity of 10,000 lb/(hr)(sq ft of cross section); the thermocouple in the gas stream attains a steady reading of 2070°F; and the temperature of the inner wall of the tube is 1850°F.

Calculate the true temperature of the gas.

8. In the heat-measurements laboratory a test was run on a cylindrical rod fin having a diameter of $\frac{4}{3}$ in. and a length of 24 in. One end was attached to a heated base maintained at t_o of 370°F, and the other end was insulated, the sides being exposed to air of the room at t_a of 70°F. When the steady state was obtained, the observed curve of fin temperature *vs.* length was used to calculate the *average* loss from the entire fin, which was 250 Btu/(hr)(sq ft). If a cylindrical rod fin had a diameter of $\frac{3}{8}$ in., t_o of 370°, h of 5, what length would be necessary to make the average heat loss 250 Btu/(hr)(sq ft), for t_a of 70°F? Assume the free end to be insulated and h of 5 in both cases.

9. A finned steam pipe, to be used in an air heater, consists of a standard $\frac{3}{4}$-in. steel pipe, on which is wound spirally a crimped steel fin (k of 26) of rectangular cross section, 0.03 in. thick by 0.50 in. wide. The fin extends radially 0.50 in. from the tube surface and makes four turns per inch of pipe length. At the air velocity used, h is 7.7, t_a is 70°F.

    a. If the pipe carries dry saturated steam condensing at 344°F, what will be the temperature at the outer tip of the fin?

    b. Calculate the "effectiveness" of the fin, $\Delta t_m/\Delta t_o$.

    c. What would be the heat loss in Btu/(hr)(ft of pipe length)?

    d. Repeat *c* for the bare pipe if no fins are used, for h of 8.0.

CHAPTER IX

CONDENSING VAPORS

Introduction.—This chapter deals with heat transfer for condensing vapors, in both the absence and presence of noncondensable gases, and is divided into five sections:

    I. Pure saturated vapors.

    II. Pure superheated vapors.

    III. Mixed vapors.

    IV. Effect of noncondensable gas.

    V. Direct contact of liquid and mixture of vapor and gas.

The first four sections deal with condensation of vapors upon a colder wall separating the vapor and cooling medium, as in surface condensers, feed heaters, and evaporators. The mechanism and theory are considered in detail, data of various observers are correlated, and recommended relations are given. An alignment chart is included to facilitate the use of the Nusselt equation. A graphical method of resolving the observed over-all thermal resistance into the individual resistances is illustrated by data for several vapors.

The fifth section deals with cases in which the cooling medium and gas are in direct contact, as in humidification and dehumidification in packed towers or spray chambers. Calculations are facilitated by combining the humidity and temperature potentials in an enthalpy potential.

Table III summarizes the coefficients for film type condensation of 20 different pure vapors on horizontal and vertical tubes and reports deviations from the theoretical relations (Eqs. 10 and 13); data for seven additional vapors are given in Table VIII. Typical results are plotted in Figs. 132, 133, and 135, which justify use of the recommended relation, Fig. 136; the alignment chart (Fig. 137) applies for streamline flow of condensate, usually obtained with film type condensation on horizontal tubes. An illustrative problem is solved on page 270. Data for mixed vapors are scarce, Figs. 141 and 142. Results for dropwise condensation of steam are given on pages 276 and 279 and over-all coefficients for the condensation of refrigerant vapors are summarized on pages 271 to 274.   The usual design procedure for pipe-coil dehumidifiers is outlined on pages 283 to 285, and that for cooling towers is developed on pages 285 to 292.   Mass-transfer coefficients for the evaporation of water into air, in terms of the height of an over-all mass-transfer unit, are summarized in Table X and Fig. 144.   Practice problems are given on pages 292 and 293.

I. CONDENSATION OF PURE SATURATED VAPOR

Mechanism: Dropwise vs. Film-type Condensation.—In a study[641] of the condensation of steam on a *vertical* water-cooled

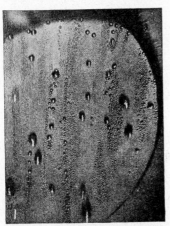 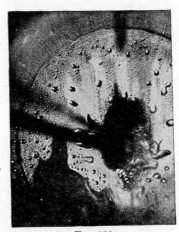

Fig. 130.   Fig. 131.

Fig. 130.—*Dropwise* condensation of steam on vertical plate.

Fig. 131.—Layer and dropwise condensation of steam on vertical plate.   (*Photographs from Schmidt, Schurig, and Sellschopp,*[641] *Technische Mechanik und Thermodynamik.*)

wall, photographs were taken of the condensate side of the plate. On a rusty or etched plate, the steam condensed in a continuous *film* over the entire wall.   With a polished surface of chromium-plated copper, the condensate was formed in *drops*, which rapidly grew in size (up to 3 mm in diameter) and ran down the plate. Dropwise condensation could also be brought about, for a while, by coating the surface with a thin petroleum oil that later washed away.   Figure 130 shows dropwise condensation on the polished chromium-plated surface of copper; Fig. 131 shows dropwise condensation on clean areas and film condensation on areas coated with rust brought in by the steam.   Dropwise condensation gave coefficients of heat transfer four to eight times as high as film condensation, and the latter type gave results agreeing with the theoretical equation of Nusselt given later. Spoelstra[687] found dropwise condensation of steam promoted by a small concentration of oil vapor in the steam, and an increase in heat transfer compared with results for oil-free steam. A more complete discussion of dropwise condensation is given on page 275.

TABLE I.—NOMENCLATURE FOR CONDENSATION

A Area of heat-transfer surface, square feet; A_i for inside, A_L for coolant side, A_0 for outside, A_v for vapor side, A_w for tube wall (mean of A_L and A_v).

a Total heat-transfer surface divided by total volume of tower, $a = A/S_0z$, square feet per cubic foot.

a_0 Dimensional constant in Eq. 21, equal to h_L for a water velocity of 1 ft/sec but based on outside surface.

a_1 Dimensionless constant in Eq. 15.

a_2 Dimensional constant in Eq. 20.

a_4 $\lambda_o - 0.45t_o$; with t_o of 32°F, $a_4 = 1061.4$ Btu/lb of steam.

b Breadth of condensing surface, feet; for a vertical tube, b equals πD; for a horizontal tube, b equals L_H.

c Specific heat, Btu/(lb fluid)(deg F); c_L for liquid coolant, c_p for constant pressure, c_{pv} for vapor.

c_s Humid heat, Btu/(lb dry gas)(deg F); for air at ordinary temperatures, c_s equals $0.24 + 0.45H$.

D Diameter of tube, feet; D_0 for o.d., D_i for i.d., D_i' for *inches*.

D_v Diffusivity of vapor (volumetric units), square feet per hour (see $\mu_v\rho_v/D_v$).

d Prefix, indicating derivative, dimensionless.

e Base of Napierian or natural logarithms.

F_t Dimensionless factor to allow for variation in tube temperature, see Table II.

F_V Dimensionless factor to allow for finite velocity of vapor, see Table IV.

G_f Mass velocity of film of condensate, lb/(hr)(sq ft of cross section of film).

G_G Superficial mass velocity of dry gas; equals w_G/S_o, lb/(hr)(sq ft of total cross section).

G_L Superficial mass velocity of coolant, equals W/S_o, lb/(hr)(sq ft of gross cross section).

g Acceleration due to gravity, ordinarily taken as 4.17×10^8 ft/(hr)(hr).

g_c Conversion factor 4.17×10^8 lb force $\times$ ft/(pounds fluid)(hr)(hr), or 32.2 with time in seconds.

H "Absolute" humidity, pounds of water vapor per pound of dry gas; H_i is saturation value at t_i; H_G is H of bulk of vapor-gas stream, H_{G1} at gas inlet, and H_{G2} at gas outlet; H_L is saturation value of H at t_L.

h Local coefficient of heat transfer, Btu/(hr)(sq ft)(deg F).

TABLE I.—NOMENCLATURE FOR CONDENSATION.—(*Continued*)

h_m Mean value of h with respect to height of condensing surface, Btu/(hr) (sq ft)(deg F).

h_d Mean coefficient for dirt deposit, Btu/(hr)(sq ft)(deg F), see Chap. VI.

h_G Mean coefficient for transfer of sensible heat through gas film, Btu/ (hr)(sq ft)(deg F), see Chaps. VII and VIII.

h_L Mean coefficient of heat transfer to coolant, Btu/(hr)(sq ft)(deg F), see Chaps. VII and VIII.

h_r Coefficient of heat transfer due to radiation, Btu/(hr)(sq ft)(deg F), see Chap. III.

i Enthalpy, Btu per pound; for gas vapor mixture, i_G equals $c_s t + a_4 H_G$; i_i is value of i_G at t_i; i_L equals i_G based on t_L.

K_G Mass transfer coefficient through gas film, lb of vapor condensed/(hr) (sq ft)(unit potential difference expressed in atmospheres).

K' Mass transfer coefficient, expressed in lb of vapor condensed/(hr) (sq ft)(unit humidity potential difference); K'_G for **gas film,** based on $H_i - H_G$; K'_o for **over-all** value based on $H_L - H_G$.

k_f Thermal conductivity of condensate at t_f, Btu/(hr)(sq ft)(deg F per ft).

k_G Thermal conductivity of gas-vapor mixture.

k_w Thermal conductivity of tube wall, Btu/(hr)(sq ft)(deg F per ft).

L Length of a straight tube, feet; L_H for horizontal and L_v for vertical tube.

M Molecular weight; M_n for noncondensable gas (28.97 for air), M_v for vapor (18.02 for steam).

N Number of rows of tubes in a vertical tier; N_H is a horizontal plane.

P Total absolute pressure, *atmospheres*.

p Partial pressure, *atmospheres* absolute; p_n for noncondensable gas, p_{nm} for logarithmic mean of p_{ni} at gas-liquid interface, and p_{nv} in main body of gas stream; p_v for condensable vapor in main body of gas stream; p_{vi} is vapor pressure of liquid at t_i, p_L is vapor pressure of condensate at temperature t_L of coolant.

q Rate of heat transfer, Btu per hour; in general, q or Σq is total by all mechanisms; q_G is based on transfer of sensible heat by means of h_G, q_λ of latent heat by means of conduction through film x of condensate, q_L total transfer to coolant.

R Thermal resistance, degrees Fahrenheit times hours divided by Btu; R_d for dirt deposit, R_L for coolant, R_v for vapor side, R_w for tube wall, ΣR for total resistance ($= 1/U$).

$(Re)_f$ Reynolds number, $4 r_h G/\mu_f$, dimensionless; for a horizontal tube $(Re)_f = 2\Gamma'/\mu_f$; for a vertical tube $(Re)_f = 4\Gamma/\mu_f$; $r_h = S/b$.

S_o Total cross section (ground area) of vertical tower, square feet.

S Cross section of film of condensate, square feet.

t Temperature, degrees Fahrenheit; $t_f = t_{sv} - 3\Delta t/4$ for condensate film; t_G for gas stream (bulk temperature); t_{G1} and t_{G2} for inlet and outlet gas, respectively; t_i for liquid-gas interface; t_L for coolant (bulk temperature); t_{L1} and t_{L2} for inlet and outlet coolant; t_s for condensing surface; t_{sv} for saturation temperature or dew-point tem-

TABLE I.—NOMENCLATURE FOR CONDENSATION.—(*Continued*)

perature of vapor; t_{wb} for wet-bulb temperature; t_v for actual temperature of vapor.

U Over-all coefficient of heat transfer, Btu/(hr)(sq ft)(deg F); U_G is based on q_G and $t_G - t_L$; U' is based on Σq and $t_i - t_L$.

V Average velocity, feet per hour.

V' Average velocity of coolant, feet per second.

W Coolant rate, pounds per hour; W_1 at inlet and W_2 at outlet.

w_G Dry-gas rate, pounds per hour.

w Mass rate of flow of condensate from *lowest* point on condensing surface, pounds per hour; w_z at distance z from top of condensing surface.

x Length of conduction path, thickness of film of condensate, feet.

x_i Mol fraction of more volatile component in condensate at t_i.

x_w Thickness of tube wall, feet.

X Abscissas of graphs.

Y Ordinates of graphs.

y Linear distance in Eq. 20, feet.

z Distance of a point from top of a vertical tube; height of a vertical tower, feet.

z_G Height or length of a "mass-transfer unit," feet, based on gas-film resistance; $z_G = G_G/K_G'a$.

z_{OG} Height of an **over-all** "mass-transfer unit," feet, based on overall humidity difference; $z_{OG} = G_G/K_O'a$.

z_{ot} Height of an **over-all** "heat-transfer unit," feet; $z_{ot} = G_G c_s/U_G a$.

z_t Height of a "heat-transfer unit," feet; $z_t = G_G c_s/h_G a$.

Z Complex dimensionless term defined below (Table IV).

Γ Mass rate of flow of condensate from lowest point on condensing surface, divided by the breadth, lb/(hr)(ft); for a vertical tube, Γ equals $w/\pi D$; for a horizontal tube, Γ' equals w/L; in general, Γ is used to designate both Γ and Γ': Γ_z is the local value of Γ at position z.

ΔP Pressure drop, force pounds per square foot of cross section.

Δt Temperature difference, degrees Fahrenheit. For condensing pure vapors, saturated or superheated, Δt equals $t_{sv} - t_s$.

Δt_o Over-all temperature difference, $t_{sv} - t_L$, degrees Fahrenheit; Δt_{ob} and Δt_{ot} refer to bottom and top, respectively.

λ Ethalpy change, latent heat of condensation, Btu per pound; λ at saturation temperature, λ_{32} at 32°F, and λ_o at base temperature.

μ_f Absolute viscosity of condensate film at t_f, lb/(hr)(ft); μ equals $2.42 \times \mu_f'$ in centipoises. If μ_f is viscosity in force pounds $\times$ hours per square foot, $\mu_f = \mu_F g_c$.

μ_v Absolute viscosity μ of gas-vapor stream, lb/(hr)(ft).

$\mu_v/\rho_v D_v$ Schmidt number, dimensionless; for air-steam mixtures at ordinary pressures, $\mu_v/\rho_v D_v$ equals 0.71.

π 3.1416 $\cdots$.

ρ_f Density of condensate film at t_f, pounds per cubic foot.

ρ_v Density of gas-vapor mixture, pounds per cubic foot.

ϕ Prefix, indicating function.

ψ Angle of inclination from horizontal.

Film-type Condensation

Theoretical Relations.—In 1916, Nusselt[525]* derived theoretical relations for predicting the coefficient of heat transfer between a pure saturated vapor and a colder surface. It was assumed that streamline motion exists throughout the thickness of the continuous film of condensate on the cooling surface. In deriving the simple relations given below, it was further assumed that the force of gravity alone causes the flow of condensate over the surface, thus neglecting the possible effect of vapor velocity upon the thickness of the condensate film. By employing the definition of viscosity and assuming zero velocity of the condensate at the wall and a maximum velocity at the liquid-vapor interface, theoretical equations were obtained for the thickness of the film of condensate at a given point on the surface. The local coefficient of heat transfer may then be calculated upon assuming that the total thermal resistance lies in the film of condensate, through which the latent heat of condensation is conducted, neglecting the cooling of the condensate. Upon assuming that the temperature difference between vapor and wall is constant at all points, the resulting theoretical equations for the mean coefficients of heat transfer involve the thermal conductivity, viscosity, and density of the condensate, the temperature difference between vapor and solid, and certain dimensions of the apparatus.

Upon increase of the difference in temperature between saturated vapor and surface, it is clear that the rate of heat transmission q would be increased and the average thickness of the condensate layer would increase. Since heat is assumed to flow through the condensate film only by conduction, it follows that the coefficient of heat transfer should decrease with increase in the temperature difference. Since the physical properties involved, especially viscosity, depend upon temperature, changes in film temperatures should theoretically affect the coefficient of heat transfer.

At any distance z below the top of the tube where condensation starts, heat is transferred solely by conduction through the condensate film having local thickness x:

$$h = \frac{k_f}{x} = \frac{dq}{(dA)(\Delta t)} = \frac{\lambda \, dw_z}{(b \, dz)(\Delta t)} = \frac{\lambda \, d\Gamma_z}{dz \, \Delta t} \tag{1}$$

* The derivations are given in English in references 148, 484, and 339 and in German in references 713, 697, 271, and 479. In reference 413, it is shown that the accelerating force in the film is negligible compared with the viscous drag.

Let $d\Gamma_z$ equal dw/b, where b is the perimeter πD. For the entire tube, of length L, by definition,

$$h_m = \frac{q}{(A)(\Delta t)} = \frac{\lambda w}{(bL)(\Delta t)} = \frac{\lambda \Gamma}{L \, \Delta t} \tag{2}$$

Combining Eqs. 1 and 2 to eliminate Δt, which is assumed constant,

$$\frac{k_f}{x} = \frac{h_m L}{\Gamma} \frac{d\Gamma_z}{dz} \tag{3}$$

From the theory of isothermal streamline flow down vertical wetted walls,*

$$\Gamma_z = \rho_f^2 g x^3 / 3\mu_f \tag{4}$$

Elimination of x from Eqs. 3 and 4 gives

$$k_f \left(\frac{\rho_f^2 g}{3\mu_f} \right)^{1/3} dz = \frac{h_m L}{\Gamma} \Gamma_z^{1/3} \, d\Gamma_z \tag{5}$$

Integration from 0 to L and from 0 to Γ gives

$$h_m = \frac{4}{3} k_f \left(\frac{\rho_f^2 g}{3\mu_f \Gamma} \right)^{1/3} = 0.925 k_f \left(\frac{\rho_f^2 g}{\mu_f \Gamma} \right)^{1/3} \tag{6}$$

Equation 6 may be rearranged to involve the Reynolds number based on μ_f:

$$(Re)_f = \frac{4 r_h G}{\mu_f} = \frac{4}{\mu_f} \left(\frac{S}{b} \right) \left(\frac{w}{S} \right) = \frac{4w}{\mu_f b} = \frac{4\Gamma}{\mu_f}$$

giving

$$h_m \left(\frac{\mu_f^2}{k_f^3 \rho_f^2 g} \right)^{1/3} = 1.47 \left(\frac{4\Gamma}{\mu_f} \right)^{-1/3} = 1.47 (Re)_f^{-1/3} \tag{7}$$

Elimination of Γ from Eqs. 6 and 2 gives

$$h_m = 0.943 \left(\frac{k_f^3 \rho_f^2 g \lambda}{L \mu_f \, \Delta t} \right)^{1/4} \tag{8}$$

The local coefficient h at any z is obtained by eliminating x from Eqs. 1 and 4.

Vertical Surfaces.—As shown above, the theoretical dimensionless equations of Nusselt for film-type condensation on vertical surfaces are

$$h = (k_f^3 \rho_f^2 g / 3\mu_f \Gamma_z)^{1/3} \tag{9}$$

$$h_m = 0.943 (k_f^3 \rho_f^2 g \Gamma / \mu_f L \, \Delta t)^{1/4} \tag{10}$$

$$h_m \left(\frac{\mu_f^2}{k_f^3 \rho_f^2 g} \right)^{1/3} = 1.47 \left(\frac{4\Gamma}{\mu_f} \right)^{-1/3} \tag{11}$$

These equations should for streamline flow not be used for $4\Gamma/\mu_f$ exceeding 2100 or for dropwise or mixed condensation. For

---

* Assuming a linear gradient in temperature through the film, and that $1/\mu$ is linear in t, Drew[188] shows that μ_f should be evaluated at $t_f = t_{sv} - 3 \, \Delta t/4$.

planes inclined at an angle ψ with the horizontal, the values of h and h_m are to be multiplied by $(\sin \psi)^{1/4}$. Comparison of Eqs. 9 and 11 shows that the local coefficient at the end of the condensing section is three-fourths of the mean value for the condensing section.

When a liquid flows isothermally down vertical tubes,[154] measurements of the average thickness of the liquid film substantiate Eq. 4 for values of the Reynolds number $4w/b\mu$ ranging from 1 to 2000. Wave motion in the film may cause the *maximum* thickness at the crest of a ripple to be as much as 2.5 times[236] that predicted by Eq. 4, although the *mean* thickness of the film is found to check the theoretical value.[236] For a given amount of liquid on the wall, the occurrence of ripples causes a variation in x and gives a larger *average* value[251] of k_f/x than when no ripples occur and x is constant. Consequently, ripples should cause the coefficient of heat transfer to exceed that predicted from theory.

Variation in Tube-wall Temperature.—In the Nusselt derivations, it was assumed that the temperature difference was constant. In the usual condenser, cooled by a liquid that rises considerably in temperature, the temperature difference varies substantially. The heat balance shows that the over-all temperature difference, Δt_o, from condensing vapor to coolant, is linear in q_z or Γ_z. Modification[188,313] of the derivation[741] for condensation of pure saturated vapors shows that the value of h_m should be taken as F_t times those obtained from Eqs. 10 and 11, where the dimensionless factor F_t varies slightly with the ratio of over-all temperature differences at bottom and top of the vertical condenser, $\Delta t_{ob}/\Delta t_{ot}$, as shown in Table II.

TABLE II

$\Delta t_{ob}/\Delta t_{ot}$	0.5	1.0	2.0	5.0
F_t	0.96	1.0	1.06	1.15

Single Horizontal Tubes.—By a derivation similar to that for vertical surfaces, Nusselt[525] obtained the following dimensionless equations:

$$h = 0.693(k_f^3 \rho_f^2 g \sin \phi / \Gamma_z' \mu_f)^{1/3} \tag{12}$$
$$h_m = 0.725(k_f^3 \lambda \rho_f^2 g / D \mu_f \, \Delta t)^{1/4} \tag{13}*$$

* By assuming that the local rate of condensation was uniform with perimeter, instead of assuming constant Δt, Parr[548] obtained a constant of 0.75 instead of the 0.725 obtained by Nusselt.

$$h_m \left(\frac{\mu_f^2}{k_f^3 \rho_f^2 g}\right)^{1/3} = 1.2(Re_f)^{-1/3} = 1.51 \left(\frac{4\Gamma'}{\mu_f}\right)^{-1/3} \tag{14}*$$

wherein Γ' designates w/L_H. These equations are subject to the same limitations as those for vertical tubes. In the derivation, it was shown that 59.4 per cent of the condensate is formed on the upper half of the tube. For N horizontal tubes arranged in a vertical plane so that the condensate from one tube flows onto the tube directly below without splashing, h_m in Eq. 13 theoretically depends on the fourth root of N. This effect of N is automatically allowed for in Eq. 14, which contains Γ', based on the total condensate from the lowest tube in the tier.

Vertical vs. Horizontal Tube.—Comparison of Eqs. 10 and 13 for a given Δt shows that vertical and horizontal tubes should give the same h_m if the length of the vertical tube is 2.87 times the outside diameter of the horizontal tube. If a tube had a ratio of length to diameter of 100:1, theoretically, h_m for the horizontal position would be 2.44 times that for the vertical position.

The term Γ of the equation for vertical surface equals $w/\pi D$, and Γ' of the equation for horizontal tubes equals w/L_H where w is the total condensation rate per tube, D is the diameter of the vertical tube, and L_H is the length of the straight horizontal tube. If Γ is used to designate both Γ for vertical tubes and Γ' for horizontal tubes, Eqs. 11 and 14 become

$$h_m \left(\frac{\mu_f^2}{k_f^3 \rho_f^2 g}\right)^{1/3} = a_1 \left(\frac{4\Gamma}{\mu_f}\right)^{-1/3} \tag{15}$$

where the purely numerical constant a_1 is 1.47 for a vertical and 1.5 for a horizontal tube. Hence little error is introduced by using Eq. 15 for both vertical and horizontal tubes,[193] with a_1 taken as 1.5. To facilitate calculations, the term $(k_f^3 \rho_f^2 g/\mu_f^2)^{1/3}$ for water is tabulated as a function of temperature on page 413.

Given measured coefficients h_1, h_2, . . . h_N for each of N rows of horizontal pipes[784a] in a vertical tier, or for successive sections of a vertical surface.[652] The coefficients for the top tube or section

---

* For a horizontal tube,

$$(R\epsilon)_f = \frac{4 r_h G}{\mu_f} = \frac{4}{\mu_f}\left(\frac{S}{L}\right)\left(\frac{w/2}{S}\right) = \frac{2\Gamma'}{\mu_f} \tag{14a}$$

Hence the critical Reynolds number of 2100 corresponds to $4\Gamma'/\mu_f$ of 4200 for a **horizontal** tube.

TABLE III.—DATA OF VARIOUS OBSERVERS CONDENSING PURE SATURATED VAPORS[a] OUTSIDE HORIZONTAL H AND VERTICAL V TUBES

Ref. No.	Vapor	Range of h_m	Range of Δt, deg F	Range Obs. h_m / Pred.* h_m	V or H	Diam- eter, in.	Length, ft	Observer
457	Steam	2100–3400	22–43	1.0–1.3	H	0.675	4.0	McAdams and Frost
541	Steam	1700–5000	2–19	0.7–1.2	H	3.0	3.9	Othmer
40	Steam	2800–4100	3–13	....	H	1.31	3.67	Baker and Mueller
742	Steam	3800–4300	9–11	1.5–1.7	H	0.84	2.5	Wallace and Davison
41[a]	Steam	3200–6500	7–66	1.5–2.2	H	0.625	3.67	Baker and Tsao
292	Steam	680–1900	5–39	Av. 1.5	V	1.0	12.0	Hebbard and Badger
475	Steam[b]	840–1800	5–48	Av. 1.5	V	1.0	12.0	Meisenburg *et al.*
39	Steam	1300–2500	2–23	*Ca.* 1.7	V	0.875	8.0	Fragen
39	Steam	700–1500	3–34	Av. 1.2	V	2.0	20.0	Baker *et al.*
652	Steam	....		Av.	V	Plate	.....	Shea and Krase
457	Benzene	310–370	23–28	0.8–0.9	H	0.675	4.0	McAdams and Frost
393	Benzene	242–381	42–67	0.84–1.22	H	1.31	8.2	Kirkbride
40	Benzene	235–262	31–62	....	H	1.31	3.67	Baker and Meuller
742	Benzene	264–289	56–79	0.98–1.07	H	0.84	.....	Wallace and Davison
41	Benzene	307–315	114	1.07–1.10	H	0.625	3.67	Baker and Tsao
485	Diphenyl	225–400	8–27	....	H	1.7	9.4	Montillon *et al.*
31	Diphenyl	120–430	23–130	Turbulent	V	0.75	12.0	Badger *et al.*
28	Dowtherm *A*	118–545	35–72	Turbulent	V	0.875	11.7	Badger
393	Naphtha[c]	174–361	22–85	0.84–1.16	H	1.31	8.2	Kirkbride
393	Oleum spirits[d]	212–362	17–38	0.81–1.05	H	1.31	8.2	Kirkbride
393	Oil vapor[e]	190–260	55–60	0.80–1.27	H	1.31	8.2	Kirkbride
722	Tetrachloroethylene[f]	170–190	58–135	0.64–0.90	H	1.00	3.67	Tsao
457	Tetrachloromethane (CCl₄)	280	27	0.9	H	0.675	4.0	McAdams and Frost
722	Trichloroethylene[f]	244–262	54–85	0.84–0.99	H	1.00	3.67	Tsao
722	Toluene[f]	203–300	21–115	0.76–1.04	H	1.00	3.67	Tsao
742	Toluene	193–241	55–72	0.77–0.96	H	0.84	2.5	Wallace and Davison
553	Turpentine[g]	326–514	24–84	....	H	1.31	6.0	Patton and Feagen
543	Methanol[h]	500–600	14–28	1.06	H	2.0	1.63	Othmer and White
543	Ethanol[h]	320–450	11–39	1.02	H	2.0	1.63	Othmer and White
277	Ethanol	200–340	20–98	0.78–1.03	V	0.405	0.47	Hagenbuch
543	Propanol[h]	250–300	23–47	0.87	H	2.0	1.63	Othmer and White
543	Butanol[h]	250–300	22–50	0.85	H	2.0	1.63	Othmer and White
543	*i*-propanol[h]	235–263	17–45	0.73–0.95	H			
543	*i*-butanol[h]	194–210	26–56	....	H	2.0	1.63	Othmer and White
543	Sec-butanol[h]	191–213	21–58	....	H	2.0	1.63	Othmer and White
543	Tert-butanol[h]	154–192	15–46	....	H	2.0	1.63	Othmer and White

* Based on observed Δt and Eqs. 10 or 13.

[a] Data of Jakob and coworkers are discussed on p. 266; values of h_m for a number of vapors, deduced from U, are tabulated on p. 275.

[b] With 3 per cent air by weight, the observed h_m checked Eq. 10.

[c] 58° API; IBP, 220°F; 50 per cent off at 258°F; EP, 340°F.

[d] 48° API; IBP, 254°F; 50 per cent off at 346°F; EP, 423°F.

[e] 42° API; IBP, 348°F; 50 per cent off at 424°F; EP, 504°F.

[f] Data made available through the courtesy of Prof. E. M. Baker.

[g] Condensate (turpentine and water) boils at 204°F.

[h] Figure 6 of reference 543 shows an alignment chart based on data of reference 543.

may properly be compared with Eqs. 13 or 8 for the local coefficients
on a surface having no condensate fed to the highest point. Since
the second row or section receives condensate from the first, the
'ocal coefficients for these sections should not be compared with
Eqs. 13 or 8. However, the mean coefficient for the two highest
sections may correctly be compared with Eq. 15, involving Γ leaving
the second section. If each of the two sections are equal in size,

$$h_m = \frac{(q_1 + q_2)/2A_1}{(\Delta t_1 + \Delta t_2)/2}$$

and hence $h_m\sqrt[3]{\mu_f^2/k_f^3\rho_f^2 g}$ should be plotted *vs.* $4\Gamma/\mu_f$ and compared
with Eq. 15, wherein $\Gamma_2' = (q_1 + q_2)/\lambda L$ for two horizontal tubes
in a vertical tier, and $\Gamma_2 = (q_1 + q_2)/\lambda\pi D$ for the two highest sections
of a vertical tube. A similar procedure applies for any number of
sections, so long as the Reynolds number is less than 2100 for the
condensate leaving the section.

Data.—A number of experiments have been published on heat-
transfer between pure saturated vapors and single horizontal or
vertical tubes. Because the coefficients of heat transfer are so high
for vapors such as saturated steam, temperature differences between
vapor and solid are relatively small. As pointed out on page 151,
the measurement of small differences in temperature offers considerable difficulty, and, in general, the available coefficients of
heat transfer between pure saturated vapors and single horizontal
tubes are not so precise as might be desired.

Table III describes the apparatus and operating conditions
employed by a number of different investigators and gives deviations from Eqs. 10 and 13.

Figure 132 shows data* for steam condensing on the outer
surface of vertical tubes, 8 to 20 ft high, compared with the theoretical Eq. 15. For a given Reynolds number $4\Gamma/\mu_f$ at the bottom
of the tube, the observed coefficients of heat transfer average
roughly 75 per cent above the values predicted from Eq. 15. If

* The data were taken from the paper[39] by Baker, Kazmark, and Stroebe,
which gave data of Stroebe, Hebbard, and Fragen for tube lengths of 20, 12,
and 8 ft, respectively.

Data of Kirchbaum and Kranz[398a] are available for the condensation of
steam at various pressures outside a vertical tube having a height of 6.46 ft and
a diameter of 0.157 ft. Since tube-wall temperatures are available for only
one point along the tube, the data are not plotted; with X ranging from
300 to 2000, Y ranged from 0.20 to 0.27 for absolute steam pressures of 3.5 to
16.2 lb/sq in and from 0.38 to 0.43 for steam pressures of 20.6 to 42.6.

compared on the basis of a given Δt, the observed coefficients average roughly 50 per cent higher than predicted from Eq. 10.

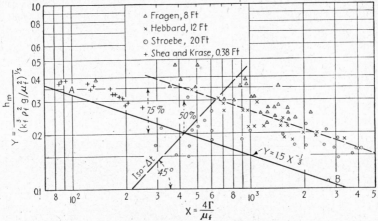

Fɪɢ. 132.—Data for steam condensing on vertical tubes or plates, compared with the theoretical relation for film type condensation, Eq. 15.

Figure 133 shows data of several observers for condensation of single pure saturated vapors outside single horizontal tubes* and on a short vertical plate. From Fig. 133, it is seen that the deviations from Eq. 15 range from -50 to $+25$ per cent.

Effect of Vapor Velocity.— When the velocity of the uncondensed vapor is substantial compared with the velocity of the condensate at the vapor-condensate interface, because of friction between the vapor and the condensate film, the vapor velocity influences the velocity and thickness of the condensate film and, consequently, the coefficient of heat transfer. Thus upward flow of vapor in a vertical tube

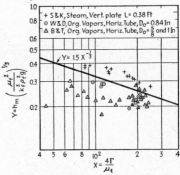

Fɪɢ. 133.—Film type condensation of single vapors on horizontal tubes or short vertical plates, compared with Eq. 15.

* Data of Clement and Garland[128] and of Morris and Whitman[490] for condensing steam on horizontal tubes and those of Bray and Sayler[87] for organic vapors were plotted in reference 454a; on the whole, h_m exceeded the theoretical values except for the data of reference 490, which gave values of h_m averaging 2500, somewhat below the theoretical values.

tends to increase the thickness of the film, and with high vapor velocities condensate may be carried out the top of the condenser. To avoid this, it may be necessary to use a number of short reflux condensers in parallel instead of one tall condenser of limited cross section.*

Using the Fanning equation to estimate the frictional drag at the interface and assuming a constant downward vapor velocity and laminar flow of the condensate down the inner wall of a vertical

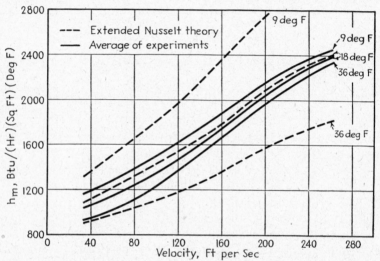

Fig. 134.—Effect of steam velocity on h_m for steam condensing on vertical tubes; both steam and water flowed downward. (Jakob, Erk, and Eck,[344] Physik. Z.)

tube, Nusselt[525] found that the constant of Eq. 9 theoretically increases with increase in vapor velocity, as shown by the following table:

TABLE IV.—DIMENSIONLESS FACTOR F_V TO ALLOW FOR EFFECT OF VAPOR VELOCITY FOR DOWNWARD FLOW OF VAPOR AND CONDENSATE INSIDE VERTICAL TUBES (TEN BOSCH[713])

Z	0	1	2	3	5	10	20	40
F_V	1.0	1.3	1.5	1.68	1.95	2.44	3.08	3.91

$$Z = \left(\frac{\Delta p g_c D_i}{3gL\rho_f k_f}\right)\left(\frac{k_f^3 \rho_f^2 g\lambda}{4L\mu_f \,\Delta t}\right)^{\frac14}; \qquad F_V = \frac{h_m}{h_m \text{ from Eq. 10}}$$

* Data on the loading velocities are given in references 736 and 85.

Where only a small fraction (say, one-tenth) of the steam is condensed, the data of Jakob *et al.*[343,339] agree well with the theory, both for saturated and superheated steam. When a large fraction of the vapor condenses, as in most practical cases, allowance[344] for the change in interfacial friction per unit length, which is roughly proportional to the 1.8 power of the vapor velocity, leads to a complex differential equation, for which the general integral is not available for all possible combinations of surface temperature and tube length.

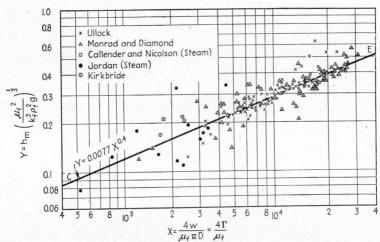

Fig. 135.—Kirkbride type plot of data for single vapors condensing on vertical tubes; the increase in Y with increase in X is attributed to turbulence in the condensate layer on the lower portion of the tube.

However, Jakob *et al.*[344] integrated the equations for the conditions of their experiments in which a large fraction of the steam condensed. Figure 134 compares the extended theory and data.

Effect of Turbulence.—With film condensation of vapor on a tall vertical tube, one can easily obtain condensation rates such that the Reynolds number $4\Gamma/\mu_f$ exceeds the critical value (*ca.* 2100) at which turbulence begins[484]; this is not the case with horizontal tubes where the condensing height $(\pi D_o/2)$ is inherently small. Because of turbulence in the layer of condensate on the lower part of the tube, the mean coefficient for the entire tube should lie above the line predicted from Eq. 15. Figure 135 shows data[31,723] for the condensation of diphenyl oxide and Dowtherm A on vertical tubes, correlated by Kirkbride[394] and Badger,[28] giving the recommended dimensionless equation for $4\Gamma/\mu_f$ exceeding 2100:

$$h_m \left(\frac{\mu_f^2}{k_f^3 \rho_f^2 g} \right)^{1/3} = 0.0077 \left(\frac{4\Gamma}{\mu_f} \right)^{0.4} \tag{16}$$

which is plotted as line CE in Fig. 135.   Data for steam are included.

A semitheoretical relation of Colburn[143] is available for the condensate film for the case where $4\Gamma/\mu_f$ exceeds 2100 before reaching the bottom of a vertical tube.   At the top of the tube the local coefficient for the streamline region is given by Eq. 9, and that for the turbulent region is based on an equation similar to Eq. 7,

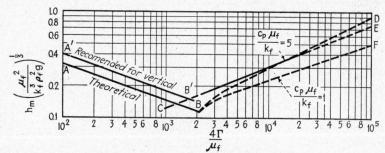

Fig. 136.—Recommended curves $A'B'$ and CE for film type condensation of single vapors on vertical tubes or plates.

page 182, with G_f replaced by Γ_z/x, DG/μ_f replaced by $4\Gamma/\mu_f$, and 0.023 replaced by 0.027, giving

$$\left(\frac{hx}{c_p \Gamma_z} \right) \left(\frac{c_p \mu_f}{k_f} \right)^{2/3} = 0.027 \left(\frac{4\Gamma_z}{\mu_f} \right)^{-0.2} \tag{17}$$

The resulting integrated relation, involving the mean coefficient for the entire tube and Γ, is shown in Fig. 136, as Curves BD and BF for two values of $c_p \mu_f / k$.

Recommended Relations.—For film-type condensation of a pure saturated vapor outside of a vertical tier of N **horizontal** tubes, the use of Eq. 18 is recommended, depending on whether it is more convenient to estimate Δt or Γ', giving

$$h_m = 0.725 \left(\frac{k_f^3 \rho_f^2 g \lambda}{N D_o \mu_f \, \Delta t} \right)^{1/4} = 0.95 \left(\frac{k_f^3 \rho_f^2 g L_H}{\mu_f w} \right)^{1/3} \tag{18}$$

This recommendation is probably conservative, since it contains no special allowable for turbulence due to high vapor velocity or splashing of condensate.

For **vertical** tubes, where $4\Gamma/\mu_f$ is less than 2100, the data in Fig. 132 average[455] at least 20 per cent above the theoretical line

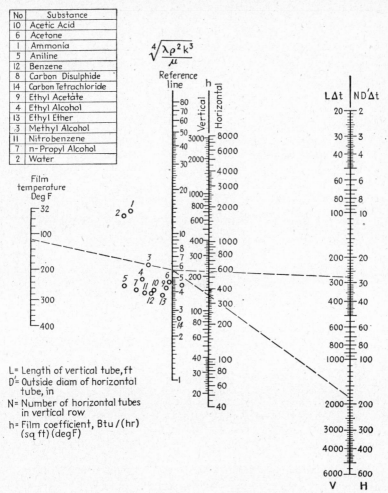

No	Substance
10	Acetic Acid
6	Acetone
1	Ammonia
5	Aniline
12	Benzene
8	Carbon Disulphide
14	Carbon Tetrachloride
9	Ethyl Acetate
4	Ethyl Alcohol
13	Ethyl Ether
3	Methyl Alcohol
11	Nitrobenzene
7	n-Propyl Alcohol
2	Water

$$\sqrt[4]{\frac{\lambda\rho^2 k^3}{\mu}}$$

L= Length of vertical tube, ft
D'= Outside diam of horizontal tube, in
N= Number of horizontal tubes in vertical row
h= Film coefficient, Btu/(hr) (sq ft)(deg F)

FIG. 137.—Alignment chart for film type condensation of single vapors, with streamline flow of condensate, based on Nusselt's theoretical relations (Eqs. 10 and 18). For vertical tubes, multiply h by 1.2. For $4\Gamma/\mu_f$ exceeding 2100, use Fig. 136 or Eq. 16. (*Chilton, Colburn, Genereaux, and Vernon.*[118])

AB; hence line $A'B'$ of Fig. 136 is recommended or the alternate form

$$h_m = 1.13\left(\frac{k_f^3\rho_f^2 g\lambda}{L\mu_f\,\Delta t}\right)^{1/4} = 1.11\left(\frac{k_f^3\rho_f^2 g\pi D}{\mu_f w}\right)^{1/3} \qquad (19)$$

Figure 137 facilitates evaluation of h_m for single horizontal tubes and for vertical tubes.

For values of $4\Gamma/\mu_f$ above 2100 for vertical tubes, the use of Eq. 16, which is plotted as line CE of Fig. 136, is recommended.*

For film-type condensation of **steam** at atmospheric pressure the Nusselt theoretical relations reduce to the following approximation:

$$h_m = \frac{a_2}{y^{\frac{1}{4}} \Delta t^{\frac{1}{3}}} \tag{20}$$

where Δt ranges from 10 to 150°F. For a single horizontal tube, y is the outside diameter in feet and a_2 is 3100; for a vertical tube y is the tube length in feet, and a_2 is 4000. Similar relations for other vapors can readily be obtained by plotting readings from the alignment chart, Fig. 137.

Illustration 1.—Dry saturated steam at 212°F is condensing outside a bank of horizontal tubes, 16 pipes high, and the average temperature of the outer surface of the tubes is 200°F. The o.d. of the tubes is 1 in. Estimate the value of h_m from steam to metal.

Solution.—The value of t_f is $(212 + 200)/2 = 206$°F. In Fig. 137, align 206°F with point 2, thus obtaining an intersection with the reference line. The product $D' \Delta t$ is $1 \times 12 = 12$. Aligning 12 on the right-hand scale and the point already found on the reference line, read h_m of 2500 Btu/(hr)(sq ft) (deg F) for a single horizontal pipe. For 16 pipes high, $h_m = 2500/(16)^{0.25} = 1250$.

In case $2\Gamma/\mu_f$ exceeds, say, 2100 because of turbulence, Eq. 15 will be too conservative, and one should use Eq. 16 or the right-hand part of Fig. 136. For a single tier of 16 tubes each L_H ft long, the corresponding A equals (16) $(\pi)(D_o)(L_H) = 16(\pi)(\frac{1}{12})(L_H) = 4.18 \, L_H$ sq ft. The corresponding value of w equals $(h_m)(A_m)(t_{sv} - t_s)/\lambda = (1250)(4.18 \, L_H)(212 - 200)/(970 + 6) = 64.3 \, L_H$ lb/hr, and Γ equals $w/L_H = 64.3$ lb/(hr)(ft), from the lowest tube. Since, from page 407, μ_f' equals 0.294 centipoises, μ_f equals 2.42 $\mu_f' = 2.42$ $(0.294) = 0.711$ lb/(hr)(ft), and $2\Gamma/\mu_f = 2 \, (64.3)/(0.711) = 181$; since this is less than the critical value of *ca.* 2100, the value of h_m of 1250 from Fig. 137 is satisfactory, unless a promoter be used to secure dropwise condensation.

Subcooling.—When it is desired to condense a vapor and cool the condensate in a single apparatus, one could employ a vertical tubular condenser with downflow of vapor and upflow of coolant, thus securing counter flow. With isothermal streamline flow of single-phase condensate under the influence of gravity, the velocity distribution is parabolic and is given by the relation: $u_x = [(x_f x) - (x^2/2)](\rho g/\mu)$, where u_x is the local velocity at the distance x from

---

* For horizontal tubes, data are not available for $2\Gamma'/\mu_f$ exceeding 2100, but if such cases are encountered, Eq. 16 would be employed.

the wall and x_f is the thickness of the film, defined* by

$$t_m = \left(\int_0^{x_f} t_x c \rho u_x b \, dx \right) \Big/ \left(\int_0^{x_f} c \rho u_x b \, dx \right).$$

Upon assuming a linear gradient in temperature through the film, and neglecting change in physical properties with change in temperature, integration gives

$$t_m = t_{sv} - 3(t_{sv} - t_s)/8.$$

The coefficient of heat transfer in the subcooling section is given by Eq. 30, Chap. VII, and that for the condensing section by Eq. 19, Chap. IX. A recent paper* shows that this procedure is satisfactory for interpreting the data for condensing and subcooling several organic vapors. Coefficients for subcooling ranged from 50 to 130.

Condensing Ammonia.—Kratz *et al.*[406] condensed ammonia vapor at a gauge pressure of 145 lb/sq in. in several types of condensers, using cooling water at 60 to 75°F, and obtained the over-all coefficients given in Tables V, VI, and VII.

TABLE V.—U_o FOR STANDARD 2- BY 3-INCH HORIZONTAL DOUBLE-PIPE CONDENSER WITH AMMONIA IN THE ANNULAR SPACE

Δt_m, deg F	$V' = 4$ ft/sec	$V' = 6$ ft/sec	$V' = 8$ ft/sec
1.5	350	410	470
3.5	270	320	390
7.0	230	280	350

TABLE VI.—U_i FOR STANDARD 2-INCH HORIZONTAL CONDENSER, WATER FILM OUTSIDE

$\Gamma = w/L_H$, lb water/(hr)(ft)	400	800	1200
U, Btu/(hr)(sq ft)(deg F)	250	330	400

Graphical Method of Interpreting Over-all Coefficients of Heat Transfer in Surface Condensers.—In surface condensers, a vapor is being condensed on the outer surface of a tube, while a liquid, usually cooling water, flows in turbulent motion inside the tube. Although in some cases tube temperatures have been measured, especially in testing single-tube experimental apparatus, in the majority of cases tube temperatures have not been measured;

* Colburn, A. P., L. L. Millar, and J. W. Westwater, paper presented at the 1942 Spring Meeting, American Institute of Chemical Engineers, Boston, Mass.

TABLE VII.—U_o FOR VERTICAL SHELL-AND-TUBE CONDENSER, WATER FILM INSIDE TUBES[a]

Δt_m, deg F	$\Gamma = 400$	$\Gamma = 800$	$\Gamma = 1200$	$\Gamma = 1600$	$\Gamma = 2000$	$\Gamma = 2400$
1.5	220	275	310	350		
3.5	170	225	270	315	390	430
7.0	150	215	260	300	340	370

$\Gamma = w/\pi D_i = $ lb water/(hr)(ft inside perimeter).

[a] Additional data are given by Horne,[315] Horne and Ophuls,[316] and Zumbro.[788]

hence only over-all coefficients of heat transfer U are available. In attempting to correlate these over-all coefficients, many engineers have failed to take advantage of the fact that the over-all resistance to heat flow ($\Sigma R = 1/U$) is numerically equal to the sum of the individual series resistances, namely, the resistance on the vapor side R_v, that of the wall itself R_w, that of the dirt deposit R_d, and that on the water side R_L. In 1915, Wilson[769] employed a valuable graphical analysis of the over-all coefficient of heat transfer. The following treatment presents the method and illustrates the application to several sets of data.

Consider a series of runs made in condensing substantially air-free vapor at a given temperature, employing different water velocities. From the concept of resistances in series (page 136) it is clear that the total resistance is equal to the sum of the individual resistances $1/U = R_v + R_w + R_d + R_L$. According to the theoretical equation of Nusselt, the resistance on the vapor side depends upon the temperature difference and the temperature of the condensate film; hence R_v should vary somewhat as water velocity is changed. Also, the thermal resistance of any scale on the heating surface might differ in the various runs; and changes in tube-wall temperature, brought about by changes in water velocity, would cause minor variations in the thermal conductivity of the tube wall. However, except where very high water velocities are used, the water-side resistance is usually the major resistance from condensing steam to water, and, under these conditions, serious error would not be introduced by assuming that the sum of the first three individual resistances $R_v + R_w + R_d$ is approximately constant. As is well known, the water-side resistance is an inverse function of the water velocity V' through the tubes, and, neglecting the effects of changes in water temperature, due to changes in water velocity, the water-side resistance R_L could be taken as a function of the water velocity alone. As Wilson points out, a plot of $1/U$ *vs.* $1/\phi(V')$ should give a straight line when plotted to ordinary rectangular coordinates. For turbulent flow of the water in a given apparatus, $\phi(V')$ may be taken as $a_o(V')^{0.8}$, and hence

$$\frac{1}{U_o} = R_v + R_w + R_d + \frac{1}{a_o(V')^{0.8}} \qquad (21)$$

wherein a_o is an empirical constant and may be considered as the apparent individual coefficient of heat transfer from tube to water, based on the **outside** surface for water velocity of 1 ft/sec. Figure 138 shows experimental data of Orrok,[537] plotted as suggested by Wilson. The crosses represent data for a new clean tube; and, for a given abscissa, the total thermal resistances are lower for the new tube than for the old tube. Empirical equations for the two sets of data are as follows:

For the old tube:

$$\frac{1}{U_o} = 0.00092 + \frac{1}{268(V')^{0.8}} \qquad (21a)$$

for the clean tube:

$$\frac{1}{U_o} = 0.00040 + \frac{1}{268(V')^{0.8}} \qquad (21b)$$

where U_o is expressed as Btu/(hr)(sq ft on the steam side)(deg F *over-all* temperature difference) and V' = water velocity in the tubes in feet per second.

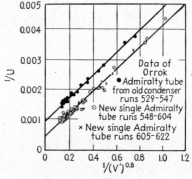

Fig. 138.—Wilson plot.

The reciprocal slope a_o for each set of tests was 268, indicating that the water-side coefficient, at a water velocity of 1 ft/sec, was 268 Btu/(hr)(sq ft)(deg F, difference from tube to water). Since the tube had outside and inside diameters of 1.00 and 0.902 in., respectively, the water-side coefficient per square foot of inside surface was $h_i = 268/0.902 = 297$. The tube-wall thickness was 0.00408 ft, and taking $k_w = 63$ Btu/(hr)(sq ft)(deg F/ft) for the Admiralty-metal tube, $R_w = 0.000068$. Referring to the curve for the clean tube, R_w may be deducted from the intercept of 0.00040, giving by difference

$$R_v = 0.00040 - 0.000068 = 0.000332 = 1/3010$$

i.e., the vapor-side coefficient of heat transfer was 3010.

Thus, by the aid of this graphical method, the observed over-all resistance has been subdivided into the three component resistances $R_v = 0.000332$, $R_w = 0.000068$, and $R_L = 1/268(V')^{0.8}$. By comparing the empirical equations for the old and new tubes, the resistance of the scale is found by difference to be $0.00092 - 0.00040 = 0.00052 = 1/1920$, *i.e.*, the apparent coefficient of heat transfer through the scale is 1920 based on the steam side, or $1920/0.902 = 2130$ per square foot of water side.

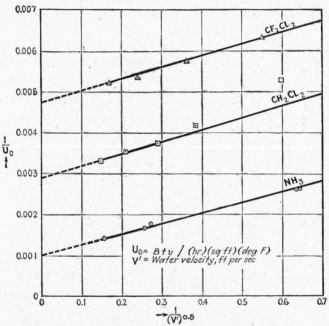

Fig. 139.—Data of Carrier[107] for condensation of vapors.

Even if one does not wish to evaluate the individual thermal resistances as outlined above, the graphical method gives a straight line, thereby facilitating interpolation and extrapolation. When the water velocity becomes too low, the assumption of 0.8 exponent will be incorrect, and hence this relation will break down at low water velocities. The graphical method is applied to a number of sets of data in reference 458. Graphical analysis of over-all coefficients[11] for surface condensers gives[139] scale-deposit coefficients h_d of 760 before cleaning the inside surface, 1200 after cleaning with rubber plugs, 2000 after using a mechanical tube cleaner, and 4200 after sand blasting; the combined coefficient for the tube wall and steam side was 1300, and the water-side coefficient was equal to $370(V')^{0.8}$.

In condensing a vapor whose condensate has a low thermal conductivity, theory shows that the thermal resistance on the vapor side should be much larger than for condensing steam, and hence some of the assumptions underlying this graphical method will appear somewhat questionable. Nevertheless, even for such cases, the method has value, as illustrated by Fig. 139, which shows data obtained in condensing three different vapors at from 100 to 105°F on the outside of a horizontal clean tube of copper having an outside diameter of ⅝ in. and a tube-wall thickness of 0.04 in. Although the tests on the three vapors are comparative, the heat-transfer coefficients are higher than usually obtained in practice.

TABLE VIII.—VAPOR-SIDE COEFFICIENTS h_m FROM RHODES AND YOUNGER[589] OBTAINED GRAPHICALLY FROM OVERALL COEFFICIENTS

Vapor	Clean tube	Oxidized tube
Benzene	412	328
Toluene	382	
Pentane	341	
Hexane	315	
Octane	263	
Acetone	473	398
Ethanol (95 per cent)	442	366
Ethyl ether	403	343
Ethanol (absolute)	364	
n-propyl alcohol	335	292
n-butyl alcohol	310	269
n-pentyl alcohol	276	257

If refinements in the method be desired, it is possible to introduce factors for water viscosity and tube diameter into the abscissa.[454] The graphical method may also be applied to cases in which neither fluid changes phase, as in liquid-to-liquid or gas-to-gas heat exchangers, provided that the velocity of one of the fluids is held constant. If the liquid being heated or cooled flows in streamline motion, one should plot $1/U$ vs. $1/(V')^{1/3}$ (see page 190).

DROPWISE CONDENSATION OF PURE VAPORS

Mechanism.—Dropwise condensation has been obtained with mixtures of steam and other vapors, but steam is the only pure vapor for which conclusive evidence of dropwise condensation is available. The subject has been studied by numerous investigators,* and a number of erroneous conclusions were drawn by the early workers. The situation was investigated and clarified in papers by Nagle[498] and coworkers, and the following summary is based on the paper by Drew, Nagle, and Smith.[196]

1. Film-type condensation is always obtained with clean steam condensing on clean surfaces, whether rough or smooth, regardless of the presence of simple noncondensable gases.

2. Dropwise condensation of steam is obtained only when the condensing surface is contaminated with a suitable promoter that prevents the condensate from wetting the surface.

3. Although many substances (including hydrocarbon oils) will make the surface nonwettable temporarily, only those that are adsorbed or otherwise firmly held are significant as promoters. Some of the important promoters are specific for certain surfaces (*e.g.*, mercaptans on copper and its alloys); others are effective with a number of surfaces (*e.g.*, oleic acid on copper, brass, nickel, and chromium).†

TABLE IX.—DROPWISE CONDENSATION OF STEAM

Reference number	Height, ft	Steam filter used	Range h_m	Range Δt, deg F	Range q/A, Btu/(hr)(sq ft)
500[a]	2.0	Yes	11,000–17,000	5.2–13.9	77,000–170,000
226[b]	6.08	Yes	7,000–16,000	....	68,000–252,000
652[c]	1.92	No	7,000–75,000	1.36–28.8	74,000–276,000
226[d]	10.0	No	4,200		
641	0.49	?	6,400– 8,700		

[a] Based on thesis of Bays and Blenderman, reference 54, using oleic acid on chrome plate.

[b] Based on thesis of Baum, reference 52, using benzyl mercaptan on copper.

[c] The steam was passed through an entrainment separator, and the condensing surface was not fouled.

[d] Based on thesis of Fitzpatrick, reference 225; benzyl mercaptan was used on a fouled surface of copper.

If the surface contaminant reduces the interfacial tension sufficiently to render the surface nonwettable, the condensate will collect in drops that grow in size until downward forces cause them to roll down the surface. Since at any moment a substantial fraction of the condensing surface is free of condensate, much higher

* References, 641, 687, 63, 338, 196 and 351.

† The use of promoters to induce dropwise condensation is disclosed in U.S. Patent 1,995,361 granted to W. M. Nagle.

rates of condensation will be obtained with a given temperature difference than with a nonpromoted or wettable surface that is insulated with a continuous film of condensate.*

Emmons[211] used the Blodgett technique[66] to form a monomolecular layer of molecules and found that two layers of suitable promoter on the condensing surface were adequate to produce dropwise condensation of steam.

Data.—Table IX† summarizes the results of several investigators who report film coefficients for the dropwise condensation of steam.

With filtered steam condensing on well-promoted surfaces from 2 to 6 ft high, the data of references 500 and 226 show that h_m averages 13,000 and is independent of heat flux in range from 70,000 to 250,000 Btu/(hr)(sq ft); the lower values were obtained with insufficient promoter.[226] According to reference 652, h_m decreases from 18,000 at heights of one-sixth of 1 ft to 15,000 at heights of 2 ft, and h_m also depends somewhat on steam velocity and heat flux. With steam containing rust that deposited on the condensing surface,[226] h_m was 4200.

The following examples[226] are based on the results with commercial steam (not filtered) condensing on a 10-ft vertical No. 18 BWG tube having an outside diameter of ⅝ in., comparing chrome-plated copper promoted with benzyl mercaptan vs. copper mildly promoted with oleic acid. In order to transfer 200,000 Btu/hr with each surface, the former would require 2000 lb of cooling water/hr as compared with 4200 for the latter. When using 9400 lb/hr of water in each case, the former transferred 580,000 Btu/hr, and the latter, 270,000. In order to preheat water from 65 to 150°F, with steam condensing at 216°F, the former would heat 5100 lb/hr of water and the latter, 1090.

Figure 140 shows over-all coefficients from steam condensing at atmospheric pressure outside a vertical 10-ft length of ⅝-in. condenser tube having a wall thickness of 0.049 in., internally cooled by water flowing upward. Since the steam used contained a small concentration of oleic acid introduced in the lubricant for the boiler feed-water pump, the reference Curve DI for film condensation is based on work by Drew[187] using uncontaminated

---

* Unless the layer of contaminant is so thick as to introduce a substantial resistance to conduction.

† The results of Gnam[252] are omitted because of lack of data on the variation of tube temperature with length.

steam. For a water velocity of 7 ft/sec, the over-all coefficient is 2100 with promoted chrome plate as compared with 520 for film condensation. The water-side coefficient was 630 $(V')^{0.8}$ and k/x_w for the tube wall 54,000; Curve 1 is based on h_m of 14,000 (as obtained in reference 500), and Curve 2 is based on h_m of infinity.

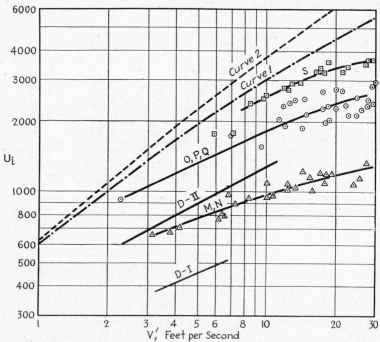

Fig. 140.—Condensation of steam at 1 atm. on a vertical 10-ft length of $\frac{5}{8}$-in copper tube.[226]

Curve 2, h_m of ∞ on vapor side.

Curve 1, h_m of 14,000 on vapor side.

Curve *S*, chrome plated on steam side, and promoted with oleic acid or benzyl mercaptan.

Curve *OPQ*, copper tube promoted with benzyl mercaptan.

Curve *MN*, copper tube, trace of oleic acid present.

Curve *D*-I, film type condensation on vertical admiralty tube (6 ft $\times$ $\frac{5}{8}$ in.) not promoted; Curve *D*-II, same tube, with benzyl mercaptan.

In the range of economical water velocity, 6 to 10 ft/sec, it is seen that U is increased but little as h_m on the vapor side increases from 14,000 to infinity.

With a single horizontal-tube condenser, over-all coefficients of reference 351 analyzed by plotting $1/U$ *vs.* $1/(V')^{0.8}$ indicate an approximate value of h_m of 10,000 with a dropwise condensation of steam on a tube of Muntz metal.

Because of the very high coefficients obtained with fine-grained dropwise condensation of steam, in many cases the resistance on the steam side will be negligible compared with other resistances involved, thus eliminating the necessity for using thermocouples in the tube wall; if the latter are used, because of the very small temperature drop from steam to thermocouple junction, the error due to thermal conduction through the leads is materially reduced.

Cleaning of Condensers.—The tubes of surface condensers may be cleaned by turbine-driven cleaners, rubber plungers, sand blast, or in some cases by chemical agents.[13] Cooling water is sometimes treated with 4 parts of chlorine per million to prevent algae growth and consequent reduction in U.[239,703,75] A number of articles* deal with the economic intervals between cleaning of condenser tubes. Scale effects are further discussed on pages 137, 138, 273, 274, and 279.

II. COOLING OF A SINGLE SUPERHEATED VAPOR

Case 1.—The mechanism of the condensation of superheated vapor differs from that of saturated vapor. However, with corresponding surface temperatures and steam pressures, superheated steam has been found to transfer heat at a rate only slightly higher than saturated steam. For example, Merkel[479] showed that, in condensing steam with 180°F superheat, the rate of heat transfer q/A was only 3 per cent more than for saturated steam at the same pressure and with the same wall temperature. Similar findings have been reported by others.† Hence, for the condensation of superheated steam, little error is made in computing the rate of heat flow per unit area q/A by multiplying the value of h_m for a saturated vapor (Fig. 136) by the difference between the saturation temperature of the steam t_{sv} and the surface temperature t_s.

$$q = hA(t_{sv} - t_s)$$

Case 2.—If the pipe wall is hotter than the saturation temperature of the vapor, no condensation will take place; the vapor will merely lose some of its superheat.[314,565] The heat-transfer mechanism is the same as that for cooling a non-condensable gas; the recommended equation is given on page 174.

Case 3.—It may happen that the temperature of the tube wall is *above* the saturation temperature of the pure vapor near the

* References 657, 144, 11, and 8.
† References 697, 342, 362, 397, and 76.

vapor inlet and *below* the saturation temperature at the outlet. Under these conditions, the vapor will be cooled without condensation in the first part of the apparatus and will condense in the latter part. It should be remembered that the coefficient of heat transfer in the desuperheating section is very small compared with that in the condensing section, and such problems should be divided into two stages: desuperheating and condensing.

III. CONDENSATION OF MIXTURES OF VAPORS

If several vapors are condensing simultaneously in the absence of noncondensable gas, the results differ, depending on the nature of the condensates. Thus, if the various components, when condensed, are not miscible in all proportions, such as condensed hydrocarbons and water, dropwise condensation occurs.

For a condensate forming a true solution, h_m should be predictable from the physical properties of the solution and Fig. 136.*

When a mixture of condensable vapors at temperature t_v is exposed to a surface having a temperature t_s below the dew point of the vapor mixture, condensation occurs. The temperature t_i of the interface between the condensate film and the vapor film will be intermediate between t_v and t_s. Under the influence of the temperature difference $t_v - t_i$, sensible heat dq_g flows through the gas film to the interface. Simultaneously, vapor condenses on the element dA of condensing surface, and the corresponding enthalpy change dq_λ (largely latent heat) is liberated at the interface. The sum of $dq_G + dq_\lambda$ is transferred through the film of condensate, flows through the tube wall and dirt deposit, and is absorbed by the cooling medium.

With film-type condensation, as is usually obtained with a single-phase condensate, the coefficient h for the condensate film is predicted by the methods given above for pure vapors, and the corresponding rate dq of heat transfer is calculated from the equation

$$dq = h \, dA(t_i - t_s) \tag{22}$$

The interfacial temperature is evaluated by assuming equilibrium at the interface, *i.e.*, that t_i is the boiling temperature corresponding

---

* If special heat effects, such as heat of solution, are important compared with latent heat of condensation, due allowance should be made for such effects.

to the total pressure P and the composition of the liquid at the interface.*

Colburn and Drew[146] give the complex equations from which the mol fraction of the more volatile component x_i may be computed for a binary mixture. In an example of the differential condensation of a saturated vapor containing 70 mol per cent methanol and 30 per cent steam at 1 atm, they show that the local condensate varies in composition from 50 mol per cent methanol when the

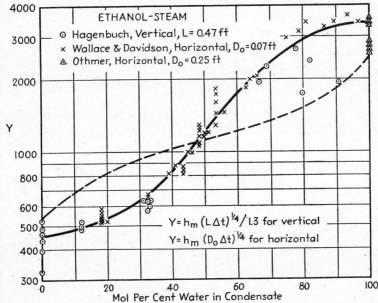

ETHANOL-STEAM
- ⊙ Hagenbuch, Vertical, L= 0.47 ft
- × Wallace & Davidson, Horizontal, D_0 = 0.07 ft
- △ Othmer, Horizontal, D_0 = 0.25 ft

$Y = h_m (L \Delta t)^{1/4} / 1.3$ for vertical
$Y = h_m (D_0 \Delta t)^{1/4}$ for horizontal

Mol Per Cent Water in Condensate

FIG. 141.—Condensation of mixtures of ethanol and steam at 1 atm; the dotted curve shows the approximate location of the theoretical curve for film type condensation; $h_m = q/(A)(t_i - t_s)_m$, in which t_i is the boiling point of the condensate.

cooling surface is at 60°C, t_i is 74°C, and $t_i - t_s$ is 14°C to 67 mol per cent methanol when the cooling surface is at 0°C, t_i is 70°C, and $t_i - t_s$ is 70°C.†

To avoid the laborious computations necessary to calculate t_i, one assumes that the condensate has the same composition as the original vapor and hence computes too small a temperature

---

* In the analogous fields of absorption and distillation, equilibrium at the interface is a satisfactory assumption; in heat transfer, this assumption is employed for condensation of mixtures in references 393, 40, 146, and 41.

† A coefficient of 500 was taken for the condensate film, independent of condensate composition.

drop through the condensate layer. This conservative approximation involves values of $t_i - t_s$ of $70 - 60$ or $10°C$ and $70 - 0$ or $70°C$, respectively, instead of the correct values of 14 and $70°C$. These approximate values are used in Eq. 22, to obtain h from Eqs. 9 or 12, evaluating the physical properties at the film temperature $t_f = t_{sv} - 3 \Delta t/4$.

Data for Condensation of Vapors Giving Single-phase Condensate.—Two sets of data[742,277] are available for the condensation of binary mixtures; in one case,[742] nearly all the vapor was condensed; in the other,[277] only a small fraction was condensed in the test condenser. In both cases, the condensate from the test condenser was collected and analyzed. Taking t_i as the boiling point of the condensate, the values of h_m were computed from the equation

$$h_m = q/A(t_i - t_s)_m \qquad (23)$$

Figure 141 shows the data of both observers, plotted vs. the mol per cent water in the condensate. To facilitate comparison of the results with theory, the ordinates are $h_m(D_o \Delta t)^{1/4}$ for the horizontal tubes and $[h_m(L \Delta t)^{1/4}]/1.3$ for the vertical tube. The data of these observers for steam was omitted, since dropwise or mixed condensation was obtained, and those of Othmer[541] for film-type condensation of steam were included. The maximum deviations of h_m, from the theoretical values, are $+80$ and -25 per cent.

Condensation of Vapors Giving Immiscible Condensates.—Cogan[135] noticed that mixtures of steam and benzene, when condensed, gave partial dropwise condensation. A film of benzene preferentially wet the tube, and drops of water were present in the film. This observation was confirmed by Baker and coworkers,[40,41] who determined values of h_m for condensation of binary mixtures of steam and benzene, toluene, chlorobenzene, heptane, and trichloroethylene outside horizontal tubes having diameters of 0.625, 1.00, and 1.31 in. Although the vapor was superheated $(t_v > t_i)$ in a number of cases, as suggested by Kirkbride[393] h was based on $t_i - t_s$, where t_i is the equilibrium temperature at which the sum of the vapor pressures of water and organic substance equals the total pressure (1 atm) and t_s is the mean temperature of the outer surface of the tube. It was found that h for the different mixtures and a given diameter could be correlated in terms of the weight per cent water in the condensate. Since, in most runs, nearly all the entering vapor was condensed, the composition of the withdrawn condensate differed little from that of the entering vapor, and equally good correlation could be obtained in terms of composition of entering vapor. The effect of diameter, if any, is difficult to determine; the data are plotted in Fig. 142.

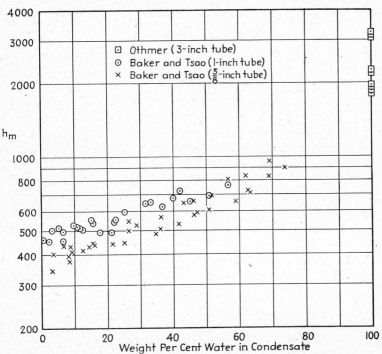

FIG. 142.—Condensation of mixtures of steam and organic vapors (benzene, toluene, chlorobenzene, or trichloroethylene) giving two-phase condensate; $h_m = q/(A)(t_i - t_s)_m$; t_i is the temperature at which sum of the vapor pressures of the water and the substantially immiscible organic liquid equals the total pressure.

IV. EFFECT OF NONCONDENSABLE GAS IN CONDENSATION OF VAPORS (DEHUMIDIFICATION)

Introduction.—When a mixture of a condensable vapor and a noncondensable gas is exposed to a surface colder than the dew point of the mixture, some condensation occurs. In the absence of dropwise condensation, a layer of condensate forms on the cooling surfaces, and a film of a mixture of noncondensable gas and vapor collects next to the condensate layer, the concentration of vapor in the gas film being lower than in the main body of the mixture. As pointed out by Lewis,[432] because of the difference in partial pressure of the vapor between the main body of the mixture and that at the interface between gas and liquid films, the vapor diffuses from the main body through the gas film to liquefy at the interface. Thus both the latent heat of condensation and the sensible heat lost by the vapor are transferred through the condensate layer. However, the latent heat is not transferred through the gas film unless, under special conditions, with a very cold surface, the dew point might be reached in the gas film, causing "fogging" in the gas film. As the main body of the mixture flows past the cooling surface, it is cooled, and the sensible heat so removed is transferred through the gas film by conduction and convection, later to pass through the condensate layer and metal wall to the cooling medium on the other side. The rate of condensation is thus governed by the laws of diffusion of vapor through a film of noncondensable gas, whereas sensible heat transmission is governed by the usual laws of heat transfer by conduction and convection.

Data[440,148,541] are available for dehumidifying air-steam mixtures, but these are strictly applicable only for the conditions of the experiments.

The following design procedure is that recommended by Colburn and Hougen.[149] A partial resistance $1/U'$ is computed that includes only the resistances of the water side, the dirt deposit, the tube wall, and the condensate film:

$$\frac{1}{U'} = \frac{1}{h_L A_L / A_v} + \frac{1}{h_d A_w / A_v} + \frac{L}{k_w A_w / A_v} + \frac{1}{h_m} \qquad (24)$$

Since the heat transferred to the cooling water, neglecting subcooling of the condensate, equals that delivered to the gas-liquid interface, for an element of surface dA_v the following heat balance is employed:

$$W \, dt_L = U'(t_i - t_L) = h_G(t_v - t_i) + \lambda[K_G(p_v - p_i)] \qquad (25)$$

One assumes a value of t_i and substitutes t_i, together with the corresponding vapor pressure p_i, into Eq. 25 and repeats the procedure until the equation balances, thus giving the correct value of t_i. The total area required is then determined by graphically or otherwise integrating the following equation:

$$A = \int_0^q \frac{dq}{U'(t_i - t_L)} \qquad (26)$$

A detailed example of the use of these equations, in designing a tubular dehumidifier, is given elsewhere.[149] The mass-transfer coefficient K is obtained by substituting the dimensionless terms

$$\left(\frac{Kp_{nm}}{G}\right)\left(\frac{\mu_v}{\rho_v D_v}\right)^{2/3} \quad \text{or} \quad \left(\frac{Kp_{nm}}{G_{\max}}\right)\left(\frac{\mu_v}{\rho_v D_v}\right)^{2/3}$$

for the corresponding dimensionless terms

$$\left(\frac{h_G}{c_{pv}G}\right)\left(\frac{c_p\mu_G}{k_G}\right)^{2/3} \quad \text{or} \quad \left(\frac{h_G}{c_{pv}G_{\max}}\right)\left(\frac{c_p\mu_v}{k}\right)^{2/3}$$

appearing on pages 182 and 229.

V. DIRECT CONTACT OF LIQUID AND GAS

In a previous section, methods of calculation were given for an indirect type of dehumidifier, where the gas and cooling medium were separated by a metal wall through which the heat was conducted. In some instances, the cooling water is brought into *direct* contact with the gas, as in a spray chamber or in a packed tower. However, the same general method of calculation applies, except that it may be difficult to evaluate the square feet of cooling surface, in which case performance is reported on a basis of unit volume of the apparatus. Thus, let a represent the square feet of cooling surface per cubic foot of chamber, having height z, gross cross section S_o, and consequently gross volume $S_o z$; the total cooling surface A is equal to the product $aS_o z$.

Basic Equations.—Consider steady operation of a vertical tower in which air and water are brought into direct countercurrent contact. Air of dry-bulb temperature t_{G1} enters at constant mass rate w_G at the bottom and leaves at t_{G2} at the top, and water enters the top at mass rate W_1 and temperature t_{L1} and leaves the bottom at W_2 and t_{L2}. Let H_G represent the absolute humidity of the gas stream, expressed as pounds of water vapor per pound of dry air. The water balances are

$$W - W_2 = w_G(H - H_{G1}) \tag{27}$$
$$dW = w_G\, dH \tag{27a}$$

The enthalpy i_v of 1 lb of low-pressure steam at any temperature t equals the enthalpy change λ_o due to vaporization at the base temperature t_o plus the enthalpy corresponding to the superheat: $i_v = \lambda_o + 0.45(t - t_o)$. The enthalpy i_a of 1 lb of dry air having a specific heat of 0.24 is $i_a = 0.24(t - t_o)$. The enthalpy i_G of 1 lb of dry air plus H_G lb of water vapor is consequently

$$i_G = i_a + i_v H_G = 0.24(t - t_o) + H_G[\lambda_o + 0.45(t - t_o)] \tag{28}$$

As suggested in 1908 by Grosvenor,[272] the term $0.24 + 0.45\, H_G$ is designated as the **humid heat** c_s, and hence

$$i_G = c_s(t - t_o) + \lambda_o H_G \tag{28a}$$

The enthalpy of 1 lb of liquid of specific heat c_L is $c_L(t_L - t_o)$. For adiabatic operation, an enthalpy balance (above a base temperature t_o for both gas and liquid) for the upper part of the tower gives

$$W_1 c_L(t_{L1} - t_o) + w_G[\lambda_o H_G + c_s(t_G - t_o)] = W c_L(t_L - t_o) + w_G[\lambda_o H_{G2} + c_{s2}(t_{G2} - t_o)] \quad (29)$$

Differentiating Eq. 29 and neglecting unimportant terms, one obtains

$$w_G \, di_G = W c_L \, dt_L \quad (29a)$$

The rate of transfer of heat from the stream of liquid at t_L through the liquid

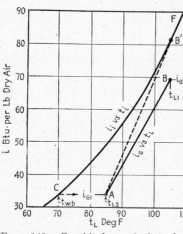

film to the liquid-gas interface at t_i is

$$W c_L \, dt_L = h_L a S_o \, dz(t_L - t_i) \quad (30)$$

and the rate of transfer of sensible heat from the interface through the gas film to the gas stream at t_G is

$$w_G c_s \, dt_G = h_G a S_o \, dz(t_i - t_G) \quad (31)$$

where S_o is the total cross section and z is the height. The rate of diffusion of water vapor from the interface through the gas film to the gas stream is proportional to the humidity H_i at the interface (based on the saturation humidity at t_i) less the humidity H_G of the gas stream:

$$w_G \, dH_G = K_G' a S_o \, dz(H_i - H_G) \quad (32)*$$

FIG. 143.—Graphical method[661] for design of cooling towers.

Since, fortuitously, for air and water vapor at ordinary temperatures, the ratio of thermal and mass-transfer diffusivities is such that h_G is substantially equal† to $K_G' c_s$, Eq. 31 becomes

$$w_G c_s \, dt_G = K_G' a S_o \, dz(c_s t_i - c_s t_G) \quad (31a)$$

Upon multiplying both sides of Eq. 32 by λ_o and adding to Eq. 31a, defining i_i as $\lambda_o H_i + c_{si} t_i$ and neglecting the differences between c_s and c_{si}, the following relation is obtained‡

$$w_G \, di_G = K_G' a S_o \, dz(i_i - i_G) \quad (33)$$

* The mass transfer coefficients K_G' of Eq. 32 and K_G of Eq. 25 are related by the relation $K_G'(H_i - H_G) = K_G(p_i - p_G)$, and H_G and p_v are related by the definition (based on the gas laws):

$$H_G = \left(\frac{p_v}{P - p_v}\right)\left(\frac{M_v}{M_n}\right)$$

As an approximation, $K_G' = P K_G M_v / M_n$.

† Based on pp. 587 to 592 of reference 741.

‡ Merkel,[479a] Goodman,[254b] Boelter,[68,69,442] and Sherwood.[661]

Figure 143 shows values of i_i vs. t_i for air saturated with water vapor at several total pressures,* based on the relation $i_i = 1061.4H_i + c_s t_i$.

Let the wet-bulb temperature of the entering air be represented by t_{wb}. Since for air and water the usual equation, relating the wet- and dry-bulb temperatures and the corresponding humidities H_{wb} and H_G, takes the form $i_{wb} = i_G$, the enthalpy i_G of the vapor stream is fixed by t_{wb}, and hence the wet-bulb lines start on the saturation curve and run horizontally to the right on Fig. 143.

The relation between i_G and t_L is given by Eq. 29a, but ordinarily the fractional change in W is so small that little error is made by assuming W constant, and for these conditions Eq. 29a shows that t_L is linear in i_G, the slope di_G/dt_L being equal to Wc_L/w_G.

Since the enthalpy i_{G1} and water temperature t_{L2} are fixed at the bottom of the tower, point A of Fig. 143, the enthalpy balance line is a straight line[661] passing through point A. In order to reach the abscissa t_{L1}, corresponding to the temperature of the water entering the top of the tower, the steepest possible line is AB', which is tangent to the saturation curve CF at point B'. The corresponding maximum slope is $(i_{G2} - i_{G1})/(t_{L2} - t_{L1}) = (Wc_L/w_G)_{max}$, but since the potential difference $i_{G2} - i_{i2}$ is zero, Eq. 33 shows that the corresponding height of tower is infinite. Consequently, it will be necessary to decrease the ratio of water to dry air, using a flatter operating line such as AB.

Approximate Method.—Since it is difficult to measure the interfacial temperature, it usually is assumed equal to the bulk temperature of the liquid, and Eq. 33 is written to involve an over-all coefficient K'_{OG}:

$$w_G \, di_G = K'_{OG} a S_o \, dz(i_L - i_G) \qquad (33a)†$$

At any t_L, the potential difference $i_L - i_G$ corresponds to the vertical distance[661] between the saturation curve (i_L vs. t_L) and the operating

* In such calculations, one usually employs base temperatures of 0°F for the dry air and 32°F for the steam. Since the latent heat of vaporization at 32°F is 1075.8 Btu/lb of steam and the specific heat of low-pressure steam is 0.45, $i_v = 1075.8 + 0.45(t - 32) = 1061.4 + 0.45t$. Per pound of dry air, containing H lb of water vapor, the enthalpy is $i_G = 0.24t + i_v H = c_s t + 1061.4H$.

If t_o is taken as 0°F for *both* air and steam, and since the extrapolated value of λ_o is 1094, $i = 0.24t + (1094 + 0.45t)H = c_s t + 1094H$. Each of the two procedures gives $i = a_4 H + c_s t$; a_4 is 1061.4 when 0 and 32°F are used as base temperatures for air and steam, respectively, and a_4 is 1094 when 0°F is used for both air and steam. Since both the equilibrium curve and the operating line will be based on the same value of a_4, it makes little difference which value of a_4 is used; in the derivation of the approximate method (Eq. 33a) larger errors are introduced by certain assumptions discussed later.

† Since $t_i - t_L$ has been assumed negligible, this is equivalent to assuming h_L of infinity. Since t_L must exceed t_i, the derivation of Eq. 33a involves over-all coefficients U_G and K'_{OG} defined in the following modified forms[69,442,443] of

line (i_G vs. t_L) and the height z of the tower is found by integration

$$z = \frac{G_G}{K'_{OG}a} \int \frac{di_G}{i_L - i_G} = z_{OG} \int \frac{di_G}{i_L - i_G} \qquad (33b)$$

It is noted that the ratio w_G/S_o, or G_G, is the mass velocity based on the dry-gas rate and the total cross section. Since for a given G_L of the liquid ($G_L = W/S_o$) in a given type of contacting device, the over-all mass-transfer coefficient $K'_{OG}a$ is a function of G_G, the ratio $G_G/K'_{OG}a = z_{OG}$ is sometimes called[117a] the *height of an over-all mass-transfer unit*. For a given type of contacting device and a fixed value of G_L, one may plot either $K'_{OG}a$ or z_{OG} vs. G_G.

Illustration 2.—It is desired to design a forced-draft tower to cool 7450 lb/hr of water from 105 to 85°F, using air entering with a wet-bulb temperature of 70°F at the bottom. In order to avoid entrainment of liquid by the gas stream, it is agreed to use G_G of 600 lb/(hr)(sq ft of total cross section). In order that the height of the tower be not excessive, it is planned to use a ratio of water to air equal to three-fourths of the maximum value.

Calculate the total cross section and number of over-all mass-transfer units required.

Solution.—The enthalpy i_{G1} of the entering air is obtained from Fig. 143 by reading 34 Btu/lb from the saturation curve at $t_{wb} = 70°F$. This is plotted in Fig. 143 as the ordinate of point A, corresponding to the bottom of the tower, the abscissa being $t_{L2} = 85°F$. The maximum value of w_G/W corresponds to equilibrium at the top of the tower; reference to Fig. 143 shows that at t_{L1} of 105°F, i_{G2} is 81 Btu/lb of dry air. From the approximate enthalpy balance

$$\frac{W}{w_G} = \frac{i_{G2} - i_{G1}}{c_L(t_{L1} - t_{L2})} = \frac{81 - 34}{(1)(105 - 85)} = 2.35 \frac{\text{lb water}}{\text{lb dry air}}$$

This is the slope of the dotted line AB'. Then the actual ratio of water to air will be 2.35(3/4) = 1.76, and the air rate will be (7450)/(1.76) = 4230 lb/hr of dry air, which corresponds to a tower having gross cross section S_o of $4230/600$ = 7.05 sq ft.

From point A in Fig. 143, the actual operating line AB is drawn with a slope of 1.76, and the point B is located at the intersection of this line with t_{L1} of 105°F at an ordinate of i_{G2} of 69.3. From Eq. 33b,

$$z = z_{OG} \int_{34}^{69.3} \frac{di_G}{i_L - i_G}$$

Eqs. 31 and 32:

$$w_G c_s \, dt_G = U_G a S_o \, dz(t_L - t_G) \qquad (31b)$$

$$w_G \, dH_G = K'_{OG} a S_o \, dz(H_L - H_G) \qquad (32a)$$

and the further assumption that $U_G/K'_{OG} = c_s$, which is known to be in error.[741] However, since the enthalpy change due to the transfer of sensible heat (Eq. 31b) is small compared to that due to evaporation (Eq. 32a), the error caused by assuming $U_G/K'_{OG} = c_s$ is not serious, and the use of experimental values of K'_{OG}, defined by Eq. 33a, is helpful in the design of cooling towers.

where i_L corresponds to saturation at t_L. At any point the over-all driving force $i_L - i_G$ is the difference between the ordinates of the saturation line and the operating line, and, in general, the preceding equation for z must be solved by a graphical integration.* Since, over the range of i_L from 34 to 81, the curvature of the saturation line is not great, a sufficiently accurate approxima-

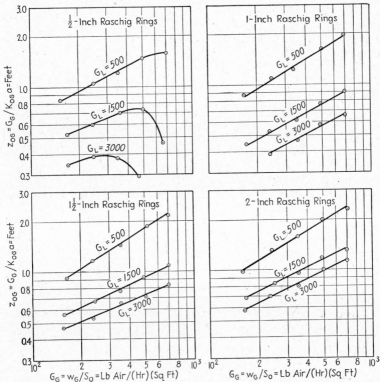

Fig. 144.—Performance data for packed cooling towers; by Parekh.[547]   (*Courtesy T. K. Sherwood.*)

tion may be made by using the arithmetic average of the driving forces at five points:

$$(i_L - i_G)_a = \frac{15 + 13 + 11 + 11 + 11.7}{5} = 12.3$$

$$\int \frac{di}{i_L - i_G} = \frac{i_{G2} - i_{G1}}{(i_L - i_G)_a} = \frac{69.3 - 34.5}{12.3} = 2.83 \text{ over-all mass-transfer units.}$$

Incidentally, the wet-bulb temperature of the exit air is found to be 99°F.

The value of $G_L = 7450/7.05 = 1060$ lb of water/(hr)(sq ft of total cross section). The value of z_{OG} may depend upon both G_G amd G_L, as well as the

---

* A simple geometrical method for determining the integral has been devised by Baker.[38a]

type of contacting device used; values of z_{OG} are given in Table X.   The height z of the tower is 2.83 z_{OG}.

Performance data are available for several types of cooling towers: atmospheric type with cross flow of air,[*] forced draft with counterflow of air,[†] and spray ponds.[‡]   Table X summarizes data for cooling water by air in several types of contacting devices. Cost data are available.[469a,557]

TABLE X.—DATA FOR FORCED-DRAFT COOLING TOWERS

Observer	Type of contacting device	z_{OG}, ft	G_G	G_L
Niederman et al.[510a]	Vertical spray tower	10–2.5	420	200–600
		4.7	300–700	420
Geibel[243]	Grid packing	14.4	550	720
Robinson[602]	Grid packing	19	1020–2280	3180
Johnstone and Singh[355]	Crossed grids[a]			
	Spacing 0.625 in.	1.1	2460	1100
	Spacing 1.25 in.	2.5	2460	1100
	Spacing 1.75 in.	3.7	2460	1100
	Spacing 2.25 in.	3.2–5.2	2460	1100
London et al.[442]	Ovate slats			
Parekh[547]	1-in. Raschig rings	See Fig. 144		
Hooker and Sackheim[314a]	Spined tubing, horizontal, staggered	3.5–3.9	430–760	700

[a] Air was cooled by feeding water at wet-bulb temperature, and hence the values are for z_G, not z_{OG}.   Wooden grids were 0.25 in. thick, 4.0 in. high and were crossed to form an "eggcrate" pattern.

Allowance for Liquid-film Resistance.—Comparison of Eqs. 33 and 30 shows that

$$\frac{i_i - i_G}{t_i - t_L} = -\frac{h_L}{K_G'} \tag{34}$$

and hence a line having a negative slope equal to h_L/K_G' may be used to relate i_i and t_i and i_G and t_L, as shown by the dotted lines in Fig. 145.   The potential differences $i_i - i_G$ may be read from Fig. 145 and the tower height calculated from Eq. 33:

$$z = \frac{G_G}{K_G'a} \int \frac{di_G}{i_i - i_G} = z_G \int \frac{di_G}{i_i - i_G} \tag{35}$$

where z_G is the height of a mass-transfer unit, based on the resistance of the gas film itself.

[*] Coffey and Horne,[134] Geibel,[243] and Perry.[557]

[†] Geibel,[243] Johnstone and Singh,[355] London et al.,[442] Niederman et al.,[510a] Perry,[557] and Robinson.[602]

[‡] Coffey and Dauphinee[133] and Perry.[557]

Since it is difficult to measure t_i, the film coefficients h_G, h_L, and K'_G are best obtained by measuring K'_{OG} and U_G for cases in which the liquid-film resistance is inoperative, *i.e.*, in an adiabatic humidifier in which water is fed at the wet-bulb temperature and consequently the change in water temperature is negligible, and substantially all the latent heat for evaporation is furnished by the cooling of the air. Since the heat lost or gained by the water is negligible, t_i is

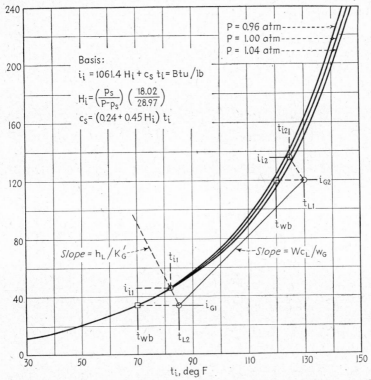

Fig. 145.—Method of allowing for thermal resistance of the liquid film. In the example shown, water is to be cooled from 130 to 85°F by air initially having a wet-bulb temperature of 70°F, using 1.91 lb water per pound of dry air. Assuming h_E/K'_G of 3.4, the terminal values of t_i are found to be 125 and 82°F, and the gas-film driving forces are $136 - 120 = 16$ and $46 - 34 = 12$ Btu/lb dry air; if the liquid film resistance is neglected, the corresponding values are $156 - 120 = 36$ and $49 - 34 = 15$.

substantially equal to t_L; hence K'_{OG} equals K'_G and U_G equals h_G. Then, with the same values of G_G and G_L, the same apparatus is operated adiabatically as a water cooler or water heater (dehumidifier), and the new over-all values of K'_{OG} and U_G, particularly the former, should be smaller than before. Davis and Shipman[170] made this comparison for a vertical wetted-wall tower* having an

* Water-cooling runs in this type of tower are reported by Barnett and Kobe,[45] and wet-bulb runs are given by Chambers and Sherwood.[112]

i.d. of 2.13 in. and a height of 11.6 ft and, at $D_i G_G/\mu_G$ of 10,000, obtained z_{OG} of 9 ft in water-cooling runs and z_{OG} of 6 ft in "wet-bulb" runs, *i.e.*, runs in which water at the wet-bulb temperature was recirculated and consequently was neither heated nor cooled.

At present, most of the available data are over-all values for K'_{OG} for cooling towers, defined by Eq. 33a.

If for any reason one is interested in the relations between H_G and t_G, and H_i and t_i, division of Eq. 32 by Eq. 31 and substitution of $h_G = K'_G c_s$ give

$$dH_G/dt_G = (H_i - H_G)/(t_i - t_G) \qquad (32b)$$

Thus, on the usual humidity chart, a straight line connecting the point H_G, t_G with the point H_i, t_i gives the slope dH_G/dt_G in the vicinity of the point H_G, t_G, as shown in reference 741. Upon neglecting the temperature drop $t_L - t_i$ through the liquid film, H_L and t_L can be used[374] instead of H_i and t_i. Supporting data are given in references 374 and 404. However, in designing direct-contact water coolers or dehumidifiers, the procedure given on pages 286 to 291 is more convenient.

Constant Water Temperature.—In an adiabatically operated humidifier wherein the unevaporated water is recirculated, the water reaches an equilibrium temperature t_e, substantially equal to t_{wb}. The heat given up by the cooling of the air is transferred to the water and is largely consumed in evaporating water that humidifies the air. In this case, where the rates of heat transfer and vapor diffusion are substantially equal, the performance of the apparatus may be expressed in terms of either $h_G a$ or $K_G a$, obtained by integrating Eqs. 31 and 32:

$$\ln_e \frac{t_{G1} - t_e}{t_{G2} - t_e} = \frac{h_G a S_o z}{w_G c_s} = \frac{h_G a z}{G_G c_s} = \frac{z}{z_t} \qquad (36)$$

$$\ln_e \frac{H_e - H_{G1}}{H_e - 'H_{G2}} = \frac{K'_G a S_o z}{w_G} = \frac{K'_G a z}{G_G} = \frac{z}{z_G} \qquad (37)$$

Since for air and water h_G equals $K'_G c_s$, Eqs. 36 and 37 show that H_G is linear in t_G, as is also found by integrating the heat balance, calling c_s constant.

Problems

1. Steam at 310°F and 1 atm absolute enters a vertical standard 3-in. iron pipe and flows up through the pipe with a negligible drop in pressure.

   a. If the inner walls of the pipe are maintained at 220°F and the steam exhausts at 229°F, what equation should be used to obtain the coefficient of heat transfer between the steam and the inside wall of the pipe? Calculate the proper mean value of Δt to use with this coefficient when computing the heat flow rate.

   b. If the inner walls of the pipe are maintained constant at 177°F and the exit temperature of the steam is 240°F, what equation should be used to compute the coefficient of heat transfer between the steam and the inside pipe wall? Calculate the proper Δt_m to use in this case.

c. In which case is q/A the greater?

2. An experimental vertical $\frac{5}{8}$-in. o.d. condenser tube (No. 16 BWG, page 417) is 20 ft high, and cooling water at 70°F is to enter the tube at the average velocity (V') specified below. The vapor to be condensed is to be supplied to the well-insulated jacket that surrounds the tube. Calculate the number of pounds of vapor to be condensed per hour in each of the following runs:

Run 1. Film-type condensation of benzene at 176°F, V' of 1 ft/sec.

Run 2. Film-type condensation of steam under vacuum at 176°F, V' of 5 ft/sec.

Run 3. Fine-grained dropwise condensation of steam at 176°F ($h = 10,000$) with V' of 5 ft/sec.

Note.—It is agreed to assume no deposits of dirt or scale on any of the surfaces.

3. Repeat Problem 2, assuming the tube to be horizontal.

4. Steam is condensing at 216°F on the outside surface of 10-ft vertical section of No. 18 gauge copper condenser tube, page 417. Cooling water enters the bottom of the tube at 65°F and leaves at 150°F, flowing at the rate of 1420 lb/hr. From measurements of the temperature of the outside surface of the tube by suitably placed thermocouples, it is found that the resistance on the steam side is 50 per cent of the total resistance to heat flow.

If the copper tube were chrome-plated, because of the shift to predominantly dropwise condensation, it is estimated that thereafter the coefficient on the steam side would be 6000 Btu/(hr)(sq ft)(deg F). How many pounds of water per hour could be heated from 65 to 150°F, with the use of the chrome-plated tube, with steam condensing at 216°F?

5. Air at 100°F with a wet-bulb temperature of 65°F is flowing in series through a humidifier consisting of two spray chambers. The spray chambers are of equal size, have an equal number of sprays, and operate with the same water pressure on the nozzles. There is no reheater between the chambers. The unevaporated water from each chamber is recirculated to the same chamber, and make-up water is added at 65°F. The operation involves negligible heat losses to the surroundings.

The air leaving the second spray chamber is at 67.4°F. Calculate the temperature of the air as it leaves the first spray chamber.

6. It is planned to design a forced-draft tower to cool continuously 50,000 lb/hr of water from 120 to 95°F. Assume that the following air conditions are typical of the worst to be met at the air temperatures listed:

Air temperature, deg F	85	92	100	110
Absolute humidity, lb/lb	0.0260	0.0300	0.0230	0.0150
Wet bulb temperature, deg F	85	90	85	80

For which set of conditions should the tower be designed so it will surely cool the water from 120 to 95°F or lower under all the conditions listed? Explain briefly but clearly the factor or factors that determine the choice.

CHAPTER X

HEAT TRANSFER TO BOILING LIQUIDS

The first section deals with the calculation of surface and over-all coefficients from test data and the mechanism of boiling liquids by submerged heat-transfer surfaces; high-speed photographs are included for liquids boiling at various rates. The available data are presented in detail, and the various factors affecting the coefficients are evaluated. Conclusions are summarized on pages 319 to 321, with reference to the supporting graphs and tables. The second section discusses the mechanism of boiling inside tubes and presents coefficients for both forced and natural circulation in vertical tubes and for forced flow in horizontal tubes; conclusions are summarized on pages 333 to 334. The third section treats prediction of over-all coefficients and gives a new graphical analysis of over-all coefficients, involving a plot of $1/U$ $vs.$ $(A/q)^m$.

TABLE I.—NOMENCLATURE

A	Area of heat-transfer surface, square feet; unless otherwise specified, A refers to the boiling side.
A_m	Mean area of boiling side and of A_x corresponding to location of tube-wall thermocouple, square feet.
A_w	Mean area of tube wall, square feet.
a_1	Factor defined by the equation $\log_{10} (h_a/h) = a_1(t_a - t)$.
a_2, a_3, a_4	Empirically determined constants.
c	Specific heat of liquid, Btu/(lb)(deg F).
D	Diameter of tube on boiling side, square feet.
h	Coefficient of heat transfer on boiling side, Btu/(hr)(sq ft)(deg F); h_a is based on apparent temperature difference, $t_s - t_o$; h_B in section wherein boiling occurs; h_{NB} for section in which liquid is not boiling.
h_d	Value of h for the dirt deposit; Btu/(hr)(sq ft)(deg F).
h_m	Mean coefficient for entire tube (based on $t_s - t_m$), Btu/(hr)(sq ft)(deg F).
k	Thermal conductivity of liquid, Btu/(hr)(sq ft)(deg F per ft).
k_w	Thermal conductivity of tube wall, Btu/(hr)(sq ft)(deg F per ft).
m	Exponent; $m = n/(n + 1)$.
n	Exponent in $h_B = a_5 \Delta t_B^n$.
Q	Heat transferred in time θ, Btu.
q	Rate of heat transfer, Btu per hour.
q/A	Flux, Btu/(hr)(sq ft on boiling side).

Table I.—Nomenclature.—(Continued)

R	Over-all resistance less that on boiling side, deg F $\times$ hr/(Btu).
t	Temperature of boiling liquid, degrees F; t_a is boiling temperature at atmospheric pressure; t_B is length-mean value in section in which boiling occurs; t_{NB}, in "nonboiling" section; t_o is temperature in vapor-liquid separator or at inlet to tubes.
t_s	Mean temperature of surface, degrees Fahrenheit.
t_{sv}	Saturation temperature of vapor, degrees Fahrenheit.
U	Over-all coefficient of heat transfer, usually in boiling section and based on boiling-side surface, Btu/(hr)(sq ft)(deg F); U_a is based on apparent temperature drop, $t_{sv} - t_o$; U_B in "boiling" section is based on $t_{sv} - t_B$; U_{NB} in "nonboiling" section is based on $t_{sv} - t_{NB}$; $U_{\theta=0}$ is the initial value of U_B for clean surface.
V'	Velocity of liquid entering tubes, feet per *second*.
x_w	Thickness of tube wall, feet; x' is the distance in feet from tube-wall thermocouple to the boiling side.
y	Weight fraction of feed vaporized, dimensionless.
Greek	
Δt, Δt_B	Temperature difference between surface on boiling side and the boiling liquid, $t_s - t_B$, degrees Fahrenheit; $\Delta t_a = t_s - t_o$; Δt_c, critical value of Δt corresponding to maximum flux.
Δt_m	Mean Δt between boiling side and liquid, for combined "nonboiling" and "boiling" sections, degrees Fahrenheit.
Δt_{NB}	Mean Δt between boiling side and liquid, in section wherein boiling does not occur, degrees Fahrenheit.
Δt_o	Over-all temperature difference, based on saturation temperature of vapor and temperature of the boiling liquid, degrees Fahrenheit; Δt_{oc}, critical Δt_o corresponding to maximum flux.
θ	Time of boiling, starting with a clean surface, hours.
μ	Absolute viscosity of liquid, lb/(hr)(ft); μ equals 2.42 $\times$ centipoises
π	3.1416 $\cdots$.
ρ	Density of liquid, pounds per cubic foot.
Σ	Summation.
ϕ_4	$(h_a D/k)(c\mu/k)^{-0.4}(DG/\mu)^{-0.8}$, dimensionless.

In commercial practice a pool of liquid may be boiled by means of heat supplied by submerged internally heated tubes, or the liquid may flow through externally heated tubes. The two cases will be discussed separately.*

I. SUBMERGED HEATING SURFACE

Mechanism.—Visualize a horizontal-tube evaporator (Fig. 146) internally heated by dry saturated steam condensing at any desired pressure and submerged in a pool of a pure liquid boiling at atmospheric pressure in a suitable container. Feed is introduced to

---

* A more detailed description of evaporators and discussion of methods of operation are given in references 749, 26, 288, 30, 741, and 557.

compensate for liquid evaporated. The rate of heat transfer q is calculated from the measured rate of condensation, and the outside area A of the tube is computed from the exposed length and diameter of the tube. By means of suitable thermocouples* located at a distance x' from the outer surface, the mean temperature at x' is measured. The temperature t_s of the outer surface is calculated from the conduction

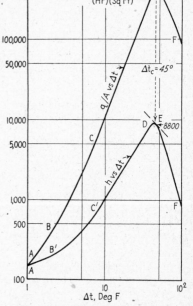

Fig. 147.—Water boiling at 1 atm outside a horizontal submerged tube, based on data of Fig. 156.

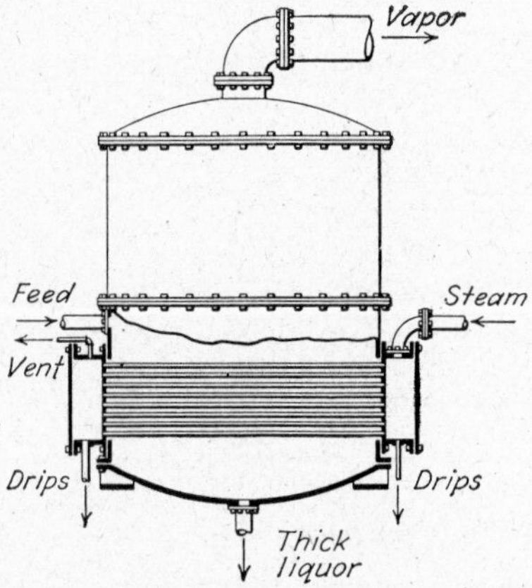

Fig. 146.—Submerged-tube evaporator. (*Courtesy of Swenson Evaporator Company.*)

equation $q = k_m A_m(t_x - t_s)/x'$. The **true** coefficient h on the outside is computed from its definition:

$$h = q/A(t_s - t_L) \qquad (1)$$

where t_L is the boiling temperature of the liquid as measured by a thermometer.†

---

* Methods of installing thermocouples are discussed in Chap. VI.

† In some cases t_L is replaced by the saturation temperature t_{sv} corresponding to the pressure in the vapor space, giving the so-called "apparent" coefficient h_a, which is somewhat lower than the true coefficient based on $t_s - t_L$, if the liquid is superheated ($t_L > t_{sv}$).

In the case of boiling solutions of electrolytes, the evolved vapor is always superheated, since the temperature of the boiling solution is higher than the saturation temperature of the vapor at the pressure in the vapor space. Where the temperature of the boiling solution is not measured, it is calculated from the

A plot on logarithmic paper of the observed flux q/A as ordinates *vs.* the temperature difference Δt $(= t_s - t_L)$ would give a series of experimental points for the various values at Δt, and these could be represented by a curve $ABCDEF$, shown diagrammatically in Fig. 147. In the range AB, the temperature drop Δt and consequently the rate of boiling are so small that the flux is of the same order of magnitude[345] as that obtained in warming the liquid without phase change. As Δt is increased, more rapid boiling occurs, and the slope in the range CD is quite large. Finally, at the point E, the *maximum flux* is reached, which for water is as large as 400,000 Btu/(hr)(sq ft), and the corresponding **critical temperature difference** is 45°F. As Δt is further increased, the flux decreases because of the formation of a film of vapor of low thermal conductivity that insulates the heating surface from the liquid. This phenomenon was first mentioned in 1756 by Leidenfrost,[435a]* who observed that drops of water evaporate more slowly on a red-hot surface than on a considerably colder surface. On the former, the drop assumes the spheroidal form and is separated from the heating surface by a film of vapor. This may be demonstrated by use of an ordinary electric hot plate. With a clean surface at, say, 230°F, the drop wets the surface and evaporates rapidly, but, if the plate temperature is raised to 310°, the drop dances on a film of steam and evaporates slowly. The curve of Fig. 147 is reversible under steady conditions, unless, while operating past the hump E, in the range EF, irreversible changes occur in the condition of the heating surface. If one had used electric heat instead of steam heat and thus had regulated q/A instead of Δt, the same curve $ABCD$ would be obtained. At the point E, a further increase in heat supply would burn out the electric heater unless the heat input was immediately reduced as soon as the critical Δt is exceeded.

Figure 148 shows two high-speed photographs of ethyl acetate boiling at atmospheric pressure in a pool heated by steam condensing inside a horizontal tube of aluminum having an outside diameter of 0.5 in. In using an over-all Δt (from steam to boiling liquid) of 104°F, the flux is only 14 per cent as large as when Δt_o is 73°F. The critical Δt will be discussed in detail later.

---

pressure in the vapor space and data on the boiling-point elevation of the solution in question.

* Drew and Mueller[195] show photographs of boiling at various values of Δt and give a bibliography of 42 references.

Range of Low Flux.—In boiling water with small to moderate temperature differences, of the order of 2 to 20°F, the rate of vapor evolution is sufficiently small to permit visual study of the mechanism of vaporization. Jakob and Fritz[345]* investigated the mechanism of vaporization of water from a flat, horizontal, electrically heated copper plate, for values of q/A not exceeding 20,000 Btu/(hr)(sq ft).

At a given temperature, the vapor pressure from a very small concave liquid surface, such as that generated by a steam bubble

Fig. 148.—Photographs by E. T. Sauer[620] and W. B. Tucker of ethyl acetate boiling at 1 atm. Nuclear boiling is shown in the left-hand picture; $\Delta t_o = 73°F$, $q/A = 41,000$, and $U_o = 560$. Film boiling, typical of a vapor-bound surface, is shown in the right-hand picture, where an excessive Δt_o of 104°F was used, giving q/A of 5800 and U_o of 56. Photographs were taken with an exposure of 1/100,000 sec, using the Edgerton technique.

in water, is less than the vapor pressure from a flat liquid surface. Hence, for a given pressure, a liquid must be hotter to evaporate into a small bubble of vapor than into the vapor space above the liquid. The difficulty in forming vapor bubbles then becomes apparent, since the curvature of the liquid surface of a very small newly formed bubble is very great and the vapor pressure is reduced substantially requiring a higher temperature than the saturation temperature corresponding to the pressure. Therefore it is not surprising that vaporization occurs only from those spots on the heating surface where the temperature and the nature of the

---

* This paper confirms the prediction of Bosnjakovic[75a] of the important role played by superheat and some of the speculations of a pioneer paper by Claasen,[126] in 1902, and throws considerable light on the mechanism of vaporization; consequently it is discussed in detail.

surface are favorable. Jakob and Fritz[345] showed that on some surfaces the vapor bubbles form readily and quickly detach themselves, whereas on others they form only when the liquid has a higher degree of superheat. These investigators studied the effect of roughness of the heating surface on heat-transfer rates and made temperature explorations in the boiling liquid and in the vapor space above it. In Fig. 149, some of these temperature explorations

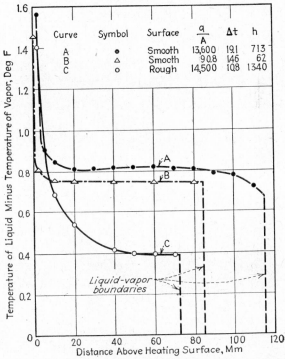

Curve	Symbol	Surface	$\dfrac{q}{A}$	Δt	h
A	⊙	Smooth	13,600	19.1	713
B	△	Smooth	90.8	146	62
C	○	Rough	14,500	10.8	1340

Fig. 149.—Temperature explorations in water boiling at 1 atm on a horizontal plate.
(*Data of Jakob and Fritz.*)

are plotted as degrees of superheat of liquid (temperature of liquid minus saturation temperature) *vs.* the vertical distance from the heated plate. For the rough heating surface, Curve *C*, the Δt required to transfer 14,500 Btu/(hr)(sq ft) was 10.8°F, whereas for the smooth surface, Curve *A*, the corresponding temperature drop from plate to vapor required to transfer 13,600 Btu/(hr)(sq ft) was 19.1°F. In these two runs, the rough plate gave a coefficient ($h = q/A\ \Delta t$) of 1340, and the smooth plate gave 713; this was attributed to the larger number of vaporization nuclei on the

rough plate. It should be noted further that the liquid boiling
on the rough plate had about half as much superheat as the liquid
boiling on the smooth plate.* Curve B, with a very low rate of
heat transfer, 91 Btu/(hr)(sq ft) and Δt of 1.46°F, shows, nevertheless, approximately the same liquid superheat as Curve A with

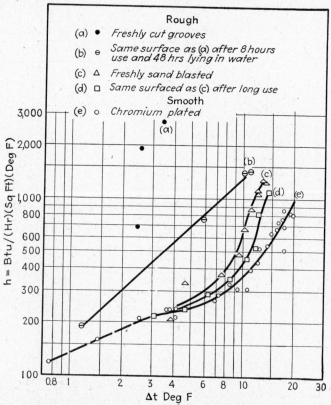

Fig. 150.—Effects of surface conditions on heat-transfer coefficient from horizontal
plates to water boiling at 1 atm. (*Data of Jakob and Fritz.*)

150 times the heat flux. In the region near the heating surface,
these diagrams show a very sharp increase in the temperature of
the liquid with decrease in distance from the heated plate, indicating
substantial superheat in the liquid film. Figure 150 shows the
individual coefficients of heat transfer measured by Jakob and Fritz
with water boiling over copper plates having both smooth and rough

* Heidrich[294] evaporated very pure water and found negligible vapor
formation beneath the liquid surface, obtaining superheats as high as 16°F.

surfaces. It is seen that the rougher surfaces give the higher coefficients. Adsorbed air on the heating surface was found to increase the rate of vaporization, but this effect gradually disappeared with continued boiling and returned if the surface was allowed to stand in contact with air. When the temperature difference is only a few degrees, the observed coefficients are of the

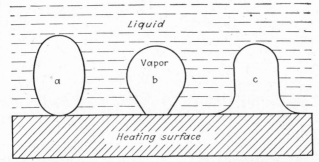

Fig. 151.—Effect of interfacial tension on shape of bubbles of vapor.[345]

(a)   (b)

Fig 152.—Photographs of water boiling at approximately equal rates on (a) clean rough plate of copper and (b) on same plate covered with a film of oil. (*From Jakob and Fritz, Forsch. Gebiete Ingenieurw.*)

order of magnitude[345] of those computed from the usual relations for natural-convection heating without phase change, and consequently h varies as a fractional power of Δt; but when the product of the Grashof and Prandtl numbers (page 242) exceeds approximately 10^9, the convection currents are greatly enhanced by the agitation due to the rising bubbles, and h increases rapidly with increase in Δt.

The effect of the surface tension at the interface between liquid and heating surface is believed to play a part in the mechanism of vaporization, as illustrated in Fig. 151.[345] If the liquid has a high tendency a to wet the surface, the vapor bubbles will be pinched in at the heating surface and readily set free. In contrast, if the liquid has a low tendency c to wet the surface, the vapor bubble will spread out at the surface and be set free only when compara-

FIG. 153.
(*Photograph by Jakob and Fritz, Forsch. Gebiete Inge-nieurw.*)

tively large. Figure 152 shows photographs of water boiling at approximately equal rates on a clean, rough copper plate, whose surface was readily wetted, and on the same plate covered with a thin layer of oil, which the water wetted much less readily. It is seen that the bubbles are smaller and much more numerous in the first picture. When the boiling liquid does not readily wet the surface, the vapor bubbles are large and cover nearly the entire heating surface, giving a lower coefficient of heat transfer, since the rate of heat transfer to vapor is much less than to liquid and since less room is available for the formation of new bubbles.

At low flux, since a substantial portion of the heating surface is covered with liquid, a considerable fraction of the heat transferred from the surface is first used to superheat liquid. As a bubble leaves the heating surface and rises through the pool, the superheat is consumed in vaporizing additional liquid, thus increasing the volume of the bubble. By means of stroboscopic photography, Jakob and Fritz[345] measured the increase in volume of typical bubbles (Fig. 153). As shown in Table II, the increase in volume of the bubble after leaving the heating surface, expressed as a percentage of its volume leaving the heating surface, ranged from 4500 to 140, depending on the original size of the liberated bubble.

TABLE II.—BUBBLE VOLUMES, CUBIC MILLIMETERS
Measured by Jakob and Fritz

Leaving heating surface	Leaving surface of pool	Increase	Increase, per cent of original volume
0.5	23	22.5	4500
35.	100	65.	185
53.	172	119.	224
84.	200	116.	138

In all cases, more heat was transferred to the bubble after it left the surface than before, and hence the superheating of liquid played an important role. The coefficients of heat transfer from the pool to the rising bubble were estimated to range from 2600 to 4600, somewhat less than predicted from the theory of Bosnjakovic.[75a]

FACTORS AFFECTING THE COEFFICIENT

Analysis of the existing data shows that there are a number of factors of importance.

Nature of Surface.—As already noted, Jakob and Fritz[345] found that a rough copper surface adsorbed air and gave initially much higher coefficients in the range of moderate flux, although with continued boiling the coefficients decreased and approached more closely those for the smooth chromium-plated surface. In both cases, A was taken as the projected area of the plate, regardless of the fact that the roughened surface had an actual area 1.8 times that of the smooth plate. At Δt of 10°F the coefficient based on the *actual* area was less for the rough than for the smooth plate.

In boiling ethanol at atmospheric pressure, Sauer[620]* found that the over-all coefficient U, based on the projected area, was increased by grooving the copper, but the percentage of increase varied with the Δt_o employed. Deutsch and Rhode[174] boiled distilled water at atmospheric pressure and for a given Δt_o found that U based on the projected area was not increased by roughening the surface and that U based on the total surface was less than for the smooth tube.

Effect of Addition Agents.—A saturated solution of benzyl mercaptan in distilled water, boiled at atmospheric pressure by a single horizontal chrome-plated tube, raised the value of q/A approximately 30 per cent over that for distilled water in the region to the left of the hump. An excess of mercaptan on a copper tube caused deposition of a yellow scale, lowering the flux at the various temperature differences. With a steel tube, 0.2 per cent of sodium oleate in distilled water raised the flux at the smaller values of Δt and lowered it at values of Δt above 34°F. However, check runs were not made, and hence the data are not given.[153a]

For water boiling at atmospheric pressure, Rhodes and Bridges[588] show the effect of small concentrations of contaminants upon h at a given Δt to water boiling at atmospheric pressure. With a

* The data are plotted in reference 620a.

clean steel tube, addition of a film of mineral oil seriously reduces h, and subsequent addition of sodium carbonate gives intermediate values.* Abnormally low values of h were obtained with a chrome-plated tube, but considerably higher values were obtained upon adding one-sixth of 1 per cent of sodium carbonate, which may have removed grease accidentally present. Jakob and Linke[346] found that for a given flux, for water boiling at atmospheric pressure, h was increased 23 per cent by adding a wetting agent (Nekal BX), which reduced the surface tension 45 per cent. At a constant flux of 12,800, Insinger and Bliss[335] found that a wetting agent (Triton W-30) increased h 20 per cent while reducing surface tension 27 per cent.

Figure 154 shows data[73] for boiling ethanol at atmospheric pressure on a horizontal flat plate provided with several different surfaces. For a Δt of 40°F, h is 4800 for freshly polished copper, 2200 for fresh gold plate, 1300 for fresh chrome plate, and 580 for aged chrome plate. With water or methanol boiling at atmospheric pressure in a small submerged-tube evaporator, Cooper[153a,620a] found that U was larger with iron than with copper tubes, indicating that the increase in the number of vaporization nuclei more than compensated for the decrease in thermal conductivity.

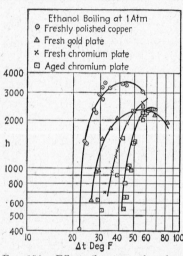

Fig. 154.—Effect of nature of surface. (*Data of Bonilla and Perry.*[73])

When boiling a given liquid at a given pressure and Δt, one is interested in reproducibility of results, for until these are obtainable, the true effect of a change in operating conditions cannot be determined. This point is overlooked by some workers, who make few duplicate runs and even then say little or nothing about the discrepancies. In some cases, this is due to plotting h *vs.* q/A, which is equivalent to plotting $q/(A)(\Delta t)$ *vs.* q/A. In the range CD of Fig. 147, where a large fractional change in q/A is caused by a small fractional change in Δt, if the values of h are plotted against

*The coefficients were estimated from over-all coefficients from liquid mercury to boiling water, by the use of Eq. 4c of Chap. VII.

the values of q/A the results will seem to be quite reproducible, despite the fouling that may have occurred. The true situation

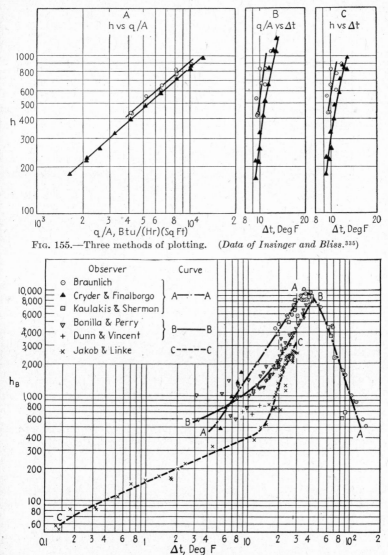

FIG. 155.—Three methods of plotting. (*Data of Insinger and Bliss.*[335])

FIG. 156.—Water boiling at 1 atm in pools heated by horizontal tubes (*AA*) and horizontal flat plates (*BB* and *CC*).

would be disclosed by plotting the q/A *vs.* Δt. Both methods of plotting a given set of data are shown in Fig. 155. Since one is often interested in the value of h rather than that of q/A, the same data are also plotted as h $vs.$ Δt in Fig. 155. If, owing to fouling, Δt

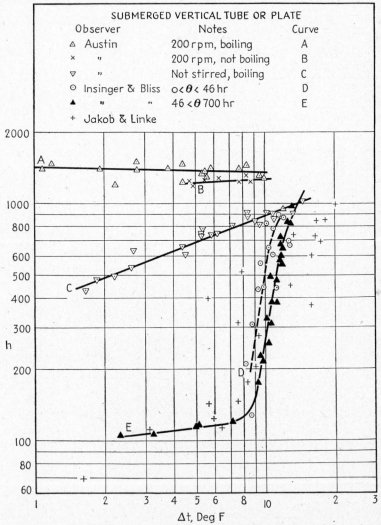

Fig. 157.—Water boiling at 1 atm in pools heated by vertical tubes or plates; the data of Austin should be given less weight than those of the others, but the relative effects are probably significant.

must be larger than before to deliver the same q/A, the point will be moved to the right and downward, thus bringing it vertically far below the curve for the clean surface; consequently this is the most revealing method of plotting the data and will be used herein.

Effect of Δt.—Clearly one should operate the heat-transfer surface at Δt not greater than the critical value, beyond which q/A decreases. Since in the desirable range CDE of Fig. 147, q/A and consequently h increase with increase in Δt, one may select either Δt or q/A as an important variable affecting h. As explained previously, Δt will be employed rather than q/A. Figure 156 shows data of various observers for distilled water boiling at atmospheric pressure, heated by submerged horizontal tubes or

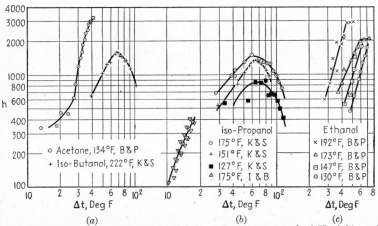

FIG. 158.—(*a*) Data of Bonilla and Perry[73] for acetone, and of Kaulakis and Sherman[369,5] for *i*-butanol, at 1 atm; (*b*) data of Kaulakis and Sherman, and of Insinger and Bliss,[335] for *i*-propanol; (*c*) data of Bonilla and Perry for ethanol at several pressures.

flat horizontal plates. These data are the basis of the curves in Fig. 147.

Figure 157 shows data for vertical heating surfaces. The data of Austin,[20] obtained in 1902, lie in the low-flux range and fall on a relatively flat curve. The data of Insinger and Bliss[335] lie on a flat curve for Δt below 9°F and on a very steep curve at larger values. At Δt of 10°F, the long-time run[335] gives h 55 per cent of that in the shorter run, and the decrease is attributed to fouling or development of a less favorable condition of the heating surface.* The data of Jakob and Linke[346] are for long runs in which h had already fallen to substantially constant values.

* If compared on the basis of equal flux, the coefficients would differ only 12 per cent, Fig. 155.

For the boiling of isopropanol at atmospheric pressure, Fig. 158 shows good agreement by extrapolation of the data of Insinger and Bliss[335] and of Kaulakis and Sherman.[369a]*   Figure 159 shows data for the boiling of carbon tetrachloride at atmospheric pressure.

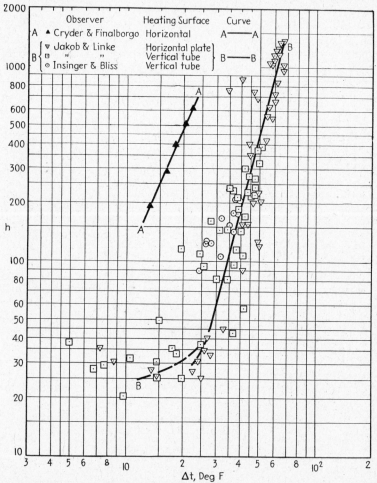

Observer	Heating Surface	Curve
A ▲ Cryder & Finalborgo	Horizontal	A——A
B ▽ Jakob & Linke	Horizontal plate	B——B
□ " "	Vertical tube	
⊙ Insinger & Bliss	Vertical tube	

FIG. 159.—Carbon tetrachloride boiling at 1 atm; data for the horizontal tube give Curve A (n of 2.5); data for the vertical tubes and horizontal plate suggest Curve B (n of 3.9).

Effect of Temperature or Pressure.—Figure 160 shows data of several observers who boiled a given liquid at atmospheric pressure and at several reduced pressures. Cryder and Finalborgo,[160] who

* The data are published in reference 5.

worked only in the range of low to moderate flux—2000 to 20,000 Btu/(hr)(sq ft)—obtained parallel curves of h vs. Δt for each temperature and found that the data could be correlated by the equation

$$\log (h_a/h) = a_1(t_a - t) \qquad (2)$$

where t_a is the boiling point at atmospheric pressure and t is the boiling temperature under reduced pressure and both h_a and h

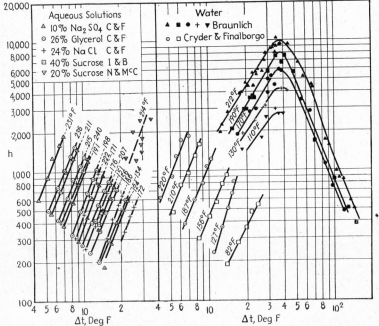

FIG. 160.—Effect of temperature (or pressure) upon h, for a given Δt; single horizontal tubes.

are for the same value of Δt. For eight liquids, including three aqueous solutions, water, and four organic liquids, a_1 ranged from 0.017 to 0.012. However, this simple relation did not correlate the data of Kaulakis and Sherman[369a] or of Braunlich,[86] who used considerably higher values of Δt and three different liquids. Figure 161 shows the values of h_a/h, plotted on a logarithmic scale, vs. the corresponding value of $t_a - t$ plotted on an arithmetic scale, for the data of several observers. It is seen that the slope a is considerably more for the data of Finalborgo,[160] who used small temperature differences. However, it is noted that in every case a decrease in temperature, accompanied by a corresponding decrease in pressure, gave a decrease in h at a given Δt. Bogart and Johnson[71a] built a high-duty electric heater encased in a horizontal nickel tube, submerged in liquid in a high-pressure shell. In

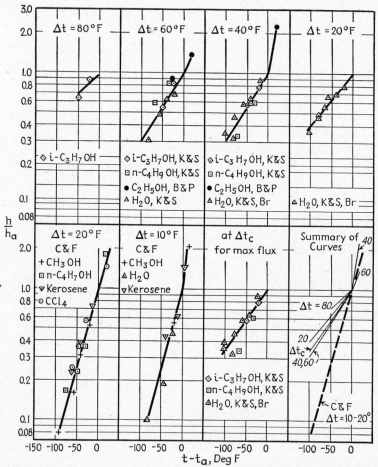

Fig. 161.—For the Δt shown in the legend, h/h_a is the ratio of h at the temperature t to h at t_a, the boiling point at 1 atm. For a given Δt, the data for the various liquids are well correlated by a single curve, but the slope a_1 is not independent of Δt.

preliminary runs with benzene, at a given Δt an increase in temperature and pressure gave an increase in h all the way from atmospheric pressure to the critical pressure, in spite of the fact that a carbonaceous deposit formed on the tube due to thermal decomposition that occurred when excessive Δt was used in the region to the right of the hump. Since the surface was fouled to an unknown degree the results are not included.

TABLE III.—EVAPORATION OF WATER BY SUBMERGED COPPER COIL (Claassen)

Δt_o, °F	20	30	40	50	60	70	80	90
U for 212°F	390	490	560					
U for 187°F	...	360	440	520	600			
U for 158°F	...	...	...	...	510	600	660	720

Table III shows the effect of reduced boiling temperature upon the over-all coefficient U from steam to water for an experimental

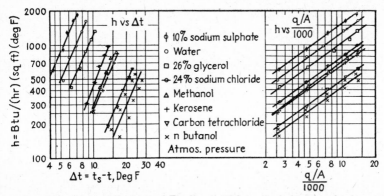

FIG. 162.—Data of Cryder and Finalborgo,[160] for a single horizontal tube.

evaporator[126] with steam condensing inside a copper coil having a heating surface of 5.4 sq ft. Additional data for two solutions boiling at atmospheric pressure in the same evaporator are shown in Table IV.

TABLE IV.—DATA OF CLAASSEN FOR SOLUTIONS

Weight, per cent solids	0	10	20	30	40	50	60	70
U, salt solutions, $\Delta t_o = 18$°F	420	430	440					
U, molasses, $\Delta t_o = 12$°F	360	350	340	320	290	250	210	170

Nature of the Liquid.—Data of different observers, for the boiling of a number of liquids, have been shown in Figs. 154 to 161. Figure 162 shows the data of Cryder and Finalborgo,[160] who boiled a number of liquids in the range of moderate flux. For a given Δt, the value of h for methanol is 12 per cent of that for water, but for a given flux, shown in the right-hand part of Fig. 162, the value of h is 55 per cent of that for water.* The data of various

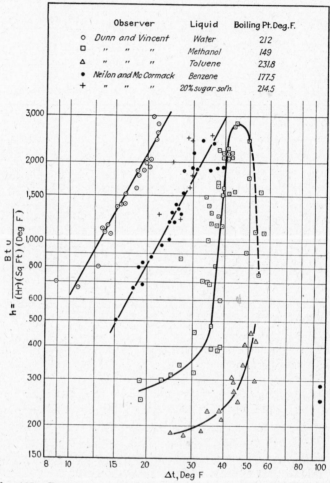

Fig. 163.—Data for several liquids boiling at 1 atm on horizontal plates.

observers for several liquids and solutions boiled at a number of pressures are given in Figs. 154 to 162. Miscible binary mixtures

* A similar comparison may be made of the earlier data of Cryder and Gilliland,[161] as shown on p. 292 of reference 454a, but since the data of these observers are considerably higher than those of later observers (references 5, 73, 160, 202, 335, 345–348), the data are not plotted herein. As noted earlier, an error of even 1° in Δt is particularly serious in the range of low flux, where Δt is quite small. However, Curve a of Fig. 150 gave even higher results than the water runs of reference 161.

give results lying between those for the pure components.[73] As shown in Fig. 162, aqueous solutions of salts or organic substances usually give lower coefficients than water at the same pressure, for a given Δt or flux.

Effect of Agitation.—In 1902, Austin[20] clearly showed that agitation may increase the heat-transfer coefficients for boiling water in the range of moderate flux. Line C of Fig. 157 represents the data for heat transfer to water boiling at 212°F, with no agitation other than that caused by the evolution of bubbles; it is seen that the heat-transfer coefficient increases with increase in temperature difference (or with rate of heat transfer). This increase is generally considered to be due to an increase in agitation caused by more vigorous evolution of bubbles. The data represented by Curve A were obtained by boiling water in the same apparatus with mechanical stirring (200 rpm) and show no increase of h with increase in temperature difference. Mechanical agitation has been used in commercial equipment.[749] Drew and Mueller[195] find that stirring did not prevent vapor binding and that the critical over-all Δt was not affected substantially. Further data on the effect of velocity of the liquid are given under Boiling Inside Tubes, page 322.

Number and Arrangement of Tubes.—Most of the data in the literature for laboratory apparatus are for a single tube or a horizontal plate. Abbott and Comley[1] tested a model evaporator containing 60 nearly horizontal chrome-plated copper tubes, each 10 in. long, having inside and outside diameters of 0.438 and 0.500 in., respectively. When the tubes were placed on 1-in. centers, giving horizontal and vertical clearances of 0.50 in., with 10 rows deep, the results shown in Fig. 164 were obtained, which are approximately the same as those obtained by Kaulakis and Sherman[369a] and by Dreselly[182a] with single tubes. In all three cases the copper surface inside the tube was treated with benzyl mercaptan (page 276) to promote dropwise condensation, thus minimizing the resistance on the steam side. When the clearance between tubes was increased 50 per cent, at a given over-all Δt the flux decreased but 8 per cent, which is not significant. The heat transfer was measured for the five pairs of adjacent rows, and no significant variations were found. Figure 164 also shows data of Pridgeon and Badger[576] for the boiling of distilled water at atmospheric pressure outside polished copper tubes in an evaporator containing a bundle of horizontal tubes (⅞-in. outside diameter, ¾-in. inside diameter) 4 rows deep and 12 rows wide. At a given

Δt_o, the flux is roughly one-half that obtained in the 60-tube model, and this is attributed, at least in part, to the fact that a promoter was not used in the steam.

The only observers who have published data for a given fluid boiled with both horizontal and vertical surfaces are Jakob and Linke;[346] the comparison shows that the horizontal plate gives nearly as good results as the vertical surface for both water and carbon tetrachloride boiling at atmospheric pressure.

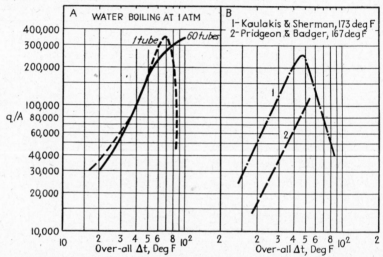

Fig. 164.—In the graph at the left, surprisingly good agreement is shown between data for small evaporators containing 60 tubes and 1 tube; in the graph at the right, the 48-tube evaporator (Curve 2) with nonpromoted steam required more over-all Δt, to give the same flux, than the single-tube evaporator (Curve 1), which was supplied with steam promoted to give dropwise condensation.

Effect of Tube Diameter.—As shown by Akin,[4a] the data of Nukiyama[518a] for water boiled at atmospheric pressure by an electrically heated platinum wire having a diameter of 0.0055 in. give substantially the same coefficients as those of other observers who used tubes having diameters of 0.5 in. or more.

Maximum Flux and Corresponding Critical Temperature Difference.—In the literature, attempts have been made to measure the minimum temperature difference at which a drop of liquid assumes the spheroidal form when placed on a heated surface, but the experimental technique was such that the results probably have little precision. Such data show that the critical Δt varies both with the metal and liquid.* The critical Δt, as reported herein, is

* Results are summarized by Drew and Mueller.[195]

TABLE V.—MAXIMUM FLUX FOR VARIOUS LIQUIDS

Liquid	Surface on boiling side	t, deg F	Maximum flux, q_{max}/A	Critical Δt	
				Δt_L, deg F	Δt_o, deg F
Ethyl acetate[620a]	Aluminum[d]	162[a]	42,000	..	80
Ethyl acetate[620a]	Slightly dirty copper[d]	162[a]	62,000	..	57
Ethyl acetate[620a]	Chrome-plated copper[d]	162[a]	77,000	..	70
Benzene[620a]	Slightly dirty copper[d]	177[a]	43,000	..	100
Benzene[620a]	Aluminum[d]	177[a]	50,000	..	80
Benzene[620a]	Copper[d]	177[a]	55,000	..	80
Benzene[620a]	Chrome-plated copper[d]	177[a]	69,000	..	100
Benzene[620a]	Copper[d]	177[a]	72,000	..	60
Benzene[620a]	Chrome-plated copper[d]	177[a]	70,000	..	100
Benzene[620a]	Steel[d]	177[a]	82,000	..	100
Carbon tetrachloride[620a]	Dirty copper[d]	170[a]	47,000	..	83
Carbon tetrachloride[620a]	Copper[d]	170[a]	58,000	..	79
Heptane[620a]	Copper[d]	209[a]	53,000	..	55
Ethanol[620a]	Aluminum[d]	173[a]	54,000	..	90
Ethanol[620a]	Copper[d]	173[a]	80,000	..	66
Ethanol[620a]	Slightly dirty copper[d]	173[a]	93,000	..	65
Ethanol[620a]	Grooved copper[d]	173[a]	120,000	..	55
Ethanol[620a]	Chrome-plated copper[d]	173[a]	126,000	..	65
i-Propanol[369a]	Polished nickel-plated copper[d]	127	67,000	85	91
i-Propanol[369a]	Polished nickel-plated copper[d]	151	90,000	75	84
i-Propanol[369a]	Polished nickel-plated copper[d]	175[a]	110,000	90	96
Methanol[620a]	Slightly dirty copper[d]	149[a]	78,000	..	92
Methanol[620a]	Chrome-plated copper[d]	149[a]	120,000	..	110
Methanol[620a]	Steel[d]	149[a]	123,000	..	105
Methanol[620a]	Copper[d]	149[a]	124,000	..	115
n-Butanol[369a]	New nickel-plated copper[d]	173	79,000	70	83
n-Butanol[369a]	New nickel-plated copper[d]	207	92,000	70	79
n-Butanol[369a]	New nickel-plated copper[d]	241[a]	105,000	60	70
i-Butanol[369a]	Polished nickel-plated copper[d]	222[a]	115,000	80	85
Water[369a]	Polished nickel-plated copper[b]	131	115,000	42	53
Water[86]	Chrome-plated copper[c]	110	150,000	45	
Water[86]	Chrome-plated copper[c]	130	175,000	45	65
Water[369a]	New nickel-plated copper[b]	155	190,000	50	
Water[86]	Chrome-plated copper[c]	150	220,000	45	64
Water[86]	Chrome-plated copper[c]	170	243,000	45	64
Water[369a]	Polished nickel-plated copper[b]	171	250,000	50	72
Water[369a]	New nickel-plated copper[b]	191	260,000	50	
Water[86]	Chrome plated copper[c]	190	300,000	45	70
Water[5]	Chrome-plated copper[b]	212[a]	330,000	45	80
Water[369a]	New nickel-plated copper[b]	212[a]	360,000	52	68
Water[369a]	Polished nickel-plated copper[b]	212[a]	370,000	45	72
Water[86]	Chrome-plated copper[c]	212[a]	390,000	45	72
Water[620a]	Steel[d]	212[a]	410,000	..	150

[a] Boiling at atmospheric pressure.
[b] Steam side was promoted with benzyl mercaptan.
[c] Steam side was promoted with octyl thiocyanate.
[d] Steam probably contained a trace of oleic acid.

that value at which the measured flux reaches a maximum value (Figs 147, 156, and 160) and is best determined by using a vapor-heated surface. Table V summarizes the values so determined.* Apparently the critical Δt for a given liquid and surface is substantially independent of the boiling temperature and corresponding total pressure (Figs. 158 and 160), and the corresponding maximum flux increases with increase in boiling temperature (Fig. 161). The over-all temperature difference Δt_o is defined as the saturation temperature of the steam less the boiling temperature of the liquid. For a given liquid and pressure, the critical value of Δt_o is increased by substantial deposits of scale and is less for dropwise than for film condensation.

Scale Deposits.—In boiling water or aqueous solutions in evaporators heated by condensing steam, the coefficients on both the steam side and the boiling-liquid side are large with clean surfaces. Hence even a thin layer of scale may have a large effect on the over-all coefficient. Pridgeon and Badger[576] measured over-all coefficients from condensing steam to water boiling at 167°F in a horizontal submerged-tube evaporator. The data of Table VI (read from their curves) show the importance of over-all temperature difference and the cleanliness and nature of the heating surface.

TABLE VI.—U_o FROM CONDENSING STEAM TO BOILING WATER[576]

Δt_o, over-all Δt, deg F	18	27	36	45	54
U_o (rusty iron)	280	300	325	350	375
U_o (clean iron)	300	385	460	535	610
U_o (slightly dirty copper)	580	780	950	1120	
U_o (polished copper)	820	1110	1470	1810	2120

Later work on the copper tubes, after acid cleaning, gave U_o as high as 3070 with $\Delta t_o = 38°F$, but it was difficult to reproduce these very high values of U_o, owing to the collection of a thin deposit on the tubes. The small amount of scale necessary to reduce a high coefficient by a substantial amount is not generally realized. By taking the thermal conductivity k of scale as 1.3†

* Additional data are given in reference 195, obtained with a very small apparatus.

† The conductivity of boiler scale has been studied by Eberle and Holzbauer,[206] Partridge,[550] Kamp,[364] and Zarnite.[785]

Btu/(hr)(sq ft)(deg F per ft), the calculated thickness of scale required to reduce the coefficients in Table VI for polished copper to those for slightly dirty copper are shown in Table VII.*

TABLE VII

Δt_o, deg F	18	27	36	45
U (polished copper)	820	1110	1470	1810
U (slightly dirty copper)	580	780	950	1120
Necessary scale thickness, in	0.0079	0.0059	0.0058	0.0053

Webre and Robinson[749] quote some tests by Kerr on a quadruple-effect evaporator in a sugar mill that show the effect of cleanliness. Tests were made $3\frac{1}{2}$ days and 6 days after the evaporators were cleaned. The effect of increasing scale formation is illustrated by the following table.

TABLE VIII.—U, BTU/(HR)(SQ FT)(DEG F)

Evaporator	1	2	3	4
After $3\frac{1}{2}$ days	321	508	203	90
After 6 days	239	270	97	79

Webre and Robinson also give data on an experimental apparatus in which the over-all coefficient U dropped from 1550 to 900 in less than 2 hr, then less rapidly to a value of 700.

Assuming that the scale collecting on the heating surface in an evaporator is strictly proportional to the total Btu, Q, transferred up to the time θ, McCabe and Robinson[462] show that $1/U^2 = a_2 + a_3\theta$, wherein a_2 and a_3 are empirical constants and U is the over-all coefficient of heat transfer.† Figure 165 illustrates how closely some data fit this relation. Where the experimental data follow

---

* For Δt_o of 18°F, the resistance x/k of the scale, assumed equal to the difference between the over-all resistance when the tube is dirty and when it is polished, is $(1/580) - (1/820)$, whence x is 0.00066 ft, or 0.0079 in.

† $\dfrac{1}{U} = \dfrac{1}{U_{\theta=0}} + a_4 Q;\quad -\dfrac{dU}{U^2} = a_4\, dQ.$ But by definition $dQ = UA\,\Delta t_o\, d\theta.$
Elimination of dQ and integration give

$$\frac{1}{U^2} = \frac{1}{U^2_{\theta=0}} + a_4 A\,\Delta t_o\,\theta = a_2 + a_3\theta.$$

this equation, the optimum cleaning cycle is readily calculated from the following equation[32] and cost data:

$$Q = A(\Delta t_o)(2)[\sqrt{a_2 + a_3\theta} - \sqrt{a_2}]/a_3 \qquad (3)$$

wherein Q represent the Btu transferred in θ hours.

Figure 166 illustrates that some data do not follow the linear relationship.

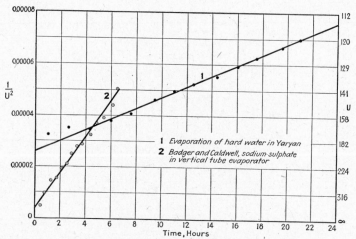

FIG. 165.—Effect of scale deposit on U. (*From Badger and Othmer.*)

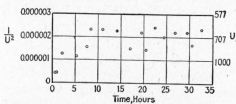

FIG. 166.—Data of Webre[749] for evaporation of sea water in a single-tube evaporator.

In boiling saturated solutions of sodium sulphate or sodium chloride at atmospheric pressure Coffey[132a] found that scale was rapidly deposited on the heating surface. Starting with clean surfaces, a number of runs were made, each with a constant over-all temperature difference, in the range 50 to 150°F. Comparison of these results, 1 hr after boiling started, showed that the largest flux of 75,000 was obtained with Δt_o of 75°F, whereas with water a maximum flux of 330,000 was found with Δt_o of 95°F. With a solute of low solubility, calcium sulphate, Bulkely finds that the fractional increase in U with increase in Δt_o is less than for water boiling in the same apparatus; at Δt_o of 25°F, the solution gave the same U as water, and with Δt_o of 120°F, U/U_w was 0.64.

With very thin scale deposits formed on tubes submerged in water boiling at atmospheric pressure, two observers[620a,86] find that h is increased for a given Δt or flux in the region BCD of Fig. 147; Akin[4a] finds that the percentage of increase due to slight fouling decreases rapidly with increase in Δt, whereas Braunlich finds the increase independent of Δt. With a thicker deposit of scale, formed

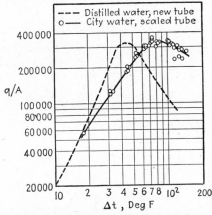

FIG. 167.—Effect of scale deposit on critical value of over-all Δt. (*Data of Dreselly.*[182a,5])

by boiling city water, Dreselly[182a] obtained the usual decrease in h for a given Δt or flux. In order to obtain the maximum flux of 330,000, fouling increased the Δt_c from 45 to 80°F, Fig. 167.

Summary, Boiling by Submerged Surfaces

In boiling a liquid at a given pressure, as the temperature difference is increased the heat flux at first increases slowly, then more rapidly, goes through a maximum, and subsequently decreases as the heat-transfer surface becomes insulated with a film of vapor (Figs. 147 to 148). Table V gives the values of the maximum flux and corresponding "critical" temperature differences for 11 liquids and several surfaces. In using exhaust steam to supply the heat to vaporize organic liquids of moderately low boiling points, to avoid exceeding the critical Δt it may be necessary to boil under pressure or to condense the steam under reduced pressure. The critical temperature difference for a given liquid and surface is nearly independent of the temperature or pressure of boiling, but the maximum flux decreases with decrease in temperature, as shown by the correlation of data for several liquids in Fig. 161. However, water or aqueous solutions are often boiled in multiple-effect evaporators, wherein a total temperature drop of 100 to 150°F is shared among the several evaporators connected in series with respect to vapor, and under such conditions there is little or no chance of exceeding the critical temperature difference.

Whereas the true situation as to reproducibility of runs is shown by plotting q/A *vs.* Δt, for the reasons given on page 305 a plot of h *vs.* Δt is preferred to a graph of h *vs.* q/A.

For a given liquid boiled at a fixed pressure in a given apparatus, the boiling-side and over-all coefficients, and consequently the flux, increase with increase in temperature difference so long as the critical Δt is not exceeded. Supporting data for 11 pure liquids and 5 solutions are shown in Figs. 154 to 164 and in Tables III and VI.

For a given liquid boiled in a given apparatus, employing a fixed Δt not exceeding the critical value, the boiling-side and over-all coefficients, and hence the flux, increase with increase in temperature or pressure of the boiling liquids, as shown in Fig. 160 and Tables III and IX. As shown in Fig. 161, the data for a given liquid may be roughly correlated by the equation $\log_{10}(h/h_a) = a_1(t - t_a)$, and the temperature coefficient a_1 varies relatively little for the various liquids for which data are available. Since for a given liquid the curves of h *vs.* Δt for the various temperatures diverge at very low Δt, a_1 increases at low Δt.

In boiling various liquids at a fixed pressure in a given apparatus, without exceeding the critical Δt, h may vary widely from one liquid to another when the comparisons are made at a given Δt, but the variation is considerably less when the comparison is made at equal flux. Data for 11 pure liquids and 5 aqueous solutions are shown in Figs. 154 to 164.

For a given liquid boiled at a fixed pressure with a given Δt, h varies widely with the nature of the heat-transfer surface at moderate Δt, but this variation is much less at large or small Δt. Usually a reduction in surface tension of water, due to addition of a wetting agent, is accompanied by an increase in h at a given Δt or flux, as shown on page 303. The effects upon h of other addition agents, including adsorbed air, are treated on pages 303 and 304.

Whereas a very thin layer of scale on the heat-transfer surface on the boiling side may increase h (page 319), a thicker deposit may seriously decrease h (page 316, Tables VI and VIII, and Figs. 165 to 167).

Substantially the same coefficients have been obtained with horizontal and vertical heat-transfer surfaces (page 314), and the meager data indicate little effect of substantial variation in the spacing of horizontal tubes in a bundle (page 313).

Available data show no significant change in h due to a one hundredfold reduction in diameter of a submerged horizontal cylinder, page 314.

II. BOILING INSIDE TUBES

In both forced- and natural-circulation evaporators, unevaporated liquid recirculates through the tubes, entering at the saturation temperature corresponding to the pressure in the vapor space of the evaporator or that in the vapor-liquid separator. However, since the pressure at the base of the tube is higher, the liquid is first warmed without evaporation as it flows through the tube until it reaches a section where boiling starts. Badger and his associates* have developed a traveling thermo-

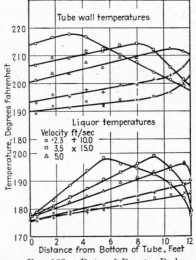

FIG. 168.—Data of Boarts, Badger, and Meisenburg[67] for a forced-circulation vertical-tube evaporator; t_{sv} = 230°F, t_o = 176°F, over-all Δt = 54°F.

couple for measuring the variation in the temperature of the fluid with distance from the inlet; tube-wall temperatures are measured by thermocouples.

Forced-circulation Vertical-tube Evaporator.—Boarts *et al.*[67] evaporated water at boiling temperatures of 212 to 139°F inside a vertical copper tube (0.76 in. by 12 ft) jacketed with condensing steam. By use of the traveling thermocouple and tube-wall thermocouples, temperature distribution curves were obtained, as shown in Fig. 168.[67] For runs in which the Reynolds number DG/μ exceeded 65,000 (V' above 3.4 ft/sec at the inlet) the true coefficients h_m for the entire tube, based on the length-mean Δt, averaged 1.26 times those predicted from Eq. 4c of Chap. VII for

* References 441, 67, 91, 706, and 232; see also reference 700.

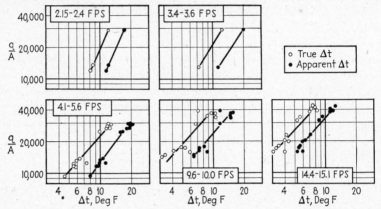

FIG. 169.—Data of Boarts, Badger, and Meisenburg[67] for heating and boiling water in a vertical-tube forced-circulation evaporator (0.76×12 ft). The ratio $\Delta t_a / \Delta t_m$ averaged 0.63.

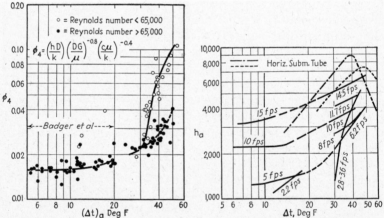

FIG. 170.—Apparent coefficients of heat transfer from tube to water in vertical forced-circulation evaporators, plotted in terms of $\phi_4 = (h_a D/k)$ $(c\mu/k)^{-0.4}(DG/\mu)^{-0.8}$ vs. apparent temperature drop. If Eq. 4c of Chap. VII applied to h_m, and if $\Delta t_m = 0.63\Delta t_a$ (Fig. 169), ϕ_4 should equal 0.63 (0.023) = 0.015. Below Δt_a of 22°F, data are those of Boarts;[67] above Δt_a of 22°F, data are those of Oliver[534a] for a short vertical tube (0.495 in. by 1.72 ft).

FIG. 171.—Apparent coefficients for heating and boiling water in vertical forced-circulation evaporators (vapor-liquid separator at 212°F), plotted vs. apparent temperature difference ($\Delta t = t_m - t_o$), compared with data of Fig. 156 for water boiling at 212°F in pools heated by a submerged horizontal tube.

warming water without vaporization. At lower feed rates, where as much as 6.5 per cent by weight of the feed evaporated per pass, the true coefficients in the boiling section *BC* averaged 140 per cent above those predicted from Eq. 4c. Figure 169 shows the data for the entire tube plotted as average flux q/A *vs.* Δt, defined in two ways: Δt_m, the true length-mean Δt described above, and Δt_a, the apparent Δt based on the length-mean temperature of the surface and the saturation temperature corresponding to the pressure in the vapor-liquid separator. The latter type of Δt is much easier to use in design calculations and gives at least as good a correlation of the data as the more involved Δt_m. The apparent Δt averaged 0.63 times the true Δt.

The observed *apparent* coefficients $h_a = q/A \, \Delta t_a$ are plotted in terms of the dimensionless term

$$\phi_4 = (h_a D/k)(c\mu/k)^{-0.4}(DG/\mu)^{-0.8}$$

vs. Δt_a in Fig. 170, together with data of Oliver[534a] for a very short vertical nickel-tube evaporator (0.495 in. by 1.72 ft) in which Δt_a ranged from 24 to 53°F and the corresponding flux was 38,000 to 260,000 Btu/(hr)(sq ft). For a given DG/μ based on the viscosity of the liquid, ϕ_4 increases with increase in Δt_a; for DG/μ above 65,000, the curve of ϕ_4 rises from 0.016 to 0.040; for lower values of the Reynolds number, ϕ_4 is 0.1 at Δt_a of 50°F. For warming water without vaporization, the standard value of ϕ_4 is 0.023. The corresponding over-all coefficients for runs with the short tube at entering velocities of 3.6 ft/sec are plotted *vs.* the steam pressure in Fig. 172, and it is seen that the oleic acid was a better promoter of dropwise condensation on nickel than was octyl thiocyanate.

Over-all coefficients for molasses and gelatin solutions are given by Coates and Badger,[130] and film and over-all coefficients for concentrated caustic solutions are reported by Badger, Monrad, and Diamond[31] for a vertical nickel tube heated by condensing vapors of diphenyl.

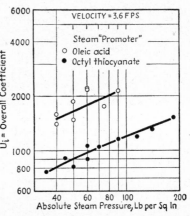

Fig. 172.—Increase in capacity of a short vertical nickel-tube forced-circulation evaporator (0.495 in. by 1.72 ft) by promoting dropwise condensation by use of oleic acid; film coefficients are given in Fig. 171. (*Data of Oliver.*[534a])

Long-tube Vertical Evaporator, Natural-circulation Type.—In this type, the feed rates are very small, compared with those used in forced-circulation evaporators, so that a large fraction of the feed is evaporated in each pass. Brooks and Badger[91] measured the distribution of temperature in a single vertical tube of copper (1.76 in. by 20 ft) jacketed by condensing steam. It was found that a substantial portion of the length was used for preheating and true over-all coefficients U_B for the boiling section were determined

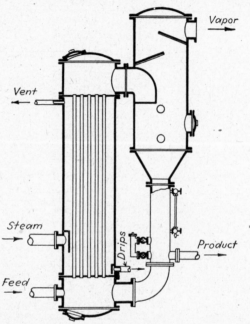

Fig. 173.—Long vertical-tube natural-circulation type of evaporator, with external vapor-liquid separator. (*Courtesy of Buffalo Foundry and Machine Company.*)

for distilled water boiling at temperatures ranging from 150 to 200°F. The data show that U_B increased with increase in over-all temperature difference and suggest that U_B decreases with increase in fraction of the feed evaporated.

Stroebe *et al.*[706] used the same apparatus to boil water at 150 to 200°F, with feed entering at velocities of 0.065 to 0.58 ft/sec and injected enough live steam to bring the feed to the boiling temperature corresponding to the pressure at the base of the tube, so that boiling occurred through the length of the tube. The corresponding true-mean coefficients h_m (based on Δt_m obtained with the aid of a traveling thermocouple) ranged from 1160 to 2640, which are considerably lower than those obtained by Boarts[67] with forced circulation. However, because of the substantial resistance on the steam side, the over-all coefficients in the forced- and natural-circulation types were more nearly equal than the coefficients on the boiling-side coefficients. Use of a promoter in the steam for both evaporators would have allowed the forced-circulation type to take advantage of the high velocity inside the tubes. Stroebe obtained U ranging from 230 to 630 based on apparent over-all Δt and 410 to 880 based on true over-all Δt. In a run with water

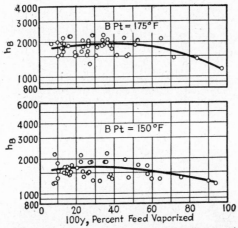

Fig. 174.—True film coefficients for water in the boiling section of a vertical-tube natural-circulation evaporator (1.76 in. by 20 ft), plotted *vs.* weight per cent vaporized. (*Data of Stroebe, Baker, and Badger.*[706])

entering at a velocity of 0.2 ft/sec and a temperature of 155°F in the vapor separator, h_B was 1500, but upon adding a small concentration of a wetting agent (Duponol) h_B increased to 3100 and U_B increased from 540 to 710. In contrast to the small weight fraction y of feed vaporized in the forced-circulation evaporator, at the low feed rates used in the long-tube vertical natural-circulation type, from 7 to nearly 100 per cent by weight of the feed is vaporized. At high values of y, the true coefficient h_B decreases, as shown by Woods[779a] in Fig. 174.[460]

Cessna, Lientz, and Badger[111] continued the program and reported over-all coefficients for a vertical copper tube 1.25 in. by 18.5 ft and calculated true over-all coefficients U_{NB} and U_B for the nonboiling and boiling sections, for water and for solutions containing from 30 to 50 per cent sucrose fed at the rate of 36 U.S. gal/hr. The values of U_{NB} were correlated by the natural-convection type equation: $U_{NB} = 0.06(c_p \, \Delta t_m \rho^2/\mu)_{NB}^{0.7}$. Since the work is still under way, the values of U_B were not correlated but are reported. Cessna

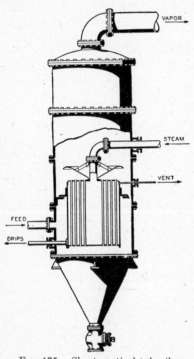

FIG. 175.—Short vertical-tube (basket type) natural-circulation evaporator. (*Courtesy of Swenson Evaporator Company.*)

and Badger[110] repeated the work described in reference 111 by substituting a vertical copper tube (0.65 in. by 18.5 ft) and gave a complex equation for correlating the maximum temperature and reported the over-all coefficients U_{NB} and U_B.

Short Vertical-tube Evaporators.—Badger and Shepard[34] used a basket-type evaporator containing 24 iron tubes (2 in. by 2 ft), and, as shown in Table IX, U increased with increase in Δt_o and with increase in the temperature of boiling.

Figure 176 shows data obtained by Cleve[129] for evaporation of water in a short vertical-tube natural-circulation evaporator. At Δt greater than 9°F, because of decrease in the velocity of the liquid entering the tube and the increase in Δt, h rose more slowly than at smaller values of Δt, where V' was increasing.

Foust, Baker, and Badger[232] studied the evaporation of water under reduced pressure in a basket-type evaporator containing 31 ten-gauge steel tubes (2.5 in. outside diameter and 4 ft long), heated by condensing steam. The liquor velocity entering the

TABLE IX.—BOILING WATER IN BASKET-TYPE EVAPORATOR

Δt_o, deg F	10	20	30	40	50	60
U for 140°F	120	205	270	320	350	370
U for 167°F	220	320	400	440	480	500
U for 212°F	320	440	500	520		

tubes, measured by a pitot tube, ranged from 1 to 4 ft/sec and for
each value of the over-all temperature drop went through a maximum with respect to liquor level.   The over-all coefficients increased
with lowered level of the liquor,
with increased Δt_o, and with
increased boiling point.   Apparent values of U ranged from 76
to 309, and true values of U
ranged from 78 to 340.

Hydrostatic Head.—The
depth of the liquid over the
heating surface in an evaporator
affects the apparent over-all coefficient of heat transfer to a substantial degree.   As shown by
Curves 1, 2, and 3 of Fig. 177,
short vertical-tube evaporators

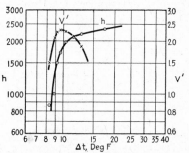

Fig. 176.—Data of Cleve[129] for heating and boiling water in a short vertical-
tube natural-circulation evaporator; V'
is liquor velocity entering tube, expressed in feet per second.

show an increase in the apparent over-all coefficient U with increase
in depth of liquid up to a certain point and then a decrease with
increase in depth.   The low coefficients at very low liquid levels

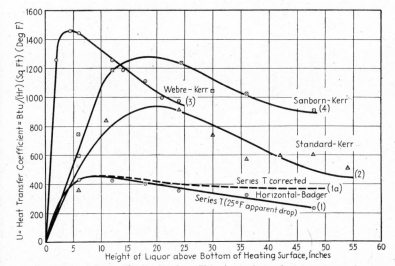

Fig. 177.—Effect of liquor level on U in natural-circulation evaporators.

may be due to incomplete submergence of the heating surface.   At
high levels the decrease with increase in liquid level is attributed
both to the effect of hydrostatic head on the temperature difference

and to a change in circulation. Badger and Shepard[34] had previously studied the variation with liquid level of the over-all coefficient from steam to boiling water in a vertical-tube evaporator and observed a behavior analogous to that illustrated in Fig. 177.

In 1920, Badger[25] published tests on a 138-sq ft horizontal-tube evaporator operated with various liquid levels. Water was evaporated by condensing steam, and the effect of the water level

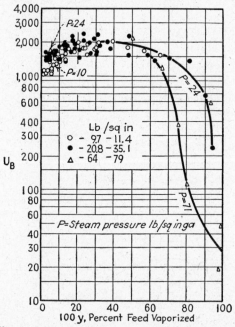

FIG. 178.—Plot of local over-all coefficient in boiling section of horizontal four-pass forced-circulation evaporator (Yaryan type) *vs.* cumulative weight per cent vaporized. The decrease in U_B at high y is due to insufficient liquid to wet the inner walls of the tube. (*Data of Woods.*[779a,460])

on the over-all coefficient is shown as Curve 1 in Fig. 177. The solid line is based on the difference between the temperature corresponding to the pressure in the steam chest and the temperature corresponding to the pressure in the vapor space. The dotted line, Curve 1*a*, is based on the temperature difference, corrected for hydrostatic head, taken as the difference between the saturation temperature in the steam chest and the arithmetic mean of the saturation temperatures of the water corresponding to the pressures at the top and at the bottom of the heating surface. The coefficient of heat transfer calculated from this corrected temperature difference decreases with increase in liquor level, although not so rapidly as the uncorrected value. Coefficients of heat transfer in evaporators may vary so much with type of evaporator, kind of liquor evaporated, cleanliness, and temperatures of steam and boiling

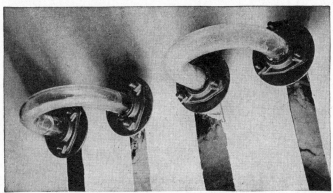

FIG. 179a.—High-speed photograph of return bends at end of first and third passes in four-pass apparatus of Woods.[779a,460] [Taken between surges at a feed rate of 530 lb of water per hr and a steam-gauge pressure of 20. Calculated cumulative vaporization equals 8 per cent of feed (by weight), in first return bend (at the left) and 47 per cent in third. Note quiet liquid layer in bottom of first return bend. A cardboard background was placed behind return bends.] (*Photograph by H. E. Edgerton with exposure of 1/100,000 sec.*)

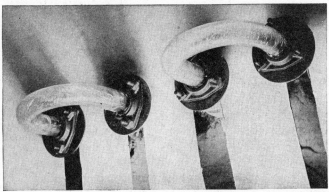

FIG. 179b.—Edgerton photograph taken a few seconds after that shown in Fig. 179a, while a surge occurred in the return bend at the left.

liquid that the use of coefficients based on an uncorrected temperature difference is usually as satisfactory as those based on a corrected temperature difference. Nevertheless, there is an optimum liquid level at which either type of coefficient of heat transfer, and hence the capacity of the evaporator, is at a maximum.

Horizontal Tubes.—Woods *et al.*[460] vaporized water or benzene flowing through a four-pass horizontal steam-jacketed standard 1-in. copper pipe. Temperatures of the fluid were determined at

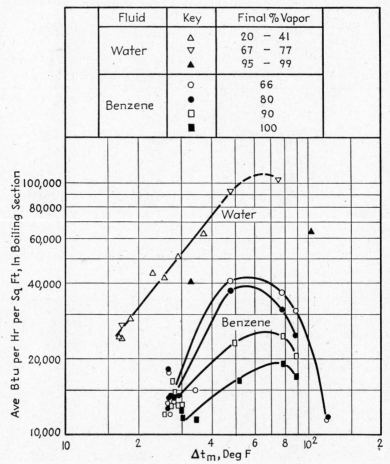

Fig. 180.—Average flux in boiling section of a Yaryan-type evaporator *vs.* length-mean over-all temperature difference, for various values of y. In the benzene runs, hot-wall vapor binding (due to excessive Δt) is clearly shown for several values of y; at a given Δt, dry-wall vapor binding is indicated by the decrease in flux with increase in y. Owing to use of a promoter of dropwise condensation on the steam side, the Δt on the boiling side should be substantially the same as the measured over-all Δt. (*Data of Woods*[779a,461] *and Bryan.*)

the end of each 12-ft pass, and condensate rates were measured from the 12 separate steam jackets. As in the case of the long-tube vertical, low feed velocities were used (0.26 to 1 ft/sec) so that nearly all the feed could be evaporated if desired. The steam-side resistance was minimized by using octyl thiocyanate (page 276) to promote dropwise condensation, and hence over-all coefficients should be nearly as large as the inside coefficients. In the benzene runs the local over-all coefficients in the preheating section ran

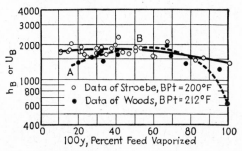

Fig. 181.—Data of Woods[460] for water in a four-pass horizontal tube, compared with those of Stroebe *et al.*[706] for a single vertical tube. Since dropwise condensation was employed by the former, the values of h_B probably were little higher than the measured values of U_B.

from two to four times as large as those predicted from Eq. 4c of Chap. VII, which may be due to increased turbulence resulting from temporary vaporization in the film near the wall and subsequent condensation in the bulk of the stream and to turbulence resulting from the surging flow inside the tubes. As shown in Fig. 178, with moderate temperature differences, as the fluid is progressively vaporized, the local over-all coefficient at first increases, goes through a maximum, and then decreases sharply toward values typical of superheating dry vapor (Eq. 4k of Chap. VII). This dry-wall vapor binding is attributed to insufficient liquid to wet the walls; at the glass return bends, small droplets of liquid were carried down the center of the tube (Fig. 179a).

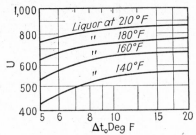

Fig. 182.—Data of Moore[488] for evaporation of water from sulphite liquor flowing in a slightly inclined steel tube (3 in. × 25 ft) jacketed by condensing steam.

With high temperature differences, there was encountered the type of hot-wall vapor binding typical of boiling pools of liquid heated with submerged tubes. Figure 180 shows the average flux in the boiling section plotted *vs.* the length-mean over-all temperature difference for various per cent vaporizations of the feed.   Figure 181 shows that the coefficients for water are of the same order of magnitude as those[706] in the long-tube vertical evaporator.

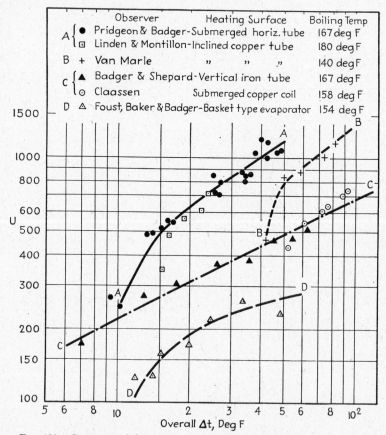

Fig. 183.—Summary of data for apparent over-all coefficients from condensing steam to water boiling under vacuum in several types of natural-circulation evaporators; for each set of data the curves are convex upward.   For a given Δt_o and t_o, Foust *et al.*[232] found that q was highest when the liquor level was below the top of the heating surface.

Figure 182 shows over-all coefficients reported by Moore[488] for evaporation of water from sulphite liquor flowing inside a steel tube (3 in. by 25 ft), slightly inclined from the horizontal and jacketed by condensing steam.   As usual, U increases with increase in over-all temperature difference and with increase in boiling temperature.

Inclined-tube Evaporators.—Table X shows the dimensions of two evaporators having tubes inclined 45 deg, in which the feed enters at the bottom and the unevaporated liquid returns by gravity to recirculate through the tubes.

TABLE X

Observer	Number of tubes	O.D., inches	I.D., inches	Heated length, feet	A_i, sq ft
Linden and Montillon[436].....	1	1.32	1.06	4.08	1.14
VanMarle[732]...............	7	3.00	2.83	4.88	25.3

Table XI gives smoothed values of the over-all coefficients of heat transfer for the evaporation of water at several temperatures.

TABLE XI.—COEFFICIENTS IN INCLINED-TUBE EVAPORATORS

Boiling temperature, deg F...........	120	130	140	180	195	210
U, Δt_o = 10°F, reference 436..........	...	...	....	...	...	300
U, Δt_o = 20°F, reference, 436..........	...	...	....	550	700	900
U, Δt_o = 60–79°F, reference 732.......	650	850	1050			

The inside coefficients, determined by Linden and Montillon, were correlated by the equation $h = a_5 \Delta t^{2.5}$, where a_5 is 0.63 at 180°, 1.0 at 195°, and 1.56 at 210°F.

SUMMARY, BOILING INSIDE TUBES

For natural-circulation evaporators having long or short vertical tubes or inclined tubes, the boiling-side and over-all coefficients increase with increase in temperature difference and with increase in temperature of boiling (pages 324 to 333), as is also true for submerged-tube evaporators. The effect of high temperature difference has not been studied. As with submerged heat-transfer surfaces, the coefficients increase with decrease in surface tension (page 325). When a solute is added to water, thus increasing viscosity, the coefficients decrease (page 326). Typical coefficients are quoted for water, and literature references are given for several aqueous solutions.

Forced-circulation evaporators, operated with high velocities in the tubes, give higher coefficients on the boiling side than natural-circulation types, but frequently the increase in over-all coefficient is not marked because of the importance of the thermal resistance on the steam side, where film type condensation prevails. The advantage of promoting dropwise condensation is shown in Fig. 172. With high feed rates, a small fraction is vaporized, and for the reasons given on page 331, the boiling-side coefficients may be roughly twice those predicted from Eq. 4c of Chap. VII. At low feed rates $(DG/\mu < 65{,}000)$, the ratio of the apparent coefficient h_a to that predicted from Eq. 4c increases approximately from 1 to 4 as Δt_a increases from 30 to 50°F, as shown in Fig. 170.

With low feed rates in a multipass horizontal-tube evaporator, it is possible to evaporate the volatile portion of the feed if desired. With such apparatus, two types of vapor binding and consequent decrease in capacity may be encountered. With moderate Δt_B, when a large fraction of the feed is evaporated, the residual liquid is carried as spray in the rapidly moving stream of vapor (Fig. 179a), and h_B decreases with further increase in fraction evaporated (Fig. 178). The coefficients are roughly the same as those for similar conditions in the long-tube vertical natural-circulation type (Fig. 181). With large Δt_B and a given substantial fraction vaporized, hot-wall vapor binding occurs at a critical Δt_B, and even the *average* flux decreases with further increase in Δt_B; typical results are shown in Fig. 180.

III. PREDICTION OF OVER-ALL COEFFICIENT

In a number of cases, values of U are already available; otherwise they are preferably determined experimentally for the solution and type of apparatus under consideration. However, it is sometimes necessary to base preliminary design on the available data for the surface coefficients, with the use of the familiar resistance equation

$$\frac{1}{U_o A_o} = \sum \frac{1}{hA} + \frac{x_w}{k_w A_w} \tag{4}$$

Values of the thermal conductivity of the tube wall are known, but except where it is necessary to use glass-lined equipment or the like, k_w has but little influence on U. Steam-side coefficients of heat transfer are given in Chap. IX, except for condensation inside horizontal tubes; as an approximation, h may be taken the same as for outside horizontal tubes. Coefficients of heat transfer for scale deposits on the steam side are given on page 275. In nearly all cases, the reported steam-side values were determined without filtering the steam, and hence the effect of dirt on the steam is already included. However, it is desirable to make separate allowance for h_d on the steam side, especially where the steam side cannot be cleaned readily. Corresponding values for the boiling side may depend on both the nature of the liquid and the surface but can be approximated from runs in small-scale apparatus. The scale-deposit factor on the boiling side is automatically included in the values of h_B determined from the results of long runs in which h, at a given Δt_B, has reached a constant value with respect to time. With these data, it is easy to compute the coordinates of a curve of U *vs.* Δt_o, or flux *vs.* Δt_o, as follows: For a given Δt_B on the boiling side, with the use of the curve of h_B *vs.* Δt_B, the flux q/A is calculated. The temperature drops through the tube wall and dirt deposit are computed as usual, and finally the Δt through the condensate film is obtained by use of the charts* on pages 268 or 269. The over-all temperature difference is obtained by adding these individual temperature drops, and flux or U_o may be plotted *vs.* Δt_o.

Graphical Analysis of U.—By assuming that the sum R of the resistances of the steam side, tube wall, and dirt deposits is constant, an approximate graphical analysis of over-all coefficients may be made by combining the following relations:

$$\frac{1}{U} = R + \frac{1}{h_B} = R + \frac{1}{a_5 \, \Delta t_B^n}$$

$$h_B \, \Delta t_B = a_5 \, \Delta t_B^{n+1} = U_o \, \Delta t_o$$

to give

$$\frac{1}{U_o} = R + \frac{1}{a_5^{\frac{1}{n+1}}(U_o \, \Delta t_o)^{\frac{n}{n+1}}} = R + \frac{1}{a_6(q/A)^m} \tag{5}$$

Hence if, by selecting a suitable value of n, a plot of $1/U_o$ as ordinates *vs.* $1/(U_o \, \Delta t_o)^{n/n+1}$ as abscissas gives a straight line on rectangular coordinates with a positive intercept on the vertical axis, the intercept equals R, and the reciprocal of the slope equals $a_5^{1/(n+1)}$.† Obviously the method will break down as the critical

---

* Note that in Fig. 136 the abscissa $4\Gamma/\mu_f$ is proportional to the flux on the steam side. Alternatively, one may use the alignment chart on p. 269.

† Alternately, one may plot $\left[\left(\dfrac{1}{U}\right) - R_w\right]$ *vs.* $\dfrac{1}{(q/A)^m}$, wherein

$$m = n/(n + 1).$$

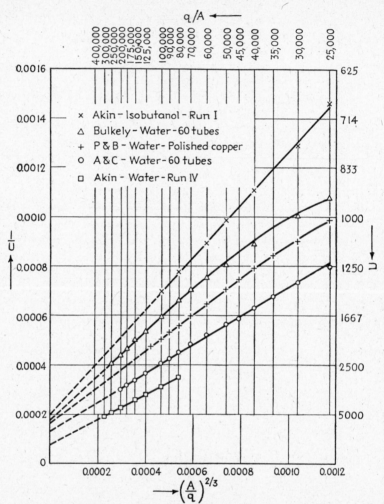

Fig. 184.—Graphical analysis of over-all coefficients from condensing steam to liquids boiling at 1 atm. in submerged horizontal-tube evaporators, based on $m = n/(n + 1) = \frac{2}{3}$. The intercept on the vertical axis represents the apparent sum of all thermal resistances except that of the boiling liquid. The reciprocal of the slope, raised to an exponent of $n + 1$ (3 in this case), represents the value of a_b in the equation $h_B = a_b \Delta t_B^n$. The weakness of the method lies in the fact that substantially straight lines are obtained by use of values of m ranging from 0.5 to 0.8, corresponding to n ranging from 1 to 4; as m is increased from 0.5 to 0.8, both the intercept and slope increase, but for these data the intercepts are small compared with the over-all resistances, for m ranging from 0.5 to 0.8.

Δt_o is approached, where the value of n falls rapidly and even reverses sign. The method also fails in the region of very low flux, along the portion AB of the curve of Fig. 147, where n is much less than in the range CD. With film-type condensation on one side and water boiling on the other, R is a substantial fraction of the total resistance $1/U$, whereas with dropwise condensation, R drops sharply. The method will also fail if R varies considerably, because of a substantial deposition of scale, a shift from one type of condensation to another, or accumulation of

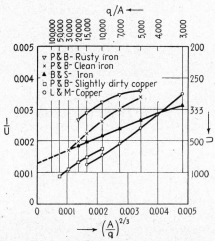

Fig. 185.—Graphical analysis of data for range of low flux, showing lack of linear relation, since in this range n and m are not constant, as shown in Fig. 147; however, intercepts are much larger than in Fig. 184.

noncondensable gas. Although it is possible to obtain a representative slope with fair accuracy, the value of a_5 computed from the slope is less reliable. As shown in Fig. 184, the data in the range of high flux give a linear relation based on n of 2. However, as shown in Fig. 185, use of n of 2 in the range of low flux is unsatisfactory in most cases.

Problems

1. An experimental evaporator shell consists of a horizontal cylinder approximately 1 ft in length by 8 in. in diameter, provided with an overhead water-cooled total condenser and a submerged horizontal chromium-plated copper tube that is heated by steam condensing on the inside surface. The submerged tube is 12.1 in. long and has an o. d. of 0.840 in. and a wall thickness of 0.109 in. Thermocouples are installed at points 4 in. from each end of the tube and 0.025 in. below the outer surface.

In a typical run, the heating surface is covered with water to a depth of 1.25 in.; steam is passed through a vapor-liquid separator, thence through a glass-wool filter, and is throttled to the desired condensing pressure before it enters the heating tube. Cooling water is supplied to the condenser.

When steady-state conditions have been obtained, the following readings are taken with the water boiling at 212°F:

Run number	1	2	3	4
Steam gauge pressure, lb/sq in.	99	13	43	78
Average temperature of thermocouples, deg F	329	234	258.5	317
Temperature of inlet condenser water, deg C	16.2	17.2	12.8	18
Temperature of outlet condenser water, deg C	54.5	58.5	57	58.5
Condenser-water rate, lb/hr	322	305	1132	317

From these data, compute the over-all coefficient and the two surface coefficients.

2. It is desired to boil methanol at 151°F in a natural-convection evaporator heated by steam condensing inside horizontal submerged tubes. In view of the data below, what should be the condensing temperature of the steam?

t_{sv}, deg F	221	226	236	246	256	266	272	286	296
U	1450	1510	1540	1500	1420	1300	1200	1040	950

3. It is proposed to feed 5000 lb/hr of a viscous solution containing 30 weight per cent solute at 175°F to an evaporator operated continuously at a fixed vacuum, to produce a product containing 40 weight per cent solute. The submerged tubes will be supplied with an adequate amount of superheated steam at 175°F, having a condensation temperature of 170°F. Further data are given below. Calculate the square feet of heating surface required.

DATA

Per cent solids	Specific heat	Boiling temperature, deg F	U
30	0.720	110	50
40	0.615	130	30

4. A two-effect vapor-compression evaporator is to concentrate 100,000 lb/hr of a colloidal solution from 10 to 40 per cent solids by weight. The feed will enter the first effect at the boiling temperature in that effect, which is to be operated with an absolute pressure on the boiling side of 21 lb/sq in. The pressure in the vapor space of the second effect will be maintained at an absolute pressure of 4 in. of mercury.

A part of the vapor from the first effect is to be compressed to an absolute pressure of 40 lb/sq in., and the remainder of the vapor will be sent to the second effect. The over-all efficiency of the compressor (based on the theoretical work of isentropic compression) may be taken as 50 per cent, and the actual compression may be assumed adiabatic. The turbine, which will supply the power to the compressor, is to be fed by dry saturated steam at 164.7 lb/sq in. abs.; and the efficiency of the turbine (based on the theoretical work output by isentropic expansion to the final pressure) is 70 per cent. The turbine may be assumed to be adiabatic in operation. The steam is to be exhausted from the turbine at an absolute pressure of 40 lb/sq in. and mixed with steam from the compressor before entering the first effect of the evaporator. If necessary, high-pressure steam may be added directly to the first effect. Assume the over-all coefficients of heat transfer in the first and second effects are 300 and 200 Btu/(hr)(sq ft)(deg F), respectively.

a. Calculate the pounds of high-pressure steam required per hour, indicating how much, if any, of this is to be fed directly to the first effect.
b. Calculate the condition of the steam entering the first effect.
c. Calculate the area of heating surface in each effect.
d. What percentage of the total evaporation will be accomplished in the first effect?

CHAPTER XI

APPLICATIONS TO DESIGN

Introduction.—The first section treats the general case of heat loss through insulated surfaces, "critical radius," and optimum thickness of insulation in reducing heat loss. The second section deals with condensers, heaters, coolers, and exchangers. Various types of tubular equipment are described, alternate methods of routing the streams are discussed, and unit cost data are included. The basic quantitative relations among the various factors are reviewed and summarized. In designing to obtain predetermined terminal temperatures with tubes of fixed diameters, the design procedure is discussed on the assumption that the designer has preselected one of the following factors: velocities, heated length, and pressure drop. A procedure is given whereby the velocity can be estimated from the pressure drop without evaluating the heated length, and an equation is developed for determining whether a given pressure drop should be utilized for flow inside or across tubes. The section dealing with optimum operating conditions treats the complex general case of optimum velocity as well as two special cases in which only one power cost need be considered; in the latter cases the equations are easy to use, as is true of those for the corresponding minimum costs of power and fixed charges. Equations and graphs are included for determining the optimum amount of cooling water for condensers and coolers, and equations are developed for the optimum temperature difference to be used in recovering waste heat. Several illustrative problems are solved, and a number of practice and review problems are given at the end of the chapter.

TABLE I.—NOMENCLATURE AND UNITS

A	Area of heat-transfer surface, square feet; A_i for inside, A_o for outside, A_s for outer surface of insulation, A_w for tube wall, A_1 and A_2 for surfaces 1 and 2.
a	Constant, dimensionless; $f_i = a_i(\mu/DG)_i^m$; $f_o = a_o(\mu/DG)_o^{m_o}$; $j_i = a_3/F_s(DG/\mu)_i^{1-n}$; $j_o = a_4/F_s(DG/\mu)_o^{1-n_o}$.
B_i, B_o	Correction factors, dimensionless, in friction relations. Eqs. 8 and 9.

TABLE I.—NOMENCLATURE AND UNITS.—*(Continued)*

C — Unit costs: C_A is first cost of apparatus, dollars per square foot of heat-transfer surface (C_{Ai} is based on A_i, C_{Ao} on A_o); C_e is cost of mechanical energy supplied to the fluid, dollars per foot-pound (C_{ei} for fluid inside tubes and C_{eo} for fluid outside tubes); C_H is cost of heat in dollars per Btu used (C_{H1} available at low temperature and C_{H2} at high); C_w is cost of cooling water in dollars per pound.

C_a — Hourly fixed charges on apparatus, dollars/(hr)(sq ft); C_{ai} is based on A_i and C_{ao} on A_o; $C_a = C_A F_A / \theta$.

C_p — Hourly power cost, dollars/(hr)(sq ft of heat-transfer surface); C_{pi} for fluid in tubes and C_{po} for fluid in shell.

c — Mean specific heat of fluid, Btu/(lb)(deg F); c' is value for colder fluid, c'' for warmer, c_i for fluid inside tubes, c_o for fluid outside tubes.

D — Diameter of tube in feet; D_i for inside, D_m for mean diameter of insulant, D_o for outside (D_c for critical o.d. of insulant), D_s for surface of insulation, D_w for tube wall.

d — Prefix, indicating derivative, dimensionless.

F — Correction factor, dimensionless; $F = \Delta t_m / \Delta t_l$ (see Chap. VI).

F_A — Fraction of first cost of apparatus charged off annually.

F_s — Factor of safety, dimensionless; value by which h in equations recommended in Chaps. VII to X should be divided to allow for deviation of data from recommended equation.

F_c, F_e, F_i, F_r — Friction, foot-pounds per pound of fluid, due to sudden contraction, sudden enlargement, friction in tubes, and reversal in direction of flow, respectively.

f_i — Friction factor, dimensionless, for flow inside tubes; $F_i = 4f_i L G_i^2 / 2g_c D_i \rho_i^2$.

f_o — Friction factor, dimensionless, for flow normal to a bank of tubes; $F_o = 4f_o N G_o^2 / 2g_c \rho_o^2$.

G — Mass velocity, lb/(hr)(sq ft of cross section); for flow inside tubes, $G_i = w/S = 4w/\pi D_i^2$; for flow across tubes, $G_o = w/S_o$, where S_o is based on the minimum free area (previously G_o was designated as $G_{\max}$).

g_c — Conversion factor in Newton's law; $g_c = 4.17 \times 10^8$ (lb fluid)(ft)/(hr)(hr)(pounds force).

h — Surface-, film-, or individual coefficient of heat transfer, Btu/(hr)(sq ft)(deg F); h_c by natural convection, h_i for inside tubes, h_o for outside tubes, h_r by radiation.

j — Dimensionless factor, $(h/cG)(c\mu/k)^{2/3}$; j_i for inside tubes, j_o for outside tubes (flow normal to axis).

K_1 — Dimensionless factor in definition of B_i (see Eqs. 15a and 15).

K_c — Dimensionless factor due to sudden contraction (see Chap. V).

K_i, K_o — Dimensional terms defined in Eqs. 21 and 22.

K_2 — Factor defined in Eq. 26.

K_3 — Sum of power costs and fixed charges, dollars/(hr)(sq ft); $K_3 = C_a(X_a + X_p)/(X_a)$.

k — Thermal conductivity, Btu/(hr)(sq ft)(deg F per ft); k_i for

TABLE I.—NOMENCLATURE AND UNITS.—(*Continued*)

fluid in tubes, k_m for insulant, k_o for fluid outside tubes, k_w for tube wall.

L	Length of each tube, feet; L_H is heated length, $L_H = N_{TP}L$, where N_{TP} is number of tube passes.
m, m_o	Exponents (dimensionless) in dimensionless equations: $f_i = a_i(\mu/DG)_i^m$ and $f_o = a_o(\mu/DG)_o^{m_o}$.
$\ln_e$	Operator, dimensionless, denoting natural logarithm to base e; $\ln_e = 2.303 \times \log_{10}$.
N	Number of rows of tubes across which shell fluid flows, dimensionless.
N_{TP}	Number of tube passes, dimensionless.
N_w	Number of tubes in each tube pass.
n, n_o	Exponents (dimensionless) in dimensional equations: $h = \alpha_i G_i^n$, $h_o = \alpha_o G_o^{n_o}$; n' and n'_o in $U_i = \alpha' G_i^{n'}$ and $U = \alpha'_o G_o^{n_o}$.
Q	Quantity of heat, Btu, transferred through a tube wall.
q	Rate of heat transfer, Btu per hour.
R	Individual thermal resistance, degrees Fahrenheit $\times$ hours per Btu; R_1 on inside of pipe, R_w of pipe wall, R_x of insulation, R_s on outer surface of insulant; ΣR is total resistance.
R_2, R_3, R_4	Thermal resistances defined in Eq. 23, based on inside surface; $R_2 = R_{wd}$, $R_3 = D_i/\alpha_o D_o$, and $R_4 = 1/\alpha_i$.
r	Radius, feet; r_1 is inside radius of insulant; r_c is critical outer radius at which dq/dL reaches maximum value.
r	Exponent (dimensionless) $= 1/(3 + n_o - m_o)$.
s	Exponent (dimensionless) $= (3 + n - m)/(3 + n_o - m_o)$.
S	Cross section, square feet, normal to flow of fluid; $S_i = $ inside section $= \pi D_i^2/4$; S_o for outside; S_H/S_i is ratio of cross sections of headers and tubes.
t	Bulk temperature of fluid, degrees Fahrenheit; t_a for air, t' for warmer fluid, t'' for colder fluid.
U	Over-all coefficient of heat transfer, Btu/(hr)(sq ft)(deg F); U_i is based on A_i and U_o on A_o; in a given case $U_iA_i = U_oA_o$.
V	Average velocity, feet per hour; $V = G/\rho$; V_i for inside tubes, V_H in headers.
w	Mass rate of flow, pounds per hour; w' for warmer fluid and w'' for colder fluid.
x	Thickness of conductor, feet, measured in direction of heat flow; x_w for tube wall, x for insulant covering tube.
X	Cost ratio, dollars per Btu transferred; X_a represents fixed charges on apparatus and equals C_aA/q (X_{ai} is for a given fluid inside the tubes and X_{ao} for a given fluid outside the tubes); $(X_{ai})_o$ represents optimum value of X_{ai}. X_p represents cost of mechanical power delivered to the fluid, allowing for over-all efficiencies of motors, pumps, etc., and equals C_pA/q (X_{pi} is for a given fluid inside the tubes, and X_{po} is for a given fluid outside the tubes).
X, Y_o, Z	Dimensionless ratios defined in Fig. 198.
y_o	Clearance (feet) between outer surfaces of tubes in a bundle, taken to correspond to the minimum free area.

TABLE I.—NOMENCLATURE AND UNITS—*(Continued)*

z	Dimensionless ratio defined on page 365.
z'	Dimensionless ratio, $w''c''/w'c'$.
Greek	
α, α'	Dimensional factors in the equations $h_i = \alpha_i G_i^n$, $U_i = \alpha_i' G_i^{n'}$, $h_o = \alpha_o G_o^{n_o}$, $U_o = \alpha_o' G_o^{n_o'}$.
Δp	Pressure drop, pounds per square foot; Δp_i for inside and Δp_o for outside (see page 357).
Δt	Mean value of temperature drop across an individual thermal resistance, degrees Fahrenheit; Δt_i for inside fluid film, Δt_o for outside fluid film, Δt_{wd} for tube wall and dirt deposits.
Δt_m	Mean value of over-all temperature drop $(t' - t'')$ from warmer to colder fluid, degrees Fahrenheit; $\Delta t_m = F \, \Delta t_l$, where Δt_l is the logarithmic mean of terminal values for counterflow.
θ	Hours of operation per year.
μ	Viscosity of fluid, lb/(hr)(ft) = $2.42 \times \mu'$ in centipoises; μ_i for fluid inside tubes, μ_o for fluid outside tubes.
π	$3.1416 \cdots$.
ρ	Density of fluid, pounds per cubic foot; ρ_i for fluid inside tubes and ρ_o for fluid outside tubes.
ϕ	Dimensionless term, defined by Eq. 11.
ψ	Dimensionless factor by which f for isothermal flow is multiplied to obtain f for nonisothermal flow (see page 121).

I. HEAT TRANSMISSION THROUGH INSULATION

Consider the general case of a hot fluid at t' inside a pipe having length L, inside and outside diameters D_i and D_o, and mean thermal conductivity k_w, insulated with any thickness x of insulant having mean thermal conductivity k_m, exposed to colder surroundings at t_a. Under steady conditions the same heat flows in turn through a number of resistances: by conduction and convection from the warm fluid to the inside surface, by conduction through the tube wall and insulation to the outer surface, and thence by conduction, convection, and radiation to the surroundings. In view of the relations developed in preceeding chapters, the following general relation may be written

$$\frac{dq}{dL} = \frac{t - t_a}{\dfrac{1}{h_i(\pi D_i)} + \dfrac{x_w}{k_w(\pi D_w)} + \dfrac{x}{k_m(\pi D_m)} + \dfrac{1}{(h_c + h_r)(\pi D_s)}} = \frac{\Delta t_o}{\Sigma R} \quad (1)$$

which applies to the usual case in which both the air and the surfaces of the surroundings have the same temperature. Values of the thermal conductivities are given in the Appendix, values of h_i are given in Chap. VII, and values of $h_c + h_r$ are given in Table VIII of Chap. VIII.

Illustration 1.—Calculate the heat loss per 100 ft of standard 1-in. steel pipe carrying saturated steam at a gauge pressure of 150 lb per sq in., insulated with a 2-in. layer of magnesia pipe covering, exposed to a room at 80°F.

Solution.—From the steam tables (page 397), it is found that the saturation temperature corresponding to an absolute pressure of 165 lb per sq in. is 366°F, and consequently the over-all Δt is $366 - 80 = 286$°F. From page 416, $D_i' = 1.049$ in., $D_o = 1.315$ in., and $x_w' = 0.133$ in.; since $x' = 2$ in., $D_s' = 5.315$ in. Since the resistance on the steam side will be small relative to that of the other resistance, h need not be predicted accurately; consequently the combined resistance of the condensate film and dirt deposit will be taken as 1000. Then

$$R_1 = \frac{1}{h_i(\pi D_i)} = \frac{1}{1000(3.14 \times 1.049/12)} = 0.0036$$

From page 380, k for steel is 26.

$$R_w = \frac{x_w}{k_w \pi D_w} = \frac{0.133/12}{26(3.14 \times 1.182/12)} = 0.0014$$

If the temperature drop in the insulation is 90 per cent of the over-all drop, the mean temperature of the insulation will be 238°F, and from Table VI of the Appendix, k_m is interpolated as 0.0418. The logarithmic mean of 1.32 and 5.32 is 2.86 in.

$$R_x = \frac{x}{k_m D_m} = \frac{2/12}{(0.0418)(3.14)(2.86/12)} = 5.33$$

With 10 per cent (29°) of the total drop through the surface resistance, reference to Table VIII of page 247, at Δt_s of 29°F and D_s' of 5.32 in., gives $h_c + h_r$ of 1.9.

$$R_s = \frac{1}{(h_c + h_r)(\pi D_s)} = \frac{1}{(1.9)(3.14 \times 5.32/12)} = 0.38$$

The total resistance ΣR is then $0.0036 + 0.0014 + 5.33 + 0.38 = 5.72$, and hence the resistances R_1 and R_w were, as usual, negligible compared with the total resistance. The estimated value of R_s is $(0.38/5.72)(100) = 6.6$ per cent of the total resistance instead of the 10 per cent assumed above, but the discrepancy is too small to warrant a second calculation based on Δt_s of 0.066 $(286) = 19$°F. The predicted heat flow per foot is then $q = (t - t_a)/\Sigma R = 286/5.72 = 50$ Btu per hr, or 5000 Btu per hr from 100 ft.

Optimum Thickness of Insulation.—This can be determined by straightforward calculation for a number of standard thicknesses and suitable cost data. Figure 186 shows the results of such a ●calculation, if it is assumed that heat is worth 20 cents per 10^6 Btu, that the installed cost of insulation per foot is 52 cents for a 1-in. layer, 96 cents for a 2-in. layer, and 141 cents for a 3-in. layer, if 15 per cent of the first cost is charged off annually, if operation for 7200 hr per year is assumed, and if k is assumed as 0.042. The resulting curve of total variable costs (annual fuel value of heat lost and fixed charges on insulation) is usually flat near the minimum point, corresponding to approximately a 2-in. layer in this case.

If bare, the pipe would lose

$$\frac{dq}{dL} = \frac{280}{\dfrac{1}{1000(\pi \times 4.03/12)} + \dfrac{0.237/12}{26(\pi \times 4.27/12)} + \dfrac{1}{3.15(\pi \times 4.5/12)}}$$

$$= \frac{280}{0.00095 + 0.00068 + 0.269} = \frac{280}{0.27} = 1030 \, \frac{\text{Btu}}{\text{(hour)(foot)}}$$

It is noted that, as usual, R_1 and R_w are negligible compared with R_s. The value of the heat saved by insulating is then (7200) $(1030 - 50)(100)(0.20)/10^6 =$ $133 per year, and since the first cost of the 2-in. layer is $96, the pay-off time is $96/133 = 0.72$ year.

Many articles* have appeared giving charts or equations to facilitate the determination of the optimum thickness from the various pertinent data.

Critical Radius.—Under spe-

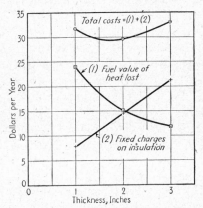

Fig. 186.—Determination of optimum thickness of insulation on a steam main.

cial conditions an increase in heat loss is caused by insulating, since the effect of the added surface more than offsets the reduced temperature of the surface. Thus, in 1910, Porter and Martin[569] showed that as the thickness x of the insulation is increased the heat loss may reach a maximum value and then decrease with further increase in x. The maximum loss occurs when the outside diameter D_c of the insulation is twice the ratio of the thermal conductivity to the surface coefficient:

$$D_c = \frac{2k_m}{(h_c + h_r)_c} \qquad (2)\dagger$$

---

* Bagley,[35] Dufton,[201] Fabry,[214] McMillan,[464-466] Nichols,[508] Patton,[552] Sanbern,[619] Stone,[704] Weidlein,[752] Wood and Rice,[779] Wunderlich,[784] Zeiner,[786] and others.

† Equation 2 may be derived by setting the derivative of the sum of R and R_s equal to zero. Let r_1 be the inside and r the outside radius of the insulation, having mean thermal conductivity k_m. Now $R = x/k_m A_m = \ln_e (r/r_1)/2\pi L k_m$, and $R_s = 1/(h_c + h_r)(2\pi L r)$, and $d(R + R_s) = 0$ gives $r_c = k/(h_c + h_r)$, neglecting change in k_m and $h_c + h_r$ with change in t_s and r.

This principle is used by the electrical engineer in insulating wires to secure a combination of electrical insulation with an increased cooling effect.

Thus the heat loss from a tube having an outside diameter of $\frac{1}{2}$ in. and a temperature of 248°F, exposed to a room at 68°F, would lose approximately 60 Btu per hr, if bare. If insulated with dense asbestos (k of 0.15), the heat loss would be 76 Btu per hr with a covering $\frac{1}{2}$-in. thick and 60 Btu per hr with a 2.8-in. layer. Had a really good insulation been used, the heat loss would have not been increased by adding the covering.

Heat loss from a bare surface depends on h_c (Chap. VIII) and upon h_r, which is directly proportional to the emissivity (Table XIII, page 393), as shown in Chap. III. Hence for a surface having a low emissivity, such as galvanized iron, the heat loss may be increased by adding a thin layer of asbestos paper having a low emissivity, as shown by Day[172]; eight layers of paper were necessary to make the heat loss as low as that from the bare pipe.

Heat Loss from Overhead Gas Mains.—Here the inside resistance may be substantial compared with other resistances, and Eq. 1 applies.*

Submerged Bodies.—Surface-resistance factors for bodies of various shapes, submerged in the ground, as given in Table II of Chap. I.

II. DESIGN OF HEAT-TRANSFER EQUIPMENT

Structural and Cost Factors.†—The designer of exchangers has to specify a number of factors. The following section describes various types of exchangers‡ and discusses temperature strains, thickness of shells and tubes, types of baffles, and unit costs of surface as affected by length, diameter and number of tubes, and material of construction. Usually the apparatus is designed to meet the requirements of the safety codes of the A.S.M.E., or the A.P.I.—A.S.M.E. Specifications, governing tubular exchangers, and the materials to be used in fabrication are given in reference 722a.

---

* A practice problem of this type is given at the end of the chapter.

† Helpful suggestions are acknowledged from M. T. Carpenter, J. J. Hogan, C. C. Lockhart, A. K. Scott, Jr., E. N. Sieder, and C. A. Stokes, who reviewed this section (pp. 346 to 354).

‡ For the sake of brevity in the descriptive section the term *exchanger* is used in the broad sense, regardless of whether the object is to cool one stream, heat the other, or to do both. Several types of evaporators are described in Chap. X.

Figure 187 shows an exchanger with fixed tube sheets. Since the tube bundle is not removable, this construction is suitable only for those cases in which the fluid in the shell does not foul the tubes. Large differences in temperature between the shell and

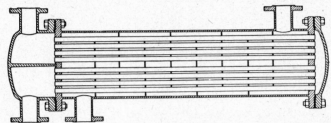

FIG. 187.—Type *N* exchanger with fixed tube sheets, two tube passes and one cross-baffled shell pass. (*Courtesy of Struthers-Wells Company.*)

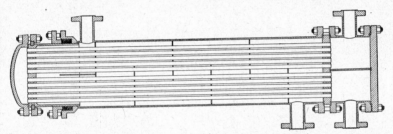

FIG. 188.—Type *F* exchanger with an expansion joint in the shell, two tube passes and one cross-baffled shell pass. (*Courtesy of Struthers-Wells Company.*)

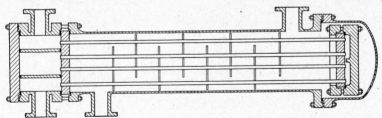

FIG. 189.—Heat exchanger with one floating head, four tube passes and one cross-baffled shell pass. (*Courtesy of M. W. Kellogg Company.*)

tubes may produce severe temperature stress, and when this is encountered the shell should be provided with some type of expansion joint. Alternatively temperature stresses may be avoided by the use of tubes bent into a U shape, which, however, are more difficult to clean inside by mechanical means.

Figures 189–190 show exchangers with floating heads and removable bundles of tubes to facilitate cleaning their outer sur-

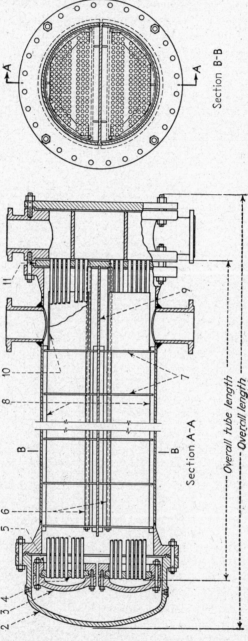

Section B-B

Section A-A

FIG. 190.—Exchanger with two floating heads, one longitudinal shell baffle, four tube passes, and two cross-baffled shell passes.
(*Courtesy of Foster-Wheeler Corporation.*)

(1) Shell; (2) shell cover; (3) floating head cover; (4) floating tube sheet; (5) split ring; (6) tie rods and spacers; (7) transverse baffles; (8) side strips; (9) longitudinal shell baffle; (10) impingement baffle; (11) fixed tube sheet.

faces and inspection of the tubes and of the shells. Sieder[667a] gives an empirical formula for calculating the number of floating heads that should be used to avoid failure due to severe temperature strains. In a single shell the use of two floating heads instead of one may increase the cost 30 per cent, and four floating heads instead of one increase the cost 50 per cent.[667a] The choice between horizontal or vertical units seldom affects the first cost of an exchanger of a given size, and the decision will depend on plant layout or process requirements and in some cases on installation costs. As

a   *b*

FIG. 191.—Photographs from Sieder[667a] of portions of exchangers; (*a*) shows split floating heads, with shell cover removed, and (*b*) shows the method of assembling tubes and baffles in an unfinished exchanger.

shown in Chap. IX, with film condensation higher coefficients are obtained with horizontal than with vertical tubes. However, if it is desired to condense the vapor and substantially subcool the condensate in one apparatus, vertical tubes are used.

If one of the fluids fouls the surface much more rapidly than the other, it should be routed through the tubes, since the inside surface may be cleaned without removing the tube bundle from the shell. If both fluids are equally nonfouling and only one is under high pressure, it should flow inside the tubes to avoid the expense of a high-pressure shell. Where only one of the fluids is corrosive it should flow inside the tubes to avoid the expense of special metal for both shell and tubes. If one of the fluids is much more viscous than the other, it may be routed through the shell to increase the over-all coefficient. The outer surface may be cleaned more readily when the tubes are arranged on a square rather than a triangular pitch as illustrated in Fig. 192. In any case, to facilitate cleaning, the clearance between tubes should be at least one-fourth the outside diameter of the tubes and in no case less than $\frac{1}{4}$-in.* At times, because of a limitation in available pressure drop, it is necessary to route a given stream through the shell.

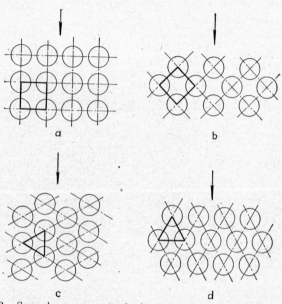

Fig. 192.—Several arrangements of tubes in bundles: (*a*) An in-line arrangement with a square pitch; (*b*) a staggered arrangement with a square pitch, (*c*) and (*d*) staggered arrangements with triangular pitches. Use of a square pitch facilitates cleaning the outer surfaces, especially where the clearances are small relative to the diameter of the tubes.

Although tube lengths of from 4 to 22 ft are readily obtainable and longer tubes are available, one often selects[722a] a standard length of 8, 12, 16, or 20 ft, using more than one pass where necessary. A typical exchanger would be reduced 24 per cent in cost by using tube lengths of 16 instead of 8 ft (Curve *a* of Fig. 193[667a]). The shorter lengths are used when the exchanger is located well above grade, to minimize the cost of platforms and equipment for removing the bundles for cleaning, where length is limited by available space or where very large shell diameters are required; the longer lengths are used when the equipment is near grade and

* With nonfouling fluids, the clearance may be made less by using a tube sheet of high strength to prevent damage in rolling in the tubes.

consequently platforms are not needed. Where maintenance work must be done frequently, location at or near grade is preferred.

As the tube diameter is decreased, the coefficients of heat transfer increase somewhat in many cases, and the first cost per square foot, and the area itself, decrease, but the pressure drop

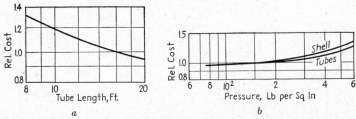

FIG. 193.—Relative costs of steel shell-and-tube exchangers as affected by (a) tube length and (b) working pressure (*Sieder*[667a]).

increases, and consequently there is an optimum diameter corresponding to the minimum sum of fixed charges and power cost. However, the difficulty of cleaning the tubes increases with decrease in diameter. In exchangers the tubes ordinarily used have outside diameters of $\frac{5}{8}$, $\frac{3}{4}$, 1, $1\frac{1}{4}$, or $1\frac{1}{2}$ in.; the larger diameters tend to be used for fluids that foul the tubes rapidly. In some cases fouling may be reduced by use of high velocity, thus permitting the use of tubes of moderate diameter. Where a number of exchangers for different duty are to be installed in a given plant, service and replacement costs are reduced by standardizing on a minimum number of tube diameters and lengths. The thickness of tube walls should be selected not only to withstand working pressures and extreme temperatures and to provide allowance for corrosion but also to facilitate expanding the tubes into the tube sheets. Manufacturers of tubes specify the outside diameter and nominal thickness of the wall. The variation in tube-wall thickness from the nominal value may be plus or minus 10 per cent for "average-wall" tubes and plus 22 per cent for "minimum-wall" tubes. The effects of these variations should not be overlooked, especially in tubes of small diameter, since pressure drop varies inversely as the diameter raised to an exponent ranging from 4 to 4.8. To provide for corrosion of the shell it is customary to add an extra thickness of $\frac{1}{8}$ in. to that needed to withstand the pressure. In some cases alloy linings are used to prevent corrosion of the shell.

The first cost per square foot decreases as the total surface increases (Fig. 194), depends considerably on the metal used for both tubes and shell,* and is a function of the working pressure (Curve *b*, Fig. 193).

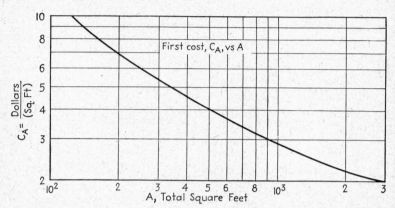

FIG. 194.—First cost, per unit surface, of a shell-and-tube heat exchanger with a steel shell for a working pressure of 150 lb/sq. in. (A.S.M.E. code) and 13-gauge steel tubes.

Figure 195 shows three types of transverse baffles used to increase velocity on the shell side. With a bored shell the clearance between baffles and shell is often from $\frac{1}{32}$ to $\frac{3}{64}$ in., but the clearance and consequently the leakage will increase because of corrosion. With unbored shells the clearance may be considerably larger because of greater tolerances.[722a] The orifice type of baffle should fit the shell closely to prevent leakage, and the baffles are spaced fairly closely to give frequent changes in the velocity; this type should not be used for fluids that rapidly foul the outer surface or where corrosion or erosion is likely to cut the tubes. In a variation of the orifice type, alternate baffles have orifices for one-half the number of tubes and support the other half. With

FIG. 195.—Three types of transverse baffles. (*Sieder*[667a].)

* Bliss[65a] gives methods for calculating separately the costs of tubes and shells of various metals.

disk-and-doughnut baffles, the disks offer no support for the central tubes unless braced to the shell. Sometimes the minimum clearance between the tubes and the edges of the holes in the segmental or disk-and-doughnut baffles is 1 per cent of the tube diameter, but since the tubes may have a diameter tolerance of 2 per cent, the maximum clearance may be 3 per cent; consequently some fluid will flow through these clearances. In reference 722a it is recommended that the tube holes in the baffles and those in the support plates be drilled $\frac{1}{32}$ and $\frac{1}{64}$ in. larger than the outside diameter of the tubes. To avoid vibration of the baffles and scoring of the tubes, the baffles should have a thickness of $\frac{1}{8}$ in. and preferably $\frac{3}{16}$ or $\frac{1}{4}$ in., and the edges of the tube holes should be chamfered.* The baffle is a fixture, whereas the tubes can be replaced individually, and the baffles may be subjected to considerable abuse when the tube bundle is being withdrawn; consequently the baffle should be at least twice as thick as the wall of the tube. Sufficient space between baffles should be provided to facilitate cleaning. The thickness of tube sheets should be at least $\frac{7}{8}$ in. and should be not less than the outside diameter of the tubes.[722a] Longitudinal baffles, if used, may be welded to the shell or may be of the removable type, with arrangement to prevent leakage. Some users of exchangers prefer two single-pass shells in series rather than one shell with a longitudinal baffle and a split floating head. Where a spare tube bundle is to be provided, it may be more economical to employ several smaller units in multiple instead of a single large unit. To avoid erosion of the tubes near the point of entry of the shell fluid, impingement baffles and flaring nozzles are sometimes installed.

Adequate vents and drains should always be provided, and relief valves or rupture disks are required for the high pressure. Since the removal of condensate becomes difficult when the gauge pressure is as low as 10 lb/sq in., gauge glasses should be provided to show the condensate level so that the operator may avoid flooding the tubes, with consequent reduction in capacity. Steam traps should be provided with by-passes so that the equipment may be operated with hand control in case of failure of the traps. With vapor-heated equipment, it is advisable to provide suitably located vents for the removal of noncondensable gas rather than to rely wholly on devices to remove both condensate and pemanent gas.

* It has been proposed to reduce scoring of tubes by use of nonmetallic baffles.

Figure 196 shows a two-pass surface condenser in which non-condensable gases are collected along the axis and pass over cold tubes before entering the air outlet line. Single-pass steam condensers have been built that contain more than 100,000 sq ft of condensing surface in a single shell.

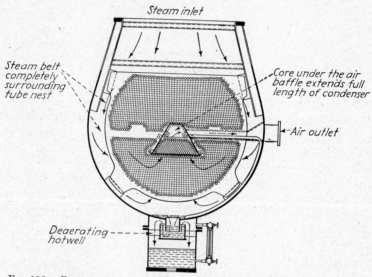

FIG. 196.—Cross section of a small radial steam-flow type of surface condenser, with two tube passes. (*Courtesy of Westinghouse Electric and Manufacturing Company.*)

Quantitative Relations.—Chapter X gives the procedure for the case in which the colder fluid is vaporized by heat supplied from the condensation of the warmer fluid; Chap. IX treats problems in which both energy and matter are transferred simultaneously by diffusion; and Chap. III deals with heat transfer at high temperature levels at which most of the energy is transferred by radiation. The following section presents quantitative relations used in the design of tubular heat-transfer apparatus such as heaters, coolers, exchangers, and condensers.

In these cases the heat is transferred from fluid to surface by the combined mechanisms of conduction and forced convection. In warming or cooling fluids flowing inside or outside tubes without change in phase, both the coefficient of heat transfer and the pressure drop increase with increase in velocity, and in many cases the designer is free to employ the optimum velocity at which the total costs are at a minimum; however, this may lead to impractical proportions of apparatus. At times, because of process requirements or for other reasons a fixed pressure drop is available, and the exchanger is designed to meet this situation. Alternatively, one may fix the tube length and diameter and use whatever velocity and pressure drop are necessary. Regardless of which factors are fixed in advance and which are computed, the same basic relations are always involved; although these have been derived and discussed in earlier chapters, they are summarized below for convenience.

Heat Balance.—As shown in Chap. V, the heat Q transferred through the wall of a tube may be expended in increasing the enthalpy of the outer stream, in changing the kinetic energy of the stream, and in doing work against gravity; some of the heat may be lost to the surroundings if the shell fluid receives the heat. Thus if the stream is a gas flowing at high velocity with large percentage change in pressure and small change in temperature, the change in kinetic energy is substantial compared with Q. With a small-scale apparatus involving a small heat flux, a substantial fraction of Q may be lost to the surroundings. Except in such special cases, substantially all the heat transferred through the wall of the tube is utilized to increase the enthalpy of the stream of fluid flowing past the heat-transfer surface, and heat loss to the surroundings is negligible. In the cases discussed below, heat is transferred from a warmer stream at t' through a heat-transfer surface to a colder stream at t'', and at least one of the streams is heated or cooled without change in phase; consequently the heat balance becomes

$$q = wc(t_2 - t_1) = SGc(t_2 - t_1) \tag{3}$$

In case neither fluid changes in phase, the heat balance is

$$q = w'c'(t_1' - t_2') = w''c''(t_2'' - t_1'') \tag{3a}$$

In these cases the heat balances have direct utility, since they fix the relation between the terminal temperatures and mass flow rates. As pointed out in Chap. VI, the ratio z' [$= w''c''/w'c'$ $= (t_1' - t_2')/(t_2'' - t_1'')$] has an important bearing on the mean overall temperature difference $(t' - t'')_m$ in multipass or cross-flow exchange of sensible heat. If this limitation is overlooked one might select four terminal temperatures that satisfy the heat balance and that seem plausible, since the lowest temperature of the warmer stream exceeds the highest temperature of the colder stream, yet the value of z' is such that the proposed heat exchange cannot occur in the particular type of apparatus under consideration, although it could readily be obtained with counterflow.

Rate Equation.—This takes the familiar form

$$q = UA \, \Delta t_m = U_i(\pi D_i L_H)F \, \Delta t_l = h_i(\pi D_i L_H)(\Delta t_i) = h_o(\pi D_o L_H) \, \Delta t_o \tag{4}$$

in which L_H is the heated length and F is the ratio of the true mean-temperature difference for the apparatus in question to the logarithmic mean value Δt_l for counterflow:

$$\Delta t_l = \frac{(t_1' - t_2'') - (t_2' - t_1'')}{\ln_e \dfrac{t_1' - t_2''}{t_2' - t_1''}} \tag{4a}$$

Values of F, given in Figs. 64 and 65, depend on two dimensionless parameters as well as on the type of exchanger. If one of the temperatures remains constant, F is always unity for any type of exchanger. It will be recalled that the values of F were derived on the assumption that U was independent of temperature. If the ratio of the terminal values of U differs substantially from unity, U is evaluated at a special temperature t_x given by Fig. 62 on page 144.

As shown in Chap. VI, the over-all coefficients are related to the individual coefficients by the resistance equation

$$\frac{1}{U} = \frac{1}{h_i} + \frac{1}{h_{di}} + \frac{x_w}{k_w D_w/D_i} + \frac{1}{h_{do}D_o/D_i} + \frac{1}{h_o D_o/D_i} \tag{5}$$

This is sometimes written as

$$\frac{1}{U_i} = \Sigma R + \frac{1}{h} \tag{5a}$$

in which ΣR represents the sum of all resistances except the resistance $1/h$ of the film under consideration; all resistances are based on the inside surface.

Coefficients.—Values of the surface coefficients h_i and h_o are given in Chaps. VII to X in terms of the pertinent physical properties, dimensions of apparatus, and operating variables; dirt-deposit factors are given in Tables I and II of Chap. VI, and various physical properties and standard diameters are given in the Appendix. For turbulent flow without change in phase, as shown in

Chaps. VII and VIII, the values of h_i and h_o are given by the following dimensionless equations:

$$\left(\frac{h}{cG}\right)_i \left(\frac{c\mu}{k}\right)_i^{2/3} = \frac{a_3/F_s}{(DG/\mu)^{1-n}} \tag{6}$$

$$\left(\frac{h}{cG}\right)_o \left(\frac{c\mu}{k}\right)_o^{2/3} = \frac{a_4/F_s}{(DG/\mu)_o^{1-n_o}} \tag{7}*$$

Various refinements are discussed in Chaps. VII and VIII; for ordinary purposes, a_3 is 0.023, n is 0.8, a_4 is 0.33, and n_o is 0.6. The proper value of the factor of safety F_s depends on the case but, in general, may be taken as 1.25 for gases or water, and 1.5 for viscous liquids.†

For a given case, these reduce to

$$h_i = \alpha_i G_i^n \tag{6a}$$
$$h_o = \alpha_o G_o^{n_o} \tag{7a}$$

Equation 7 is based on flow normal to tubes that are not baffled. If baffles are used, because of leakage of fluid from one compartment to the next, the velocity and consequently h_o will be less than computed on the basis of no leakage. Furthermore, in baffled exchangers, the flow is not strictly normal to the tubes, tending to reduce coefficients, and certain portions of the tubes are not swept by the stream, thus reducing the effectiveness of these areas. Data are scarce, but h_o for baffled exchangers is sometimes taken[120] as 0.6 times the value obtained from Eq. 7, upon assuming no leakage, but this correction factor depends on the construction of the exchanger.‡ Alternatively, one may space the baffles more closely so that the desired velocity is obtained despite leakage.

Pressure Drop.—As shown in Chap. V, the pressure drop Δp_i through the tube passes is B_i times that due to friction in the straight tubes:

$$\Delta p_i = \frac{B_i 4 f_i L_H G_i^2}{2g_c \rho_i D_i} \tag{8}$$

---

* Data for tubes of various shapes, and for finned tubes, are given in Chaps. VII and VIII.

† If a given equation predicts h within ± 20 per cent, to play safe, h is taken as 0.8 times the value from the equation, and the corresponding F_s is $1/0.8 = 1.25$.

‡ R. A. Bowman (Heat Transfer, Am. Soc. Mech. Engrs., 1933–1934, pp. 75–81) shows that a velocity, empirically corrected for leakage, permits the use of Eqs. 7 and 9.

As shown in Fig. 51, f_i depends on the Reynolds number $(DG/\mu)_i$ and somewhat on the roughness of the surface of the wall; f_i may be approximated by the relation

$$f_i = a_i(\mu/DG)_i^m \qquad (8a)$$

where the exponent m is 0.2 for turbulent flow and 1.0 for streamline flow. For D_iG_i/μ_i in the range of 16,000 to 200,000, a_i is 0.046ψ for smooth tubes and 0.055ψ for steel tubes; for isothermal flow, ψ is 1.0, and values for nonisothermal flow are given on page 121.

For flow across tubes

$$\Delta p_o = \frac{4f_o B_o N G_o^2}{2g_c \rho_o} \qquad (9)$$

in which f_o (previously designated as f''') depends on a Reynolds number D_oG_o/μ_o and the arrangement and spacing of tubes and G_o (previously called G_{max}) is the mass velocity of flow through the *minimum* free area; it will be recalled that f_o is much larger than f_i. For a given arrangement and spacing

$$f_o = a_o(\mu/DG)_o^{m_o} \qquad (9a)$$

where m_o is 0.15; values of a_o depend on the spacing and arrangement of tubes and are given on page 126. In Eq. 9, N is the number of rows of tubes in the direction of fluid flow. Since the effect of leakage of fluid through the clearances between tubes and the holes in baffles is uncertain, it is best to neglect the effect of leakage on pressure drop, unless exact details of construction are available. If baffles are used, an empirically determined value of B_o is introduced to allow for the effect on Δp_o of reversal in direction of flow and nonuniformity in cross section. For flow of fluid across banks of tubes that are not baffled, B_o is 1.0.

Fixed Terminal Temperatures

Frequently terminal temperatures and mass-flow rates are determined by process requirements and the heat balance, and consequently q and Δt_l are known. Values of D_i and D_o are selected for the reasons given on page 351. Since the physical properties of the fluids are fixed, the designer may now choose two of the remaining factors and compute the others from the relations just given.

Fixed Velocities.—The corresponding values of q, h_i, h_o, and U are computed, and the product FL_H is found from Eq. 4. If L_H is not excessive, single pass is used, and F is 1.0; otherwise F is evaluated from Figs. 64 or 65. The corresponding pressure drops are found from Eqs. 8 and 8a and 9 and 9a. This procedure may be repeated for various chosen velocities, and thus the minimum total cost for power and fixed charges may be determined. Alternatively, as shown on page 363, the optimum velocities could be found from a combination of the equations given above with cost data.

Fixed Heated Length.—One may have available or under consideration a certain exchanger which might be used for at least a portion of the total proposed load. If, as before, the desired terminal temperatures are specified, the desired value of G_i may be obtained by combining Eqs. 3, 4, and 6, if it is noted that $S = (\pi/4)(D_i^2)$

$$\left(\frac{DG}{\mu}\right)_i = \left(\frac{4a_3L_H}{D_i\phi_iF_s}\right)^5 \tag{10}$$

$$\phi_i = \frac{(t_2 - t_1)_i}{\Delta t_i}\left(\frac{c\mu}{k}\right)_i^{\frac{2}{3}} \tag{11}$$

If the inside resistance is controlling, ϕ_i is known and G_i can be obtained directly, although the term involving the exponent of 5 should be known with precision. Thus if the factor of safety F_s is to be 1.25, G_i will be 33 per cent of the velocity based on F_s of 1.0. For common gases, for which Eq. 4k of Chap. VII is applicable, this case may be solved by the use of Fig. 79.

If the inside resistance is substantial but not controlling, Eq. 10 may be used by a trial-and-error procedure but in this case ϕ_i must be closely approximated. If the outside thermal resistance controls, Eqs. 3, 4, and 7 may be combined to give

$$\left(\frac{DG}{\mu}\right)_o = \left(\frac{a_4\pi D_oN}{y_o\phi_oF_s}\right)^{2.5} \tag{12}$$

$$\phi_o = \frac{(t_1 - t_2)_o}{\Delta t_o}\left(\frac{c\mu}{k}\right)_o^{\frac{2}{3}} \tag{12a}$$

Calculation of Outlet Temperature.—Both manufacturers and users of heat exchangers may face the problem of predicting the outlet temperatures t_2' and t_2'', which a given heat exchanger should produce for fixed inlet temperatures, mass-flow rates, and physical properties. The procedure is as follows: The over-all coefficient is predicted in the usual manner, and the outlet temperature t_2' is computed from the following equation, which was obtained by eliminating t_2'' from Eqs. 3a, 4, and 4a.

$$t_2' = \frac{[t_1'(1 - z') + (a_5 - 1)t_1'']}{a_5 - z'} \tag{13}$$

$$a_5 = e^{UAF(1-z')/w'c'}$$

If the ratio $z' = w'c'/w''c''$ is unity, Δt is constant throughout the counterflow exchanger and the terminal over-all temperature differences are equal and one obtains

$$t_2' = (t_1' + a_6 t_1'')/(1 + a_6) \tag{13a}$$
$$a_6 = UAF/w'c'$$

Fixed Pressure Drop, Flow inside Tubes.—By eliminating L_H from Eqs. 3, 4, 6, 8, and 8a, one obtains

$$G_i = \sqrt[2]{\frac{2a_3 g_c \rho_i \, \Delta p_i}{a_i F_s \phi_i B_i}} \tag{14}$$

As shown below,* B_i is given by the equation

$$B_i = 1 + \frac{N_{TP} K_1 a_3/a_i}{\dfrac{(t_2 - t_1)_i}{\Delta t_i}\left(\dfrac{c\mu}{k}\right)_i^{2/3}} = 1 + \frac{N_{TP} K_1 a_3/a_i}{\phi_i F_s} \tag{15}$$

For turbulent flow in tubes in which the average velocity is twice that in the header compartments, K_1 is 0.55 for single pass and

---

* As shown in Chap. V, $B_i = (F_c + F_i + F_e + F_r)/F_i$, in which the friction F_c due to each sudden contraction is $K_c V_i^2/2g_c$, the friction F_i in each tube pass is $4f_i L V_i^2/2g_c D_i$, the friction F_e due to each sudden enlargement is $(V_i - V_H)^2/2g_c$, where V_H is the velocity in the header compartments and F_r is the friction in each header due to reversal in direction of flow. As an approximation the average value of F_r is taken as $0.45 V_i^2/2g_c$, although this depends on the details of construction. Hence

$$B_i = 1 + \frac{K_c + \left(1 - \dfrac{S_i}{S_H}\right)^2 + 0.45}{4f_i L/D_i} = 1 + \frac{K_1}{4f_i L/D_i} \tag{15a}$$

The over-all change in kinetic energy $(V_{i2}^2 - V_{i1}^2)$ can be included in K_1, so that the Δp_i will represent the over-all pressure drop; otherwise Δp_i represents the over-all pressure drop due to friction, not corrected for any net change in kinetic energy.

For S_i/S_H of 0.5, the term $[1 - (S_i/S_H)]^2$ is 0.25, Fig. 52 on page 122 shows that K_c is 0.3, and K_1 equals $0.3 + 0.25 + 0.45 = 1.0$. From Eqs. 3, 6, 8, and 8a, one obtains Eq. 15, given above.

approximately 1.0 for multipass; for a given N_{TP}, B_i can be obtained from Eq. 15 without computing L_H.

If the thermal resistance on the inside is controlling, as in the case of a vapor-heated gas heater, the procedure is simple. First the term ϕ is computed from Eq. 11, and B_i is obtained from Eq. 15. Second, G_i is calculated from Eq. 14, with turbulent flow assumed. Third, D_i is selected, and the Reynolds number D_iG_i/μ_i is computed; if, as will usually be the case with gases, D_iG_i/μ_i exceeds 2100 the value of G_i obtained from Eq. 14 applies. Fourth, one computes h_i/cG_i from Eq. 6 and obtains* L_H from the following relation, which is based on Eqs. 3 and 4 (noting that $S_i = \pi D_i^2/4$):

$$\frac{4L_H}{D_i} = \frac{(t_2 - t_1)/\Delta t_i}{(h/cG)_i} \tag{16}$$

If this value of L_H is inconveniently long for a single pass, multipass will be used.

Illustration 2.—Assume that it is necessary to heat 100,000 lb per hr of air from 70 to 200°F by means of steam condensing at 220°F outside steel tubes, that the air enters at an absolute pressure of 10 atm, and that the permissible pressure drop across the heater (exclusive of that required for change in kinetic energy) is $\frac{1}{3}$ atm. If the tubes have an i.d. of 0.834 in. and F_s is taken as 1.25, what must be the number of tubes in parallel and the length of each?

Solution.—Since the thermal resistance inside the tube is controlling, U_i equals h_i. From Eq. 11

$$\phi_i = \frac{(t_2 - t_1)}{\Delta t_i}\left(\frac{c\mu}{k}\right)^{\frac{2}{3}} = \left(\ln_e\frac{220 - 70}{220 - 200}\right)(0.74)^{\frac{2}{3}} = 1.65$$

Assume that the headers have twice the cross sections of the tubes; hence K_1 is 0.55 for single pass, and from Eq. 15

$$B_i = 1 + (1)(0.55)(0.023)/(0.055)(1.65)1.25 = 1.11$$

From Eq. 4a, the mean temperature difference is 64.4°F, and ρ_i is evaluated at $t_m = t' - \Delta t_i = 220 - 64 = 156°F$. Since 29 lb of air occupies 359 cu ft at normal pressure and 492°F abs:

$$\rho_i = \frac{29(492)(9.83)}{359(460 + 156)} = 0.633 \ \frac{\text{lb}}{\text{cu ft}}$$

If the flow is turbulent, Eq. 14 applies:

$$G_i = \sqrt{\frac{2a_3g_c\rho_i\,\Delta p_i}{a_iF_s\phi_iB_i}} = \sqrt{\frac{2(0.023)(32.2)(0.633)(705)}{0.055(1.25)(1.65)(1.11)}} = 72.4 \ \frac{\text{lb}}{(\text{sec})(\text{sq ft})}$$

$$= 260,000 \ \frac{\text{lb}}{(\text{hr})(\text{sq ft})}$$

---

* Alternatively, f_i may be computed from Eq. 8a and L_H found from Eq. 8.

In order to handle 100,000 lb of air per hr, one needs

$$N_w = \frac{100,000}{(260,000)(0.785)(0.834/12)^2} = 102 \text{ tubes in parallel}$$

As shown on page 411, μ' is 0.020 centipoises, and μ_i is 2.42(0.020) = 0.0484 lb/(hr)(ft).

$$\left(\frac{DG}{\mu}\right)_i = \frac{(0.834/12)(260,000)}{0.0484} = 373,000$$

and since this exceeds 2100 the flow is turbulent, as assumed. One could now save time by using Eq. 5b of page 175, or the corresponding chart (Fig. 79); however, the example is continued to illustrate the general procedure. From Eq. 6, with a_3 of 0.023, n of 0.2, and F_s of 1.25

$$\left(\frac{h}{c_p G}\right)_i = \frac{a_3/F_s}{(DG/\mu)_i^{0.2}(c_p\mu/k)^{2/3}} = \frac{0.023/1.25}{(373,000)^{0.2}(0.74)^{2/3}} = 0.00172$$

$$L_H = \left(\frac{D_i}{4}\right)\frac{(t_2 - t_1)_i/\Delta t_i}{(h/c_p G)_i} = \left(\frac{0.834}{48}\right)\frac{2.02}{0.00172} = 20.4 \text{ ft}$$

If F_s had been taken as 1, one would have obtained N_w of 92, L_H of 16.6, and $N_w L_H$ of 1530 ft, instead of 102, 20.4, and 2080, respectively.

If the thermal resistance inside is substantial but not controlling, one assumes a preliminary value of Δt_i based on an estimate of the resistance ratio U_i/h_i, i.e., $\Delta t_i = U_i \Delta t_m/h_i$. The value of G_i is then found by the procedure outlined above, and the corresponding ratio U_i/h_i is computed. If this value differs seriously from the assumed value, the procedure is repeated until compatible results are obtained.

Fixed Pressure Drop, Flow across Tubes.—The relations are similar to those for flow inside tubes; elimination of the number of rows deep from Eqs. 3, 4, 7, 9, and 9a gives

$$G_o = \left(\frac{\pi a_4 g_c \rho_o \, \Delta p_o \, \dfrac{D_o}{y_o}}{2 a_o F_s \phi_o B_o (D_o/\mu_o)^{0.25}}\right)^{0.444} \tag{17}$$

If the thermal resistance on the shell side is controlling ($h_o = U_o$, $\Delta t_o = \Delta t_m$), ϕ_o is found from Eq. 12a, G_o is obtained from Eq. 17, h_o from Eq. 7, A_o from Eq. 4, and S_o from Eq. 3. Obviously it is necessary that N be made a whole number.

If the fixed pressure drop may be used either inside or across tubes, Δp_i equals Δp_o, and if the over-all thermal resistance is controlled by the fluid for which the pressure drop is fixed, Eqs. 14 and 17 may be combined to give

$$\frac{G_i}{G_0} = \sqrt{\left(\frac{4 a_o a_3 B_o y_o}{\pi a_i a_4 B_i D_o}\right)}\left(\frac{D_o G_o}{\mu_o}\right)^{1/8} \tag{18}$$

The corresponding ratio of apparatus costs, X_{ao}/X_{ai}, with the same Δp alternatively used inside or across tubes, is

$$\frac{X_{ao}}{X_{ai}} = \left(\frac{C_{ao}a_3}{C_{ai}a_4}\right)\left(\frac{2a_3}{a_iB_i}\right)^{0.4}\left(\frac{D_o}{D_i}\right)^{0.2}\left[\left(\frac{2a_oB_oy_o}{\pi a_4\mu}\right)^2\left(\frac{g_c\rho\ \Delta p}{F_s\phi}\right)\right]^{1/7.5} \quad (19)$$

If Δp is small, X_{ao}/X_{ai} will be substantially less than 1, and flow across tubes will be preferred; if Δp is quite large, X_{ao}/X_{ai} will exceed 1, and flow inside tubes is preferable. Although the equation is formidable in appearance it is not very difficult to use in a specific case. For example, consider the case of 1-in. tubes having a wall thickness of 0.109 in., with a transverse clearance y_o of 0.25 in.; assume that the gas is diatomic ($c\mu/k = 0.74$), μ is 0.05 lb/(hr)(ft), ρ is 0.06, and a_o is 0.69. Assume $(t_2 - t_1)/\Delta t_m$ is 2.3,* whence ϕ equals $2.3(0.740)^{2/3} = 1.88$. From Eq. 15, assuming one pass, $B_i = 1 + N_{TP}K_1a_3/a_i\phi F_s$ $= 1 + (1)(0.55)(0.023)/(0.055)(1.88)\ 1.25 = 1.1$. Substituting values in Eq. 19, assuming that the cost per foot of length is fixed (and consequently $C_{ao}/C_{ai} = D_i/D_o$), one obtains

$$X_{ao}/X_{ai} = 0.381\ \Delta p^{0.133} \quad (19a)$$

and flow across tubes would be preferred to flow inside tubes until Δp exceeded a value of 1400 lb per sq ft or 9.8 lb per sq in., at which point X_{ao} equals X_{ai}; the corresponding mass velocity G_i would be 96,000 lb/(hr)(sq ft of cross section).

In some cases, as in heating a gas at atmospheric pressure, C_{ao}/C_{ai} is much less than D_i/D_o, since the air stream can be passed through an inexpensive sheet-metal duct, and the advantage of flow across tubes is increased. If the thermal resistance on the shell side is substantial but not controlling, G_o could be found for a fixed Δp from Eq. 17 by a cut-and-try procedure similar to that outlined on page 362.

Optimum Operating Conditions

Optimum Velocities in Exchangers.—The general case, in which the surface coefficient on each side of the tube varies substantially with velocity, is complex, since the velocities and corresponding power costs can be independently varied, within limits. Let C_{ai} represent the fixed charges on the exchanger, expressed in dollars/(hr)(sq ft of inside surface); the corresponding fixed charge, expressed in dollars per Btu, is

$$X_a = \frac{C_{ai}A_i}{q} = \frac{C_{ai}}{U\ \Delta t_m} \quad (20)$$

The power theoretically required to force the fluid through the tubes is $\Delta p_i w_i/\rho_i$, and Δp_i is obtained from Eqs. 8 and 8a. Let

* For the heating of a gas by a condensing vapor, $(t_2 - t_1)/\Delta t_m = \ln_e \Delta t_1/\Delta t_2$; for $\Delta t_1/\Delta t_2$ of 10, $(t_2 - t_1)/\Delta t_m = 2.3$.

C_{ei} represent the cost of supplying mechanical energy to the fluid, expressed in dollars per foot-pound, allowing for the over-all efficiency of the pump. By use of Eqs. 3 and 4, and the relations just given, the corresponding cost of power, expressed in dollars per Btu transferred, is found to be*

$$X_{pi} = \frac{C_{pi}A_i}{q} = C_{ei}\left(\frac{B_i a_i \mu_i^m}{2g_c \rho_i^2 D_i^m}\right)\frac{G_i^{3-m}}{U_i\,\Delta t_m} = \frac{C_{ei}K_i G_i^{3-m}}{U_i\,\Delta t_m} \tag{21}$$

Similarly, using the equations for pressure drop across tubes, the power cost for flow through the shell, expressed in dollars per Btu, is[193]

$$X_{po} = \frac{C_{po}A_i}{q} = C_{eo}\left(\frac{2}{\pi}\frac{B_o a_o \mu_o^m y_o}{g_c \rho_o^2 D_o^{m_o} D_i}\right)\frac{G_o^{3-m_o}}{U_i\,\Delta t_m} = \frac{C_{eo}K_o G_o^{3-m_o}}{U_i\,\Delta t_m} \tag{22}$$

Since the inside and outside individual coefficients of heat transfer depend on the velocities $h_i = \alpha_i G_i^n$ and $h_o = \alpha_o G_o^{n_o}$, Eq. 5 may be written

$$\frac{1}{U_i} = R_2 + \frac{D_i/D_o}{h_o} + \frac{1}{h_i} = R_2 + \frac{D_i/D_o}{\alpha_o G_o^{n_o}} + \frac{1}{\alpha_i G_i^n} = R_2 + \frac{R_3}{G_o^{n_o}} + \frac{R_4}{G_i^n} \tag{23}†$$

The total cost‡ $\Sigma X = X_a + X_{pi} + X_{po}$ may be made a minimum by using the proper combination of the two velocities, and the corresponding optimum relation between the velocities and the unit costs is found by partially differentiating ΣX with respect to both G_i and G_o, setting the resulting partial derivatives equal to zero, thus obtaining the two following symmetrical equations for optimum velocities:[249a,143c]

$$G_i^{3-m} = \frac{\left(\dfrac{n}{3-m-n}\right)\dfrac{C_{ai}}{C_{ei}K_i}}{1 + \left(\dfrac{3-m}{3-m-n}\right)\left[z_i - \dfrac{nC_{po}}{(3-m)C_{pi}}\right]} \tag{24}§$$

* References 435, 193, 143c and 249a. In one case B_i was omitted.

† It will be recalled that this equation is the basis of a graphical method of interpreting over-all resistances, as discussed in Chap. IX.

‡ Note that ΣX does not include the cost of pumping cooling water against a fixed head, since this cost is independent of water velocity. However, this item should be included in the calculation of total costs at the optimum velocity.

§ It should be noted that the term ρ^2, which appears in the definitions of K_i and K_o, represents the product $\rho_m\rho_p$, wherein ρ_m is the mean density and ρ_p that in the pump.

$$G_o^{3-m_o} = \frac{\left(\dfrac{n_o}{3 - m_o - n_o}\right)\left(\dfrac{C_{ai}}{C_{eo}K_o}\right)}{1 + \left(\dfrac{3 - m_o}{3 - m_o - n_o}\right)\left[z_o - \dfrac{n_o}{(3 - m_o)}\dfrac{C_{pi}}{C_{po}}\right]} \quad (25)*$$

$$K_i = \frac{B_i a_i \mu_i^m}{2g_c \rho_i^2 D_i^m}; \qquad K_o = \frac{2B_o a_o \mu_o^{m_o} y_o}{\pi g_c \rho_o^2 D_o^{m_o} D_i}$$

$$\frac{C_{po}}{C_{pi}} = \frac{C_{eo}K_o G_o^{3-m_o}}{C_{ei}K_i G_i^{3-m}}; \qquad z_i = \frac{\Delta t_m - \Delta t_i}{\Delta t_i} = h_i \Sigma R_o = \left(R_2 + \frac{R_3}{G_o^n}\right)\frac{G_i^n}{R_4}$$

$$z_o = \left(\frac{\Delta t_m - \Delta t_o}{\Delta t_o}\right)\left(\frac{D_o}{D_i}\right) = \frac{D_o h_o \Sigma R_i}{D_i} = \frac{D_o}{D_i}\left(R_2 + \frac{R_4}{G_i^n}\right)\frac{G_o^n}{R_3}$$

Upon dividing Eq. 24 by Eq. 25, and noting that $C_{ei}K_i G_i^{3-m}/ C_{eo}K_o G_o^{3-m_o}$ equals C_p/C_{po}, one obtains

$$\frac{C_{pi}}{C_{po}} = \frac{n(3 - m_o)(1 + z_o)}{n_o(3 - m)(1 + z_i)}.$$

For values of $D_i G_i/\mu_i$ and $D_o G_o/\mu_o$ exceeding 10,000 and 1000, respectively, the exponents have the following values: $n = 0.8$, $m = 0.2$, $n_o = 0.6$ and $m_o = 0.15$,† and Eqs. 24 and 25 become

$$G_i = \left[\frac{0.4 C_{ai}/C_{ei}K_i}{1 + 1.4\left(z_i - \dfrac{0.21(1 + z_i)}{(1 + z_o)}\right)}\right]^{0.357} \quad (24a)$$

$$G_o = \left[\frac{0.267 C_{ai}/C_{eo}K_o}{1 + 1.267\left(z_o - \dfrac{0.286(1 + z_o)}{(1 + z_i)}\right)}\right]^{0.351} \quad (25a)$$

A procedure for solving a specific problem is as follows. From the physical properties of the two streams and the proposed diameters and spacing of tubes K_i and K_o are evaluated, and the unit costs C_{ai}, C_{ei}, and C_{eo} are known. From a preliminary estimate of the thermal-resistance ratios z_i and z_o trial values of G_i and G_o are obtained from Eqs. 24a and 25a. The corresponding revised values of the resistance ratios are calculated and used to find revised values of G_i and G_o from Eqs. 24a and 25a. Since substantial variations in the numerical values of the term in the parentheses in the denominators have but little effect on the values of G_i and G_o, the values converge rapidly.

---

* See footnote § on page 364.

† For flow across tubes there is some doubt as to the exact value of m_o, but apparently it lies between 0 and 0.2. If m_o were 0, $f_o = a_o$. Use of m_o of 0.2 would simplify utilization of the equations.

Alternatively, Eqs. 24a and 24b may be combined to give a relation between the **optimum** values of the two velocities:

$$G_{oo} = 0.728 \left(\frac{C_{ei}K_iR_3}{C_{eo}K_oR_4}\right)^{0.29} G_{io}^s = K_2 G_{io}^{1.043} \qquad (26)$$

in which $R_3/R_4 = \alpha_i D_i/\alpha_o D_o$. Since the exponent s is practically 1, the ratio of optimum velocities is practically dependent only on K_2. With fluids of similar physical properties on both sides of the tubes, G_{oo} tends to be only a fraction of G_{io}. Two methods of obtaining the optimum velocity in this complex case have been outlined: the straightforward but tedious method given on page 359, or the use of Eqs. 24a and 25a.

Illustration 3.—It is desired to design a gas-to-gas exchanger for use in a continuous cyclical process. One gas stream is to be heated from 180 to 540°F, and the other is to be cooled from 750 to 390°F. Each stream will flow at the rate of 20,000 lb per hr and has the same physical properties as air, c_p of 0.25. The average absolute pressures are to be 10 atm in the tubes and 9.65 in the shell. Annual fixed charges on a suitable exchanger are estimated as $0.75 per sq ft of inside surface, and the apparatus is to operate 8640 hr per year. Power delivered to the fluid costs $0.013 per kw-hr. It is proposed to employ steel tubes having an o.d. of 1.00 in. and an i.d. of 0.782 in., arranged in line with a square pitch (center-to-center distance) of 1.25 in. It is agreed to use Eq. 19 of Chap. V, which gives a_o of 0.68 and m_o of 0.15, to employ F_s of 1.25 in Eqs. 6 and 7, and to neglect all thermal resistances except those of the two gas films.

Solution.—The problem will be solved by use of Eqs. 24a and 25a. In the present case, $C_{eo} = C_{ei} = 0.0130(0.746)/(33,000 \times 60) = 4.9 \times 10^{-9}$ dollars per ft-lb delivered to the fluid. The value of C_{ai} is $0.75/8640 = 8.68 \times 10^{-5}$. If counterflow is used, F is 1 and $\Delta t_m = 210°F$. Neglecting all resistances except those of the two gas films, assume $\Delta t_i = \Delta t_o = 105°F$; on this basis $z_i = (210 - 105)/105 = 1$ and $z_o = D_o/D_i = 1.28$. The densities ρ_o and ρ_i will be evaluated at 360 and 570°F; hence

$$\rho_0 = \left(\frac{29}{359}\right)\left(\frac{492}{460 + 360}\right)\left(\frac{9.65}{1}\right) = 0.468;$$

$$\rho_i = 0.468\left(\frac{460 + 360}{460 + 570}\right)\left(\frac{10.0}{9.65}\right) = 0.385$$

From the alignment chart in the Appendix, the corresponding viscosities are 0.0247 and 0.0283 centipoises, or $\mu_o = 0.0598$ and $\mu_i = 0.0685$ lb/(hr)(ft). From Eq. 11, $\phi_i = (360/105)(0.74)^{2/3} = 2.8$; from Eq. 15, if N_{TP} is 1, $B_i = 1 + (1)(0.55)(0.023)/(0.055)(2.8)\ 1.25 = 1.07$.

$$K_i = \frac{B_ia_i}{2g_c\rho_i^2(D/\mu)_i^m} = \frac{1.07(0.055)}{(2)(4.17 \times 10^8)(0.385)^2(0.0652/0.0685)^{0.2}} = 4.78 \times 10^{-10}$$

$$K_o = \frac{2B_oa_oy_o/D_i}{\pi g_c\rho_o^2(D/\mu)_o^{m_o}} = \frac{2(1)(0.68)(0.25/0.782)}{3.14(4.17 \times 10^8)(0.468)^2(0.0833/0.0598)^{0.15}} = 14.4 \times 10^{-10}$$

$(1 + z_i)/(1 + z_o) = 2/2.28 = 0.878$; $(1 + z_o)/(1 + z_i) = 1.14$.

From Eq. 24a

$$G_i = \left[\frac{0.4(8.68 \times 10^{-5})}{\dfrac{(4.9 \times 10^{-9})(4.78 \times 10^{-10})}{1 + 1.4(1 - 0.21 \times 0.878)}} \right]^{0.357} = 38,400 \ \frac{\text{lb}}{(\text{hr})(\text{sq ft})}$$

$$G_0 = \left[\frac{0.267(8.68 \times 10^{-5})}{\dfrac{(4.9 \times 10^{-9})(14.4 \times 10^{-10})}{1 + 1.267(1.28 - 0.286 \times 1.14)}} \right]^{0.351} = 18,700 \ \frac{\text{lb}}{(\text{hr})(\text{sq ft})}$$

From Eqs. 6 and 7

$$h_i = \frac{(0.25)(38,400)}{(0.74)^{2/3}} \frac{(0.023/1.25)}{(0.0652 \times 38,400/0.0685)^{0.2}} = 26.3$$

$$h_0 = \frac{0.25(18,700)(0.26/1.25)}{(0.74)^{2/3}(0.0833 \times 18,700/0.0598)^{0.4}} = 20.3^*$$

But $z_i = (\Delta t_o + \Delta t_i - \Delta t_i)/\Delta t_i = \Delta t_o/\Delta t_i = h_i D_i/h_o D_o = 26.3(0.782)/20.3(1.0)$ = 1.01 and $z_o = (D_o/D_i)/(\Delta t_o/\Delta t_i) = 1.28/1.01 = 1.27$. Since these values of z_i and z_o differ so little from those assumed, it is unnecessary to make a second trial.

$$\frac{1}{U_i} = \frac{1}{h_i} + \frac{D_i/D_o}{h_0} = \frac{1}{26.3} + \frac{0.782}{20.3} = \frac{1}{13.0}$$

The heated length L_H is found from Eqs. 3 and 4:

$$FL_H = \frac{D_i}{4} \left(\frac{G_i c_p}{U_i} \right) \frac{(t_1 - t_2)_i}{\Delta t_m} = \frac{0.0652}{4} \left(\frac{38,400 \times 0.25}{13.0} \right) \left(\frac{750 - 390}{210} \right) = 20.6 \text{ ft}$$

Since FL_H is nearly 20 ft, single pass may be used with counterflow; consequently F is 1, and 20-ft lengths would be used.

Since the cross section of one tube is $0.785(0.0652)^2 = 0.00334$ sq ft, the number of tubes in parallel should be $20,000/(38,400)(0.00334) = 156$. The diameter D_s of a circular shell, containing N_c inscribed circles of diameter D_c, depends on the pitch, as shown by the following equations:[†]

With square pitch, and $N > 25$:

$$D_s/D_c = 1.37 N_c^{0.475}$$

With equilateral triangular pitch, and $N > 20$:

$$D_s/D_c = 0.94 + \sqrt{(N_c - 3.7)/(0.907}$$

In the present case, D_c is 1.25 in., and for 156 tubes, $D_s = 1.37(1.25)(156)^{0.475} =$ 18.86 in. or 1.57 ft. The necessary free area S_o is $20,000/18,700 = 1.07$ sq ft. Since the maximum clearance is $1.57(0.25/1.25) = 0.314$ ft, if the baffles are spaced $1.07/0.314 = 3.41$ ft apart, the average velocity should be approximately as large as the desired value ($G_o = 18,700$) even with substantial leakage. Neglecting the thickness of the baffles, with tubes 20 ft long, the number of baffled compartments would be $20/3.41 = 5.86$; hence 5 compartments would be used.

---

* For in-line banks, a_4 was conservatively taken as 0.26, as suggested on p. 229.

† "Machinery's Handbook," p. 74, Industrial Press, New York, 1927.

Optimum Velocity in Tubes; Shell Power Immaterial.—This case has frequently been discussed in the literature,* and the corresponding equation can be obtained from the general case given above (Eq. 24) by equating C_{po} to zero or can be derived directly by setting the derivative of $X_{ai} + X_{pi}$ equal to zero, noting that $1/U_i = \Sigma R_o + 1/\alpha_i G_i^n$, giving

$$G_i^{3-m} = \frac{\left(\dfrac{n}{3-m-n}\right)\dfrac{C_{ai}}{C_{ei}K_i}}{1 + \dfrac{(3-m)z_i}{3-m-n}} \qquad (27)\dagger$$

Thus for $D_i G_i/\mu_i$ exceeding 10,000, n is 0.8, and m is 0.2, and Eq. 27 becomes

$$G_i = \left(\frac{0.4 C_{ai}/C_{ei}K_i}{1 + 1.4 z_i}\right)^{0.357} \qquad (27b)\ddagger$$

This is readily solved by assuming a value of the resistance ratio $z_i = (\Delta t_m - \Delta t_i)/\Delta t_i$, computing G_i and repeating the procedure until compatible results are obtained. Since the exponent 0.357 is small, values of G_{io} converge rapidly. It is interesting to note that at the optimum velocity the ratio of costs of power and fixed charges is

$$\left(\frac{X_{pi}}{X_a}\right)_o = \frac{C_{pi}}{C_{ai}} = \frac{n}{(3-m)(1+z_i)-n} \qquad (28)$$

Thus, for turbulent flow, where n is 0.8 and m is 0.2, the optimum ratio X_{pi}/X_a is 0.4 if the inside resistance controls and otherwise is less. The minimum total cost in dollars per Btu, except for that of the heat itself, is

$$(X_{pi} + X_a)_o = \left[\frac{3-m}{(3-m)-\left(\dfrac{n}{1+z_i}\right)}\right]\frac{C_{ai}}{U_{io}\,\Delta t_m}$$

$$= \frac{(3-m)C_{ai}}{(3-m-n')U_{io}\,\Delta t_m} \qquad (29)$$

* References 435, 193, 143b, 249a.

† Alternatively, by defining an exponent n' in the relation $U_i = \alpha_i G_i^{n'}$ and noting that the term $1 + z_i$ equals n/n', Eq. 27 may be written[193]

$$G_{io} = \frac{n' C_{ai}}{(3-m-n')C_{ei}K_i} \qquad (27a)$$

‡ A rearranged form is

$$G_i^{2.8} + \frac{1.4\Sigma R_o}{R_4}G_i^{3.6} = \frac{0.4 C_{ai}}{C_{ei}K_i}$$

Optimum Velocity across Tubes; Inside Power Immaterial.—
The derivation for this case is similar to that for the previous case,
except that it is based on Eqs. 9 and 9a instead of Eqs. 8 and 8a,
giving

$$G_o^{3-m_o} = \frac{\left(\dfrac{n_o}{3 - m_o - n_o}\right)\left(\dfrac{C_{ao}}{C_{eo}K_o'}\right)}{1 + \dfrac{(3 - m_o)z_o}{(3 - m_o - n_o)}} \tag{30}$$

wherein $K_o' = 2B_o a_o \mu_o^{m_o} y_o / \pi g_c \rho_o^2 D_o D_o^{m_o}$.   Equation 28 becomes

$$(X_{po}/X_{ao})_o = (C_{po}/C_{ao})_o = n_o/[(3 - m_o)(1 + z_o) - n_o] \tag{30a}$$

and Eq. 29 becomes

$$(X_{po} + X_{ao})_o = \left[\frac{3 - m_o}{(3 - m_o) - \left(\dfrac{n_o}{1 + z_o}\right)}\right] \frac{C_{ao}}{U_{oo}\,\Delta t_m} \tag{30b}$$

If the outside thermal resistance is controlling and $D_o G_o / \mu_o$ lies
between 1000 and 40,000 (where n_o is 0.6), if m_o is taken as 0.15, the
optimum ratio X_{po}/X_a is 0.267, and Eq. 30 reduces to

$$G_o = (0.267 C_{ao}/C_{eo}K_o')^{0.351} \tag{30c}$$

Illustration 4.—It is desired to compute the optimum velocity for a gas
having ρ of 0.069 lb/cu ft, ρ_p of 0.075, $c_p \mu/k$ of 0.74, and μ of 0.045 lb/(hr)(ft),
flowing normal to a bank of in-line tubes laid out with a square pitch, so that
the transverse clearance is one-fourth the o.d. of the 1-in. tubes. Assume that
power delivered to the fluid costs \$0.0133 per kw-hr and that the hourly fixed
charges are $0.44/7200 \doteq \$6.11 \times 10^{-5}/(\text{hr})(\text{sq ft of outside surface})$; since
baffles are not involved, B_o will be taken as 1.0. What would be the optimum
U_o and the optimum total costs $(X_{po} + X_a)$ for Δt_m of 105°F?

Solution.—From Eq. 19 of Chap. V, $a_o = 0.68$. Since n_o is 0.6 and m_o is
0.15, $n_o/(3 - m_o - n_o) = 0.419$. The term $y_o/D_o = 0.25$, and $D_o = \frac{1}{12}$
$= 0.0833$ ft. With time in hours, g_c is 4.17×10^8. The cost of energy delivered to the fluid, expressed in dollars per foot-pound, is

$$C_{eo} = 0.0133(0.746)/(33,000 \times 60) = 5.03 \times 10^{-9}$$

Substitution in Eq. 30c gives

$$G_o = \left[(0.267)\frac{(6.11 \times 10^{-5})}{(5.03 \times 10^{-9})}\frac{(\pi)(4.17 \times 10^8)(0.075)(0.069)(4)}{(2)(1)(0.68)(0.045/0.0833)^{0.15}}\right]^{0.351}$$

$$= 3730\ \frac{\text{lb}}{(\text{hr})(\text{sq ft})}$$

The Reynolds number $(DG/\mu)_o = (0.0833)(3730)/0.045 = 6910$, and, taking
F_s as 1.25, Eq. 7 gives

$$\left(\frac{h}{(0.24)(3730)}\right)(0.74)^{\frac{2}{3}} = \frac{0.33/1.25}{(6910)^{0.4}} = 0.00771$$

and $h_o = U_o = 8.45$.   From Eq. 29

$$(X_{po} + X_{ao})_o = \frac{(3 - m_o)}{(3 - m_o - n_o)} \frac{C_{ao}}{U_{oo} \Delta t_m} = \frac{(2.85)(6.11 \times 10^{-5})}{(2.25)(8.45)(105)} = 8.7 \times 10^{-8}$$

i.e., the sum of the cost of power and fixed charges is 8.7 cents per million Btu transferred.

In heating a gas by a condensing vapor the thermal resistance on the gas side controls, and the question arises whether the gas should flow inside or across the tubes.   The exponents usually have the following values: $n = n' = 0.8$, $m = 0.20$, $n_o = n'_o = 0.6$, and $m_o = 0.15$, and the ratio of the optimum sums of power and fixed charges is readily found to be

$$\frac{(X_{po} + X_{ao})_o}{(X_{pi} + X_{ai})_o} = 0.905 \frac{C_{ao} U_{io}(\Delta t_m)_i}{C_{ai} U_{oo}(\Delta t_m)_o} \tag{31}$$

Consequently the choice will be determined by the product of several ratios.   If a gas were to flow either outside or inside the tubes of a given type of apparatus, where the hourly fixed charge per foot of tube was the same, C_{ao}/C_{ai} would equal D_i/D_o.   If the gas were to be cooled under pressure with water, a considerably less expensive type of construction (trickle cooler) could be used with gas inside the tubes than with gas outside the tubes in a pressure shell.   Conversely, if gas were to be heated at atmospheric pressure with steam condensing under pressure, a sheet-metal tunnel could be used for gas flow across tubes, and C_{ao}/C_{ai} would now be a fractional value.   The ratio of the optimum values of U_i and U_o may be obtained from equations previously given.

Optimum Amount of Water for Condensers or Coolers.—In some cases the cooling water in the plant mains is under sufficient pressure to give the desired rate of flow through the heat-transfer apparatus, and the cost of cooling water is directly proportional to the amount used.   The optimum water rate corresponds to the minimum annual sum of the cooling-water costs and of fixed charges on the condenser or cooler.

Consider the general case in which w' lb per hr of warmer fluid enters at t'_1 and leaves at t'_2, and the heat removed $w'c'(t'_1 - t'_2)$ is absorbed by w'' lb per hr of cooling water entering at t''_1 and having specific heat c''.   The cooling water costs C_w dollars per lb and is available in adequate amount.   Let U represent the over-all coefficient from warmer fluid to water; preferably this should be evaluated at the optimum velocity for the warmer fluid, to maintain proper balance between fixed charges on the apparatus and pumping costs for the warmer fluid (page 363). The highest useful water velocity should be used, since the water is under adequate pressure. The first cost per square foot of heat-transfer surface is C_A, and the fraction F_A is charged off annually as fixed charges; the apparatus is to be operated θ hr per year. Let t_2'' represent the temperature of the cooling water leaving the apparatus, calculated from the heat balance

$$q = w'c'(t_1' - t_2') = w''c''(t_2'' - t_1'')$$

The annual water cost y_w equals $w''\theta C_w = q\theta C_w/c''(t_2'' - t_1'')$, and the annual fixed charges y_A are AC_AF_A. But q equals $UAF \Delta t_l$, where F depends on the geometrical arrangement of the shell and tube passes in the exchanger (Chap. VI) and Δt_l is evaluated for counterflow by Eq. 4a. By combining the foregoing relations, the annual sum of water costs and fixed charges is differentiated with respect to the temperature difference $t_1' - t_2''$ at the hot end, and set equal to zero to find the minimum value of the term $y_w + y_A$, giving

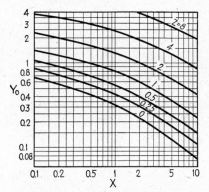

FIG. 197.—Solution of Eq. 32 for ordinary range of Z; for high values of Z, see Fig. 198.

$$\left(\frac{t_1' - t_2' + \Delta t_c - \Delta t_o}{\Delta t_o - \Delta t_c}\right)^2 \left(\frac{\Delta t_c}{\Delta t_o} - 1 + \ln_e \frac{\Delta t_o}{\Delta t_c}\right) = \frac{UFC_w\theta}{C_AF_Ac''} = \frac{UFC_w}{C_ac''}$$

$$(32)*$$

where Δt_c represents the over-all temperature difference $t_2' - t_1''$ at the cold end and Δt_o the optimum over-all difference at the hot end. Unfortunately the desired Δt_o appears in several places in Eq. 32; trial-and-error calculation is rendered unnecessary by the use of charts wherein the ratio $Y_o = (t_1' - t_2'')_o/(t_2' - t_1'') = \Delta t_o/\Delta t_c$ is plotted *vs.* $X = UFC_w\theta/C_AF_Ac''$ for various values of

* Where the temperature of the warmer fluid is constant, as in a condenser, the equation reduces to

$$\frac{t_2'' - t_1''}{\Delta t_o} - \ln_e \frac{\Delta t_c}{\Delta t_o} = \frac{UC_w}{C_ac''}$$

$$(32a)$$

$Z = (t_1' - t_2')/(t_2' - t_1'')$.   Figure 197 is a net work chart* for values of Z ranging from 0 to 4, and Fig is. 198 an alignment chart† for values of Z ranging from 0 to 100.

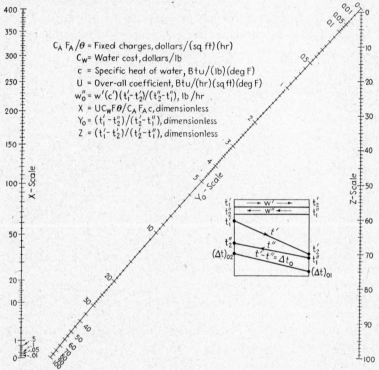

$C_A F_A/\theta$ = Fixed charges, dollars/(sq ft)(hr)
C_w = Water cost, dollars/lb
c = Specific heat of water, Btu/(lb)(deg F)
U = Over-all coefficient, Btu/(hr)(sq ft)(deg F)
$w_0'' = w'(c')(t_1'-t_2')/(t_2''-t_1'')$, lb/hr
$X = UC_w F\theta/C_A F_A c$, dimensionless
$Y_0 = (t_1'-t_2')/(t_2'-t_1'')$, dimensionless
$Z = (t_1'-t_2')/(t_2'-t_1'')$, dimensionless

Fig. 198.—Solution of Eq. 32 for high values of Z; for small values of Z, use Fig. 197.

Illustration 5.—It is desired to design a counterflow apparatus to cool 10,000 lb per hr of gas, having c' of 0.24, from 200 to 90°F by use of water entering at 85°F, costing $0.20 per 1000 cu ft.   Annual fixed charges are $0.50 per sq ft, θ is 8400, and the optimum value of U is 7.8, after including F_s of 1.25. Calculate the optimum outlet temperature of the water, the corresponding ratio of water to gas, and the square feet required.

Solution.

$$X = \frac{UFC_w\theta}{C_A F_A c''} = \frac{(7.8)(1.0)(0.2/62,300)(8400)}{(0.5)(1.0)} = 0.422$$

$$Z = (t_1' - t_2')/(t_2' - t_1'') = (200 - 90)/(90 - 85) = 22$$

and from Fig. 198, $Y_o = 15.9 = (200 - t_2'')/5$, whence $200 - t_2'' = 79.5$ and

* Courtesy of A. P. Colburn.[143a]

† Courtesy of Douglass and Adams[182] and *Industrial and Engineering Chemistry.*

$t_2 = 120.5°F$. Per pound of gas, $(200 - 95)(0.24)/(120.5 - 85.0) = 0.71$ lb of water is required. The mean over-all temperature difference is $(79.5 - 5)/\ln_e 15.9 = 26.9°F$, and $A = q/U \Delta t_m = 10,000(0.24)(200 - 95)/(7.8)(26.9) = 1200$ sq.ft.

Optimum Final Δt for Recovering Waste Heat.

—Exhaust steam having saturation temperature t' may be used to furnish part of the heat required to warm w lb per hr of a fluid without phase change from t_1 to t, the remainder of the heat being furnished by more expensive high-pressure steam condensing at t''. The problem is to determine the optimum over-all Δt at the outlet of the first heater, in which the low-pressure steam is used. Let the value of exhaust steam be $C_{H'}$ dollars per Btu of latent heat; $C_{H''}$ is the corresponding value for the high-pressure steam; $(C_a + C_p)$ or K_3 represents the optimum sum of fixed charges and power required to force the gas or liquid through the heaters, expressed as dollars/(hr)(sq ft) of heat-transfer surface. The total cost, which depends on the intermediate temperature t, is then

$$\Sigma y = wc(t - t_1)C_{H'} + A_1 K_3 + wc(t_2 - t)C_{H''} + A_2 K_3 \quad (33)$$

and A equals $q/U \Delta t_m$ for each of the two heaters; Δt_m is the logarithmic mean over-all temperature difference, which applies if U is constant (Chap. VI); F is unity for any arrangement of surface, since the vapors condense at constant temperature. Combining these relations, $d\Sigma y/dt$ is set equal to zero to find the following relation for minimum total cost:

$$(t' - t)(t'' - t) = \frac{(C_a + C_p)(t'' - t')}{U(C_{H''} - C_{H'})} \quad (34)$$

which can be used directly or solved for t by the quadratic rule.

Illustration 6.—It is planned to heat air at atmospheric pressure from 70 to 300°F. Steam condensing at 220°F costs $0.05/10^6 Btu, and steam condensing at 370°F costs $0.20 per 10^6 Btu. At the optimum velocity U_o is 8, fixed charges are estimated at $0.45/(year)(sq ft), and the equipment is to be operated 8400 hr per year. What should be the temperature of the air leaving the first heater?

Solution.—For the reasons given on page 370 it would be more economical to employ flow across tubes instead of flow inside tubes. Assume that the cost data and other factors are such that Eq. 30c gives an optimum velocity that corresponds to U of 8, after including F_s of 1.25. Since the Reynolds number would fall in the region where the exponents n_o and m_o are 0.6 and 0.15, respectively, the ratio $(X_p + X_a)/X_a = (3 - m_o)/(3 - n_o - m_o) = 2.85/2.25 = 1.27$.

$$K_3 = \left(\frac{X_p + X_a}{X_a}\right)\left(\frac{C_A F_A}{\theta}\right) = 1.27\frac{(0.45)}{(8400)} = \frac{\$6.8 \times 10^{-5}}{(\text{hours})(\text{square feet})}$$

Substitution of values in Eq. 34 gives

$$(220 - t)(370 - t) = \frac{(6.8 \times 10^{-5})(370 - 220)}{(8)(0.15 \times 10^{-6})}$$

whence t is 176°F and the optimum Δt at the outlet of the first heater is 44°F.

Problems

1. A large flat glass slab 6 in. thick ($k = 0.63$, $c = 0.3$, and $\rho = 139$) has been cooled very slowly in an annealing oven so that its temperature is substantially uniform at 900°F. It is proposed that the slab be further cooled from 900° by passing air parallel to the flat faces normal to the 6-in. dimension. To minimize thermal strains, the maximum temperature gradient allowable in the slab is 50°F per in. The air would be blown past the slab at a rate such that its temperature rise would be negligible and the coefficient from hot glass to air would be 5.0. Radiation may be neglected.

   a. When the slab is at 900°F, what is the lowest temperature of air that may be used for cooling?

   b. If air at the temperature in *a* is used for 3 hr, what is the lowest air temperature that could then be used?

   c. If the air temperature were so regulated that the slab was always being cooled at the maximum allowable rate, what would be the air temperature at the end of 3 hr?

   d. Sketch curves of temperature *vs.* thickness of the slab at the end of 3 hr for *b* and *c*.

2. A gas having a molecular weight of 86 is flowing at a rate of 1.38 kg per min through a tube having an actual i.d. of 1.20 in. At a cross section where the absolute pressure is 30 atm and the temperature is 340°F, the true density is 1.2 times that predicted by the perfect-gas law, and the viscosity is 2.0×10^{-6} force-pound $\times$ seconds per square foot. Calculate the numerical value of the *dimensionless* Reynolds number.

3. It is necessary to heat 24,000 lb per hr of air from 70 to 350°F, while it is flowing under pressure at the optimum mass velocity of 7200 lb/(hr)(sq ft) of cross section, inside tubes having an actual i.d. of 0.870 in. Low-pressure exhaust steam (220°F saturation temperature) now being discarded would be available at a cost of $0.05 per million Btu of latent heat, and high-pressure steam (370°F saturation temperature) is available at a cost of $0.20 per million Btu of latent heat. The heaters must run 8400 hr per year. The annual fixed charges, expressed in dollars per year per foot of each tube will be assumed as 0.15 for the low-pressure heater and 0.25 for the high-pressure heater, independent of the length of tube or the number of tubes. The air is to leave the high-pressure heater at an absolute pressure of 10 atm and at a temperature of 350°F. It is agreed to use Eq. 4*k* of Chap. VII. Calculate the minimum yearly costs and the tube length required for each heater.

4. A company manufacturing *n*-butanol uses Eq. 4*c* of Chap. VII in designing various butanol heaters, where the bulk temperature t ranges from 86 to 167°F. It is desired to convert Eq. 4*c* to the following form:

$$h = a(1 + bt)(V')^{0.8}/(D')^{0.2}$$

Determine the constants a and b in the preceding equation; calculate the predicted value of h for a run where the average bulk temperature is 118°F, D' is 0.494 in., and $V' = 11.8$ ft per sec, and find the percentage of deviation of the predicted h from the observed value[663] of 562.

5. The following data were obtained in a test on a vertical falling-film water heater made of copper 2.88 in. o.d. and 2.50 in. i.d., jacketed for a length of 2.0 ft by steam condensing at 227°F. The cooling water entered at 41°F at a rate of 3110 lb per hr and flowed as a layer down the inside wall, leaving with a bulk temperature of 125°F. From the readings of 10 thermocouples, the length-mean temperature of the outer surface was found to be 206°F. Predict the water-side coefficient from Eq. 28 of Chap. VII, and compare it with the observed value.

6. A multipass heat exchanger contains 1200 tubes, each 16 ft long, having an o.d. of 1.25 in. and an i.d. of 1.12 in. These tubes are arranged as a 12-6 exchanger in which the fluid in the tubes makes 12 equal single passes and that in the shell makes 6 corresponding passes. Each tube pass contains 100 tubes, and each shell pass is well baffled. It is desired to predict the performance of this apparatus if 693,000 lb per hr of a hot oil, $c = 0.540$ g-cal/(g)(deg C), were introduced continuously into the shell at a temperature of 360°F and cold oil at 60°F, $c = 0.470$ g-cal/(g)(deg C), $\rho = 56$ lb/cu ft were fed to the first pass of the tubes at a rate of 796,000 lb per hr. From the data and notes given below, calculate the temperature to which the hot oil will be cooled.

Data and Notes.—It is estimated that the average coefficient from hot oil to the outer surface of the tubes, including suitable allowance for scale deposit on both sides, will be 100 Btu/(hr)(sq ft)(deg F), based on the outside surface. The thermal conductivity of the tubes will be taken as 26 Btu/(hr) (sq ft)(deg F per ft). The coefficient h on the inside of the tube is given by Eq. 4*c* of Chap. VII. The average absolute viscosity of the oil in the tubes may be taken as 0.0416 gm/(sec)(cm); and the thermal conductivity of the oil in the tubes is 0.080 Btu/(hr)(sq ft)(deg F per ft).

7. An air cooler consisting of a bundle of 1-in. 18 BWG copper tubes, enclosed in a well-baffled shell, is being built to cool 45,000 lb of air per hr from 200 to 90°F. The air flows under pressure in a single pass through the tubes, and cooling water at 80°F, under sufficient pressure to force it through at any desired rate, flows countercurrently through the shell. The air flows inside the pipes at a mass velocity of 8600 lb/(hr)(sq ft), which is the optimum velocity; the corresponding U_i will be 7.8. Cooling water costs 20 cents per 1000 cu ft, and the annual fixed charges on the cooler are 50 cents per sq ft of heating surface. It is proposed to operate 8400 hr per year. From the standpoint of the lowest total yearly cost, calculate:

    a. The optimum pounds of cooling water per pound of air.

    b. The over-all temperature difference at the hot end.

   c. The length of each tube.
   d. The number of tubes in parallel.
   e. The total annual costs in dollars.

8. It is desired to design a horizontal tubular feed-water heater. Because of space limitations, it is agreed that the over-all length shall not exceed 11.4 ft, which corresponds to a tube length of 9.75 ft. It is agreed to use admiralty metal tubes $\frac{5}{8}$ in. o.d. No. 18 BWG, with a water velocity inside the tubes of 385 lb/(sec)(sq ft of transverse area). The tubes are to be staggered and arranged in a square bundle. The heater is to be designed to heat 190,000 lb per hr of distilled water from 114 to 215°F, with steam condensing outside the tubes at 240°F.

   a. Calculate the number of tubes in each pass.
   b. Calculate the number of passes.
   c. Calculate the tube length.
   d. Calculate the over-all pressure drop due to friction, pounds per square inch.

9. A small-scale heat exchanger, consisting of two concentric pipes, is operated in counterflow with hot water flowing inside the smaller pipe and cold water in the annular space. The inner pipe is a 1¼-in. standard copper pipe, and the outer pipe is a 2-in. standard steel pipe. The length of active heating surface is 9.43 ft.

Data.
t_1' = inlet temperature of hot water, degrees centigrade
t_2' = outlet temperature of hot water, degrees centigrade
t_1'' = inlet temperature of cold water, degrees centigrade
t_2'' = outlet temperature of cold water, degrees centigrade
w' = mass rate of flow of hot water inside smaller pipe, pounds per minute
w'' = mass rate of flow of cold water in jacket, pounds per minute

w'	t_1'	t_2'	w''	t_1''	t_2''
11.82	82.47	46.0	137.5	9.38	12.5
10.90	85.42	47.38	99.2	9.50	13.72
10.60	86.6	48.18	81.5	9.59	14.56
9.87	87.61	48.39	61.8	9.75	16.08
9.84	88.53	48.78	57.1	9.78	16.58
9.85	87.77	52.12	34.5	10.13	20.14
10.90	85.75	47.12	124.5	9.59	13.09
9.83	88.20	44.97	142.9	9.60	12.50
9.86	87.95	54.87	22.95	10.60	24.72
9.92	87.68	58.42	14.02	11.07	31.21
10.10	87.47	63.28	8.39	11.54	40.28

Using only these data, find the constants a_1 and a_2 in the equations $h_i = a_1(V_i')^{0.8}$ and $h_j = a_2(V_j')^{0.8}$, and compare them with the predicted values, expressing velocities V' in feet per second.

10. Both manufacturers and users of counterflow heat exchangers may face the problem of predicting the outlet temperatures that a given heat exchanger should produce for fixed inlet temperatures, mass flow rates, and specific heats. Find the outlet temperature of the warmer fluid for the following problems:

  a. $A = 1000$, $w' = 27,800$, $c' = 0.5$, $w'' = 41,700$, $c'' = 1.0$, $U = 50$, $t_1' = 400°$, and $t_1'' = 80°F$.

  b. $A = 1000$, $w' = 27,800$, $c' = 0.5$, $w'' = 13,900$, $c' = 1.0$, $U = 50$, $t_1' = 200°$ and $t_1'' = 80°F$.

11. 10,000 lb per hr of air are to be heated from 70 to 205°F by continuously blowing the air through apparatus heated by steam condensing at 220°F. The allowable friction drop due to flow of air through the apparatus is only 0.10 in. of water, and the air is to leave the heater at atmospheric pressure. There are already on hand ample quantities of ¾- and 1.0-in standard steel pipe, page 416. Two designs are proposed: I. The air flows inside horizontal standard 1-in. pipes, and the steam condenses on the outside. II. The air flows normal to a bank of vertical staggered standard ¾-in. pipes, the steam condensing on the inside of the pipes, which are to be mounted on 2-in. equilateral centers, but because of space restrictions, the maximum tube length cannot be greater than 8 ft.

  a. For I, calculate the total number of tubes and the length of each.
  b. For II, calculate the total number of tubes necessary and the number of rows over which the air must pass in series.
  c. Neglecting construction costs, which proposal do you favor? Why?

12. Air is being heated continuously in a refractory tube that passes horizontally through an experimental muffle furnace. The inside of the furnace is cubical, 1 ft to a side, with glazed silica brick walls that are kept at 2000°F. The air initially at 100°F and 10 atm pressure is blown through the tube at a rate of 500 lb per hr. Neglecting the effect of conduction along the length of the tube, calculate

  a. The outlet air temperature.
  b. The heat flow through the tube walls in Btu per hour.

Data.—The dimensions of the refractory tube are 2.4 in. o.d. and 2.0 in. i.d.; k for the refractory tube is the same as for the silica brick. The emissivity of the furnace walls and of the surface of the tube may be taken as 0.85.

APPENDIX

		Page
Tables I to III.	k for Metals	380–381
Tables IV to VIII.	k for Building Materials and Insulants	383–388
Tables IX to X.	k for Liquids	389–390
Table XI.	k for Gases and Vapors	391–392
Table XII.	Conversion Factors for U and h	392
Table XIII.	Emissivities of Surfaces	393–396
Table XIV.	Steam Table	397
Figure 199.	Latent Heats of Vaporization of Liquids	398
Table XV.	True Specific Heats of Solids	399
Table XVI.	Average Specific Heats of Organic Liquids	400
Figure 200.	True Specific Heats of Liquids	401
Table XVII.	Average Specific Heats of Liquefied Gases	402
Table XVIII.	True Specific Heats of Aqueous Solutions	403–405
Table XIX.	Effect of Pressure on Specific Heat of Air	406
Figure 201.	True Specific Heats of Gases	406
Table XX.	Viscosity of Water at Various Temperatures	407
Table XXI.	Conversion Factors for Viscosity	407
Figure 202.	Viscosities of Liquids *vs.* Temperature	408–409
Figure 203.	Effect of Pressure on Viscosity of Gases	410
Figure 204.	Viscosities of Gases *vs.* Temperature	410–411
Table XXIV.	Viscosity of Steam	412
Table XXV	Consistent Units for Reynolds Number	412
Table XXVI.	Some Physical Properties of Water	413
Figure 205.	$c\mu/k$ for Liquids *vs.* Temperature	414
Table XXVI*A*.	$c_p\mu/k$ for Gases and Vapors	415
Figure 206.	Surface Tension of Liquids *vs.* Temperature	415
Table XXVII.	Standard Dimensions for Wrought-iron Pipe	416
Table XXVIII.	Standard Dimensions for Condenser Tubing	417

Thermal Conductivities.—The values of k in the tables are expressed in Btu/(hr)(sq ft)(deg F per ft). Conversion factors to other units are as follows:

Multiply by 0.00413 to obtain gm-cal/(sec)(sq cm)(deg C per cm).
Multiply by 173 to obtain kilo-ergs/(sec)(sq cm)(deg C per cm).
Multiply by 0.0173 to obtain watts/(sq cm)(deg C per cm).
Multiply by 1.49 to obtain kg-cal/(hr)(sq m)(deg C per m).
Multiply by 12 to obtain Btu/(hr)(sq ft)(deg F per in.).
Multiply by 12 to obtain pcu*/(hr)(sq ft)(deg C per in.).

* The pound-centigrade unit is the amount of heat required to raise the temperature of 1 lb of water by 1°C and equals 1.8 Btu. The pcu is the same as the pound calorie or centigrade heat unit, Chu. Strictly, the pcu is the

TABLE I.—EFFECT OF TEMPERATURE UPON THERMAL CONDUCTIVITY OF
METALS AND ALLOYS*

Main body of table is k in Btu/(hr)(sq ft)(deg F per ft)

| t, deg F. | 32 | 212 | 392 | 572 | 752 | 932 | 1112 | Melting point, deg F |
t, deg C.	0	100	200	300	400	500	600	
Aluminum	117	119	124	133	144	155	...	1220
Brass (70 copper, 30 zinc).	56	60	63	66	67	...	...	1724
Cast iron	32	30	28	26	25	...	...	2192
Cast high-silicon iron	30	...	...	...	...	...	...	2300
Copper, pure	224	218	215	212	210	207	204	1976
Lead	20	19	18	18	...	...	...	621
Nickel	36	34	33	32	...	...	...	2642
Silver	242	238	...	...	...	...	...	1760
Sodium	81	...	...	...	...	...	...	208
Steel, mild	...	26	26	25	23	22	21	2507
Tantalum (at 68°F)	32	...	...	...	...	...	...	5162
Tin	36	34	33	...	...	...	...	450
Wrought iron, Swedish	...	32	30	28	26	23	...	2741
Zinc	65	64	62	59	54	...	...	786

* From "International Critical Tables," McGraw-Hill Book Company, Inc., New York, 1929, and other sources.

change in enthalpy when $\frac{1}{100}$ lb of water, at its saturation pressure, is heated from 0 to 100°C. Similarly, the Btu is the change in enthalpy when $\frac{1}{180}$ lb of water, at its saturation pressure, is heated from 32 to 212°F.

TABLE II.—THERMAL CONDUCTIVITIES OF METALS (Marks[469])

$$k = Btu/(hr)(sq ft)(deg F per ft)$$

Substance	Deg F	k	Substance	Deg F	k
Metals			Metals		
Antimony........	32	10.6	Mercury...............	32	4.8
Antimony........	212	9.7	Nickel alloy (62 Ni, 12 Cr,		
Bismuth..........	64	4.7	26 Fe)...............	68	7.8
Bismuth..........	212	3.9	Platinum...............	64	40.2
Cadmium........	64	53.7	Platinum...............	212	41.9
Cadmium........	212	52.2	Alloys		
Gold.............	64	169.0	Admiralty metal........	86	65
Gold.............	212	170.0	Bronze, commercial......	...	109
Iron, pure........	64	39.0	Constantan (60 Cu, 40 Ni)	64	13.1
Iron, pure........	212	36.6	Constantan (60 Cu, 40 Ni)	212	15.5
Iron, wrought......	64	34.9	Nickel silver............	32	16.9
Iron, wrought......	212	34.6	Nickel silver............	212	21.5
Iron, cast........	129	27.6	Manganin {84 Cu 4 Ni	64	12.8
Iron, cast........	216	26.8			
Steel (1 per cent C)	64	26.2	12 Mn	212	15.2
Steel (1 per cent C)	212	25.9	Platinoid...............	64	14.5
Magnesium........	32–212	92.0			

TABLE III.—THERMAL CONDUCTIVITY OF CHROMIUM ALLOYS (Martin[470])

$$k = Btu/(hr)(sq ft)(deg F per ft)$$

American Iron and Steel Institute type number	Cr	Ni	Si	Mn	C	k at 625°F
416	13.22	0.23	0.86	0.31	0.10	19.3
310	24.48	20.30	0.89	0.63	0.17	16.5
304	17.36	10.20	0.93	0.25	0.068	16.2
430	17.60	0.23	0.86	0.31	0.10	15.2
302	18.15	8.23	0.32	0.45	0.14	14.8
302	17.64	10.68	....	....	0.12	14.5
309	22.90	11.67	0.17	....	0.15	13.8

TABLE IV.—THERMAL CONDUCTIVITIES OF SOME BUILDING AND INSULATING
MATERIALS*

$k = \text{Btu}/(\text{hr})(\text{sq ft})(\text{deg F per ft})$

Material	Apparent density ρ, lb/cu ft at room temperature	Deg F	k
Aerogel, silica, opacified...............................	8.5	248	0.013
		554	0.026
Asbestos-cement boards.............................	120	68	0.43
Asbestos sheets.....................................	55.5	124	0.096
Asbestos slate......................................	112	32	0.087
	112	140	0.114
Asbestos...	29.3	−328	0.043
	29.3	32	0.090
	36	32	0.087
	36	212	0.111
	36	392	0.120
	36	752	0.129
	43.5	−328	0.090
	43.5	32	0.135
Aluminum foil, 7 air spaces per 2.5 in..................	0.2	100	0.025
		351	0.038
Ashes, wood..	......	32–212	0.041
Asphalt..	132	68	0.43
Boiler scale (ref. 364)...............................			
Bricks			
Alumina (92–99 % Al_2O_3 by weight) fused.............	......	801	1.8
Alumina (64–65 % Al_2O_3 by weight).................	......	2399	2.7
(See also Bricks, fire clay)...........................	115	1472	0.62
	115	2012	0.63
Building brickwork..............................	......	68	0.4
Chrome brick (32 % Cr_2O_3 by weight)................	200	392	0.67
	200	1202	0.85
	200	2399	1.0
Diatomaceous earth, natural, across strata (ref. 719)...	27.7	399	0.051
	27.7	1600	0.077
Diatomaceous, natural, parallel to strata (ref. 719).....	27.7	399	0.081
	27.7	1600	0.106
Diatomaceous earth, molded and fired (ref. 719).......	38	399	0.14
	38	1600	0.18
Diatomaceous earth and clay, molded and fired (ref. 719)	42.3	399	0.14
	42.3	1600	0.19
Diatomaceous earth, high burn, large pores (ref. 517)...	37	392	0.13
	37	1832	0.34
Fire clay, Missouri................................	......	392	0.58
		1112	0.85
		1832	0.95
		2552	1.02
Kaolin insulating brick (ref. 517).....................	27	932	0.15
	27	2102	0.26
Kaolin insulating firebrick (ref. 518).................	19	392	0.050
	19	1400	0.113
Magnesite (86.8 % MgO, 6.3 % Fe_2O_3, 3 % CaO, 2.6 % SiO_2 by weight)	158	399	2.2
	158	1202	1.6
	158	2192	1.1

TABLE IV.—THERMAL CONDUCTIVITIES OF SOME BUILDING AND INSULATING MATERIALS.*—(*Continued*)

Material	Apparent density ρ, lb/cu ft at room temperature	Deg F	k
Bricks: (*Continued*)			
Silicon carbide brick, recrystallized (ref. 517).........	129	1112	10.7
	129	1472	9.2
	129	1832	8.0
	129	2192	7.0
	129	2552	6.3
Calcium carbonate, natural.........................	162	86	1.3
White marble........................	.....	.....	1.7
Chalk................................	96	.....	0.4
Calcium sulphate (4H$_2$O), artificial....................	84.6	104	0.22
Plaster, artificial................................	132	167	0.43
Building................................	77.9	77	0.25
Cambric, varnished...............................	.....	100	0.091
Carbon, gas......................	.....	32–212	2.0
Cardboard, corrugated............................	.....	.....	0.037
Celluloid.......................................	87.3	86	0.12
Charcoal flakes................................	11.9	176	0.043
	15	176	0.051
Clinker, granular...............................	.....	32–1292	0.27
Coke, petroleum...............................	.....	212	3.4
		932	2.9
Coke, powdered................................	.....	32–212	0.11
Concrete, cinder................................	.....	.....	0.20
1:4 dry.......................................	.....	.....	0.44
Stone.......................................	.....	.....	0.54
Cotton wool................................	5	86	0.024
Cork board................................	10	86	0.025
Cork, ground................................	9.4	86	0.025
regranulated................................	8.1	86	0.026
Diatomaceous earth powder, coarse (ref. 719)..........	20.0	100	0.036
	20.0	1600	0.082
Fine (ref. 719)...................................	17.2	399	0.040
	17.2	1600	0.074
Molded pipe covering (ref. 719).....................	26.0	399	0.051
	26.0	1600	0.088
4 vol. calcined earth and 1 vol. cement, poured and fired			
(ref. 719)...................................	61.8	399	0.16
	61.8	1600	0.23
Dolomite................................	167	122	1.0
Ebonite................................	.....	.....	0.10
Enamel, silicate................................	38	.....	0.5–0.75
Felt, wool................................	20.6	86	0.03
Fiber insulating board........................	14.8	70	0.028
Fiber, red................................	80.5	68	0.27
With binder, baked............................	.....	68–207	0.097
Gas carbon................................	.....	32–212	2.0
Glass................................	.....	.....	0.2–0.73
Boro-silicate type............................	139	86–167	0.63
Soda glass................................	.....	.....	0.3–0.44
Window glass................................	.....	.....	0.3–0.61
Granite................................	.....	.....	1.0–2.3

TABLE IV.—THERMAL CONDUCTIVITIES OF SOME BUILDING AND INSULATING MATERIALS.*—(*Continued*)

Material	Apparent density ρ, lb/cu ft at room temperature	Deg F	k
Graphite, dense, commercial	......	32	86.7
Powdered, through 100 mesh	30	104	0.104
Gypsum, molded and dry	78	68	0.25
Hair felt, perpendicular to fibers	17	86	0.021
Ice	57.5	32	1.3
Infusorial earth (see Diatomaceous earth)			
Kapok	0.88	68	0.020
Lampblack	10	104	0.038
Lava	......	......	0.49
Leather, sole	62.4	......	0.092
Limestone (15.3 vol. % H_2O)	103	75	0.54
Linen	......	86	0.05
Magnesia, powdered	49.7	117	0.35
Magnesia, light carbonate	19	70	0.04
Magnesium oxide, compressed	49.9	68	0.32
Marble	......	......	1.2–1.7
Mica, perpendicular to planes	......	122	0.25
Mill shavings	......	......	0.033–0.05
Mineral wool	9.4	86	0.0225
	19.7	86	0.024
Paper	......	......	0.075
Paraffin wax	......	32	0.14
Petroleum coke	......	212	3.4
	......	932	2.9
Porcelain	......	392	0.88
Portland cement (see Concrete)	......	194	0.17
Pumice stone	......	70–151	0.14
Pyroxylin plastics	......	......	0.075
Rubber, hard	74.8	32	0.087
Para		70	0.109
Soft		70	0.075–0.092
Sand, dry	94.6	68	0.19
Sandstone	140	104	1.06
Sawdust	12	70	0.03
Scale (ref. 364)			
Silk	6.3	......	0.026
Varnished	......	100	0.096
Slag, blast furnace	......	75–261	0.064
Slag wool	12	86	0.022
Slate	......	201	0.86
Snow	34.7	32	0.27
Sulphur, monoclinic	......	212	0.09–0.097
Rhombic	......	70	0.16
Wallboard, insulating type	14.8	70	0.028
Wallboard, stiff pasteboard	43	86	0.04
Wood shavings	8.8	86	0.034
Wood, across grain			
Balsa	7–8	86	0.025–0.03
Oak	51.5	59	0.12
Maple	44.7	122	0.11

TABLE IV.—THERMAL CONDUCTIVITIES OF SOME BUILDING AND INSULATING MATERIALS.*—(*Continued*)

Material	Apparent density ρ, lb/cu ft at room temperature	Deg F	k
Wood, across grain: (*Continued*)			
Pine, white..	34.0	59	0.087
Teak...	40.0	59	0.10
White fir..	28.1	140	0.062
Wood, parallel to grain			
Pine...	34.4	70	0.20
Wool, animal..	6.9	86	0.021

* Marks, "Mechanical Engineers' Handbook," McGraw-Hill Book Company, Inc., 1941, "International Critical Tables," McGraw-Hill Book Company, Inc., 1929, and other sources. For additional data, see pp. 386–388.

TABLE V.—THERMAL CONDUCTIVITIES OF SOME MATERIALS FOR
REFRIGERATION AND BUILDING INSULATION*

k = Btu/(hr)(sq ft)(deg F per ft) at approximately room temperature

Material	Apparent density, lb cu ft room temperature	k
Soft, flexible materials in sheet form		
Chemically treated wood fiber......	2.2	0.023
Eel grass between paper...........	3.4–4.6	0.021–0.022
Felted cattle hair................	11–13	0.022
Flax fibers between paper.........	4.9	0.023
Hair and asbestos fibers, felted.....	7.8	0.023
Insulating hair and jute...........	6.1–6.3	0.022–0.023
Jute and asbestos fibers, felted.....	10.0	0.031
Loose materials		
Charcoal, 6 mesh.................	15.2	0.031
Cork, regranulated, fine particles...	8–9	0.025
Diatomaceous earth, powdered.....	10.6	0.026
Glass wool, curled...............	4–10	0.024
Gypsum in powdered form.........	26–34	0.043–0.05
Mineral wool, fibrous.............	6	0.0217
	10	0.0225
	14	0.0233
	18	0.0242
Sawdust........................	12	0.034
Wood shavings, from planer........	8.8	0.034
Semiflexible materials in sheet form	13.0	0.026
Flax fiber.......................	13.0	0.026
Semirigid materials in board form		
Corkboard......................	7.0	0.0225
Corkboard......................	10.6	0.025
Mineral wool, block, with binder....	16.7	0.031
Stiff fibrous materials in sheet form	16.2–16.9	0.028
Sugar-cane fiber.................	13.2–14.8	0.028
Cellular gypsum..................	8	0.029
	12	0.037
	18	0.049
	24	0.064
	30	0.083

* Abstracted from *U. S. Bur. Standards Letter Circ.* 227, Apr. 19, 1927. For additional data, see pp. 382–385, 387–388.

TABLE VI.—THERMAL CONDUCTIVITIES OF INSULATING MATERIALS AT HIGH TEMPERATURES*

$k = $ Btu/(hr)(sq ft)(deg F per ft)

Material	For temperatures, deg F up to	Mean temperature, deg F									
		100	200	300	400	500	600	800	1000	1500	2000
Laminated asbestos felt (approx. 40 laminations per in.)	700	0.033	0.037	0.040	0.044	0.048					
Laminated asbestos felt (approx. 20 laminations per in.)	500	0.045	0.050	0.055	0.060	0.065					
Corrugated asbestos (4 plies per in.)	300	0.050	0.058	0.069							
85% magnesia	600	0.039	0.041	0.043	0.046						
Diatomaceous earth, asbestos and bonding material	1600	0.045	0.047	0.049	0.050	0.053	0.055	0.060	0.065		
Diatomaceous earth brick	1600	0.054	0.056	0.058	0.060	0.063	0.065	0.069	0.073		
Diatomaceous earth brick	2000	0.127	0.130	0.133	0.137	0.140	0.143	0.150	0.158	0.176	
Diatomaceous earth brick	2500	0.128	0.131	0.135	0.139	0.143	0.148	0.155	0.163	0.183	0.203
Diatomaceous earth powder (density, 18 lb per cu ft)	....	0.039	0.042	0.044	0.048	0.051	0.054	0.061	0.068		
Rock wool	....	0.030	0.034	0.039	0.044	0.050	0.057				

Asbestos cement, 0.1; 85% magnesia cement, 0.05; asbestos and rock wool cement, 0.075 approx.

* Marks, "Mechanical Engineers, Handbook," McGraw-Hill Book Company, Inc., 1941.

TABLE VII.—THERMAL CONDUCTIVITIES OF INSULATING MATERIALS AT MODERATE TEMPERATURES (Nusselt)*

$k = $ Btu/(hr)(sq ft)(deg F per ft)

Material	Weight, lb per cu ft	Temperatures, deg F						
		32	100	200	300	400	600	800
Asbestos	36.0	0.087	0.097	0.110	0.117	0.121	0.125	0.130
Burned infusorial earth for pipe coverings	12.5	0.043	0.046	0.052	0.057	0.062	0.073	0.085
Insulating composition, loose	25.0	0.040	0.046	0.050	0.053	0.055		
Cotton	5.0	0.032	0.035	0.039				
Silk hair	9.1	0.026	0.030	0.034				
Silk	6.3	0.025	0.028	0.034				
Wool	8.5	0.022	0.027	0.033				
Pulverized cork	10.0	0.021	0.026	0.032				
Infusorial earth, loose	22.0	0.035	0.039	0.045	0.047	0.050	0.053	

* Marks, "Mechanical Engineers' Handbook," McGraw-Hill Book Company, Inc., 1941.

TABLE VIII.—THERMAL CONDUCTIVITIES OF INSULATING MATERIALS
AT LOW TEMPERATURES (Gröber)*

$k = $ Btu/(hr)(sq ft)(deg F per ft)

Material	Weight, lb cu ft	Temperatures, deg F				
		32	−50	−100	−200	−300
Asbestos...........	44.0	0.135	0.132	0.130	0.125	0.100
Asbestos...........	29.0	0.0894	0.0860	0.0820	0.0720	0.0545
Cotton............	5.0	0.0325	0.0302	0.0276	0.0235	0.0198
Silk..............	6.3	0.0290	0.0256	0.0235	0.0196	0.0155

* Marks, " Mechanical Engineers' Handbook," McGraw-Hill Book Company, Inc., 1941.

For certain substances for which values of k are not given in the preceding, data may be found in references 336, 9, 719, 730a, 728, 517, and 265a.

Table IX.—Thermal Conductivity of Liquids
$$k = \text{Btu}/(\text{hr})(\text{sq ft})(\text{deg F per ft})$$

A linear variation with temperature may be assumed. The extreme values given constitute also the temperature limits over which the data are recommended.

Liquid	Deg F	k	Liquid	Deg F	k
Acetic acid 100% (ref. 122)	68	0.099	Hexane (n-) (ref. 677)	86	0.080
50% (ref. 122)	68	0.20		140	0.078
Acetone (ref. 90)	86	0.102	Heptyl alcohol (n-) (ref. 163)	86	0.094
	167	0.095		167	0.091
Allyl alcohol (ref. 665)	77–86	0.104	Hexyl alcohol (n-) (ref. 163)	86	0.093
Ammonia (ref. 365)	5–86	0.29		167	0.090
Ammonia, aqueous 26% (ref. 122)	68	0.261	Kerosene (ref. 90)	68	0.086
	140	0.29		167	0.081
Amyl acetate (ref. 336)	50	0.083			
Alcohol (n-) (ref. 163)	86	0.094	Mercury (ref. 336)	82	4.83
	212	0.089	Methyl alcohol 100% (ref. 49)	68	0.124
(iso-) (ref. 677)	86	0.088	80%	68	0.154
	167	0.087	60%	68	0.190
Aniline (ref. 370)	32–68	0.100	40%	68	0.234
Benzene (ref. 677)	86	0.092	20%	68	0.284
	140	0.087	100%	122	0.114
Bromobenzene (ref. 677)	86	0.074	Chloride (refs. 365 and 51)	5	0.111
	212	0.070		86	0.089
Butyl acetate (n-) (ref. 665)	77–86	0.085			
Alcohol (n-) (ref. 90)	86	0.097	Nitrobenzene (ref. 677)	86	0.095
	167	0.095		212	0.088
(iso-) (ref. 90)	50	0.091	Nitromethane (ref. 677)	86	0.125
Calcium chloride brine 30% (ref. 122)	86	0.32		140	0.120
15% (ref. 122)	86	0.34	Nonane (n-) (ref. 677)	86	0.084
Carbon disulphide (ref. 90)	86	0.093		140	0.082
	167	0.088	Octane (n-) (ref. 677)	86	0.083
Tetrachloride (ref. 51)	32	0.107		140	0.081
	154	0.094	Oils (ref. 122,677)*	86	0.079
Chlorobenzene (ref. 677)	50	0.083	Castor (ref. 370)	68	0.104
Chloroform (ref. 51)	86	0.080		212	0.100
Cymene (para) (ref. 677)	86	0.078	Olive (ref. 370)	68	0.097
	140	0.079		212	0.095
Decane (n-) (ref. 677)	86	0.085	Paraldehyde (ref. 677)	86	0.084
	140	0.083		212	0.078
Dichlorodifluoromethane (ref. 59)	20	0.057	Pentane (n-) (ref. 677)	86	0.078
	60	0.053		167	0.074
	100	0.048	Perchloroethylene (ref. 51)	122	0.092
	140	0.043	Petroleum ether (ref. 90)	86	0.075
	180	0.038		167	0.073
Dichloroethane (ref. 51)	122	0.082	Propyl alcohol (n-) (ref. 163)	86	0.099
Dichloromethane (ref. 51)	5	0.111		167	0.095
	86	0.096	Alcohol (iso-) (ref. 677)	86	0.091
Ethyl acetate (ref. 336)	68	0.101		140	0.090
Alcohol 100% (ref. 49)	68	0.105			
80%	68	0.137	Sodium	212	49
60%	68	0.176		410	46
40%	68	0.224	Sodium chloride brine 25.0% (ref. 122)	86	0.33
20%	68	0.281	12.5% (ref. 122)	86	0.34
100% (ref. 49)	122	0.087	Sulphuric acid 90% (ref. 122)	86	0.21
Benzene (ref. 677)	86	0.086	60%	86	0.25
	140	0.082	30%	86	0.30
Bromide (ref. 90)	68	0.070	Sulphur dioxide (ref. 365)	5	0.128
Ether (ref. 90)	86	0.080		86	0.111
	167	0.078			
Iodide (refs. 90 and 122)	104	0.064	Toluene (refs. 90 and 677)	86	0.086
	167	0.063		167	0.084
Ethylene glycol (ref. 336)	32	0.153	β-trichloroethane (ref. 51)	122	0.077
Gasoline (refs. 163 and 677)	86	0.078	Trichloroethylene (ref. 51)	122	0.080
Glycerol 100% (ref. 48)	68	0.164	Turpentine (ref. 336)	59	0.074
80%	68	0.189	Vaseline (ref. 336)	59	0.106
60%	68	0.220	Water (refs. 49, 122, 471)	32	0.330
40%	68	0.259		86	0.356
20%	68	0.278		140	0.381
100% (ref. 48)	212	0.164		176	0.398
Heptane (n-) (ref. 677)	86	0.081	Xylene (ortho-) (ref. 336)	68	0.090
	140	0.079	(meta-) (ref. 336)	68	0.090

* Thermal conductivity data for a number of oils are available from reference 677. See also Table X; for many oils, an average value of 0.079 may be used.

TABLE X.—THERMAL CONDUCTIVITIES OF PETROLEUM OILS
(J. F. D. Smith)
$k = $ Btu/(hr)(sq ft)(deg F per ft)

Designation of hydro-carbon oil	Av. mol wt.*	Viscosity, centi-poises			k at 86°F	k at 212°F	Sp. gr. at 60°F
		68°F	140°F	212°F			
Light heat-transfer oil....	284	62.0	9.5	3.2	0.0765	0.0748	0.925
Rabbeth spindle oil.......	303	24.5	5.7	2.37	0.0825	0.0805	0.870
Velocite B oil...... ...	333	73.0	11.0	4.20	0.0825	0.0800	0.897
Red oil.................	418	....	44.0	9.90	0.0815	0.0796	0.928

* H. O. Forrest and L. W. Cummings.

TABLE XI.—THERMAL CONDUCTIVITIES OF GASES AND VAPORS

$$k = \text{Btu}/(\text{hr})(\text{sq ft})(\text{deg F per ft})$$

The extreme temperature values given constitute the experimental range. For extrapolation to other temperatures, it is suggested that the data given be plotted as log k vs. log T, or that use be made of the assumption that the ratio $c_{p\mu}/k$ is practically independent of temperature (or of pressure, within moderate limits).

Substance	Deg F	k	Substance	Deg F	k
Acetone (ref. 491)*................	32	0.0057	Dichlorodifluoromethane..............	32	0.0048
	115	0.0074		122	0.0064
	212	0.0099		212	0.0080
	363	0.0147		302	0.0097
Acetylene (ref. 212)*..............	−103	0.0068			
	32	0.0108	Ethane (refs. 123 and 212)...........	−94	0.0066
	122	0.0140		−29	0.0086
	212	0.0172		32	0.0106
Air (ref. 491)*....................	−148	0.0095		212	0.0175
	32	0.0140	Ethyl acetate (ref. 491)*............	115	0.0072
	212	0.0183		212	0.0096
	392	0.0226		363	0.0141
	572	0.0265	Alcohol (ref. 491)*.............	68	0.0089
Ammonia (ref. 212)*..............	−76	0.0095		212	0.0124
	32	0.0128	Chloride (ref. 491)*.............	32	0.0055
	122	0.0157		212	0.0095
	212	0.0185		363	0.0135
				413	0.0152
Benzene (ref. 491)*...............	32	0.0052	Ether (ref. 491)*...............	32	0.0077
	115	0.0073		115	0.0099
	212	0.0103		212	0.0131
	363	0.0152		363	0.0189
	413	0.0176		413	0.0209
Butane (n-) (ref. 468).............	32	0.0078	Ethylene (ref. 212)*...............	−96	0.0064
	212	0.0135		32	0.0101
(iso-) (ref. 468)...............	32	0.0080		122	0.0131
	212	0.0139		212	0.0161
Carbon dioxide (ref. 656)..........	−58	0.0068	Heptane (n-) (ref. 491)*...........	392	0.0112
	32	0.0085		212	0.0103
	212	0.0133	Hexane (n-) (ref. 468).............	32	0.0072
	392	0.0181		68	0.0080
	572	0.0228	Hexene (ref. 491)*...............	32	0.0061
Disulphide (ref. 212)*.............	32	0.0040		212	0.0109
	45	0.0042	Hydrogen..........................	−148	0.065
Monoxide (refs. 123 and 212)*........	−312	0.0041		−58	0.083
	−294	0.0046		32	0.100
	32	0.0135		122	0.115
Tetrachloride (ref. 491)*...........	115	0.0041		212	0.129
	212	0.0052		572	0.178
	363	0.0065	Hydrogen and carbon dioxide (ref. 332)..	32	
Chlorine (ref. 336)................	32	0.0043	0% H₂............................	.....	0.0083
Chloroform (ref. 491)*.............	32	0.0038	20%............................	.....	0.0165
	115	0.0046	40%............................	.....	0.0270
	212	0.0058	60%............................	.....	0.0410
	363	0.0077	80%............................	.....	0.0626
Cyclohexane......................	216	0.0095	100%............................	.....	0.10

Table XI.—Thermal Conductivities of Gases and Vapors.—(*Continued*)

Substance	Deg F	k	Substance	Deg F	k
Hydrogen and nitrogen (ref. 332).......	32		Nitric oxide (ref. 212)*	−94	0.0103
0% H₂............................	....	0.0133		32	0.0138
20%................................	....	0.0212	Nitrogen (refs. 175a and 212)*..........	−148	0.0095
40%................................	....	0.0313		32	0.0140
60%................................	....	0.0438		122	0.0160
80%................................	....	0.0635		212	0.0180
Hydrogen and nitrous oxide (ref. 332)...	32		Nitrous oxide (refs. 175a and 212)*......	−98	0.0067
0% H₂................................	....	0.0092		32	0.0087
20%................................	....	0.0170		212	0.0128
40%................................	....	0.0270			
60%................................	....	0.0410	Oxygen (refs. 123, 175a, 263)...........	−148	0.0095
80%................................	....	0.0650		−58	0.0119
Hydrogen sulphide (ref. 212)*..........	32	0.0076		32	0.0142
				122	0.0164
Mercury (ref. 336)....................	392	0.0197		212	0.0185
Methane (refs. 123, 212,* 468)..........	−148	0.0100			
	−58	0.0145	Pentane (*n*-) (refs. 468 and 491)*.......	32	0.0074
	32	0.0175		68	0.0083
	122	0.0215	(iso-) (ref. 491)*..............	32	0.0072
Methyl alcohol (ref. 491)*.............	32	0.0083		212	0.0127
	212	0.0128	Propane (ref. 468)....................	32	0.0087
Acetate (ref. 491)*.................	32	0.0059		212	0.0151
	68	0.0068			
Methyl chloride (ref. 491)*............	32	0.0053	Sulphur dioxide (ref. 175a).............	32	0.0050
	115	0.0072		212	0.0069
	212	0.0094			
	363	0.0130	Water vapor (refs. 123, 482, 491,* 735)..	115	0.0120
	413	0.0148		212	0.0137
Methylene chloride (ref. 491)*.........	32	0.0039		392	0.0187
	115	0.0049		572	0.0248
	212	0.0063		752	0.0315
	413	0.0095		932	0.0441

* Data from Eucken[212] and Moser[491] are measurements relative to air.   Data in this table from these sources are based on the thermal conductivity of air at 32°F of 0.0140 Btu/(hr)(sq ft) (deg F per ft).

Table XII.—Conversion Factors for Coefficients of Heat Transfer
  Throughout this book of h and U are expressed in Btu/(hr)(sq ft)(deg F). Conversion factors to other units are as follows:
  Multiply by 4.88 to obtain kg-cal/(hr)(sq m)(deg C).
  Multiply by 1 to obtain pcu/(hr)(sq ft)(deg C).
  Multiply by 0.0001355 to obtain gm-cal/(sec)(sq cm)(deg C).
  Multiply by 0.000568 to obtain watts/(sq cm)(deg C).
  Multiply by 0.00204 to obtain watts/(sq in)(deg F).
  Multiply by 0.000394 to obtain hp/(sq ft)(deg F).

TABLE XIII.—THE NORMAL TOTAL EMISSIVITY OF VARIOUS SURFACES
(Hottel)

A. Metals and Their Oxides

Surface	t, deg F*	Emissivity*	Reference number
Aluminum			
Highly polished plate, 98.3% pure.............................	440–1070	0.039–0.057	642
Polished plate.......................................	73	0.040	637
Rough plate......................................	78	0.055	637
Oxidized at 1110°F........................	390–1110	0.11–0.19	578
Al-surfaced roofing..........................	100	0.216	297
Calorized surfaces, heated at 1110°F			
Copper....................................	390–1110	0.18–0.19	578
Steel...................................	390–1110	0.52–0.57	578
Brass			
Highly polished			
73.2% Cu, 26.7% Zn...........................	476–674	0.028–0.031	642
62.4% Cu, 36.8% Zn, 0.4% Pb, 0.3% Al......................	494–710	0.033–0.037	642
82.9% Cu, 17.0% Zn...........................	530	0.030	642
Hard rolled, polished, but direction of polishing visible.............	70	0.038	637
but somewhat attacked........	73	0.043	637
but traces of stearin from polish left on.......	75	0.053	637
Polished.................................	100–600	0.096–0.096	297
Rolled plate, natural surface......	72	0.06	637
Rubbed with coarse emery..........................	72	0.20	637
Dull plate...................................	120–660	0.22	744
Oxidized by heating at 1110°F..................................	390–1110	0.61–0.59	578
Chromium (see Nickel alloys for Ni-Cr steels)....................	100–1000	0.08–0.26	
Copper			
Carefully polished electrolytic copper............................	176	0.018	310
Commercial emeried, polished, but pits remaining..................	66	0.030	637
Commercial, scraped shiny but not mirrorlike....................	72	0.072	637
Polished...................................	242	0.023	756
Plate, heated long time, covered with thick oxide layer............	77	0.78	637
Plate heated at 1110°F............................	390–1110	0.57–0.57	578
Cuprous oxide..................................	1470–2010	0.66–0.54	97
Molten copper..................................	1970–2330	0.16–0.13	97
Gold			
Pure, highly polished..................................	440–1160	0.018–0.035	642
Iron and steel			
Metallic surfaces (or very thin oxide layer)			
Electrolytic iron, highly polished............................	350–440	0.052–0.064	642
Polished iron...............................	800–1880	0.144–0.377	680
Iron freshly emeried...............................	68	0.242	637
Cast iron, polished..........................	392	0.21	578
Wrought iron, highly polished........................	100–480	0.28	744
Cast iron, newly turned........................	72	0.435	637
Polished steel casting............................	1420–1900	0.52–0.56	567
Ground sheet steel............................	1720–2010	0.55–0.61	567
Smooth sheet iron............................	1650–1900	0.55–0.60	567
Cast iron, turned on lathe........................	1620–1810	0.60–0.70	567
Oxidized surfaces			
Iron plate, pickled, then rusted red.........................	68	0.612	637
Completely rusted...............	67	0.685	637
Rolled sheet steel............................	70	0.657	637
Oxidized iron............................	212	0.736	689
Cast iron, oxidized at 1100°F...............	390–1110	0.64–0.78	578
Steel, oxidized at 1100°F...............	390–1110	0.79–0.79	578
Smooth oxidized electrolytic iron............................	260–980	0.78–0.82	642
Iron oxide............................	930–2190	0.85–0.89	99
Rough ingot iron............................	1700–2040	0.87–0.95	567

TABLE XIII.—THE NORMAL TOTAL EMISSIVITY OF VARIOUS SURFACES
(Hottel).—(Continued)

A. Metals and Their Oxides.—(Continued)

Surface	t, deg F*	Emissivity*	Reference number
Iron and steel—(Continued)			
Oxidized surfaces—(Continued)			
Sheet steel, strong, rough oxide layer.	75	0.80	637
Dense, shiny oxide layer.	75	0.82	637
Cast plate, smooth.	73	0.80	637
Rough.	73	0.82	637
Cast iron, rough, strongly oxidized.	100–480	0.95	744
Wrought iron, dull oxidized.	70–680	0.94	744
Steel plate, rough.	100–700	0.94–0.97	297
High-temperature alloy steels (see Nickel alloys)			
Molten metal			
Cast iron.	2370–2550	0.29–0.29	718
Mild steel.	2910–3270	0.28–0.28	718
Lead			
Pure (99.96%), unoxidized.	260–440	0.057–0.075	642
Gray oxidized.	75	0.281	637
Oxidized at 390°F.	390	0.63	578
Mercury.	32–212	0.09 –0.12	227
Molybdenum filament.	1340–4700	0.096–0.292	781
Monel metal, oxidized at 1110°F.	390–1110	0.41 –0.46	578
Nickel			
Electroplated on polished iron, then polished.	74	0.045	637
Technically pure (98.9% Ni, + Mn), polished.	440–710	0.07–0.087	642
Electroplated on pickled iron, not polished.	68	0.11	637
Wire.	368–1844	0.096–0.186	708a
Plate, oxidized by heating at 1110°F.	390–1110	0.37 –0.48	578
Nickel oxide.	1200–2290	0.59 –0.86	98
Nickel alloys			
Chromnickel.	125–1894	0.64 –0.76	708a
Nickelin (18–32 Ni; 55–68 Cu; 20 Zn), gray oxidized.	70	0.262	637
KA-2S alloy steel (8% Ni; 18% Cr), light silvery, rough, brown, after heating.	420–914	0.44 –0.36	595
after 42 hr. heating at 980°F.	420–980	0.62 –0.73	595
NCT-3 alloy (20 Ni; 25 Cr). Brown, splotched, oxidized from service.	420–980	0.90 –0.97	595
NCT-6 alloy (60 Ni; 12 Cr). Smooth, black, firm adhesive oxide coat from service.	520–1045	0.89 –0.82	595
Platinum			
Pure, polished plate.	440–1160	0.054–0.104	642
Strip.	1700–2960	0.12 –0.17	227
Filament.	80–2240	0.036–0.192	171
Wire.	440–2510	0.073–0.182	244
Silver			
Polished, pure.	440–1160	0.0198–0.0324	642
Polished.	100–700	0.0221–0.0312	297
Steel (see Iron)			
Tantalum filament.	2420–5430	0.194–0.31	781
Tin, bright tinned iron sheet.	76	0.043 and 0.064	637
Tungsten			
Filament, aged.	80–6000	0.032–0.35	229
Filament.	6000	0.39	789
Zinc			
Commercial 99.1% pure, polished.	440–620	0.045–0.053	642
Oxidized by heating at 750°F.	750	0.11	578
Galvanized sheet iron, fairly bright.	82	0.228	637
Galvanized sheet iron, gray oxidized.	75	0.276	637

TABLE XIII.—THE NORMAL TOTAL EMISSIVITY OF VARIOUS SURFACES
(Hottel).—(*Continued*)

B. Refractories, Building Materials, Paints, and Miscellaneous

Surface	t, deg F*	Emissivity*	Reference number
Asbestos			
Board	74	0.96	637
Paper	100–700	0.93–0.945	297
Brick			
Red, rough, but no gross irregularities	70	0.93	637
Silica, unglazed, rough	1832	0.80	567
Silica, glazed, rough	2012	0.85	567
Grog brick, glazed	2012	0.75	567
(See Refractory materials)			
Carbon			
T-carbon (Gebruder Siemens) 0.9% ash	260–1160	0.81–0.79	642
This started with emissivity at 260°F of 0.72, but on heating changed to values given			
Carbon filament	1900–2560	0.526	451
Candle soot	206–520	0.952	755
Lampblack-water-glass coating	209–362	0.959–0.947	310
Same	260–440	0.957–0.952	642
Thin layer on iron plate	69	0.927	637
Thick coat	68	0.967	637
Lampblack, 0.003 in. or thicker	100–700	0.945	297
Enamel, white fused, on iron	66	0.897	637
Glass, smooth	72	0.937	637
Gypsum, 0.02 in. thick on smooth or blackened plate	70	0.903	637
Marble, light gray, polished	72	0.931	637
Oak, planed	70	0.895	637
Oil layers on polished nickel (lub. oil)	68		637
Polished surface, alone		0.045	
+0.001 in. oil		0.27	
+0.002 in. oil		0.46	
+0.005 in. oil		0.72	
∞ thick oil layer		0.82	
Oil layers on aluminum foil (linseed oil)			689
Al foil	212	0.087†	
+1 coat oil	212	0.561	
+2 coats oil	212	0.574	
Paints, lacquers, varnishes			
Snow-white enamel varnish on rough iron plate	73	0.906	637
Black shiny lacquer, sprayed on iron	76	0.875	637
Black shiny shellac on tinned iron sheet	70	0.821	637
Black matte shellac	170–295	0.91	757
Black lacquer	100–200	0.80–0.95	297
Flat black lacquer	100–200	0.96–0.98	297
White lacquer	100–200	0.80–0.95	297
Oil paints, 16 different, all colors	212	0.92–0.96	689
Aluminum paints and lacquers			
10% Al, 22% lacquer body, on rough or smooth surface	212	0.52	689
26% Al, 27% lacquer body, on rough or smooth surface	212	0.3	689
Other Al paints, varying age and Al content	212	0.27–0.67	689
Al lacquer, varnish binder, on rough plate	70	0.39	637
Al paint, after heating to 620°F	300–600	0.35	642

TABLE XIII.—THE NORMAL TOTAL EMISSIVITY OF VARIOUS SURFACES
(Hottel).—*(Continued)*

B. Refractories, Building Materials, Paints, and Miscellaneous.—*(Continued)*

Surface	t, deg F*	Emissivity*	Reference number
Paper, thin			
Pasted on tinned iron plate	66	0.924	637
Rough iron plate	66	0.929	637
Black lacquered plate	66	0.944	637
Plaster, rough lime	50–190	0.91	744
Porcelain, glazed	72	0.924	637
Quartz, rough, fused	70	0.932	637
Refractory materials, 40 different	1110–1830	....	758
Poor radiators	....	$\left.\begin{matrix}0.65\\0.70\end{matrix}\right\}-0.75$	
Good radiators	....	$\left.\begin{matrix}0.80\\0.85\end{matrix}\right\}-\left\{\begin{matrix}0.85\\0.90\end{matrix}\right.$	
Roofing paper	69	0.91	637
Rubber			
Hard, glossy plate	74	0.945	637
Soft, gray, rough (reclaimed)	76	0.859	637
Serpentine, polished	74	0.900	637
Water	32–212	0.95–0.963	‡

NOTE.—The results of many investigators have been omitted because of obvious defects in experimental method. A comprehensive bibliography is given in reference 642.

* When two temperatures and two emissivities are given, they correspond, first to first and second to second, and linear interpolation is permissible.

† Although this value is probably high, it is given for comparison with the data, by the same investigator, to show the effect of oil layers (see Aluminum, part *A* of this table).

‡ Calculated from spectral data.

TABLE XIV.—STEAM TABLE*

Temp., deg F	Abs. press. lb/sq in.	Specific volume			Enthalpy			Entropy		
		Sat. liquid	Evap.	Sat. vapor	Sat. liquid	Evap.	Sat. vapor	Sat. liquid	Evap.	Sat. vapor
t	p	v_f	v_{fg}	v_g	h_f	h_{fg}	h_g	s_f	s_{fg}	
32	0.08854	0.01602	3306	3306	0.00	1075.8	1075.8	0.0000	2.1877	2.1877
35	0.09995	0.01602	2947	2947	3.02	1074.1	1077.1	0.0061	2.1709	2.1770
40	0.12170	0.01602	2444	2444	8.05	1071.3	1079.3	0.0162	2.1435	2.1597
45	0.14752	0.01602	2036.4	2036.4	13.06	1068.4	1081.5	0.0262	2.1167	2.1429
50	0.17811	0.01603	1703.2	1703.2	18.07	1065.6	1083.7	0.0361	2.0903	2.1264
60	0.2563	0.01604	1206.6	1206.7	28.06	1059.9	1088.0	0.0555	2.0393	2.0948
70	0.3631	0.01606	867.8	867.9	38.04	1054.3	1092.3	0.0745	1.9902	2.0647
80	0.5069	0.01608	633.1	633.1	48.02	1048.6	1096.6	0.0932	1.9428	2.0360
90	0.6982	0.01610	468.0	468.0	57.99	1042.9	1100.9	0.1115	1.8972	2.0087
100	0.9492	0.01613	350.3	350.4	67.97	1037.2	1105.2	0.1295	1.8531	1.9826
110	1.2748	0.01617	265.3	265.4	77.94	1031.6	1109.5	0.1471	1.8106	1.9577
120	1.6924	0.01620	203.25	203.27	87.92	1025.8	1113.7	0.1645	1.7694	1.9339
130	2.2225	0.01625	157.32	157.34	97.90	1020.0	1117.9	0.1816	1.7296	1.9112
140	2.8886	0.01629	122.99	123.01	107.89	1014.1	1122.0	0.1984	1.6910	1.8894
150	3.718	0.01634	97.06	97.07	117.89	1008.2	1126.1	0.2149	1.6537	1.8685
160	4.741	0.01639	77.27	77.29	127.89	1002.3	1130.2	0.2311	1.6174	1.8485
170	5.992	0.01645	62.04	62.06	137.90	996.3	1134.2	0.2472	1.5822	1.8293
180	7.510	0.01651	50.21	50.23	147.92	990.2	1138.1	0.2630	1.5480	1.8109
190	9.339	0.01657	40.94	40.96	157.95	984.1	1142.0	0.2785	1.5147	1.7932
200	11.526	0.01663	33.62	33.64	167.99	977.9	1145.9	0.2938	1.4824	1.7762
210	14.123	0.01670	27.80	27.82	178.05	971.6	1149.7	0.3090	1.4508	1.7598
212	14.696	0.01672	26.78	26.80	180.07	970.3	1150.4	0.3120	1.4446	1.7566
220	17.186	0.01677	23.13	23.15	188.13	965.2	1153.4	0.3239	1.4201	1.7440
230	20.780	0.01684	19.365	19.382	198.23	958.8	1157.0	0.3387	1.3901	1.7288
240	24.969	0.01692	16.306	16.323	208.34	952.2	1160.5	0.3531	1.3609	1.7140
250	29.825	0.01700	13.804	13.821	218.48	945.5	1164.0	0.3675	1.3323	1.6998
260	35.429	0.01709	11.746	11.763	228.64	938.7	1167.3	0.3817	1.3043	1.6860
270	41.858	0.01717	10.044	10.061	238.84	931.8	1170.6	0.3958	1.2769	1.6727
280	49.203	0.01726	8.628	8.645	249.06	924.7	1173.8	0.4096	1.2501	1.6597
290	57.556	0.01735	7.444	7.461	259.31	917.5	1176.8	0.4234	1.2238	1.6472
300	67.013	0.01745	6.449	6.466	269.59	910.1	1179.7	0.4369	1.1980	1.6350
310	77.68	0.01755	5.609	5.626	279.92	902.6	1182.5	0.4504	1.1727	1.6231
320	89.66	0.01765	4.896	4.914	290.28	894.9	1185.2	0.4637	1.1478	1.6115
330	103.06	0.01776	4.289	4.307	300.68	887.0	1187.7	0.4769	1.1233	1.6002
340	118.01	0.01787	3.770	3.788	311.13	879.0	1190.1	0.4900	1.0992	1.5891
350	134.63	0.01799	3.324	3.342	321.63	870.7	1192.3	0.5029	1.0754	1.5783
360	153.04	0.01811	2.939	2.957	332.18	862.2	1194.4	0.5158	1.0519	1.5677
370	173.37	0.01823	2.606	2.625	342.79	853.5	1196.3	0.5286	1.0287	1.5573
380	195.77	0.01836	2.317	2.335	353.45	844.6	1198.1	0.5413	1.0059	1.5471
390	220.37	0.01850	2.0651	2.0836	364.17	835.4	1199.6	0.5539	0.9832	1.5371
400	247.31	0.01864	1.8447	1.8633	374.97	826.0	1201.0	0.5664	0.9608	1.5272
410	276.75	0.01878	1.6512	1.6700	385.83	816.3	1202.1	0.5788	0.9386	1.5174
420	308.83	0.01894	1.4811	1.5000	396.77	806.3	1203.1	0.5912	0.9166	1.5078
430	343.72	0.01910	1.3308	1.3499	407.79	796.0	1203.8	0.6035	0.8947	1.4982
440	381.59	0.01926	1.1979	1.2171	418.90	785.4	1204.3	0.6158	0.8730	1.4887
450	422.6	0.0194	1.0799	1.0993	430.1	774.5	1204.6	0.6280	0.8513	1.4793
460	466.9	0.0196	0.9748	0.9944	441.4	763.2	1204.6	0.6402	0.8298	1.4700
470	514.7	0.0198	0.8811	0.9009	452.8	751.5	1204.3	0.6523	0.8083	1.4606
480	566.1	0.0200	0.7972	0.8172	464.4	739.4	1203.7	0.6645	0.7868	1.4513
490	621.4	0.0202	0.7221	0.7423	476.0	726.8	1202.8	0.6766	0.7653	1.4419
500	680.8	0.0204	0.6545	0.6749	487.8	713.9	1201.7	0.6887	0.7438	1.4325
520	812.4	0.0209	0.5385	0.5594	511.9	686.4	1198.2	0.7130	0.7006	1.4136
540	962.5	0.0215	0.4434	0.4649	536.6	656.6	1193.2	0.7374	0.6568	1.3942
560	1133.1	0.0221	0.3647	0.3868	562.2	624.2	1186.4	0.7621	0.6121	1.3742
580	1325.8	0.0228	0.2989	0.3217	588.9	588.4	1177.3	0.7872	0.5659	1.3532
600	1542.9	0.0236	0.2432	0.2668	617.0	548.5	1165.5	0.8131	0.5176	1.3307
620	1786.6	0.0247	0.1955	0.2201	646.7	503.6	1150.3	0.8398	0.4664	1.3062
640	2059.7	0.0260	0.1538	0.1798	678.6	452.0	1130.5	0.8679	0.4110	1.2789
660	2365.4	0.0278	0.1165	0.1442	714.2	390.2	1104.4	0.8987	0.3485	1.2472
680	2708.1	0.0305	0.0810	0.1115	757.3	309.9	1067.2	0.9351	0.2719	1.2071
700	3093.7	0.0369	0.0392	0.0761	823.3	172.1	995.4	0.9905	0.1484	1.1389
705.4	3206.2	0.0503	0	0.0503	902.7	0	902.7	1.0580	0	1.0580

* Reprinted from abridged edition of "Thermodynamic Properties of Steam," by Joseph H. Keenan and Frederick G. Keyes, John Wiley & Sons, Inc., New York, 1937, with the permission of the authors and publisher.

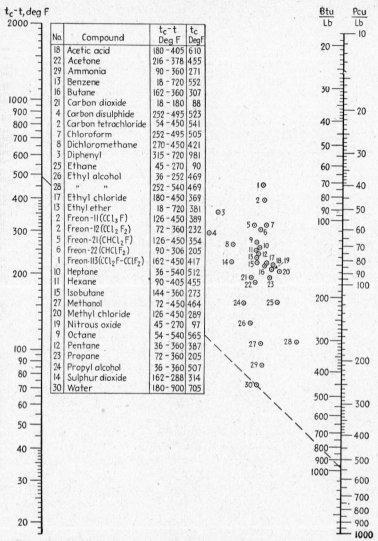

No.	Compound	t_c-t Deg F	t_c DegF
18	Acetic acid	180 – 405	610
22	Acetone	216 – 378	455
29	Ammonia	90 – 360	271
13	Benzene	18 – 720	552
16	Butane	162 – 360	307
21	Carbon dioxide	18 – 180	88
4	Carbon disulphide	252 – 495	523
2	Carbon tetrachloride	54 – 450	541
7	Chloroform	252 – 495	505
8	Dichloromethane	270 – 450	421
3	Diphenyl	315 – 720	981
25	Ethane	45 – 270	90
26	Ethyl alcohol	36 – 252	469
28	" "	252 – 540	469
17	Ethyl chloride	180 – 450	369
13	Ethyl ether	18 – 720	381
2	Freon-11(CCl$_3$F)	126 – 450	389
2	Freon-12(CCl$_2$F$_2$)	72 – 360	232
5	Freon-21(CHCl$_2$F)	126 – 450	354
6	Freon-22 (CHClF$_2$)	90 – 306	205
1	Freon-113(CCl$_2$F–CClF$_2$)	162 – 450	417
10	Heptane	36 – 540	512
11	Hexane	90 – 405	455
15	Isobutane	144 – 360	273
27	Methanol	72 – 450	464
20	Methyl chloride	126 – 450	289
19	Nitrous oxide	45 – 270	97
9	Octane	54 – 540	565
12	Pentane	36 – 360	387
23	Propane	72 – 360	205
24	Propyl alcohol	36 – 360	507
14	Sulphur dioxide	162 – 288	314
30	Water	180 – 900	705

Fig. 199.—Latent heats of vaporization. For water at 212°F, $t_c - t = 705 - 212 = 493$, and the latent heat of vaporization is 970 Btu per lb. (*Chilton, Colburn, and Vernon,*[119] *based mainly on data from International Critical Tables.*)

TABLE XV.—TRUE SPECIFIC HEATS OF SOLIDS*
Expressed in Btu/(lb)(deg F) = gm-cal/(gm)(deg C)

Deg F	Deg C	Pb	Zn	Al	Ag	Au	Cu	Ni	Fe	Co	Quartz
32	0	0.0306	0.0917	0.1813	0.0557	0.0305	0.0919	0.1050	0.1064	0.1025	0.1667
212	100	0.0315	0.0958	0.1824	0.0571	0.0312	0.0942	0.1170	0.1178	0.1081	0.2061
392	200	0.0325	0.0999	0.1836	0.0585	0.0320	0.0965	0.1288	0.1293	0.1138	0.2315
572	300	0.0335	0.1041	0.1848	0.0599	0.0327	0.0988	0.1408	0.1406	0.1194	0.2518
752	400	0.0394	0.1082	0.1860	0.0612	0.0334	0.1011	0.1289	0.1519	0.1252	0.2696
932	500	0.0328	0.1225	0.1872	0.0626	0.0341	0.1034	0.1304	0.1633	0.1308	0.2765
1112	600	0.0328	0.1233	0.1884	0.0640	0.0349	0.1057	0.1319	0.1748	0.1364	0.2624
1292	700	0.0328	0.1242	0.259	0.0654	0.0356	0.1080	0.1335	0.1863	0.1431	0.2714
1472	800	0.0328	0.1250	0.259	0.0668	0.0363	0.1103	0.1351	0.1323	0.1480	0.2808
1652	900	0.0328	0.1259	0.259	0.0682	0.0371	0.1126	0.1366	0.1440	0.1535	0.2899
1832	1000	0.0328	0.1267	0.259	0.076	0.0378	0.1149	0.1381	0.1530	0.1592	0.2993
2012	1100				0.076	0.0355	0.118	0.1397	0.1530	0.1650	0.3084
2192	1200				0.076	0.0355	0.118	0.1412	0.1530	0.1705	0.3174
2372	1300				0.076	0.0355	0.118	0.1428	0.1530	0.1762	0.3264
2552	1400							0.1443	0.1530	0.1820	0.3359
2732	1500							0.1455	0.1790	0.1440	0.3460
2912	1600							0.1455	0.1460	0.1440	0.3544
Melting points, deg F........		621	786	1220	1760	1945	1981	2646	2795	2696	

* Calculated values from equations by K. K. Kelley, *U.S. Bur. Mines Bull.* 371, 1934. These values are the true specific heats for the particular physical state or allotropic modification existing at the indicated temperatures. Melting points are from Perry (ref. 557).

TABLE XVI.—AVERAGE SPECIFIC HEATS OF ANHYDROUS ORGANIC LIQUIDS*

Compound	Deg F	Btu/(lb)(deg F)
Butane (n, iso)	32	0.549
Cresol (o)	32–68	0.497
Cresol (m)	70–387	• 0.551
Cyclohexane (ref. 547a)	50–64	0.431
Cymene (o)	32	0.398
Decylene	32–122	0.467
Diamylene	68–266	0.543
Dichloroacetic acid	70–385	0.348
Di-isoamyl	70.7–311	0.588
Dodecane	57–68	0.505
Dodecylene	32–122	0.455
Ethylene chloride	−22	0.278
	+68	0.299
	140	0.318
Formic acid	68–212	0.524
Furfural	68–212	0.416
Heptylene	32–122	0.486
Hexadecane (n)	32–122	0.496
Hexylene	32–122	0.504
Methane (ref. 762a) saturated liquid	−280	0.811
	−226	0.861
	−172	0.992
Naphthol (α)	32	0.388
Naphthol (β)	32	0.403
Pentadecane	32–122	0.497
Phenol	57–79	0.561
Propane	32	0.576
Stearic acid	167–279	0.550
Tetradecane	32–122	0.497
Tetrachlorethane	68	0.268
Tetrachlorethylene	68	0.216
Trichlorethane	68	0.266
Trichlorethylene	68	0.223
Tridecane	32–122	0.499
Undecane	32–122	0.501

* "International Critical Tables," Vol. 5, pp. 107–113. See also Fig. 200. For data on aqueous solutions of some of these substances, see Table XVIII, p. 403.

Specific heat = Btu/(Lb)(Deg F) = Pcu/(Lb)(Deg C)

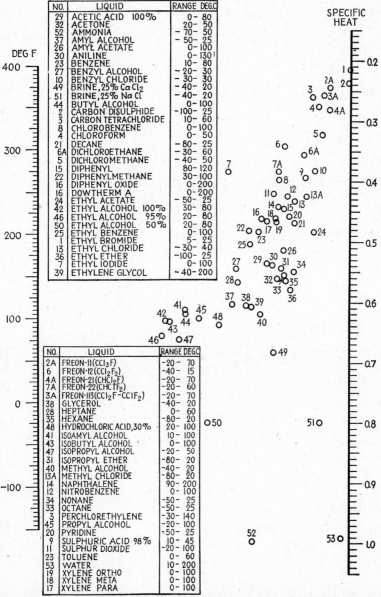

NO.	LIQUID	RANGE DEG.C
29	ACETIC ACID 100%	0- 80
32	ACETONE	20- 50
52	AMMONIA	- 70- 50
37	AMYL ALCOHOL	- 50- 25
26	AMYL ACETATE	0- 100
30	ANILINE	0- 130
23	BENZENE	10- 80
27	BENZYL ALCOHOL	- 20- 30
10	BENZYL CHLORIDE	- 30- 30
49	BRINE, 25% Ca Cl₂	- 40- 20
51	BRINE, 25% Na Cl	- 40- 20
44	BUTYL ALCOHOL	0- 100
2	CARBON DISULPHIDE	-100- 25
3	CARBON TETRACHLORIDE	10- 60
8	CHLOROBENZENE	0- 100
4	CHLOROFORM	0- 50
21	DECANE	- 80- 25
6A	DICHLOROETHANE	- 30- 60
5	DICHLOROMETHANE	- 40- 50
15	DIPHENYL	80- 120
22	DIPHENYLMETHANE	30- 100
16	DIPHENYL OXIDE	0- 200
16	DOWTHERM A	0- 200
24	ETHYL ACETATE	- 50- 25
42	ETHYL ALCOHOL 100%	30- 80
46	ETHYL ALCOHOL 95%	20- 80
50	ETHYL ALCOHOL 50%	20- 80
25	ETHYL BENZENE	0- 100
1	ETHYL BROMIDE	5- 25
13	ETHYL CHLORIDE	- 30- 40
36	ETHYL ETHER	-100- 25
7	ETHYL IODIDE	0- 100
39	ETHYLENE GLYCOL	- 40- 200

NO.	LIQUID	RANGE DEG.C
2A	FREON-11 (CCl₃F)	-20- 70
6	FREON-12 (CCl₂F₂)	-40- 15
4A	FREON-21 (CHCl₂F)	-20- 70
7A	FREON-22 (CHClF₂)	-20- 60
3A	FREON-113 (CCl₂F-CClF₂)	-20- 70
38	GLYCEROL	-40- 20
28	HEPTANE	0- 60
35	HEXANE	-80- 20
48	HYDROCHLORIC ACID, 30%	20- 100
41	ISOAMYL ALCOHOL	10- 100
43	ISOBUTYL ALCOHOL	0- 100
47	ISOPROPYL ALCOHOL	-20- 50
31	ISOPROPYL ETHER	-80- 20
40	METHYL ALCOHOL	-40- 20
13A	METHYL CHLORIDE	-80- 20
14	NAPHTHALENE	90- 200
12	NITROBENZENE	0- 100
34	NONANE	-50- 25
33	OCTANE	-50- 25
3	PERCHLORETHYLENE	-30- 140
45	PROPYL ALCOHOL	-20- 100
20	PYRIDINE	-50- 25
9	SULPHURIC ACID 98%	10- 45
11	SULPHUR DIOXIDE	-20- 100
23	TOLUENE	0- 60
53	WATER	10- 200
19	XYLENE ORTHO	0- 100
18	XYLENE META	0- 100
17	XYLENE PARA	0- 100

Fig. 200.—True specific heats of liquids. (*Chilton, Colburn, and Vernon,*[119] *based mainly on data from International Critical Tables.*)

TABLE XVII.—AVERAGE SPECIFIC HEATS OF LIQUEFIED GASES

Liquid	Range, deg K*	c_p = Btu/ (lb)(deg F)
Ammonia...........................	200–220	1.08
Carbon dioxide (at 63 atm)..........	223–263	0.465–0.539
Carbon monoxide...................	67– 83	0.0615
Chlorine..........................	68	0.229
Hydrogen.........................	15– 21	1.75 –2.33
Nitrogen..........................	64– 76	0.475
Nitric oxide.......................	115–117	0.580
Oxygen...........................	57– 73	0.398
Sulphur dioxide...................	273	0.317

* Degrees Kelvin equals 273.1 plus degrees centigrade.

TABLE XVIII.—TRUE SPECIFIC HEATS OF AQUEOUS SOLUTIONS*
Btu/(lb)(deg F)
HCl and Water

Weight % HCl	32°F	50°F	68°F	104°F	140°F
0.0	1.00				
16.8	0.72	0.72	0.74	0.75	0.78
28.9	0.61	0.605	0.631	0.645	0.67
33.6	0.58	0.575	0.591	0.615	0.638
41.4	0.55	.....	.....	.....	0.61

Acetic Acid and Water (at 100°F)

Weight % acetic acid...........	0	20	60	80	100
Btu/(lb)(deg F)................	1.0	0.911	0.73	0.631	0.535

NH₃ and Water

Weight % NH₃	36.3°F	69.1°F	105.8°F	141.8°F
0	1.01	1.0	0.995	1.0
10	0.98	0.995	1.06	1.02
20	0.96	0.99	1.03	
31	0.956	1.0		
40	0.985			

Aniline and Water (at 68°F)

Weight % aniline......	100	99.0	98.0	96.0	94.0
Btu/(lb)(deg F)........	0.497	0.52	0.53	0.56	0.581

NaOH and Water (at 68°F)

Weight % NaOH................	0	1.1	2.2	18.2	30.8	47.2	57.2
Btu/(lb)(deg F)................	1.0	0.985	0.97	0.835	0.80	0.784	0.782

Methyl Alcohol and Water

Weight % CH₃OH	41°F	68°F	104°F
10	1.02	1.0	0.995
20	0.975	0.982	0.98
40	0.877	0.917	0.92
60	0.776	0.811	0.83
80	0.681	0.708	0.726
100	0.576	0.60	0.617

TABLE XVIII.—TRUE SPECIFIC HEATS OF AQUEOUS SOLUTIONS.*—(*Continued*)

Ethyl Alcohol and Water

Weight % C_2H_5OH	37°F	73°F	106°F
10	1.05	1.02	1.02
25	1.02	1.03	1.03
60	0.805	0.86	0.875
80	0.67	0.727	0.748
100	0.54	0.577	0.621

Normal Propyl Alcohol and Water

Weight % C_3H_7OH	41°F	68°F	104°F
5	1.03	1.02	1.01
15	1.07	1.06	1.03
30	1.035	1.032	0.99
50	0.877	0.90	0.91
70	0.75	0.78	0.815
90	0.612	0.645	0.708
100	0.534	0.57	0.621

Glycerol and Water

Weight % $C_3H_5(OH)_3$	59°F	90°F
10	0.961	0.960
20	0.929	0.924
40	0.851	0.841
60	0.765	0.758
80	0.67	0.672
100	0.555	0.576

KOH and Water (at 66°F)

Weight % KOH.......	0	1.6	4.9	13.5	23.7
Btu/(lb)(deg F).......	1.0	0.975	0.93	0.814	0.75

NaCl and Water

Weight % NaCl	43°F	68°F	91°F	135°F
0.8	.....	0.99		
3.2	0.96	0.97	0.97	
7.5	0.91	0.915	0.915	0.923
24.5	0.805	0.81	0.81	0.82

TABLE XVIII.—TRUE SPECIFIC HEATS OF AQUEOUS SOLUTIONS.*—(*Continued*)
KCl and Water

Weight % KCl	43°F	68°F	91°F	104°F
4	0.945	0.947	0.947	0.947
14	0.828	0.831	0.835	0.837
20	0.77	0.775	0.778	0.775
25	.....	0.727		

ZnSO$_4$ and Water

Weight % ZnSO$_4$	Range	Specific heat
15.2	68–126°F	0.842
4.3	68–126°F	0.952

CuSO$_4$ and Water

Weight % CuSO$_4$	Range	Specific heat
15.1	54–59°F	0.848
4.2	54–57°F	0.951
2.2	55–63°F	0.975

* For additional data, see "International Critical Tables," Vol. 5, pp. 115–116, 122–125.

TABLE XIX.—SPECIFIC HEAT OF AIR AT HIGH PRESSURES*

Temperature, deg C	c_p, specific heat of air					
	1 atm	10 atm	20 atm	40 atm	70 atm	100 atm
100	0.237	0.239	0.240	0.245	0.250	0.258
0	0.238	0.242	0.247	0.251	0.277	0.298
−50	0.238	0.246	0.257	0.279	0.332	0.412
−100	0.239	0.259	0.285	0.370	0.846	
−150	0.240	0.311	0.505			

* For the specific heats of other gases as a function of the pressure, see "International Critical Tables," Vol. 5, pp. 82–83.

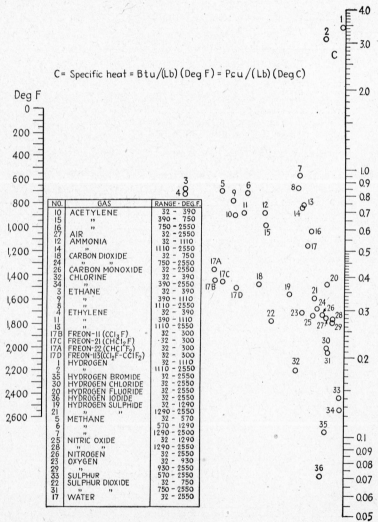

FIG. 201.—True specific heats c_p of gases and vapors at 1 atmosphere pressure. (*Chilton, Colburn, and Vernon,*[119] *based mainly on data from International Critical Tables.*)

TABLE XX.—VISCOSITY OF WATER AT VARIOUS TEMPERATURES*
t in deg F and μ' in centipoises

t	μ'	t	μ'	t	μ'	t	μ'	t	μ'
32	1.79	74	0.929	116	0.582	158	0.407	200	0.305
34	1.73	76	0.905	118	0.571	160	0.400	202	0.301
36	1.66	78	0.887	120	0.560	162	0.394	204	0.298
38	1.60	80	0.861	122	0.549	164	0.388	206	0.294
40	1.55	82	0.840	124	0.539	166	0.383	208	0.291
42	1.49	84	0.820	126	0.530	168	0.377	210	0.287
44	1.44	86	0.800	128	0.520	170	0.372	212	0.284
46	1.40	88	0.782	130	0.511	172	0.367	220	0.270
48	1.35	90	0.764	132	0.502	174	0.362	230	0.255
50	1.31	92	0.747	134	0.493	176	0.357	240	0.242
52	1.27	94	0.731	136	0.485	178	0.352	250	0.229
54	1.23	96	0.715	138	0.477	180	0.347	260	0.218
56	1.19	98	0.699	140	0.470	182	0.343	270	0.208
58	1.16	100	0.684	142	0.461	184	0.338	280	0.199
60	1.12	102	0.670	144	0.454	186	0.333	290	0.191
62	1.09	104	0.654	146	0.446	188	0.329	300	0.185
64	1.06	106	0.643	148	0.439	190	0.325	310	0.179
66	1.03	108	0.630	150	0.432	192	0.321	320	0.174
68	1.01	110	0.617	152	0.425	194	0.317	330	
70	0.978	112	0.605	154	0.419	196	0.313	340	
72	0.953	114	0.593	156	0.412	198	0.309	350	

* Condensed from "International Critical Tables," Vol. 5, p. 10, 1929.

TABLE XXI.—CONVERSION FACTORS FOR VISCOSITY

Viscosity in centipoises $\div$ 100 = viscosity in poises = gm/(sec)(cm)

Viscosity in centipoises $\times$ 0.000672 = viscosity in lb/(sec)(ft)

Viscosity in centipoises $\times$ 0.0000209 = viscosity in (lb force)(sec)/(sq ft)

Viscosity in centipoises $\times$ 2.42 = viscosity in lb/(hr)(ft)

Viscosity in centipoises $\times$ 3.60 = viscosity in kg/(hr)(m)

Example.—At a temperature of slightly greater than 68°F and at atmosperic pressure, liquid water has a viscosity of 1.00 centipoise, 0.0100 poise, 0.0000209 (lb force)(sec)/(sq ft), 0.000672 lb/(sec)(ft), 2.42 lb/(hr)(ft), or 3.6 kg/(hr)(m).

EFFLUX VISCOSIMETERS

These instruments are designed to conform to the equation $\mu'/\rho' = A'\theta - B'/\theta$, where μ' is expressed in poises and ρ' in grams per cubic centimeter; θ is the time of efflux expressed in seconds. The ratio μ'/ρ' is called the **kinematic viscosity** and in the preceding equation is expressed in stokes.

Saybolt Universal Viscosimeter, $A' = 0.0022$, $B' = 1.8$

Redwood Viscosimeter, $A' = 0.0026$, $B' = 1.72$

Redwood Admiralty Viscosimeter, $A' = 0.027$, $B' = 20.0$

Engler Viscosimeter, $A' = 0.00147$, $B' = 3.74$

Such instruments should not be used outside the range of calibration.

TABLE XXII.—VISCOSITIES OF LIQUIDS*
Coordinates for Fig. 202

No.	Liquid	X	Y	No.	Liquid	X	Y
1	Acetaldehyde	15.2	4.8	56	Freon-22	17 2	4.7
2	Acetic acid, 100%	12.1	14.2	57	Freon-113	12.5	11.4
3	Acetic acid, 70%	9.5	17.0	58	Glycerol, 100%	2.0	30.0
4	Acetic anhydride	12.7	12.8	59	Glycerol, 50%	6.9	19.6
5	Acetone, 100%	14.5	7.2	60	Heptene	14.1	8.4
6	Acetone, 35%	7.9	15.0	61	Hexane	14.7	7.0
7	Allyl alcohol	10.2	14.3	62	Hydrochloric acid, 31.5%	13.0	16.6
8	Ammonia, 100%	12.6	2.0	63	Isobutyl alcohol	7.1	18.0
9	Ammonia, 26%	10.1	13.9	64	Isobutyric acid	12.2	14.4
10	Amyl acetate	11.8	12.5	65	Isopropyl alcohol	8.2	16.0
11	Amyl alcohol	7.5	18.4	66	Kerosene	10.2	16.9
12	Aniline	8.1	18.7	67	Linseed oil, raw	7.5	27.2
13	Anisole	12.3	13.5	68	Mercury	18.4	16.4
14	Arsenic trichloride	13.9	14.5	69	Methanol, 100%	12.4	10.5
15	Benzene	12.5	10.9	70	Methanol, 90%	12.3	11.8
16	Brine, CaCl₂, 25%	6.6	15.9	71	Methanol, 40%	7.8	15.5
17	Brine, NaCl, 25%	10.2	16.6	72	Methyl acetate	14.2	8.2
18	Bromine	14.2	13.2	73	Methyl chloride	15.0	3.8
19	Bromotoluene	20.0	15.9	74	Methyl ethyl ketone	13.9	8.6
20	Butyl acetate	12.3	11.0	75	Naphthalene	7.9	18.1
21	Butyl alcohol	8.6	17.2	76	Nitric acid, 95%	12.8	13.8
22	Butyric acid	12.1	15.3	77	Nitric acid, 60%	10.8	17.0
23	Carbon dioxide	11.6	0.3	78	Nitrobenzene	10.6	16.2
24	Carbon disulphide	16.1	7.5	79	Nitrotoluene	11.0	17.0
25	Carbon tetrachloride	12.7	13.1	80	Octane	13.7	10.0
26	Chlorobenzene	12.3	12.4	81	Octyl alcohol	6.6	21.1
27	Chloroform	14.4	10.2	82	Pentachloroethane	10.9	17.3
28	Chlorosulfonic acid	11.2	18.1	83	Pentane	14.9	5.2
29	Chlorotoluene, ortho	13.0	13.3	84	Phenol	6.9	20.8
30	Chlorotoluene, meta	13.3	12.5	85	Phosphorus tribromide	13.8	16.7
31	Chlorotoluene para	13.3	12.5	86	Phosphorus trichloride	16.2	10.9
32	Cresol, meta	2.5	20.8	87	Propionic acid	12.8	13.8
33	Cyclohexanol	2.9	24.3	88	Propyl alcohol	9.1	16.5
34	Dibromoethane	12.7	15.8	89	Propyl bromide	14.5	9.6
35	Dichloroethane	13.2	12.2	90	Propyl chloride	14.4	7.5
36	Dichloromethane	14.6	8.9	91	Propyl iodide	14.1	11.6
37	Diethyl oxalate	11.0	16.4	92	Sodium	16.4	13.9
38	Dimethyl oxalate	12.3	15.8	93	Sodium hydroxide, 50%	3.2	25.8
39	Diphenyl	12.0	18.3	94	Stannic chloride	13.5	12.8
40	Dipropyl oxalate	10.3	17.7	95	Sulphur dioxide	15.2	7.1
41	Ethyl acetate	13.7	9.1	96	Sulphuric acid, 110%	7.2	27.4
42	Ethyl alcohol, 100%	10.5	13.8	97	Sulphuric acid, 98%	7.0	24.8
43	Ethyl alcohol, 95%	9.8	14.3	98	Sulphuric acid, 60%	10.2	21.3
44	Ethyl alcohol, 40%	6.5	16.6	99	Sulphuryl chloride	15.2	12.4
45	Ethyl benzene	13.2	11.5	100	Tetrachloroethane	11.9	15.7
46	Ethyl bromide	14.5	8.1	101	Tetrachloroethylene	14.2	12.7
47	Ethyl chloride	14.8	6.0	102	Titanium tetrachloride	14.4	12.3
48	Ethyl ether	14.5	5.3	103	Toluene	13.7	10.4
49	Ethyl formate	14.2	8.4	104	Trichloroethylene	14.8	10.5
50	Ethyl iodide	14.7	10.3	105	Turpentine	11.5	14.9
51	Ethylene glycol	6.0	23.6	106	Vinyl acetate	14.0	8.8
52	Formic acid	10.7	15.8	107	Water	10.2	13.0
53	Freon-11	14.4	9.0	108	Xylene, ortho	13.5	12.1
54	Freon-12	16.8	5.6	109	Xylene, meta	13.9	10.6
55	Freon-21	15.7	7.5	110	Xylene, para	13.9	10.9

* From J. H. Perry, "Chemical Engineers' Handbook," p. 794, McGraw-Hill Book Company, Inc., 1941.

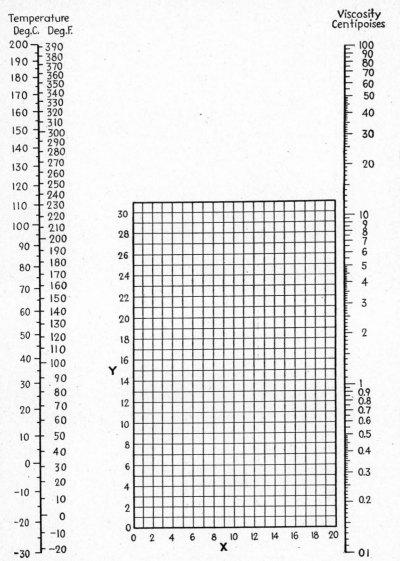

Fig. 202.—Viscosities of liquids at 1 atm. For coordinates, see Table XXII.
(*Genereaux, personal communication.*)

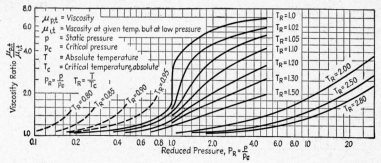

Fig. 203.—Effect of pressure on viscosities of gases at several temperatures. For steam, see Table XXIV. (*Comings and Egly,*[152] *Industrial and Engineering Chemistry.*)

TABLE XXIII.—VISCOSITIES OF GASES*
Coordinates for use with Fig. 204

No.	Gas	X	Y	No.	Gas	X	Y
1	Acetic acid	7.7	14.3	29	Freon-113	11.3	14.0
2	Acetone	8.9	13.0	30	Helium	10.9	20.5
3	Acetylene	9.8	14.9	31	Hexane	8.6	11.8
4	Air	11.0	20.0	32	Hydrogen	11.2	12.4
5	Ammonia	8.4	16.0	33	$3H_2 + 1N_2$	11.2	17.2
6	Argon	10.5	22.4	34	Hydrogen bromide	8.8	20.9
7	Benzene	8.5	13.2	35	Hydrogen chloride	8.8	18.7
8	Bromine	8.9	19.2	36	Hydrogen cyanide	9.8	14.9
9	Butene	9.2	13.7	37	Hydrogen iodide	9.0	21.3
10	Butylene	8.9	13.0	38	Hydrogen sulphide	8.6	18.0
11	Carbon dioxide	9.5	18.7	39	Iodine	9.0	18.4
12	Carbon disulphide	8.0	16.0	40	Mercury	5.3	22.9
13	Carbon monoxide	11.0	20.0	41	Methane	9.9	15.5
14	Chlorine	9.0	18.4	42	Methyl alcohol	8.5	15.6
15	Chloroform	8.9	15.7	43	Nitric oxide	10.9	20.5
16	Cyanogen	9.2	15.2	44	Nitrogen	10.6	20.0
17	Cyclohexane	9.2	12.0	45	Nitrosyl chloride	8.0	17.6
18	Ethane	9.1	14.5	46	Nitrous oxide	8.8	19.0
19	Ethyl acetate	8.5	13.2	47	Oxygen	11.0	21.3
20	Ethyl alcohol	9.2	14.2	48	Pentane	7.0	12.8
21	Ethyl chloride	8.5	15.6	49	Propane	9.7	12.9
22	Ethyl ether	8.9	13.0	50	Propyl alcohol	8.4	13.4
23	Ethylene	9.5	15.1	51	Propylene	9.0	13.8
24	Fluorine	7.3	23.8	52	Sulphur dioxide	9.6	17.0
25	Freon-11	10.6	15.1	53	Toluene	8.6	12.4
26	Freon-12	11.1	16.0	54	2, 3, 3-trimethylbutane	9.5	10.5
27	Freon-21	10.8	15.3	55	Water	8.0	16.0
28	Freon-22	10.1	17.0	56	Xenon	9.3	23.0

* From J. H. Perry, "Chemical Engineers' Handbook," p. 790, McGraw-Hill Book Company, Inc., 1941.

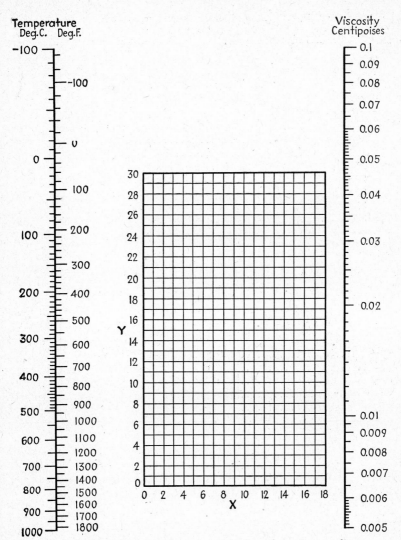

Fig. 204.—Viscosities of gases and vapors at 1 atmosphere; for coordinates, see Table XXIII. (*Genereaux, personal communication.*)

TABLE XXIV.—VISCOSITY OF STEAM, POUNDS PER HOUR PER FOOT
(Keenan and Keyes)[372]*

Absolute pressure, lb force per sq in.	Saturated vapor	32°F	200°F	400°F	600°F	800°F	1000°F	1200°F
0	......	0.0212	0.030	0.0405	0.0505	0.0601	0.0695	0.0785
500	0.0685	......	......	......	0.0751	0.0847	0.094	0.103
1000	0.0949	......	......	......	0.0975	0.107	0.116	0.125
1500	0.118	......	......	......	0.118	0.128	0.137	0.146
2000	0.138	......	......	......	......	0.146	0.155	0.165
2500	0.157	......	......	......	......	0.162	0.172	0.181
3000	0.172	......	......	......	......	0.176	0.186	0.195
3500	......	......	......	......	......	0.189	0.198	0.208

* The values in the original reference[372] are reported in pounds force × seconds per square foot and were multiplied by 32.2 × 3600 to convert to the units shown above.

TABLE XXV.—SETS OF CONSISTENT UNITS FOR DIMENSIONLESS
REYNOLDS NUMBER*

Diameter, D	Mass velocity $G = V\rho$	Viscosity, μ	DG/μ
Feet........................	Lb/(sec)(sq ft)	Lb/(sec)(ft)	No units
Feet........................	Lb/(hr)(sq ft)	Lb/(hr)(ft)	No units
Centimeters.................	Gm/(sec)(sq cm)	Gm/(sec)(cm)	No units
Centimeters.................	Gm/(hr)(sq cm)	Gm/(hr)(cm)	No units
Meters.....................	Kg/(hr)(sq m)	Kg/(hr)(m)	No units

* See also Chap. IV, pp. 88 and 96.

In equations for film type condensation, and in other cases, the term $\phi = (k^3\rho^2 g/\mu^2)^{1/3}$ appears. The following table gives values of t, μ, $v = 1/\rho$, k, and ϕ, expressed in units involving feet, pounds, hours, degrees Fahrenheit, and Btu; ϕ is expressed in Btu/(hr)(sq ft)(deg F).

TABLE XXVI.—SOME PROPERTIES OF LIQUID WATER*

Deg F	μ	k	$v = 1/\rho$	$\phi = \left(\dfrac{k^3\rho^2 g}{\mu^2}\right)^{\frac{1}{3}}$
32	4.33	0.325	0.01602	1440
40	3.73	0.329	0.01602	1610
50	3.17	0.334	0.01603	1810
60	2.71	0.339	0.01604	2040
70	2.36	0.344	0.01606	2280
80	2.08	0.348	0.01608	2480
90	1.85	0.353	0.01610	2740
100	1.66	0.358	0.01613	2960
110	1.49	0.363	0.01617	3260
120	1.36	0.368	0.01620	3500
130	1.24	0.372	0.01625	3760
140	1.14	0.377	0.01629	4020
150	1.04	0.382	0.01634	4290
160	0.970	0.387	0.01639	4570
170	0.900	0.392	0.01645	4860
180	0.840	0.396	0.01651	5120
190	0.786	0.401	0.01657	5440
200	0.738	0.406	0.01663	5700
210	0.695	0.411	0.01670	6000
220	0.654	0.416	0.01677	6310
230	0.618	0.420	0.01684	6510
240	0.585	0.425	0.01692	6870
250	0.555	0.430	0.01700	7200
260	0.528	0.435	0.01709	7400
270	0.504	0.440	0.01717	7710
280	0.482	0.444	0.01726	8060
290	0.463	0.449	0.01735	8390
300	0.448	0.454	0.01745	8620
310	0.434	0.459	0.01755	8880
320	0.421	0.464	0.01765	9090

* The values of k were computed from the equation $k = 0.31 + 0.00048t$, and the values of v and μ were based on references 372 and 336, respectively.

NOTE.—Recent measurements by Timrot and Vargaftik (*J. Tech. Phys.* (U.S.S.R.) **10,** 1063 (1940)) show that k goes through a maximum.

t, deg. F	100	200	300	320	420	520	620
k, sat. liq	0.363	0.393	0.395	0.394	0.376	0.340	0.275
k, 200 atm			0.404	0.403	0.388	0.353	0.290

Hence at 320°F., the new values of k and ϕ are 15 per cent below those given in Table XXVI.

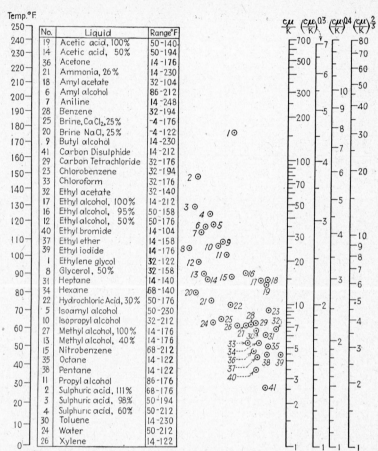

No.	Liquid	Range°F
19	Acetic acid, 100%	50-140
14	Acetic acid, 50%	50-194
36	Acetone	14-176
21	Ammonia, 26%	14-230
18	Amyl acetate	32-104
6	Amyl alcohol	86-212
7	Aniline	14-248
28	Benzene	32-194
25	Brine, CaCl₂, 25%	-4-176
20	Brine NaCl, 25%	-4-122
9	Butyl alcohol	14-230
41	Carbon Disulphide	14-212
29	Carbon Tetrachloride	32-176
23	Chlorobenzene	32-194
33	Chloroform	32-176
32	Ethyl acetate	32-140
17	Ethyl alcohol, 100%	14-212
16	Ethyl alcohol, 95%	50-158
12	Ethyl alcohol, 50%	50-176
40	Ethyl bromide	14-104
37	Ethyl ether	14-158
39	Ethyl iodide	14-176
1	Ethylene glycol	32-122
8	Glycerol, 50%	32-158
31	Heptane	14-140
34	Hexane	68-140
22	Hydrochloric Acid, 30%	50-176
5	Isoamyl alcohol	50-230
10	Isopropyl alcohol	32-212
27	Methyl alcohol, 100%	14-176
13	Methyl alcohol, 40%	14-176
15	Nitrobenzene	68-212
35	Octane	14-122
38	Pentane	14-122
11	Propyl alcohol	86-176
2	Sulphuric acid, 111%	68-176
3	Sulphuric acid, 98%	50-194
4	Sulphuric acid, 60%	50-212
30	Toluene	14-230
24	Water	50-212
26	Xylene	14-122

Fig. 205.—Prandtl numbers $c\mu/k$ for liquids. (*Chilton, Colburn, and Vernon*,[119] *based mainly on data from International Critical Tables.*) NOTE.—To obtain $c\mu/k$ at a specified temperature for a given liquid, as usual a straight line is drawn from the specified temperature through the numbered point for the liquid to the $c\mu/k$-scale; to obtain $c\mu/k$ raised to one of the three fractional powers shown, a *horizontal* alignment is made from the $c\mu/k$-scale.

TABLE XXVIA.—PRANDTL NUMBERS $c_p\mu/k$ FOR GASES AND VAPORS AT 1 ATM
AND 212°F

	$\dfrac{c_p\mu}{k}$	$\left(\dfrac{c_p\mu}{k}\right)^{0.3}$	$\left(\dfrac{c_p\mu}{k}\right)^{0.4}$	$\left(\dfrac{c_p\mu}{k}\right)^{2/3}$
Air, carbon monoxide, hydrogen, nitrogen, oxygen.............................	0.74	0.915	0.899	0.818
Ammonia..............................	0.78	0.928	0.905	0.848
Carbon dioxide, sulphur dioxide.........	0.80	0.935	0.914	0.862
Ethylene..............................	0.83	0.947	0.928	0.883
Hydrogen sulphide....................	0.77	0.925	0.900	0.840
Methane..............................	0.79	0.932	0.909	0.855
Steam (low pressure)..................	0.78	0.928	0.905	0.848

NOTE.—The effects of temperature and pressure are uncertain, and for the present it is
recommended that $c_p\mu/k$ for gases be taken as independent of temperature and pressure, except
near the critical region. Heat-transfer data for natural convection to gases at high pressures
indicate that $c_p\mu/k$ is independent of pressure (p. 243).

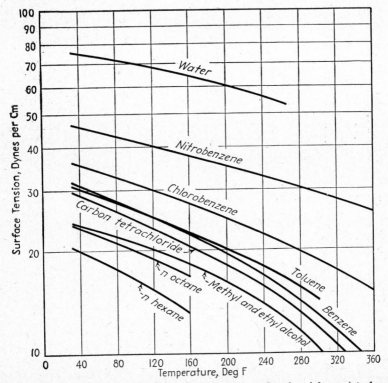

FIG. 206.—Surface tension of liquids *vs.* temperature. (*Based mainly on data from
International Critical Tables.*)

TABLE XXVII.—STANDARD DIMENSIONS FOR STANDARD-WEIGHT WROUGHT-IRON PIPE (Crane Company)

Nominal size, in.	Nominal size, mm	Actual diameters		Nominal thickness, in.	Circumference		Transverse areas			Length of pipe per sq ft		Length of pipe containing 1 cu ft, ft	Nominal weight, lb/ft		Number of threads per in. of screw
		External, in.	Approximate internal, in.		External, in.	Internal, in.	External, sq in.	Internal, sq in.	Metal, sq in.	External surface, ft	Internal surface, ft		Plain ends	Threaded and coupled	
⅛	3	0.405	0.269	0.068	1.272	0.845	0.129	0.057	0.072	9.431	14.199	2533.775	0.244	0.245	27
¼	6	0.540	0.364	0.088	1.696	1.144	0.229	0.104	0.125	7.073	10.493	1383.789	0.424	0.425	18
⅜	10	0.675	0.493	0.091	2.121	1.549	0.358	0.191	0.167	5.658	7.747	754.360	0.567	0.568	18
½	13	0.840	0.622	0.109	2.639	1.954	0.554	0.304	0.250	4.547	6.141	473.906	0.850	0.852	14
¾	19	1.050	0.824	0.113	3.299	2.589	0.866	0.533	0.333	3.637	4.635	270.034	1.130	1.134	14
1	25	1.315	1.049	0.133	4.131	3.296	1.358	0.864	0.494	2.904	3.641	166.618	1.678	1.684	11½
1¼	32	1.660	1.380	0.140	5.215	4.335	2.164	1.495	0.669	2.301	2.767	96.275	2.272	2.281	11½
1½	38	1.900	1.610	0.145	5.969	5.058	2.835	2.036	0.799	2.010	2.372	70.733	2.717	2.731	11½
2	50	2.375	2.067	0.154	7.461	6.494	4.430	3.355	1.075	1.608	1.847	42.913	3.652	3.678	11½
2½	64	2.875	2.469	0.203	9.032	7.757	6.492	4.788	1.704	1.328	1.547	30.077	5.793	5.819	8
3	76	3.500	3.068	0.216	10.996	9.638	9.621	7.393	2.228	1.091	1.245	19.479	7.575	7.616	8
3½	90	4.000	3.548	0.226	12.566	11.146	12.566	9.886	2.680	0.954	1.076	14.565	9.109	9.202	8
4	100	4.500	4.026	0.237	14.137	12.648	15.904	12.730	3.174	0.848	0.948	11.312	10.790	10.889	8
4½	113	5.000	4.506	0.247	15.708	14.156	19.635	15.947	3.688	0.763	0.847	9.030	12.538	12.642	8
5	125	5.563	5.047	0.258	17.477	15.856	24.306	20.006	4.300	0.686	0.756	7.198	14.617	14.810	8
6	150	6.625	6.065	0.280	20.813	19.054	34.472	28.891	5.581	0.576	0.629	4.984	18.974	19.185	8
7	175	7.625	7.023	0.301	23.955	22.063	45.664	38.738	6.926	0.500	0.543	3.717	23.544	23.769	8
8	200	8.625	8.071	0.277	27.096	25.356	58.426	51.161	7.265	0.442	0.473	2.815	24.696	25.000	8
8	200	8.625	7.891	0.322	27.096	25.073	58.426	50.027	8.399	0.442	0.478	2.878	28.554	28.809	8
9	225	9.625	8.941	0.342	30.238	28.089	72.760	62.786	9.974	0.396	0.427	2.294	33.907	34.188	8
10	250	10.750	10.192	0.279	33.772	32.019	90.763	81.585	9.178	0.355	0.374	1.765	31.201	32.000	8
10	250	10.750	10.136	0.307	33.772	31.843	90.763	80.691	10.072	0.355	0.376	1.785	34.240	35.000	8
10	250	10.750	10.020	0.365	33.772	31.479	90.763	78.855	11.908	0.355	0.381	1.826	40.483	41.132	8
11	275	11.750	11.000	0.375	36.914	34.558	108.434	95.033	13.401	0.325	0.347	1.515	45.557	46.247	8
12	300	12.750	12.090	0.330	40.055	37.982	127.676	114.800	12.876	0.299	0.315	1.254	43.773	45.000	8
12	300	12.750	12.000	0.375	40.055	37.699	127.676	113.097	14.579	0.299	0.318	1.273	49.562	50.706	8

TABLE XXVIII.—STANDARD CONDENSER-TUBE DATA*

Outside diameter, in.	Size number, B-W G	Weight per ft, lb†	Thickness, in.	Inside diameter, in.	Surface, sq ft per ft of length		Inside sectional area, sq in	Velocity, ft/sec for 1 U. S. gal/min	Capacity at 1 ft/sec velocity	
					Outside	Inside			U. S. gal/min	Lb water/hr
½	12	0.493	0.109	0.282	0.1309	0.0748	0.0624	5.142	0.1945	97.25
	14	0.403	0.083	0.334	0.1309	0.0874	0.0876	3.662	0.2730	136.5
	16	0.329	0.065	0.370	0.1309	0.0969	0.1076	2.981	0.3352	167.5
	18	0.258	0.049	0.402	0.1309	0.1052	0.1269	2.530	0.3952	197.6
	20	0.190	0.035	0.430	0.1309	0.1125	0.1452	2.209	0.4528	226.4
⅝	12	0.656	0.109	0.407	0.1636	0.1066	0.1301	2.468	0.4053	202.7
	14	0.526	0.083	0.459	0.1636	0.1202	0.1655	1.939	0.5157	258.9
	16	0.424	0.065	0.495	0.1636	0.1296	0.1925	1.667	0.5999	300.0
	18	0.329	0.049	0.527	0.1636	0.1380	0.2181	1.472	0.6793	339.7
	20	0.241	0.035	0.555	0.1636	0.1453	0.2420	1.326	0.7542	377.1
¾	10	0.962	0.134	0.482	0.1963	0.1262	0.1825	1.758	0.5688	284.4
	12	0.812	0.109	0.532	0.1963	0.1393	0.2223	1.442	0.6935	346.8
	14	0.644	0.083	0.584	0.1963	0.1528	0.2678	1.198	0.8347	417.4
	16	0.518	0.065	0.620	0.1963	0.1613	0.3019	1.063	0.9407	470.4
	18	0.400	0.049	0.652	0.1963	0.1706	0.3339	0.9611	1.041	520.5
⅞	10	1.16	0.134	0.607	0.2291	0.1589	0.2893	1.108	0.9025	451.3
	12	0.992	0.109	0.657	0.2291	0.1720	0.3390	0.9465	1.057	528.5
	14	0.769	0.083	0.709	0.2291	0.1856	0.3949	0.8126	1.230	615.0
	16	0.613	0.065	0.745	0.2291	0.1951	0.4360	0.7360	1.358	679.0
	18	0.472	0.049	0.777	0.2291	0.2034	0.4740	0.6770	1.477	738.5
1	10	1.35	0.134	0.732	0.2618	0.1916	0.4208	0.7626	1.311	655.5
	12	1.14	0.109	0.782	0.2618	0.2048	0.4803	0.6681	1.497	748.5
	14	0.887	0.083	0.834	0.2618	0.2183	0.5463	0.5874	1.702	851.0
	16	0.708	0.065	0.870	0.2618	0.2277	0.5945	0.5398	1.852	926.0
	18	0.535	0.049	0.902	0.2618	0.2361	0.6390	0.5022	1.991	995.5
1¼	10	1.74	0.134	0.982	0.3271	0.2572	0.7575	0.4236	2.362	1181
	12	1.45	0.109	1.032	0.3271	0.2701	0.8369	0.3834	2.608	1304
	14	1.13	0.083	1.084	0.3271	0.2839	0.9229	0.3477	2.877	1439
	16	0.898	0.065	1.120	0.3271	0.2932	0.9852	0.3257	3.070	1535
	18	0.675	0.049	1.152	0.3271	0.3015	1.043	0.3075	3.253	1627
1½	10	2.12	0.134	1.232	0.3925	0.3227	1.193	0.2688	3.720	1860
	12	1.76	0.109	1.282	0.3925	0.3355	1.292	0.2482	4.030	2015
	14	1.36	0.083	1.334	0.3925	0.3491	1.398	0.2292	4.362	2181
	16	1.09	0.065	1.370	0.3925	0.3585	1.473	0.2180	4.587	2294
2	10	2.94	0.134	1.732	0.5233	0.4534	2.355	0.1362	7.342	3671
	12	2.40	0.109	1.782	0.5233	0.4665	2.494	0.1287	7.770	3885
	14	1.85	0.083	1.834	0.5233	0.4803	2.643	0.1213	8.244	4122
	16	1.47	0.065	1.870	0.5233	0.4896	2.747	0.1168	8.562	4281

* Prepared by T. B. Drew.
† In brass, specific gravity = 8.56; specific gravity of steel = 7.8.

BIBLIOGRAPHY AND AUTHOR INDEX

In the references to journal articles, the volume number appears in **bold-faced** type, followed by the range of page numbers and year of publication. The numerals in the right-hand column are page numbers in this book; where such numbers appear in parentheses the literature reference pertains to the subject matter of the page given although it is not cited specifically.

PAGE

1. Abbott, M. D., and W. D. Comley, S.M. Thesis in Chemical Engineering, Massachusetts Institute of Technology, 1938.... 313
1a. Ackermann, G., *Z. Angew. Math. Mech.*, **11**, 192 (1931)........ 43
2. Ackermann, G., *Forsch. Gebiete Ingenieurw.*, **3**, 42–50 (1932) 243, 244
3. Adams, F. W., G. Broughton, and A. L. Conn, *Ind. Eng. Chem.*, **28**, 537–541 (1936)... 205
4. Aerofin, *Bull. H. P.* 2, Aerofin Corporation, Newark, N.J., 1927. (235)
4a. Akin, G. A., Sc.D. Thesis in Chemical Engineering, Massachusetts Institute of Technology, 1940..................... 314, 319
5. Akin, G. A., and W. H. McAdams, *Trans. Am. Inst. Chem. Engrs.*, **35**, 137–155 (1939); *Ind. Eng. Chem.* **31**, 487–491 (1939)................................. 307, 308, 312, 315, 319
6. Allen, J. R., *Trans. Am. Soc. Heating Ventilating Eng.*, **23**, 141–159 (1917)... 227
7. Andreas, J. M., S.M. Thesis in Chemical Engineering, Massachusetts Institute of Technology, 1927...................... 126
8. Anne, J. W., *Power Plant Eng.*, **35**, 1018–1019 (1931)........... 279
9. Anonymous, Heat Transmission of Insulating Materials, Rept. Insulation Comm., Am. Soc. Refrig. Engrs., New York, 1924.. 388
10. Anonymous, *Nat. Research Council Bull.*, **11**, Part III, 1926.... 64
10a. Anonymous, "Machinery's Handbook," p. 74, Industrial Press, New York, 1927..................................... 367
11. Anonymous, Rept. Prime Movers Comm., *NELA Publ.* 069, July, 1930, 420 Lexington Ave., New York................... 274, 279
12. Anonymous, *Blast Furnace Steel Plant*, **19**, 1475 (1931)
13. Anonymous, *Gas. J.* **196**, 135 (1931); *Z. Ver. deut. Ing.*, **75**, 1193 (1931)... 279
14. Anonymous, *Ind. Chemist*, **82**, 374 (1931)..................... 250
15. Anonymous, *Power*, **75**, 717 (1932)........................... 9
16. Anonymous, *Trans. Am. Inst. Chem. Engrs.*, **34**, 93–100 (1938).. 5
17. Anonymous, "Refrigerating Data Book," Am. Soc. Refrig. Engrs., p. 191, 1939–1940................................... (287)
17a. Anonymous, "Temperature, Its Measurement and Control in Science and Industry," Reinhold, New York, 1941........... 149
17b. Ashley, C. M., *Refrig. Eng.*, **43**, 89–95 (1942)............... (321)

PAGE

18. Assman, R., *Veroffenlichen Preuss. meteorol. Inst. Abhand.* **1,** 117
    (1892)... 225
19. Atherton, D. H., *Trans. Am. Soc. Mech. Engrs.,* **48,** 145–175 (1926) 123
20. Austin, L., *Mitt. Forsch.,* **7,** 75 (1903)................. 306, 307, 313
21. Awbery, J., and F. Schofield, *Proc. Intern. Congr. Refrig.,* 5th
    Congress, **3,** 591–610 (1929)................................ 16
22. Ayrton, W. E., and H. Kilgour, *Trans. Roy. Soc. (London),* **A183,**
    371 (1892)... 243
23. Babcock & Wilcox Company, "Experiments on Rate of Heat
    Transfer from Hot Gas to a Cooler Metallic Surface," New
    York, 1916... 169, 173
24. Backstrom, R. E., "House Insulation," Government Printing
    Office, Washington, D.C., 1931........................... (382)
25. Badger, W. L., *Trans. Am. Inst. Chem. Engrs.,* **13,** Part II, 139
    (1920)... 328
26. Badger, W. L., "Heat Transfer and Evaporation," Chemical
    Catalog Co., New York, 1926.............................. 295
27. Badger, W. L., *Ind. Eng. Chem.,* **19,** 677 (1927)............... (321)
28. Badger, W. L., *Trans. Am. Inst. Chem. Engrs.,* **33,** 441–446 (1937);
    Ind. Eng. Chem., **29,** 910–912 (1937)................... 263, 267
29. Badger, W. L., and F. C. Cutting, *Trans. Am. Inst. Chem. Engrs.,*
    16, Part II, 145–157 (1925)............................. (330)
30. Badger, W. L., and W. L. McCabe, "Elements of Chemical
    Engineering," McGraw-Hill, New York, 1936................ 295
31. Badger, W. L., C. C. Monrad, and H. W. Diamond, *Ind. Eng.
    Chem.,* **22,** 700 (1930)......................... 263, 267, 323
32. Badger, W. L., and D. F. Othmer, *Trans. Am. Inst. Chem. Engrs.,*
    16, Part II, 159–168 (1925)............................. 318
33. Badger, W. L., and P. W. Shephard, *Trans. Am. Inst. Chem.
    Engrs.,* **13,** Part I, 101–137 (1920)...................... 332
34. Badger, W. L., and P. W. Shephard, *Trans. Am. Inst. Chem.
    Engrs.,* **13,** Part I, 139–168 (1920).................... 326, 328
35. Bagley, G. D., *Trans. Am. Soc. Mech. Engrs.,* **40,** 667 (1918).... 345
36. Bailey, N. P., *Mech. Eng.,* **53,** 797–804 (1931); **54,** 553 (1932)..... 149
37. Bailey, A., and W. F. Cope, *Aeronautical Research Comm. (Great
    Britain), Tech. Rept.* 43, p. 199 (1933)................. 197, 198
38. Bailey, A., and N. C. Lyell, *Engineering,* **147,** 60–62 (1939)...... 247
38a. Baker, T., *Ind. Eng. Chem.,* **27,** 977 (1935).................. 289
39. Baker, E. M., E. W. Kazmark, and G. W. Stroebe, *Trans. Am.
    Inst. Chem. Engrs.,* **35,** 127–134 (1939); *Ind. Eng. Chem.,* **31,**
    214–218 (1939)...................................... 263–265
40. Baker, E. M., and A. C. Mueller, *Trans. Am. Inst. Chem.
    Engrs.,* **33,** 531–558 (1937); *Ind. Eng. Chem.* **29,** 1067–1072
    (1937)... 150, 263, 281, 282
41. Baker, E. M., and U. Tsao, *Trans. Am. Inst. Chem. Engrs.,*
    36, 517–539, 783 (1940); *Ind. Eng. Chem.,* **32,** 1115–1121
    (1940)...................................... 150, 263, 265, 281–283
42. Bakhmeteff, B. A., "The Mechanics of Turbulent Flow," Prince-
    ton University Press, Princeton, 1936.................... (110)

PAGE

43. Baldwin, J. T., and T. K. Sherwood, S.M. Thesis in Chemical
Engineering, Massachusetts Institute of Technology, 1924.... 179
44. Barker, M., *Proc. Roy. Soc. (London)*, **A101,** 435–445 (1922)..... 104
45. Barnett, W. I., and K. A. Kobe, *Ind. Eng. Chem.*, **33,** 436–442
(1941)... 291
46. Barratt, T., *Proc. Phys. Soc. (London)*, **28,** 14–20 (1915)........ (24)
47. Barratt, T., and H. R. Nettleton, "International Critical Tables,"
Vol. V, p. 227, McGraw-Hill, New York, 1929............... 20
48. Bates, O. K., *Ind. Eng. Chem.*, **28,** 494 (1936).................. 389
49. Bates, O. K., G. Hazzard, and G. Palmer, *Ind. Eng. Chem.
Anal. Ed.*, **10,** 314–318 (1938).............................. 389
50. Bates, O. K., G. Hazzard, and G. Palmer, *Ind. Eng. Chem.
Anal. Ed.*, **10,** 314–318 (1938); see also Bates, *Ind. Eng. Chem.*,
25, 431 (1933)... 19, 20
51. Bates, O. K., G. Hazzard, and G. Palmer, *Ind. Eng. Chem.*, **33,**
375–376 (1941)... 389
52. Baum, S., S.M. Thesis in Chemical Engineering, Massachusetts
Institute of Technology, 1936............................. 276
53. Bays, G. S., Sc.D. Thesis in Chemical Engineering, Massachusetts
Institute of Technology, 1936............................. 203
54. Bays, G. S., and L. M. Blenderman, S.M. Thesis, Massachusetts
Institute of Technology, 1935............................. 276
55. Bays, G. S., and W. H. McAdams, *Ind. Eng. Chem.*, **29,** 1240–1246
(1937)... 204
56. Beckett, H. E., *Proc. Phys. Soc. (London)*, **43,** 227 (1931)....... (51)
56a. Beckmann, W., *Forsch. Gebiete Ingenieurw.*, **2,** 165–178, 213–219
(1931)... (238)
57. Bell, J. E., *Intern. Eng. Congr.*, Mech. Eng. Sec., San Francisco,
6, 368 (1915)... 169
58. Benke, R., *Arch. Wärmewirt*, **19,** 287–291 (1938)....... 219, 221, 227
59. Benning, A. F., personal communication, 1940................ 389
60. Bichowsky, F. R., *Ind. Eng. Chem.*, **14,** 62 (1922)............. 169
61. Bider, M., *Strahlentherapie*, **39,** 541 (1931)..................... 236
62. Biermann, A. E., and B. Pinkel, *Nat. Advisory Comm. Aeronaut.
Tech. Rept.*, 488 (1934)................................... 235
63. Billings, R. T., and W. F. Wadt, S.M. Thesis, Massachusetts
Institute of Technology, 1933............................. 276
63a. Binkley, E. R., "Heat Transfer," *Am. Soc. Mech. Engrs.*, 1933–
1934, pp. 40–46... 50
63b. Biskamp, H., *Z. tech. Physik*, **12,** 30–33 (1931)............... 137
64. Blackett, P. M. S., P. S. H. Henry, and E. K. Rideal, *Proc. Roy.
Soc. (London)*, **A126,** 319–354 (1930)...................... 189
65. Blasius, H., *Mitt. Forschungsarb*, **131,** 1–40 (1913)............. 87
65a. Bliss, H., *Trans. Am. Inst. Chem. Engrs.*, **37,** 763–804 (1941)... 352
66. Blodgett, K., and I. Langmuir, *Phys. Rev.*, **51,** 964 (1937)....... 277
67. Boarts, R. M., W. L. Badger, and S. J. Meisenburg, *Trans. Am.
Inst. Chem. Engrs.*, **33,** 363–389 (1937); *Ind. Eng. Chem.*, **29,**
912–918 (1937)................................. 321, 322, 325

Page

68. Boelter, L. M. K., *Heating, Piping, Air Conditioning*, **11**, 639–647
   (1939).. 286
69. Boelter, L. M. K., "Heating, Ventilating, and Air Conditioning
   Guide," p. 251, ASHVE, New York, 1941................ 286, 287
70. Boelter, L. M. K., R. C. Martinelli, and F. Jonassen, *Trans. Am.
   Soc. Mech. Engrs.*, **63**, 447–455 (1941)................ (110), 164
71. Boertlein, J. C., personal communication, 1930................ 249
71a. Bogart, N. T., and A. L. Johnson, S.M. Thesis in Chemical
   Engineering, Massachusetts Institute of Technology, 1938.... 310
72. Bond, W. N., *Proc. Phys. Soc. (London)*, **43**, Part I, 46–52 (1931) 101
73. Bonilla, C. F., and C. H. Perry, *Trans. Am. Inst. Chem. Engrs.*, **37**,
   685–705 (1941)..................... 304, 305, 307, 310, 312, 313
74. Borne, A. v.d., *Ann. Hydrographie*, **58**, 409 (1930)............. 236
75. Boruff, C. S., and K. E. Stoll, *Ind. Eng. Chem.*, **24**, 398–400 (1932) 279
75a. Bosnjakovic, F., *Tech. Mech. Thermodynam.*, **1**, 358 (1930). 298, 303
76. Bosnjakovic, F., *Forsch. Gebiete Ingenieurw.*, **3**, 135 (1932)...... 279
77. Boussinesq, J., *J. math. pures et appl.* (2), **13**, 377 (1868)........ 124
78. Boussinesq, J., *Compt. rend.*, **113**, 9–15, 49–51 (1891)........... 190
79. Boussinesq, J., "Théorie analytique de le chaleur," Vol. III,
   Gouthier-Villars et Fils, Paris, 1903; *J. math. pures et appl.*,
   1, 285 (1905).. 222
80. Bowen, J. T., *Agr. Eng.*, **11**, 27 (1930)........................ 250
81. Bowman, R. A., *Ind. Eng. Chem.*, **28**, 541–544 (1936)........ (146)
82. Bowman, R. A., A. C. Mueller, and W. M. Nagle, *Trans. Am.
   Soc. Mech. Engrs.*, **62**, 283–294 (1940)................ 146, 147
83. Brandon, G. E., and W. H. George, S.B. Thesis in Business and
   Engineering Administration, Massachusetts Institute of Technology, 1940... (290)
84. Brandt, H., *Wärme*, **59**, 367–369 (1936)...................... 227
85. Braunlich, R. H., S.B. Thesis in Chemical Engineering, Massachusetts Institute of Technology, 1940..................... 266
86. Braunlich, R. H., S.M. Thesis in Chemical Engineering, Massachusetts Institute of Technology, 1941..... 305, 309, 310, 315, 319
87. Bray, W. W., and G. H. Sayler, S.M. Thesis in Chemical Engineering, Massachusetts Institute of Technology, 1923............ 265
88. Breitung, M., *Refrig. Eng.*, **22**, 11–14 (1931)................... 9
89. Bridgman, P. W., "Dimensional Analysis," Yale University
   Press, New Haven, 1922, 1931.............................. 87
90. Bridgman, P. W., *Proc. Am. Acad. Arts Sci.*, **59**, 141 (1923). 19, 389
91. Brooks, C. H., and W. L. Badger, *Trans. Am. Inst. Chem. Engrs.*,
   33, 392–413 (1937); *Ind. Eng. Chem.*, **29**, 918–923 (1937). 321, 324
92. Bryant, E. M., *Proc. Inst. Civil Engrs. (London)*, **132**, Part II,
   274–287 (1897–1898)...................................... (294)
93. Bryant, L. W., E. Ower, A. S. Halliday, and V. M. Falkner, *Brit.
   Aero. Res. Comm., Rept. and Memo.*, 1163, May, 1928......... 236
94. Buckingham, E., *Phys. Rev.*, **4**, 345–376 (1914)................. 87
95. Buhne, W., *Wärme*, **61**, 162–165 (1938)....................... 194
96. Burbach, T., and R. Hermann, "Stromungswiderstand und War-
   meubergang in Rohren," *Akad. Verlag*, Leipzig, 1930......... 179

PAGE

97. Burgess, G. K., *Nat. Bur. Standards Bull.* 6, Sci Paper 121, p. 111
(1909).. 393

98. Burgess, G. K., and P. D. Foote, *Nat. Bur. Standards Bull.* 11, Sci.
Paper 224, pp. 41–64 (1914)...................................... 394

99. Burgess, G. K., and P. D. Foote, *Nat. Bur. Standards Bull.* 12, Sci.
Paper 249, pp. 83–89 (1915)...................................... 393

100. Busey, F. L., *J. Am. Soc. Heating Ventilating Engrs.*, **18**, 172 (1912) 227

101. Buttner, K., *Veröffentl. Preuss. Meteorol. Inst. Abhand.*, **10**, No. 5,
1934.. 236

102. Byerly, W. E., "Elementary Treatise on Fourier Series," Ginn,
Boston, 1928.. 30

103. Bylevelt, van, Dissertation, Dresden, 1915..................... 219

104. Callendar, H. L., and J. T. Nicolson, *Engineering* **64**, 481–482
(1897).. 149, 267

105. Carey, J. S., Sc.D. Thesis in Chemical Engineering, Massachusetts Institute of Technology, 1929......................... (294)

106. Carne, J. B., *Phil. Mag.*, (7) **24**, 634–653 (1937)................ 241

107. Carrier, W. H., personal communication, 1932........ 166, 169, 274

108. Carrier, W. H., and F. L. Busey, *Trans. Am. Soc. Mech. Engrs.*,
33, 1055 (1911)..................................... 227, 228

109. Carslaw, "Mathematical Theory of Heat," Macmillan, New
York, 1921.. 30, 43

110. Cessna, O. C., and W. L. Badger, *Trans. Am. Inst. Chem. Engrs.*,
37, 311–331 (1941).. 326

111. Cessna, O. C., J. R. Lientz, and W. L. Badger, *Trans. Am. Inst.
Chem. Engrs.*, **36**, 759–779 (1940)......................... 325

112. Chambers, F. S., and T. K. Sherwood, *Ind. Eng. Chem.*, **29**, 1415–
1422 (1937).. 291

113. Chambers, I. D., and J. H. Steves, personal communication,
1930.. 249, 250

114. Chappell, E. L., and W. H. McAdams, *Trans. Am. Soc. Mech.
Engrs.*, **48**, 1201–1231 (1926).................. 217, 223, 227, 228

115. Chilton, T. H., and A. P. Colburn, du Pont Expt. Sta., Rept.
B-197-199 (1930)... 249

116. Chilton, T. H., and A. P. Colburn, *Ind. Eng. Chem.*, **23**, 913 (1931);
Trans. Am. Inst. Chem. Engrs., **26**, 178 (1931)............... 124

117. Chilton, T. H., and A. P. Colburn, *Ind. Eng. Chem.*, **26**, 1183–1187
(1934).. (285)

117a. Chilton, T. H., and A. P. Colburn, *Ind. Eng. Chem.*, **27**, 255–260
(1935).. 288

118. Chilton, T. H., A. P. Colburn, R. P. Generaux, and H. C. Vernon,
Trans. Am. Soc. Mech. Engrs., *Petroleum Mech. Eng.*, **55**, 7–14
(1933)............................... 174, 176, 185, 245, 269

119. Chilton, T. H., A. P. Colburn, and H. C. Vernon, personal
communications, 1929–1941; based mainly on data from
"International Critical Tables," McGraw-Hill, New York,
1929....................................... 398, 401, 406, 414

120. Chilton, T. H., and T. B. Drew, "The Science of Petroleum,"
Oxford, New York, pp. 2211–2222..................... 230, 357

121. Chilton, T. H., and R. P. Generaux, *Trans. Am. Inst. Chem. Engrs.*, **29,** 161–173 (1933)............................ 126, 127

122. Chilton, T. H., and R. P. Generaux, personal communication, 1939, based on data selected from the literature.............. 389

123. Chilton, T. H., and R. P. Generaux, personal communication, 1940..391, 392

124. Church, J. W., and H. B. Cobb, S.M. Thesis in Chemical Engineering, Massachusetts Institute of Technology, 1922........... (294)

125. Claassen, H., *Z. Ver. Deut. Zuckerind.*, **43,** 236 (1893)........ (294)

126. Claassen, *Mitt. Forschung*, **4,** 49 (1902).............. 298, 311, 332

127. Clapp, M. H., and O. FitzSimons, S.M. Thesis in Chemical Engineering, Massachusetts Institute of Technology, 1928.......................................120, 189, 193, 194

128. Clement, J. K., and C. M. Garland, *Univ. Illinois Eng. Expt. Sta. Bull*, 40, pp. 3–17, 1909..................................... 265

129. Cleve, K., *Mitt. Forschung.*, **322,** 1 (1929)................. 326, 327

130. Coates, J., and W. L. Badger, *Trans. Am. Inst. Chem. Engrs.*, **32,** 49–61 (1936)... 323

131. Coblentz, W. H., "Investigation of Infra-red Spectra," Carnegie Institute, Washington, D.C. 1905............................. 71

132. Coblentz, W. H., *Nat. Bur. Standards Bull.* 9, pp. 283–324 (1913) (51)

132a. Coffey, J. F., S.B. Thesis in Chemical Engineering, Massachusetts Institute of Technology, 1939......................... 318

133. Coffey, B. H., and G. S. Dauphinee, *Am. Soc. Refrig. Engrs. J.*, **8,** 177–202 (1921); **9,** 74 (1922)............................... 290

134. Coffey, B. H., and G. A. Horne, *Am. Soc. Refrig. Engrs. J.*, **7,** 173–201 (1920)... 290

135. Cogan, C. A., S.M. Thesis in Chemical Engineering, Massachusetts Institute of Technology, 1934......................... 282

136. Colburn, A. P., personal communication, 1930................. 170

137. Colburn, A. P., *Ind. Eng. Chem.*, **23,** 910 (1931); *Trans. Am. Inst. Chem. Engrs.*, **26,** 166 (1931)............................... 178

138. Colburn, A. P., *Food Industries*, **4,** 155–158 (1932).............. 29

139. Colburn, A. P., personal communications, 1932, 1940.. 249–251, 274

140. Colburn, A. P., *Ind. Eng. Chem.*, **25,** 873–877 (1933)............ 144

141. Colburn, A. P., personal communication, 1933................. 197

142. Colburn, A. P., *Trans. Am. Inst. Chem. Engrs.*, **29,** 174–210 (1933)............... 166–168, 182, 188, 191, 196, 205, 206, 229

143. Colburn, A. P., *Trans. Am. Inst. Chem. Engrs.*, **30,** 187–193 (1933–34); *Ind. Eng. Chem.*, **26,** 432–434 (1934).................... 268

143a. Colburn, A. P., personal communication, 1937................ 372

143b. Colburn, A. P., *Purdue Univ. Eng. Bull.* **26,** No. 1, 1942... 368

143c. Colburn, A. P., personal communication, Feb., 1942........... 364

144. Colburn, C. E., *Power*, **58,** 803 (1923)....................... 279

145. Colburn, A. P., and C. A. Coghlan, *Trans. Am. Soc. Mech. Engrs.*, **63,** 561–566 (1941).................................... 164, 169

146. Colburn, A. P., and T. B. Drew, *Trans. Am. Inst. Chem. Engrs.*, **33,** 197–212 (1937)... 281

PAGE

147. Colburn, A. P., and O. A. Hougen, *Ind. Eng. Chem.*, **22**, 522
(1930).. 149, 150, 185

148. Colburn, A. P., and O. A. Hougen, *Univ. Wis. Eng. Expt. Sta. Bull.*
70, p. 29, 1930................................. 191, 259, 284

149. Colburn, A. P., and O. A. Hougen, *Ind. Eng. Chem.*, **26**, 1178–1182
(1934)... 284

150. Colburn, A. P., and W. J. King, *Ind. Eng. Chem.*, **23**, 910–923
(1931); *Trans. Am. Inst. Chem. Engrs.*, **26**, 166–206 (1931). 125, 178

150a. Colburn, A. P., L. L. Millar, and J. W. Westwater, Am. Inst.
Chem. Engrs., Boston Meeting, May, 1942.................. 271

151. Comings, E. W., *Ind. Eng. Chem.*, **32**, 984–987 (1940)..... 87, 89, 92

152. Comings, E. W., and R. S. Egly, *Ind. Eng. Chem.*, **32**, 714–718
(1940).. 410

153. Compan, P., *Ann. chim. phys.*, **26** (7), 488–573 (1902).......... 237

153a. Cooper, H. B. H., S.M. Thesis in Chemical Engineering, Massachusetts Institute of Technology, 1938................. 303, 304

153b. Cooper, A. H., R. H. Morrison, and H. E. Henderson, *Ind. Eng.
Chem.*, **34**, 79–84 (1942)................................ (254)

154. Cooper, C. M., T. B. Drew, and W. H. McAdams, *Trans. Am.
Inst. Chem. Engrs.*, **30**, 158–169 (1933–34); *Ind. Eng. Chem.*,
26, 428–431 (1934)...................................... 261

155. Cope, W. F., *Proc. Inst. Mech. Engrs. (London)*, **137**, 165–194
(1937)... (199)

155a. Cope, W. F., *Proc. Inst. Mech. Engrs. (London)*, **145**, 99–105
(1941)... 175

156. Cornish, R. J., *Proc. Roy. Soc. (London)*, **A120**, 69 (1928)... 123, 124

157. Couch, W. H., and C. E. Herrstrom, Thesis in Chemical Engineering, Massachusetts Institute of Technology, 1924............ 101

158. Cox, E. R., *Trans. Am. Soc. Mech. Engrs.*, PET **50**, 13 (1928)... 166

159. Cragoe, *Nat. Bur. Standards Misc. Pub.* 97, 1929............ 20, 194

160. Cryder, D. S., and A. C. Finalborgo, *Trans. Am. Inst. Chem.
Engrs.*, **33**, 346–361 (1937)...................... 305, 308–312

161. Cryder, D. S., and E. R. Gilliland, *Ind. Eng. Chem.*, **24**, 1382–1387
(1932); *Refrig. Eng.*, **25**, 78–83 (1933)...................... 312

162. Dahl, O. G. C., *Trans. Am. Soc. Mech. Engrs.*, **46**, 161 (1924)..... 152

163. Daniloff, M., *J. Am. Chem. Soc.*, **54**, 1328–1332 (1932).......... 389

163a. Darrow, K. K., *Rev. Mod. Phys.*, **12**, 257–266 (1940)........... 19

164. Davidson, W. F., *et al.*, *Am. Soc. Mech. Engrs.*, Advance Paper,
Dec., 1941... (172)

165. Davies, S. J., and C. M. White, *Proc. Roy. Soc. (London)*, **A119**,
92–107 (1928); *Engineering*, **128**, 69, 98, and 131 (1929)....... 124

166. Davis, A. H., *Phil. Mag.*, **40**, 692 (1920); **43**, 329 (1922)......... 242

167. Davis, A. H., *Phil. Mag.*, **41**, 899 (1921); **44**, 940 (1922); reprinted
in Collected Researches, Nat. Phys. Lab. (Teddington, Eng.),
19, 203 (1926)..................................... 219, 242

168. Davis, A. H., *Phil. Mag.*, **44**, 920 (1922)................. 242–244

169. Davis, A. H., *Phil. Mag.* **47**, 972, 1057 (1924); reprinted in Collected Researches, Nat. Phys. Lab. (Teddington, Eng.), **19**,
243 (1926).. 225, 226, 242

PAGE

170. Davis, W. K., and J. J. Shipman, S.B. Thesis in Chemical Engineering, Massachusetts Institute of Technology, 1940 291
171. Davisson, C., and J. R. Weeks, Jr., *Optical Soc. Am.*, **8,** 581–606 (1924) 394
172. Day, V. S., *Univ. Ill. Eng. Expt. Sta. Bull.* 117, 1920 346
173. DeBaufre, W. L., *Trans. Am. Soc. Mech. Engrs.*, FSP **55,** 73–103 (1933) 152
174. Deutsch, R. K., and J. C. Rhode, S.M. Thesis in Chemical Engineering, Massachusetts Institute of Technology, 1940.... 303
175. Dehn, K., *Forschungsheft,* **342** (1931) 227
175a. Dickens, B. G., *Proc. Roy. Soc. (London)*, **A143,** 517–540 (1934). 392
176. Dittus, F. W., and L. M. K. Boelter, *Univ. Calif. Pub. in Eng.,* **2,** 443 (1930) 164, 166, 167
177. Dittus, F. W., and A. Hildebrand, *Soc. Mech. Engrs.*, Advance Paper, June, 1941 .... (120)
178. Dixon, W. T., from p. 149, ref. 740 173
179. Doetsch, H., *Diss. Aero. Inst. Tech. Hochschule Aachen,* **14,** 3–23 (1934) 232
180. Dönch, F., *Mitt. Forschungsarb.,* **282,** 1–58 (1926) 122
181. Dorno, C., *Meteorol. Z.,* **45,** 401 (1928) 236
182. Douglass, R. D., and D. P. Adams, *Ind. Eng. Chem.,* **33,** 1082–1083 (1941) 372
182a. Dreselly, R. A., S.M. Thesis in Chemical Engineering, Massachusetts Institute of Technology, 1937 .... 313, 319
183. Drew, T. B., personal communication, 1931 123
184. Drew, T. B., *Trans. Am. Inst. Chem. Engrs.*, **26,** 26 (1931). 187, 188, 222
185. Drew, T. B., *Ind. Eng. Chem.* **24,** 152–157 (1932) 189
186. Drew, T. B., personal communication, 1932 .... 123, 124
187. Drew, T. B., personal communication, 1935 277
188. Drew, T. B., personal communication, 1938 .... 203, 260
189. Drew, T. B., personal communication, 1939 417
190. Drew, T. B., personal communication, 1940 261
191. Drew, T. B., and R. P. Generaux, *Trans. Am. Inst. Chem. Engrs.,* **32,** 17–19 (1936) 119, 120
192. Drew, T. B., J. J. Hogan, and W. H. McAdams, *Ind. Eng. Chem.,* **23,** 936–945 (1931); *Trans. Am. Inst. Chem. Engrs.,* **26,** 81 (1931). 189
193. Drew, T. B., H. C. Hottel, and W. H. McAdams, *Trans. Am. Inst. Chem. Engrs.,* **32,** 271–305 (1936); *Chem. Eng. Congr. World Power Cong.,* London, **3,** 713–745 (1936) 93, 188, 262, 364, 368
194. Drew, T. B., E. C. Koo, and W. H. McAdams, *Trans. Am. Inst. Chem. Engrs.,* **28,** 56–72 (1932) 119, 120
195. Drew, T. B., and A. C. Mueller, *Trans. Am. Inst. Chem. Engrs.,* **33,** 449–471 (1937) 297, 313, 314, 316
196. Drew, T. B., W. M. Nagle, and W. Q. Smith, *Trans. Am. Inst. Chem. Engrs.,* **31,** 605–621 (1935) 276
197. Drew, T. B., and W. P. Ryan, *Ind. Eng. Chem.,* **23,** 945–953 (1931); *Trans. Am. Inst. Chem. Engrs.,* **26,** 118–147 (1931)..... 216
198. Dropkin, D., *Cornell Univ. Eng. Expt. Sta., Bull.* 23, 1936 ..... (286)

PAGE

198a. Dryden, H. L., "Aerodynamics of Cooling," Div. T, pp. 223–282, of "Aerodynamic Theory," vol. VI, by N. F. Durand, Springer, Berlin, 1936.. 110

199. Dryden, H. L., and A. M. Keuthe, *Nat. Adv. Comm. Aeronaut. Rept.* 320, 1929, Government Printing Office, Washington, D.C. 103, 215

200. Dryden, H. L., F. D. Murnaghan, and H. Batemann, *Nat. Research Council, Bull.* 84, pp. 3–634, February, 1932............. 100, 162

201. Dufton, A. F., *Heating, Piping Air Conditioning*, **4**, 355 (1932)... 345

202. Dunn, P. S. and A. D. Vincent, S.M. Thesis in Chemical Engineering, Massachusetts Institute of Technology, 1931..... 305, 312

203. Eagle, A., and R. M. Ferguson, *Proc. Roy. Soc. (London)*, **A127**, 540–566 (1930); *Engineering*, **130**, 691, 788, 821 (1930); *Proc. Inst. Mech. Engrs. (London)*, **2**, 985 (1930)...... 163, 164, 180, 183

204. Eberhardt, J. E., and H. C. Hottel, *Trans. Am. Soc. Mech. Engrs.*, **58**, 185–193 (1936); *Heat Treatment Forging*, **22**, 144–149, 193–198 (1936)... 80

205. Eberle, C., *Z. Ver. deut. Ing.*, **52**, 481–487, 539–544, 567–564, 626–632, 663–668 (1908); *Mitt. Forschungsarb.*, **78**, 1 (1909)... 243, 244

206. Eberle, C., and C. Holzhauer, *Arch. Warmewirt.*, **9**, 171–179 (1928); **10**, 334–336 (1929)................................ 316

207. Eckert, E., *Forschungsheft* **387**, 1–20 (1937)................... 72

208. Egbert, R. B., Sc.D. Thesis in Chemical Engineering, Massachusetts Institute of Technology, 1941...................... 66, 67

209. Elias, F., *Ahhandl. aerodyn. Inst., Tech. Hochschule Aachen*, **9**, 10 (1930); *Z. angew. Math. Mech.*, **9**, 434 (1929); **10**, 1 (1930); translated in *Nat. Adv. Comm. Aeronaut. Tech. Memo.* 614, April, 1931, Government Printing Office, Washington, D.C. 103, 149, 159

210. Elmer, L., *Refrig. Eng.*, **24**, 17 (1932)........................ 43

211. Emmons, H., *Trans. Am. Inst. Chem. Engrs.*, **35**, 109–122 (1939) 277

212. Eucken, A., *Physik Z.*, **12**, 1101–1107 (1911); **14**, 324 (1913). 21, 391, 392

213. Eustice, J., *Proc. Roy. Soc. (London)*, **A84**, 107–118 (1910); **A85**, 119–131 (1911)...................................... 122

214. Fabry, C., *Wärme*, **55**, 163 (1932)........................... 345

215. Fage, A., *Phil. Mag.* (7) **7**, 253 (1929)...................... 215

216. Fage, A., and V. M. Falkner, *Brit. Adv. Comm. Aero. Rept. and Memo.* 1408 (1931)................................. 206, 216

217. Fage, A., and H. C. H. Townsend, *Proc. Roy. Soc. (London)*, **A135**, 656–677 (1932)...................................... 101

218. Feldmeier, H., "Heat Transfer," pp. 69–74, Am. Soc. Mech. Engrs., New York, 1936.................................. 249

219. Fessenden, E. A., *Penn. State Coll. Eng. Expt. Sta. Bull.* 32, p. 1, 1924... 169, 173

220. Fessenden, E. A., and J. W. Haney, *Univ. Mo. Eng. Expt. Sta.*, Series 18, p. 3, October, 1916.......................... 169, 173

221. Finck, J. L., *Nat. Bur. Standards J. Research, Sci. Paper* 243, **5**, 973 (1930)... 9

222. Fischer, J., *Ingenieur-Archiv* **10**, 95–112 (1939)................ 30

223. Fishenden, M., *Engineering*, **138**, 478 (1934)................. 72

PAGE

224. Fishenden, M., and O. A. Saunders, "The Calculation of Heat Transmission," H. M. Stationery Office, London, 1932..... 30, 40
225. Fitzpatrick, J. P., S.M. Thesis in Chemical Engineering, Massachusetts Institute of Technology, 1936; also research reports, February and September, 1937............................ 276
226. Fitzpatrick, J. P., S. Baum, and W. H. McAdams, *Trans. Am. Inst. Chem. Engrs.*, **35**, 97–107, (1939)............. 204, 276–278
227. Foote, P. D., *Nat. Bur. Standards, Bull.* 11, *Sci. Paper* 243, p. 607, 1914; *J. Wash. Acad. Sci.*, **5**, 1 (1914)....................... 394
227a. Foote, P. D., C. O. Fairchild, and T. R. Harrison, *Nat. Bur. Standards, Tech. Paper* 170, Feb. 16, 1921................... 149
228. Forrest, H. O., and L. W. Cummings, personal communication, 1932................................. 390
229. Forsythe, W. E., and A. G. Worthing, *Astrophys. J.* **61**, 146–185 (1925)................................. 394
230. Fortsch, A. R., and W. G. Whitman, *Ind. Eng. Chem.*, **18**, 795–800 (1926)................................. 194
231. Fourier, J. B., "Théorie analytique de la chaleur," Oeuvres de Fourier, Gauthier-Villars et Fils, Paris, 1822; German transl. by Weinstein, Springer, Berlin, 1884; *Ann. chim. phys.*, **37**, 2, 291 (1828); *Pogg. Ann.*, **13**, 327 (1828)..................... 6, 30
232. Foust, A. S., E. M. Baker, and W. L. Badger, *Trans. Am. Inst. Chem. Engrs.*, **35**, 45–71 (1939); *Ind. Eng. Chem.*, **31**, 206–214 (1939)... 321, 326, 332
233. Foust, A. S., and G. A. Christian, *Trans. Am. Inst. Chem. Engrs.*, **36**, 541–554 (1940)... 202
234. Fragen, N., and W. L. Badger, *Ind. Eng. Chem.*, **28**, 534–537 (1936) 294
235. Frank, A., *Gesundh.-Ing.*, **52**, 541 (1929)..................... 207
236. Friedman, S. J., and C. O. Miller, *Ind. Eng. Chem.*, **33**, 885–891 (1941)................................. 261
237. Froessel, W., *Forsch. Gebiete Ingenieurw*, **7**, 75–84 (1936)........ 120
238. Fromm, K., *Z. angew. Math. Mech.*, **3**, 339 (1923). Data in *Abhandl. aero. Inst.*, *Tech. Hochschule Aachen*, 1923.......... 123
239. Frost, V. M., and W. F. Rippe, *Trans. Am. Soc. Mech. Engrs.*, FSP **53**, 131 (1931)... 279
240. Furnas, C. C., *U.S. Bur. Mines Bull.* 307, 1929................. 124
241. Gardner, K. A., *Ind. Eng. Chem.*, **33**, 1215–1223 (1941)......... 148
242. Gardner, K. A., *Ind. Eng. Chem.*, **33**, 1495–1500 (1941)......... 148
243. Geibel, C., *Mitt. Forschung.*, **242**, 1–98 (1921)................. 290
244. Geiss, W., *Physica*, **5**, 203 (1925)............................ 394
244a. Genereaux, R. P., personal communication, 1940.......... 409, 411
245. Gibson, A. H., *Proc. Inst. Auto. Engrs.*, **14**, 243 (1919).......... 235
246. Gibson, A. H., *Engineering*, **117**, 325–357, 391; 422 (1924)....... 96
247. Gibson, A. H., *Phil. Mag.* (6) **47**, 324 (1924)...... 219, 220, 221, 223
248. Gibson, A. H., "Hydraulics and Its Applications," 4th ed., Van Nostrand, New York, 1930............................ 122
249. Gilliland, E. R., *Ind. Eng. Chem.*, **30**, 506–514 (1938)........... 162
249a. Gilliland, E. R., personal communication, Jan., 1942...... 364, 368

PAGE

250. Gilliland, E. R., and T. K. Sherwood, *Ind. Eng. Chem.*, **26**, 516–523 (1934)... (284)

251. Ginabat, A., *Wärme*, **47**, 573–578, 588–592, (1924).............. 261

252. Gnam, E., *Forschungsheft*, **382**, 17–31 (1937).................. 277

253. Goldschmidt, H., and E. P. Partridge, "Industrial Heat Transfer" (English translation of ref. 627), Wiley, New York......... 30, 43

253a. Goldstein, S., "Modern Developments in Fluid Mechanics," Oxford Univ. Press, 1938................................... 99

254. Goodman, W., *Refrig. Eng.*, **32**, 225 (1936).................. (284)

254a. Goodman, W., *Heating, Piping Air Conditioning*, **9**, 11–14, 89–91, 165–169, 179–180 (1937)................................. (284)

254b. Goodman, W., *Heating, Piping Air Conditioning*, **10**, 697–701, 707, 777–781 (1938); **11**, 13–19, 83–86, 157–160, 233–236, 305–308 (1939)... 286

255. Goukhman, A., V. Joukovsky, and L. Loiziansky, *Tech. Phys.* (U.S.S.R.), **1**, 221–242 (1934)........................ 221, 223

256. Graetz, L., *Z. Math. Physik*, **25**, 316, 375 (1880)................ 124

257. Graetz, L., *Ann. Physik.*, **18**, 79–94 (1883); **25**, 337 (1885)....... 187

258. Grebe, J. J., *Mech. Eng.*, **53**, 719, (1931)...................... 193

259. Greenhill, A. G., *Proc. London Math. Soc.*, **13**, 43 (1881)......... 124

260. Gregg, J. L., *Refrig. Eng.*, **23**, 279, 288, 290, 304 (1932)......... 9

261. Gregory, H. S., *Proc. Roy. Soc.* (*London*), **A149**, 35–56 (1935). (391)

262. Gregory, H. S., and C. T. Archer, *Proc. Roy. Soc.* (*London*), **A110**, 91–122 (1926)... (391)

263. Gregory, H. S., and J. H. Marshall, *Proc. Roy. Soc.* (*London*), **A118**, 594 (1928)... 392

264. Griffiths, E., *Brit. Adv. Comm. Aero. Rept. and Memo.* 308, 1917. 232

265. Griffiths, E., Food Investigation Board, *Spec. Rept.* 5, Dept. Scientific and Industrial Research, H.M. Stationery Office, London, 1921.. 8

265a. Griffiths, E., Food Investigation Board, *Spec. Rept.* 35, Dept. Scientific and Industrial Research, H.M. Stationery Office, London, 1929.. 388

266. Griffiths, E., and J. H. Awbery, *Engineering*, **136**, 692–694 (1933); *Proc. Inst. Mech. Engrs.* (London), **125**, 319–382 (1933); *Ice and Cold Stor.* **37**, 14–16 (1934).................... 219, 227, 228

267. Griffiths, E., and J. H. Awbery, *Proc. Inst. Mech. Engrs.* (London), **137**, 195–216 (1937)......................... 219, 221, 227, 235

268. Griffiths, E., and A. H. Davis, Food Investigation Board, *Spec. Rept.* 9, Dept. Scientific and Industrial Research, H.M. Stationery Office, London, 1922. See also rev. ed., 1931. 237, 241, 248

269. Grimison, E. D., *Trans. Am. Soc. Mech. Engrs.*, **59**, 583–594 (1937); **60**, 381–392 (1938)...................... 126, 227–229

270. Grober, H., *Mitt. Forsch.*, **130**, 1–24 (1912)............... 166, 169

271. Grober, H., "Warmeubertragung," Springer, Berlin, 1926.... 43, 259

272. Grober, H., and S. Erk, "Die Grundgesetze der Warmeubertragung," Springer, Berlin, 1933.............. 30, 166, 169, 187, 285

272a. Grosvenor, W. M., *Trans. Am. Inst. Chem. Engrs.*, **1**, 184–202 (1908).. 285

PAGE

273. Guchmann, A., N. Iljuchin, W. Taassowa, and G. Warschaw-
ski, *Tech. Phys.* (U.S.S.R.), **2**, 375–413 (1935).......... 169, 219

274. Guerrieri, S. A., personal communication, 1932................ 71

275. Gurney, H. P., "Heating and Cooling of Solid Shapes," unpublished monograph, Massachusetts Institute of Technology
Library....................................... 30, 32, 36–38

276. Gurney, H. P., and J. Lurie, *Ind. Eng. Chem.* **15**, 1170–1172 (1923)　30

277. Hagenbuch, W. H., S.M. Thesis in Chemical Engineering,
Massachusetts Institute of Technology, 1941....... 263, 281, 282

278. Hansen, M., *Abhandl. aerodyn. Inst., Tech. Hochschule Aachen*,
8, (1928); *Z. angew. Math. Mech.*, **8**, 185 (1928); translated in
Nat. Adv. Comm. Aeronaut. Tech. Memo. 585, October, 1930,
Government Printing Office, Washington, D.C.............. 103

279. Hansen, G., *Z. tech. Physik* **12**, 436–440 (1931)................ 212

280. Harbert, W. D., D. C. Cain, and R. L. Huntington, *Trans. Am.
Inst. Chem. Engrs.*, **37**, 267–290 (1941); *Ind. Eng. Chem.*, **33**,
257–263 (1941).. 43

281. Harlow, J. H., and R. A. Bowman, *Trans. Am. Soc. Mech. Engrs.*,
61, 133–138 (1939)..................................... (354)

282. Harper, D. R., and W. B. Brown, *Nat. Adv. Comm. Aeronaut. Rept.*
158, 1922, Government Printing Office, Washington, D.C...... 232

283. Harris, R. G., L. E. Caygill, and R. A. Fairthorne, *Brit. Aero.
Research Comm., Rept. and Memo.* 1326, June, 1930.......... 236

284. Hartmann, I., *J. Franklin Inst.*, **218**, 593–612 (1934)........ 237

285. Haslam, R. T., and M. W. Boyer, *Ind. Eng. Chem.*, **19**, 4–6 (1927)　76

286. Haslam, R. T., and H. C. Hottel, *Trans. Am. Soc. Mech. Engrs.*,
FSP **50**, 9 (1928)..................................... 76

287. Haucke, E., *Arch. Wärmewirt.*, **116**, 53 (1930)............... 207

288. Hausbrand, E., and M. Hirsch, "Verdampfen, Kondensieren und
Kuhlen," 7th ed., Springer, Berlin, 1931.................... 295

289. Hausen, H., *Z. angew. Math. Mech.*, **9**, 173–200 (1929).......... 43

290. Hausen, H., *Tech. Mech. Thermodynam.*, **1**, 219 (1930); *Z. angew.
Math. Mech.*, **11**, 105 (1931).............................. 43

291. Hauser, E. A., and D. R. Dewey, *J. Phys. Chem.*, **46**, 212
(1942)... 215, 216

292. Hebbard, G. M., and W. L. Badger, *Ind. Eng. Chem., Anal. Ed.*,
5, 359–362 (1933)................................... 150, 263

293. Hebbard, G. M., and W. L. Badger, *Trans. Am. Inst. Chem.
Engrs.*, **30**, 194–216 (1933–34); *Ind. Eng. Chem.*, **26**, 420–424
(1934)... 153

294. Heidrich, A., *Diss. Tech. Hochschule Aachen*, 1931; abstracted in
ref. 337.. 300

295. Heiligenstaedt, W., "Regeneratoren, Rekuperatoren, Winderhit-
zer," Spamer, Leipzig, 96, 1931........................... 43

296. Heilman, R. H., *Ind. Eng. Chem.*, **16**, 445–452 (1924).......... 246

297. Heilman, R. H., *Trans. Am. Soc. Mech. Engrs.*, FSP **51**, 287–304
(1929)..................................... 241, 248, 393–895

298. Heinrich, E., and R. Stückle, *Mitt. Forsch.*, **271**, 1–60 (1925)..... 202

PAGE

299. Helmholtz, H., *Sitzber, Akad. Wiss. Wien*, **40**, 607 (1860); *Akad. Wiss.*, Berlin, p. 501, 1873................................. 87

300. Henry, P. S. H., *Proc. Roy. Soc.* (*London*), **A133**, 492–505 (1931). 189

301. Hermann, R., *Forschungsheft*, **7**, No. 319, 1–24 (1936).. 241, 242, 249

302. Hersey, M. D., and H. S. Snyder, *J. Rheol.*, **3**, 298 (1932)...... 120

303. Hiliger, B., *Z. Ver. deut. Ing.*, **60**, 877–883 (1916)............. (166)

304. Hilpert, R., *Forschungsheft*, **335**, 1–22 (1932).................. 249

305. Hilpert, R., *Forsch. Gebiete Ingenieurw.*, **4**, 215–224 (1933)... 219, 221

306. Hinton, A. G., quoted by H. M. Spiers, "World Power Conference, London, 1928, Technical Data on Fuel," pp. 101–103, published by World Power Conference, London, 1928........ 166, 167, 183

307. Hixson, A. W., and S. J. Baum, *Ind. Eng. Chem.*, **33**, 1433 (1941) 237

308. Hoffmann, E., *Z. ges. Kälte-Ind.*, **44**, 99–107 (1937)............. 163

309. Hoffmann, E., *Forsch. Gebiete Ingenieurw.*, **11**, 159–169 (1940).... 164

310. Hoffmann, K., *Z. Physik.*, **14**, 310 (1923)................. 393, 395

311. Holborn and Dittenberger, *Mitt. Forsch.*, **2**, 56 (1901)........ (254)

312. Holden, P. B., Thesis in Chemical Engineering, Massachusetts Institute of Technology, 1923. Data are published in ref. 192.. 193, 194

313. Holloway, F. A., personal communication, 1940............... 261

314. Holmboe, C. F., *Dinglers Polytech. J.*, **324**, 803–806 (1909); **325**, 88 (1910)...................................... 166, 169, 279

314a. Hooker, T., and R. B. Sackheim, S.M. Thesis in Chemical Engineering, Massachusetts Institute of Technology, 1941..... 290

315. Horne, G., *Refrig. Eng.*, **9**, 143 (1922)...................... 272

316. Horne, G., and F. Ophuls, *Refrig. Eng.*, **11**, 1–13 (1924)........ 272

317. Hottel, H. C., *Trans. Am. Inst. Chem. Engrs.*, **19**, 173 (1927); *Ind. Eng. Chem.*, **19**, 888 (1927)........................... 72

318. Hottel, H. C., 2d *World Power Conf.*, vol. 18, Sec. 32, No. 243, 1930; *Mech. Eng.*, **52**, 699 (1932).......................... 55

319. Hottel, H. C., *Trans. Am. Soc. Mech. Engrs.*, FSP **53**, 265–273 (1931).. 55, 62

319a. Hottel, H. C., personal communication, 1937................. (78)

319b. Hottel, H. C., personal communication, 1938............ 33–35, 80

320. Hottel, H. C., and F. P. Broughton, *Ind. Eng. Chem., Anal. Ed.*, 4, 166–175 (1932)....................................... 74

321. Hottel, H. C., and R. B. Egbert, *Trans. Am. Soc. Mech. Engrs.*, **63**, 297 (1941)... 72

322. Hottel, H. C., and J. D. Keller, *Trans. Am. Soc. Mech. Engrs., Iron and Steel*, **55–6**, 39–49 (1933)............................ 57

323. Hottel, H. C., and H. G. Mangelsdorf, *Trans. Am. Inst. Chem. Engrs.*, **31**, 517–549 (1935)................................ 72

324. Hottel, H. C., and V. C. Smith, *Trans. Am. Soc. Mech. Engrs.*, **57**, 463–70 (1935):.................................... 72

325. Hougen, O. A., and K. M. Watson, "Industrial Chemical Calculations," Wiley, New York, 1936........................... 82

326. Houghten, F. C., J. L. Blackshaw, E. M. Pugh, and D. McDermott, *Heating Piping Air Conditioning*, **4**, 288 (1932)......... 43

PAGE

327. Huge, E. C., *Trans. Am. Soc. Mech. Engrs.*, **59,** 573–581 (1937).   227–229

328. Huggins, F. E., Jr., *Ind. Eng. Chem.*, **23,** 749–753 (1931)....... 250

329. Hughes, J. A., *Phil. Mag.* (6) **31,** 118 (1916).......... 219, 221, 236

330. Hughes, H. J., and A. T. Safford, "Hydraulics," p. 298, Macmillan, New York, 1911.................................... 122

331. Hutte, 25th ed., Vol. I, W. Ernst P. Sohn, Berlin

332. Ibbs, T. L., and A. A. Hirst, *Proc. Roy. Soc. (London)*, **A123,** 134–142 (1929).. 391, 392

333. Imes, E. S., *Astrophys. J.*, **50,** 251 (1919)..................... (71)

334. Ingersoll, L. R., and O. J. Zobel, "Mathematical Theory of Heat," Ginn, Boston, 1913................................... 30, 43

335. Insinger, T. H., Jr., and H. Bliss, *Trans. Am. Inst. Chem. Engrs.*, **36,** 491–516 (1940)...................... 149, 150, 304–309, 312

336. "International Critical Tables," McGraw-Hill, New York, 1929.....8, 380, 382–385, 387–389, 391–392, 398, 400–407, 413–415

337. Jakob, M., *Chem. App.*, **19,** 109 (1932)...................... (299)

338. Jakob, M., *Z. Ver deut. Ing.*, **76,** 1161–1170 (1932); reviews work of Roecke... 276

339. Jakob, M., *Mech. Eng.*, **58,** 643–660, 729–739 (1936); reprinted in *Univ. Ill. Bull.* 34, No. 37, pp. 1–75 (1937).............. 259, 267

339a. Jakob, M., *Trans. Am. Soc. Mech. Engrs.*, **60,** 384–386 (1938).. 126

340. Jakob, M., *Phil. Mag.*, **28,** 571–578 (1939)................... 232

341. Jakob, M., *Proc. Fifth Intern. Congr. Appl. Mech.*, Massachusetts Institute of Technology, 1938; revised in *Armour Inst. Tech., Tech. Bull.* vol. 2, No. 1, July, 1939................. (294)

342. Jakob, M., and S. Erk, *Mitt. Forsch.*, **310,** 1 (1928); *Z. Ver. deut. Ing.*, **73,** 176, 761 (1929)................................. 279

343. Jakob, M., S. Erk, and H. Eck, *Forsch. Gebiete Ingenieurw.*, **3,** 161–170 (1932)... 267

344. Jakob, M., S. Erk, and H. Eck, *Physik. Z.*, **36,** 73–84 (1935).. 266, 267

345. Jakob, M., and W. Fritz, *Forsch. Giebete Ingenieurw.*, **2,** 434–447 (1931)....................................... 297–303, 312, 314

346. Jakob, M., and W. Linke, *Forsch. Giebete Ingenieurw.*, **4,** 75–78 (1933)....................................... 304–308, 312, 314

347. Jakob, M., and W. Linke, *Physik. Z.*, **36,** 267–280 (1935)... 93, 94, 312

348. Jakob, M., and W. Linke, *Mech. Eng.*, **58,** 59 (1936)............ 312

349. Jakob, M., and K. A. Rees, *Trans. Am. Inst. Chem. Engrs.*, **37,** 619–645 (1941).. 202

350. Jeans, J. H., "Dynamical Theory of Gases," 4th ed., p. 291, Cambridge, London, 1925................................ 20

351. Jeffrey, J. O., and J. R. Moynihan, *Mech. Eng.*, **55,** 751–754 (1933)... 276, 278

352. Jeschke, D., *Z. Ver. deut. Ing.*, **69,** 1526 (1925); *Z. Ver. deut. Ing. Erganzungsheft*, **24,** 1 (1925)............................. 352

353. Jodlbauer, K., *Forsch. Gebiete Ingenieurw.*, **4,** 157–172 (1933).... 242

354. Johnstone, H. F., R. L. Pigford, and J. H. Chapin, *Trans. Am. Inst. Chem. Engrs.*, **37,** 95–133 (1941)...................... 236

355. Johnstone, H. F., and A. D. Singh, *Ind. Eng. Chem.*, **29,** 286–298 (1937)... 290

PAGE

356. Jordan, H. P., *Proc. Inst. Mech. Engrs. (London)*, Parts III–IV,
    1317–1357 (1909)..................... 169, 173, 201, 263, 267

357. Joslyn, M. A., and G. L. Marsh, *Ind. Eng. Chem.*, **22**, 1192–1197
    (1930).. 43

358. Josse, E., *Engineering*, **86**, 802–806 (1908); *Mitt. Maschinenlabora-
    torium Tech. Hochschule Berlin*, Heft 5, 1913............. 169, 173

359. Josse, E., *Z. Ver. deut. Ing.*, **53**, 322 (1909)................... 166

360. Jurgensen, D. F., Jr., and G. H. Montillon, *Ind. Eng. Chem.*, **27**,
    1466–1475 (1935)..................................... 180

361. Jürges, W., *Gesundh.-Ing.*, Beiheft 19, Reihe 1, p. 1 (1924). 103, 160, 207

362. Kaiser, F., *Z. bäyer. Revisions-Ver.*, **33**, 167 (1929); *Arch. Wärme-
    wirt.*, **11**, 247–250 (1930).................................. 279

363. Kambara, S., and M. Matsui, *J. Soc. Chem. Ind.* (Japan), **34**,
    167–172 (1931), supp. binding.......................... 150

364. Kamp, H., see Biskamp............................... 316, 382

365. Kardos, A., *Z. Ver. deut. Ing.*, **77**, 1158 (1933); *Z. ges. Kälte-Ind.*,
    41, 1, 29 (1934)... 389

366. von Karman, T., *Nat. Adv. Comm. Aeronaut. Tech. Memo.* 611,
    Government Printing Office, Washington, D.C., 1931; transl. of
    Nachr. Geo. Wiss. Gottingen, Fachgruppe I (Math.), **5**, 58–76 (1930) 162

367. von Karman, T., *J. Aeronaut. Sci.*, **1**, 1–20 (1934)............ (110)

368. von Karman, T., *Proc. 4th Intern. Congr. Appl. Mech.*, 1934,
    pp. 54–91... 163

369. von Karman, T., *Engineering*, **148**, 210–213 (1939); *Trans. Am.
    Soc. Mech. Engrs.*, **61**, 705–710 (1939).............. 108–110, 163

369a. Kaulakis, A. F., and L. M. Sherman, S.B. Thesis in Chem-
    ical Engineering, Massachusetts Institute of Technology,
    1938.................................. 305, 307–310, 313–315

370. Kaye, G. W. C., and W. F. Higgins, *Proc. Roy. Soc. (London)*,
    A117, 459 (1928).. 389

371. Keenan, J. H., *J. Appplied Mechanics*, **6**, A-11-20 (1939)........ 120

372. Keenan, J. H., and F. G. Keyes, "Thermodynamic Properties of
    Steam," Wiley, New York, 1937..................... 397, 412

373. Keevil, C. S., Sc.D. Thesis in Chemical Engineering, Massachu-
    setts Institute of Technology, 1930.... 120, 166, 189, 191, 193, 194

374. Keevil, C. S., and W. K. Lewis, *Ind. Eng. Chem.*, **20**, 1058 (1928) 292

375. Keevil, C. S., and W. H. McAdams, *Chem. Met. Eng.*, **36**, 464
    (1929)... 120

376. Kemler, E., *Trans. Am. Soc. Mech. Engrs.*, HYD **55**, 7–32 (1933) 120

377. Kennard, R. B., *Nat. Bur. Standards J. Research*, **8**, 787 (1932).. 212

378. Kennard, R. B., "Temperature, Its Measurement and Control in
    Science and Industry," pp. 685–706, Reinhold, New York,
    1941.. 212, 213

379. Kennelly, A. E., and H. S. Sanborn, *Proc. Am. Phil. Soc.*, **53**,
    55–77 (1914)....................................... 219, 221

380. Kennelly, A. E., C. A. Wright, and J. S. van Bylevelt, *Trans.
    Am. Inst. Elec. Engrs.*, **28**, 363–393 (1909).............. 219, 221

381. Kerr, E. W., *La. State Agr. Expt. Sta. Bull.* 138, 1913......... (294)

PAGE

382. Kerr, E. W., *Trans. Am. Soc. Mech. Engrs.*, **35**, 731 (1913); *La. State Agr. Expt. Sta. Bull.* 149, 1914 .... (294)

383. Kerr, E. W , *La. State Agr. Expt. Sta. Bull.* 159, 1916 .... (294)

384. Kerr, E. W., *Trans. Am. Soc. Mech. Engrs.*, **38**, 67 (1916) ..... (294)

385. Kerr, H. J., *Trans. Am. Soc. Mech. Engrs.*, *Research Pub.* 54–1a, appearing in FSP **54**, 1 (1932); personal communication, 1932 .... 172, 208

386. King, L. V., *Trans. Roy. Soc. (London)*, **A214**, 373 (1914) 216, 219, 221, 222

387. King, W. J., II. Conduction, *Mech. Eng.*, **54**, 275–279 (1932) .... (5)

388. King, W. J., III. Free Convection, *Mech. Eng.*, **54**, 347 (1932) 241, 242, 248, 249

389. King, W. J., IV. Forced Convection, *Mech. Eng.*, **54**, 410 (1932) 220, 225

390. King, W. J., V. Radiation, *Mech. Eng.*, **54**, 492 (1932) .... (45)

391. King, W. J., VI. Evaporation and Condensation, *Mech. Eng.*, **54**, 560 (1932) .... (294)

392. King, W. J., *Refrig. Eng.*, **25**, 83–85, 107 (1933) .... (294)

393. Kirkbride, C. G., *Ind. Eng. Chem.*, **25**, 1324–1331 (1933) . 263, 281, 282

394. Kirkbride, C. G., *Trans. Am. Inst. Chem. Engrs.*, **30**, 170–186 (1933–1934); *Ind. Eng. Chem.* **26**, 425–428 (1934) 267

395. Kirkbride, C. G., and W. L. McCabe, *Ind. Eng. Chem.*, **23**, 625–631 (1931) 189

396. Kirpitscheff, M., *Trans. Fuel Conf. World Power Conf. London*, **2**, 1165 (1928) 249

397. Kirschbaum, E., *Arch. Wärmewirt.*, **12**, 265 (1931) 279

398. Kirschbaum, E., *Chem. Fabrik*, **10**, 337–339 (1937) .... (326)

398a. Kirschbaum, E., and B. Kranz, *Chem. Fabrik*, **7**, 176–180 (1934) . 264

399. Kirst, W. E., W. M. Nagle, and J. B. Kastner, *Trans. Am. Inst. Chem. Engrs.*, **36**, 371–394 (1940) 196

400. Klein, V., *Arch. Wärmewirt.*, **15**, 150 (1934) 216, (219)

400a. Knaus, W. L., *Refrig. Eng.*, **29**, 23–26, 82–85 (1935) .... (286)

401. Knoblauch, O., and K. Hencky, "Introduction to Accurate Technical Temperature Measurements," p. 59, Oldenbourg, Munich and Berlin, 1926 149

402. Koch, W., *Gesundh.-Ing.*, Beiheft 22, Reihe 1, pp. 1–27, 1927 .... 238, 241, 242, 244

403. Koo, E. C., D. Sc. Thesis in Chemical Engineering, Massachusetts Institute of Technology, 1932. See also ref. 194 .... 110, 111, 119

404. Kraft, W. W., S.M. Thesis in Chemical Engineering, Massachusetts Institute of Technology, 1929 292

405. Kratz, A. P., and M. K. Fahnestock, *Heating, Piping Air Conditioning*, **4**, 283 (1932) 250

406. Kratz, A. P., H. J. Macintire, and R. E. Gould, *Univ. Ill. Eng. Expt. Sta. Bull.* 171, 1927; 186, 1928; 209, 1930 271

407. Kratz, A. P., H. J. Macintire, and R. E. Gould, *Univ. Ill. Eng. Expt. Sta. Bull.* 222, 1931 123

408. Kraus, F. M., S.M. Thesis in Chemical Engineering Practice, Massachusetts Institute of Technology, 1936 .... (234)

409. Kraussold, H., *Forsch. Gebiete Ingenieurw.*, **2**, *Forschungsheft*, **351**, 20 (1931).................................... 189, 193, 194
410. Kreisinger, H., and J. F. Barkley, *U.S. Bur. Mines Bull.* 145, 1918 224
411. Kreisinger, H., and M. Ray, *U.S. Bur. Mines Bull.* 8, 1912...... 169
412. Kröner, R., *Mitt. Forsch.*, **222**, 1–85 (1920).................... 122
413. Krujilin, G., *Tech. Phys.* (U.S.S.R.), **5**, 59–66 (1938)............ 259
414. Krujilin, G., *Tech. Phys.* (U.S.S.R.), **5**, 289–297 (1938).... 216 (259)
415. Krujilin, G., and B. Schwab, *Tech. Phys.* (U.S.S.R.), **2**, 312–323 (1935)... 216 (222)
416. Kundt, A., and E. Warburg, *Pogg. Ann.* **156**, 177–250 (1875).. 22
417. Lamb, H., "Hydrodynamics," 5th ed., pp. 545 and 628, Cambridge, London, 1924.................................... 87
418. Lamb, H., "Hydrodynamics," 5th ed., pp. 555 and 556, Cambridge, London, 1924.................................... 124
419. Langmuir, I., *Phys. Rev.*, **34**, 401 (1912)...................... 243
420. Langmuir, I., *Phys. Rev.*, **34**, 421 (1912); *Trans. Am. Inst. Elec. Engrs.*, **31**, 1229 (1912); *Trans. Am. Electrochem. Soc.*, **23**, 53 (1913)... 222, 249
421. Langmuir, I., *Trans. Am. Electrochem. Soc.*, **23**, 299 (1913)...... 241
422. Langmuir, I., *Trans. Am. Electrochem. Soc.*, **23**, 318 (1913)...... 243
423. Langmuir, I., Adams, and Meikle, *Trans. Am. Electrochem. Soc.*, **24**, 53 (1913)...................................... 14, 18
424. Lasareff, P., *Ann. Physik.*, **37**, 233 (1912)..................... 22
425. Latzko, H., *Z. Angew. Math. Mech.*, **1**, 268, (1921)........... 162
426. Lawrence, A. E., and T. K. Sherwood, *Ind. Eng. Chem.*, **23**, 301–309 (1931)... 179, 185
427. Lea, F., *Phil. Mag.*, **11**, 1235 (1931).................... 123, 124
428. Lee, A., W. O. Nelson, V. H. Cherry, and L. M. K. Boelter, *Proc. Intern. Congr. Appl. Mech.* 5th Congr., pp. 571–577, Massachusetts Institute of Technology, 1938......................... 121
429. Lehman, T., *Elektrotech. Z.*, **30**, 995 (1909)................... 16
430. Lent, H., *Wärme*, **49**, 145 (1926)............................ 76
431. Leveque, J., *Ann. mines* (12) **13**, 201, 305, and 381 (1928).. 187, 188
432. Lewis, W. K., *Trans. Am. Inst. Chem. Engrs.*, **20**, 9 (1927); *Chem. Met. Eng.*, **34**, 735 (1927)................................ 283
433. Lewis, W. K., W. H. McAdams, and T. H. Frost, *J. Am. Soc. Heating Ventilating Engrs.*, **28**, 321 (1922)................ (173)
434. Lewis, W. K., and A. H. Radasch, "Industrial Stoichiometry," McGraw-Hill, New York, 1926........................... 82
435. Lewis, W. K., J. T. Ward, and E. Voss, *Ind. Eng. Chem.*, **16**, 467 (1924).. 364, 368
435a. Leidenfrost, J. G., "De aquae communis nonnullis qualitatibus tractatus," Duisburg, 1756............................... 297
436. Linden, C. M., and G. H. Montillon, *Am. Inst. Chem. Engrs.*, **24**, 120 (1930).. 332, 333
437. Lindmark, T., *Tek. Tid.*, **56**, 125–131 (1926).............. 227, 228
438. Lindmark, T., and L. Kignell, *Ing. Vetenskaps Akad. Handl.*, No. 91, pp. 1–36 (1929); No. 109, pp. 1–20 (1931)................ 76

PAGE

439. Lobo, W. E., and J. E. Evans, *Trans. Am. Inst. Chem. Engrs.*, **35,** 743–778 (1939); **36,** 173–175 (1940) 80, 81

440. Lockhart, C., personal communication, 1929; data abstracted on pp. 274–276 of ref. 454*a* 284

441. Logan, L. A., N. Fragen, and W. L. Badger, *Ind. Eng. Chem.*, **26,** 1044–1047 (1934) 321

442. London, A. L., W. E. Mason, and L. M. K. Boelter, *Trans. Am. Soc. Mech. Engrs.*, **62,** 41 (1940) 286, 287, 290

443. London, A. L., H. B. Nottage, and L. M. K. Boelter, *Ind. Eng. Chem.*, **33,** 467–473 (1941) 287

444. Lorenz, H., *Z. tech. Physik*, **15,** 155–162; 201–206 (1934) 164

445. Lorenz, L., *Wied. Ann.*, **13,** 582 (1881) 241

446. Lorenz, L., *Ann. Physik*, **13,** 422 (1882) 8

447. Lorenz, R., *Z. Ver. deut. Ing.*, **51,** 743 (1907) 152

448. Lorisch, W., "Handbuch der Experimental Physik," 1929 ed., vol. 9, Part I, pp. 299, 302, and 303; *Mitt. Forsch.*, **322,** 1 (1929) 213–216

449. Loyzansky, L. D., and B. A. Schwab, *Central Aero-Hydrodynamic Institute, U.S.S.R.*, *Rept.* 329 (1935) 236

450. Lubojatsky, S., *Metall u. Erz*, **28,** 205–214 (1931) 43

451. Lummer, O., *Elektrotech. Z.*, **34,** 1428 (1913) 395

452. Luster, E. W., *Trans. Am. Soc. Mech. Engrs.*, FSP **53,** 161 (1931) 152

453. McAdams, W. H., *Refrig. Eng.*, **11,** 279 (1925) 104

454. McAdams, W. H., *Chem. Met. Eng.*, **34,** 599 (1927) . . . . (273)

454*a*. McAdams, W. H., "Heat Transmission," 1st ed., McGraw-Hill, New York, 1933 . . . . 121, 168, 312

455. McAdams, W. H., *Trans. Am. Inst. Chem. Engrs.*, **36,** 1–20 (1940) 268

456. McAdams, W. H., T. B. Drew, and G. S. Bays, Jr., *Trans. Am. Soc. Mech. Engrs.*, **62,** 627–631 (1940) 203, 205

457. McAdams, W. H., and T. H. Frost, *Ind. Eng. Chem.*, **14,** 13–18 (1922) 263

458. McAdams, W. H., T. K. Sherwood, and R. L. Turner, *Trans. Am. Soc. Mech. Engrs.*, **48,** 1233 (1926) . . . . (273)

459. McAdams, W. H., and S. D. Turner, *J. Am. Soc. Heating and Ventilating Engrs.*, **34,** 385 (1928); discusses Sage, *ibid.*, **33,** 707 (1927) 232, 233

460. McAdams, W. H., W. K. Woods, and R. L. Bryan, *Trans. Am. Soc. Mech. Engrs.*, **63,** 545–552 (1941) 325, 328–331

461. McAdams, W. H., W. K. Woods, and L. C. Heroman, Jr., *Trans. Am. Soc. Mech. Engrs.*, **64,** 193–200 (1942) 330

462. McCabe, W. L., and C. S. Robinson, *Ind. Eng. Chem.*, **16,** 478 (1924) 317

463. MacLean, J. D., *Proc. Am. Wood Preservers' Assoc.*, p. 197, 1930 . . . . 27, 463

464. McMillan, L. B., *Trans. Am. Soc. Mech. Engrs.*, **37,** 961 (1915) 246, 345

465. McMillan, L. B., *Trans. Am. Soc. Mech. Engrs.*, **48,** 1269–1317 (1926) 345

PAGE

466. McMillan, L. B., *Mech. Eng.*, **51**, 349 (1929).................. 345

467. Mandell, W., and J. West, *Proc. Phys. Soc. (London)*, **37**, 20 (1925).. 22

468. Mann, W. B., and B. G. Dickens, *Proc. Roy. Soc. (London)*, **A134**, 77–96 (1931).. 391, 392

469. Marks, L. S., "Mechanical Engineers' Handbook," McGraw-Hill, 4th ed., New York, 1941.......................... 381–385, 387

469a. Mart, L. T., *Refrig. Eng.*, **43**, 17–21 (1942).................... 290

470. Martin, K. W., Thesis in Physics, Massachusetts Institute of Technology, 1929.. 381

471. Martin, L. H., and K. C. Lang, *Proc. Phys. Soc. (London)*, **45**, 523–529 (1933).. 389

472. Martinelli, R. C., and L. M. K. Boelter, *Proc. Intern. Congr. Appl. Mech.*, 5th Congr., Massachusetts Institute of Technology, 1938, pp. 578–584.. 242

472a. Martinelli, R. C., C. J. Southwell, *et al.*, Am. Inst. Chem. Engrs., Boston Meeting, May, 1942.......................... 121, 191

473. Mattioli, G. D., *Forsch. Gebiete Ingenieurw.*, **11**, 149–158 (1940).. 164

474. Maxwell, J. C., "Collected Works," Vol. II, p. 1, Cambridge, London, 1890.. 20

475. Meisenburg, S. J., R. M. Boarts, and W. L. Badger, *Trans. Am. Inst. Chem. Engrs.*, **31**, 622–637 (1935); **32**, 100–104 (1936).... 263

476. Meissner, T., *Z. ges. physik. Therap.*, **43**, 162 (1932)............ 236

477. Mekler, L. A., *Nat. Petroleum News*, **30**, (30), R355–368, 398–400, 402, 405 (1938).. 81

478. Merkel, F., *Mitt. Forsch.*, **275**, 1–48 (1925).................. (290)

479. Merkel, F., "Die Grundlagen der Warmeubertragung," Stein-kopff, Leipzig, 1927.. 259, 279

479a. Merkel, F., *Z. ges. Kalte-Ind.*, **34**, 117 (1927)................. 286

480. Mikrjukov, V., *Tech. Phys. (U.S.S.R.)*, **4**, 961–977 (1937)....... 123

481. Mills, V., and R. C. Daniels, *Ind. Eng. Chem.*, **26**, 248–250 (1934) 249

482. Milverton, S. W., *Proc. Roy. Soc. (London)*, **A150**, 287 (1935).... 392

483. Monrad, C. C., *Ind. Eng. Chem.*, **24**, 505 (1932)............. (229)

484. Monrad, C. C., and W. L. Badger, *Trans. Am. Inst. Chem. Engrs.*, **24**, 84–116 (1930); *Ind. Eng. Chem.*, **22**, 1103 (1930). 259, 267

484a. Monrad, C. C., and J. F. Pelton, Am. Inst. Chem. Engrs., Boston Meeting, May, 1942.. 201

485. Montillon, G. H., K. L. Rohrbach, and W. L. Badger, *Ind. Eng. Chem.*, **23**, 763–769 (1931).......................... 191, 263

486. Montsinger, V. M., and W. H. Cooney, *Trans. Am. Inst. Elec. Engrs.*, **43**, 803–812 (1924).......................... 248–250

487. Moore, A. D., *Ind. Eng. Chem.*, **28**, 704–708 (1936)............. 43

488. Moore, H. K., *Trans. Am. Inst. Chem. Engrs.*, **15**, Part II, 233 (1923).. 352

489. Morris, J. T., *Engineering*, **96**, 178–181 (1913)................ 215

490. Morris, F. H., and W. G. Whitman, *Ind. Eng. Chem.*, **20**, 234 (1928)...................... 164, 166, 167, 179, 193, 194, 265

491. Moser, Dissertation, Berlin, 1913........................ 391, 392

PAGE

492. Mull, W., and H. Reiher, *Gesundh.-Ing.*, Beiheft 28, Reihe 1,
 pp. 1–26 (1930)... 241

493. Mullikin, H. F., *Trans. Am. Soc. Mech. Engrs.*, **57**, 517–530
 (1935) 81

494. Mullikin, H. F., "Temperature, Its Measurement and Control,"
 pp. 775–804, Reinhold, New York, 1941 225

495. Mullikin, H. F., and W. J. Osborn, "Temperature, Its Measurement and Control," pp. 805–829, Reinhold, New York, 1941.. 225

496. Murphree, E. V., *Ind. Eng. Chem.*, **24**, 726–736 (1932).......... 162

497. Nagaoka, J., and A. Watanabe, *Proc. Intern. Congr. Refrig.*, 7th
 Congr., The Hague, Amsterdam, 1936, vol. 3, No. 16, pp. 221–
 245 (1937)....................................... 125, 178, 179

498. Nagle, W. M., Sc.D. Thesis in Chemical Engineering, Massachusetts Institute of Technology, 1934........................ 276

499. Nagle, W. M., U.S. Patent 1,995,361, Mar. 26, 1935............ 276

500. Nagle, W. M., G. S. Bays, Jr., L. M. Blenderman, and T. B.
 Drew, *Trans. Am. Inst. Chem. Engrs.*, **31**, 593–604 (1935)..... 276

501. Nagle, W. M., and T. B. Drew, *Trans. Am. Inst. Chem. Engrs.*,
 30, 217–255 (1933–1934)................................. (276)

502. Naumann, F., *Z. ges. Kalte-Ind.*, **37**, 82 (1930)................. 9

503. Neilon, D. F., and C. E. McCormack, S.B. Thesis in Chemical
 Engineering, Massachusetts Institute of Technology, 1932. 309, 312

504. Nessi, A., *Bull. soc. encour. ind. nat.*, **131**, 289 (1932)........... 43

505. Nessi, A., and L. Nisolle, "Methodes Graphiques pour l'étude des
 Installations de Chauffage," pp. 46ff., Dunod, Paris, 1929..... 43

506. Newman, A. B., *Trans. Am. Inst. Chem. Engrs.*, **24**, 44 (1930)... 30

507. Newman, A. B., *Trans. Am. Inst. Chem. Engrs.*, **27**, 310–333
 (1931); *Ind. Eng. Chem.*, **28**, 545–548 (1936)................. 38

508. Nichols, P., *Refrig. Eng.*, **9**, 152 (1922); **9**, 254 (1923)........... 345

509. Nichols, P., *J. Am. Soc. Heating Ventilating Engrs.*, **30**, 35 (1924);
 Ind. Eng. Chem., **16**, 490 (1924)........................... 24

510. Nicolson, *Trans. Junior Inst. Engrs.*, **19**, Part V, p. 199, 1907.... 169

510a. Neiderman, *et al.*, *Heating, Piping Air Conditioning*, **13**, 591–597
 (1941).. 290

511. Nikuradse, J., *Mitt. Forsch.*, **289** (1929)..................... 122

512. Nikuradse, J., *Ingenieur-Arch.*, **1**, 306 (1930).............. 123, 124

513. Nikuradse, J., *Proc. Intern. Congr. Appl. Mech.*, 3d Congr., Stock-
 holm, 1930, **1**, 239 (1931)............................ 143, 162

514. Nikuradse, J., *Forschungsheft*, **361**, 1–22 (1933); *Petroleum Engr.*,
 11 (6), 164–166 (1940); **11** (8), 75–82 (1940); **11** (9), 124–130
 (1940); **11** (11), 38–42 (1940); **11** (12), 83 (1940)... 107–110, 163

515. Norris, R. H., and W. A. Spofford, *Am. Soc. Mech. Engrs.*,
 Advance Paper, New York, Dec. 1941................. 233, 234

516. Norris, R. H., and D. D. Streid, *Trans. Am. Soc. Mech. Engrs.*,
 62, 525–533 (1940)................................. 188, 200

517. Norton, F. H., "Refractories," McGraw-Hill, New York,
 1931... 382, 383, 388

518. Norton, F. H., personal communication, 1939................. 382

PAGE

518a. Nukiyama, S., *J. Soc. Mech. Engrs.* (Japan), **37**, 367–374, 553–554 (1934)... 314

519. Nukiyama, S., and H. J. Yosikata, *Soc. Mech. Engrs.* (Japan), vol. 33, No. 1 (1930)..................................... 14, 18

520. Nusselt, W., *Mitt. Forsch.*, **63/64**, 72–83 (1909)................ 249

521. Nusselt, W., *Z. Ver. deut. Ing.*, **53**, 1750 and 1808 (1909); *Mitt. Forsch.*, **89**, 1 (1910).............. 87, 164, 165, 169, 173, 187, 191

522. Nusselt, W., *Z. Ver. deut. Ing.*, **54**, 1154 (1910)................ 187

523. Nusselt, W., *Z. Ver deut. Ing.*, **57**, 199 (1913)................. 200

524. Nusselt, W., *Gesundh.-Ing.*, **38**, 477 (1915).................... 242

525. Nusselt, W., *Z. Ver. deut. Ing.*, **60**, 541, 569 (1916).... 259, 261, 266

526. Nusselt, W., *Z. Ver. deut. Ing.*, **61**, 685 (1917)................ 200

527. Nusselt, W., *Gesundh.-Inɡ.*, **49**, 97 (1922)................. 207, 220

528. Nusselt, W., *Z. Ver. deut. Ing.*, **67**, 206 (1923)................... 205

529. Nusselt, W., *Z. Ver. deut. Ing.*, **71**, 85 (1927); **72**, 1052 (1928)... 43

530. Nusselt, W., *Z. Ver. deut. Ing.*, **73**, 1475 (1929)............... 242

531. Nusselt, W., *Tech. Mech. Thermodynam.*, **1**, 277 (1930); *Z. Ver. deut. Ing.*, **74**, 1767 (1930)................................... 173

532. Nusselt, W., *Tech. Mech. Thermodynam.*, **1**, 417 (1930)........ (147)

533. Nusselt, W., *Z. Math. Mech.*, **10**, 105 (1930).............. 216 (215)

534. Nusselt, W., and W. Jurges, *Z. Ver. deut. Ing.*, **72**, 597–603 (1928)... 237, 248

534a. Oliver, E., S.M. Thesis in Chemical Engineering, Massachusetts Institute of Technology, 1939......................... 322, 323

535. Olson, F. C. W., and O. T. Schultz, *Ind. Eng. Chem.*, **34**, July (1942).. 33

536. Ombeck, H., *Mitt. Forsch.*, **158, 159**, 1–64 (1914)............. (119)

537. Orrok, G. A., *Trans. Am. Soc. Mech. Engrs.*, **32**, 1773 (1910); **32**, 1139 (1910)....................................... 273

538. Orrok, G. A., *Trans. Am. Soc. Mech. Engrs.*, **33**, 1673 (1911)..... 273

539. Orrok, G. A., *Trans. Am. Soc. Mech. Engrs.*, **47**, 1148 (1925).... (81)

540. Orrok, G. A., *Trans. Am. Soc. Mech. Engrs.*, FSP **50**, 47 (1928).. 152

541. Othmer, D. F., *Ind. Eng. Chem.*, **21**, 576 (1929)....... 263, 281–284

542. Othmer, D. F., and H. B. Coates, *Ind. Eng. Chem.*, **20**, 124–128 (1928).. 149

543. Othmer, D. F., and R. E. White, *Trans. Am. Inst. Chem. Engrs.*, **37**, 135–156 (1941)..................................... 263

544. Paltz, W. J., and C. E. Starr, Thesis in Chemical Engineering, Massachusetts Institute of Technology, 1931........ 216, 219, 221

545. Pannell, J. R., *Brit. Aero. Research Comm.*, *Rept.*, *Memo.* 243, June, 1916, H.M. Stationery Office, London...................... 158

546. Pannell, J. R., *Tech. Rept. Brit. Adv. Comm. Aero.*, vol. 1, p. 22, 1916–1917.. 169

547. Parekh, M., Sc.D. Report in Chemical Engineering, Massachusetts Institute of Technology, 1941.................. 289, 290

547a. Parks, G. S., H. M. Huffmaun, and S. B. Thomas, *J. Am. Chem. Soc.*, **52**, 1032 (1930)...................................... 400

548. Parr, S. W., *Engineer*, **113**, 559 (1921)...................... 261

PAGE

549. Parsons, S. R., and D. R. Harper, *Nat. Bur. Standards Technol. Paper* 211, p. 326, 1922 .... 169, 173, 232

550. Partridge, E. P., *Engineering Research Bull.* 15, Univ. Michigan, 1930 .... 137, 316

550a. Paschkis, V., ASHVE Section, *Heating, Piping Air Conditioning*, **14**, 133 (1942) 43

550b. Paschkis, V., and H. D. Baker, *Trans. Am. Soc. Mech. Engrs.*, **64**, 105–112 (1942) 43

551. Patterson, W. C., J. H. Weiland, S. L. Reeburgh, R. A. King, and R. L. Huntington, *Trans. Am. Inst. Chem. Engrs.*, **33**, 216–239 (1937) .... (281)

552. Patton, T. C., *Heating, Piping Air Conditioning*, **4**, 6–11 (1932) 345

553. Patton, E. L., and R. A. Feagan, Jr., *Ind. Eng. Chem.*, **33**, 1237–1239 (1941) 150

554. Péclet, J. C. E., "Traite de la chaleur, considerée dans ses applications," Masson, Paris, 1860 .... (241)

555. Pekeris, C. L., and L. B. Slichter, *Applied Phys.*, **10**, 135–137 (1939) 43

556. Perks, A. A., and R. W. Griffiths, *India-Rubber J.*, **67**, 24 (1924). 43

557. Perry, J. H., "Chemical Engineers' Handbook," McGraw-Hill, New York, 1941 ... 121, 124, 125, 249–251, 290, 295, 399, 408, 410

558. Petavel, J. E., *Trans. Roy. Soc.* (*London*), **A197**, 229–254 (1901). 243

559. Petavel, J. E., *Trans. Manchester Assoc. Engrs.*, 1915–1916, p. 33 243

560. Pierce, D. E., and P. B. Terry, *Chem. Met. Eng.*, **30**, 872–873 (1924) 243

561. Pierson, O. L., *Trans. Am. Soc. Mech. Engrs.*, **59**, 563–572 (1937) 227–229

562. Pigott, R. J. S., *Mech. Eng.*, **55**, 497–501 (1933) 120

563. Pilling, N. P., *Phys. Rev.*, (2) **14**, 222 (1919) .... (36)

563a. Planck, H., *Verhandl. deut. Phys. Ges.*, **2**, 237 (1900) .... (50)

564. Planck, R., *Z. ges. Kälte-Ind.*, **39**, 56 (1932) 43

565. Poensgen, R., *Z. Ver. deut. Ing.*, **60**, 27–32, 47–51 (1916); *Mitt. Forsch.*, **191, 192**, 1 (1917) 166, 169, 279

566. Poisson, S. D., "Théorie mathématique de la chaleur," Bachelier, Paris, 1835 188

567. Polak, V., *Z. tech. Physik*, **8**, 307 (1927) 393, 395

568. Port, F. J., Sc.D. Thesis in Chemical Engineering, Massachusetts Institute of Technology, 1940 .... 69, 72

569. Porter, A. W., and T. R. Martin, *Phil. Mag.*, **20**, 511 (1910) 345

570. Poste, E. P., *Ind. Eng. Chem.*, **16**, 469–470 (1924) 250

571. Praminik, S. C., *Proc. Indian Assoc. Cultivation Sci.*, **7**, 115–123 (1922) 211, 239

572. Prandtl, L., *Z. Physik*, **11**, 1072 (1910) 163

573. Prandtl, L., *Engineering*, **123**, 627 (1927); *Nat. Advisory Comm. Aeronaut., Tech. Memo.* 452, 1928, Government Printing Office, Washington, D. C. 213

574. Prandtl, L., *Physik Z.*, **29**, 487–489 (1928) 163

575. Prandtl, L., *Z. Ver. deut. Ing.*, **77**, 105–113 (1933) 108

576. Pridgeon, L. A., and W. L. Badger, *Ind. Eng. Chem.*, **16**, 474–478 (1924) 313, 314, 316, 332

PAGE

577. Ramdas, L. A., and M. K. Paranjpe, *Current Sci.*, **4**, 642 (1936). 212

578. Randolph, C. F., and M. J. Overholtzer, *Phys. Rev.*, **2**, 144
(1913).. 393, 394

579. Ray, B. B., *Proc. Indian Assoc. Cultivation Sci.*, **5**, 95
(1920)... 211, 238, 239

580. Rayleigh, Lord, *Nature*, **95**, 66 (1915); *Phil. Mag.*, **34**, 59 (1892);
8, 66 (1904)... 87

581. Read, G. M., *Proc. duPont Chem. Eng. Soc.*, **1**, 14th meeting
(1925–1926)... 249, 250

582. "Refrigerating Data Book," Am. Soc. Refrig. Engrs., 4th ed., p.
190, (1939)... (287)

583. Reiher, H., *Mitt. Forsch.*, **269**, 1–85 (1925)... 213, 219, 221, 227, 228

584. Reynolds, O., *Proc. Manchester Lit. Phil. Soc.*, vol. 8, 1874;
reprinted in "Scientific Papers of Osborne Reynolds," Vol. II,
Cambridge, London, 1901............................... 162, 165

585. Reynolds, O., *Trans. Roy. Soc. (London)*, **174**, 935 (1883)........ 87

586. Reynolds, O., *Trans. Roy. Soc. (London)*, **A186**, 123 (1894);
"Scientific Papers of Osborne Reynolds," Vol. II, p. 535,
Cambridge, London, 1901............................... 162

587. Reynolds, O., "Scientific Papers of Osborne Reynolds," Vol. I,
pp. 81–85, Cambridge, London, 1901.................... 99, 102

588. Rhodes, F. H., and C. H. Bridges, *Trans. Am. Inst. Chem. Engrs.*,
35, 73–93 (1939); *Ind. Eng. Chem.*, **30**, 1401–1406 (1938)...... 303

589. Rhodes, F. H., and K. R. Younger, *Ind. Eng. Chem.*, **27**, 957–961
(1935).. 275

590. Rice, C. W., *Trans. Am. Inst. Elec. Engrs.*, **42**, 653 (1923);
abstracted in *J. Am. Inst. Elec. Engrs.*, **42**, 1288 (1923); revised
in *Trans. Am. Inst. Elec. Engrs.*, **43**, 131 (1924); abstracted in
Ind. Eng. Chem., **16**, 460 (1924); revised in "International
Critical Tables," Vol. V, p. 234, McGraw-Hill, New York,
1929... 220, 243, 244

591. Rice, C. W., *J. Am. Inst. Elec. Engrs.*, **42**, 1288 (1923).......... 222

592. Rice, C. W., *Ind. Eng. Chem.*, **16**, 460 (1924).............. 104, 222

593. Rice, C. W., *Trans. Am. Inst. Elec. Engrs.*, **43**, 131 (1924)..... (243)

594. Rice, C. W., "International Critical Tables," Vol. V, p. 234,
McGraw-Hill, New York, 1929.......................... 222

595. Rice, H. S., Thesis in Chemical Engineering, Massachusetts
Institute of Technology, 1931.............................. 394

596. Richter, G. A., *Trans. Am. Inst. Chem. Engrs.*, **12**, Part II, pp. 147–
185, 1919... 184

597. Riedel, L., *Forsch. Gebiete Ingenieurw.*, **11**, 340–347 (1940)..... (389)

598. Rietschel, H., *Mitt. Prufungsanstalt f. Heizungs u. Luftungseinrich-
tungen*, Konigl. Tech. Hochschule Berlin, vol. 3, September,
1910....................................... 166, 169, 227, 228

599. Robertson, R., and J. J. Fox, *Proc. Roy. Soc. (London)*, **120**, 161–
210 (1928)... (71)

600. Robertson, J. M., and H. Rouse, *Civil Eng.*, **11**, 169–171 (1941). 101

601. Robinson, C. S., personal communication, 1919....... 166, 169, 173

PAGE

602. Robinson, C. S., *Refrig. Eng.*, **9,** 169–173 (1922); *Mech. Eng.*, **45,** 99–102 (1923)... 290

603. Robinson, C. S., *Refrig. Eng.*, **10,** 201–204 (1923); *Refrig. World*, **58,** 11 (1923)... (290)

604. Robinson, C. S., and E. R. Gilliland, "Elements of Fractional Distillation," McGraw-Hill, New York, 1939

604a. Robson, *Australian Chem. Inst. J. and Proc.*, **3,** 47–54 (1936)... 250

605. Roeser, W. F., *Nat. Bur. Standards J. Research*, **7,** 485–494 (1931) 150

606. Roeser, W. F., *J. Applied Phys.*, **11,** 388–407 (1940).......... (149)

607. Roeser, W. F., and E. Mueller, *Nat. Bur. Standards J. Research*, **5,** 793 (1930)... 149

608. Rosi, A., *Bull. Intern. Inst. Refrig.*, **17,** 122 (1936)............ (234)

609. Rowley, F. B., A. B. Algren, and J. L. Blackshaw, *Heating, Piping Air Conditioning*, **2,** 501–508 (1930)........................ 207

610. Royds, R., *Trans. Inst. Engrs. Shipbuilders Scot.*, **58,** 155 (1914–1915); see also ref. 611.................................... 169

611. Royds, R., "Heat Transmission by Radiation, Conduction and Convection," Constable, London, 1921

612. Royds, R., and J. W. Campbell, *Trans. Inst. Engrs. Shipbuilders Scot.*, **50,** 53 (1911–1912)................................... 166

613. Rubach, H. L., *Mitt. Forsch.*, **185,** 1–35 (1916)............. 213, 214

613a. Rudenberg, R., *Elektrotech. Z.*, **46,** 1342–1346 (1925).......... 16

614. Ruhl, C., *Wärme*, **55,** 189 (1932)............................. 43

615. Rummel, K., *Arch. Eisenhuttenw.*, **4,** 367 (1931)................ 44

616. Rummel, K., *J. Inst. Fuel*, **4,** 160–173 (1931)... 43

617. Rummel, K., and A. Schack, *Stahl u. Eisen*, **49,** 1300 (1929)..... 43

618. Russell, A., *Phil. Mag.*, (6) **20,** 591 (1910)..................... 222

619. Sanbern, E. N., *J. Am. Soc. Heating Ventilating Engrs.*, **34,** 197 (1928)... 345

620. Sauer, E. T., S.M. Thesis in Chemical Engineering, Massachusetts Institute of Technology, 1935......................... 298, 303

620a. Sauer, E. T., H. B. H. Cooper, G. A. Akin, and W. H. McAdams, *Mech. Eng.*, **60,** 669–675 (1938).............. 303, 304, 315, 319

621. Saunders, O. A., *Proc. Roy. Soc. (London)*, **A157,** 278–291 (1936)................................. (239, 240), 243, 248

622. Saunders, O. A., *Proc. Roy. Soc. (London)*, **172,** 55–71 (1939).... (248)

623. Saunders, O. A., and M. Fishenden, *Engineering*, **139,** 483 (1935)... 239, 240

624. Sawada, M., *J. Soc. Mech. Engrs.* (Japan), **37,** 15 (1934)........ 43

625. Schack, A., *Z. tech. Physik*, **5,** 266 (1924)..................... 72

626. Schack, A., *Arch. Eisenhuttenw.*, **2,** 223, 481 (1929); *Stahl u. Eisen*, **51,** 163–164 (1931)................................... 43

627. Schack, A., "Der industrielle Wärmeubergang," Verlag Stahleisen, Dusseldorf, 1929........................ 30, 43, 173, 207

628. Schack, A., *Stahl u. Eisen*, **50,** 1289 (1930)................. 30, 248

629. Schey, O. W., and H. H. Ellerbrock, *Nat. Advisory Comm. Aeronaut.*, *Tech. Note* 587 (1937)............................. 235

630. Schiller, L., *Physik, Z.*, **26,** 566–594 (1925).............. 100, 101

PAGE

631. Schmidt, E., "Foppls Festschrift," p. 179, Springer, Berlin, 1924; abstr. in ref. 664 39

632. Schmidt, E., *Z. ges.Kälte-Ind.*, **44**, 163–169 (1937).............. 9

633. Schmidt, E., *Z. ges Kälte-Ind.*, **35**, 213 (1928)............... 237, 241

634. Schmidt, E., *Z. ver. deut. Ing.*, **75**, 969 (1931)................. (16)

635. Schmidt, E., *Forsch. Gebiete Ingenieurw.*, **3**, 57 (1932)........... 72

636. Schmidt, E., *Forsch. Gebiete Ingenieurw.*, **3**, 181 (1932)...... 211, 212

637. Schmidt, E., *Gesundh.-Ing.*, Beiheft 20, Reihe 1, pp. 1–23, 1927.. 393–396

638. Schmidt, K., *Veroffentl. Badischen Landeswetterworte*, No. 18, 1932 236

639. Schmidt, Th. E., *Forsch. Gebiete Ingenieurw.*, **4**, 183–186 (1933). (272)

640. Schmidt, E., and W. Beckmann, *Tech. Mech. Thermodynam.*, **1**, 341, 391 (1930).................................... 237, 241, 248

641. Schmidt, E., W. Schurig, and W. Sellschopp, *Tech. Mech. Thermodynam.*, **1**, 53 (1930).................................... 255, 276

642. Schmidt, H., and L. Furthmaun, *Mitt. Kaiser-Wilhelm Inst. Eisenforsch Dusseldorf, Abhandl.*, **109**, 225 (1928).......... 51, 393–396

643. Schmidt, R. J., and S. W. Milverton, *Proc. Roy. Soc. (London)*, **A152**, 586–594 (1935).................................... (240)

644. Schmidt, R. J., and O. A. Saunders, *Proc. Roy. Soc. (London)*, **165**, 216–228 (1938)..................................... 239

645. Schneider, E., *Ann. Physik*, **79**, 177 (1926).................... 22

646. Schofield, F. H., *Phil. Mag.* (7) **12**, 329–348 (1931)............. 16

647. Schulze, E., *Arch. Eisenhuttenw.*, **4**, 223 (1928)................. 173

648. Schulze, E., Dissertation, Tech. Hochschule Darmstadt, July 21, 1928... 169

649. Schutt, H. C., *Trans. Am. Soc. Mech. Engrs.*, HYD, **51**, 83 (1929) 122

650. Seibert, O., *Wärme*, **54**, 737–739 (1931)....................... 55

651. Sexauer, T., *Forsch. Gebiete Ingenieurw.*, **10**, 286–296 (1939).... (203)

652. Shea, F. L., Jr., and N. W. Krase, *Trans. Am. Inst. Chem. Engrs.*, **36**, 463–489 (1940)...................... 262, 263, 265, 276, 277

653. Shephard, J. R., and W. B. Wiegand, *Ind. Eng. Chem.*, **20**, 953–959 (1928).. 43

654. Sherman, R. A., *Trans. Am. Soc. Mech. Engrs.*, **56**, 177–185 (1934) 76

655. Sherman, R. A., *Trans. Am. Soc. Mech. Engrs.*, **56**, 401–410 (1934) 76

656. Sherrat, G. G., and E. Griffiths, *Phil. Mag.*, **27**, 68–75 (1939).... 391

657. Sherwood, T. K., *Refrig. Eng.*, **13**, 253 (1923).................. 279

658. Sherwood, T. K., *Ind. Eng. Chem.*, **20**, 1181 (1928)............. 43

659. Sherwood, T. K., personal communication, 1929............... 173

660. Sherwood, T. K., "Absorption and Extraction," McGraw-Hill, New York, 1937.

661. Sherwood, T. K., *Ind. Eng. Chem.*, **33**, 424–429 (1941)...... 286, 287

662. Sherwood, T. K., D. D. Kiley, and G. E. Mangsen, *Ind. Eng. Chem.*, **24**, 273–277 (1932)........................ 189, 193, 194

663. Sherwood, T. K., and J. M. Petrie, *Ind. Eng. Chem.*, **24**, 736 (1932)........................ 166, 167, 180–182, 193, 194, 375

664. Sherwood, T. K., and C. E. Reed, "Applied Mathematics in Chemical Engineering," McGraw-Hill, New York, 1939....... 43

PAGE

665. Shiba, S., *Sci. Papers Inst. Phys. Chem. Research* (Tokyo), **16,** 205 (1931).. 389

666. Short, B. E., *Univ. Tex. Pub.* 3819, May 15, 1938......... 202, 231

667. Short, B. E., and M. M. Heller, *Univ. Tex. Bull.* 3128, July 22, 1931... 202

667a. Sieder, E. N., *Chem. Met. Eng.*, **46,** 322–325 (1939)....... 349–352

668. Sieder, E. N., and G. E. Tate, *Ind. Eng. Chem.*, **28,** 1429–1436 (1936)........................ 121, 166–168, 188–190, 193, 194

669. Siegel, K., *Sitzber. Akad. Wiss. Wien*, **116,** Part 2a, p. 1203 (1907).. (393)

670. Simmons, L. F. G., and N. S. Dewey, *Brit. Aeronaut. Research Comm., Rept. and Memo.* 1335, Ae 466, May, 1930, H.M. Stationery Office, London.................................. 105

671. Slichter, L. B., *Bull. Geol. Soc. Am.*, **52,** 561–600 (1941)........ (43)

672. Small, J., *Phil. Mag.* (7), **19,** 251–260 (1935).......... 216, 219, 221

673. Smith, D. M., *Engineering*, **138,** 479–481, 606–607 (1934)...... (147)

674. Smith, I. B., *Trans. Am. Inst. Elec. Engrs.*, **42,** 349 (1923)...... 149

675. Smith, J. F. D., *Ind. Eng. Chem.*, **22,** 1246 (1930).. 19, 150, 194, 390

676. Smith, J. F. D., *Trans. Am. Inst. Chem. Engrs.*, **31,** 83–112 (1935)....................................164, 189, 193, 194

677. Smith, J. F. D., *Trans. Am. Soc. Mech. Engrs.*, **58,** 719 (1936).19, 389

678. Smoluchowski, M., *Phil. Mag.* (5), **46,** 192 (1898).............. 22

679. Sneeden, O., *J. Roy. Tech. Coll.* (Glasgow), **2,** 476 (1931)........ 169

680. Snell, F. D., *Ind. Eng. Chem.*, **29,** 89–91 (1937)

681. Soennecken, A., *Mitt. Forsch.*, **108–109,** 32–37 (1911)........... 179

682. Soule, L. C., *Trans. Am. Soc. Heating Ventilating Engrs.*, **19,** 391–411 (1913)... 227

683. Spear, E. B., and J. F. Purdy, *Ind. Eng. Chem.*, **15,** 842–845 (1923) 150

684. Spencer-Gregory, H., and E. H. Dock, *Phil. Mag.*, **25,** 129–147 (1938).. (391)

685. Spencer, J. W., Ross Heater and Manufacturing Company, Inc., *Bull.* 350, Buffalo, N. Y................................... (147)

686. Spitzglass, J. M., *Trans. Am. Soc. Mech. Engrs.*, **52,** *Hydraulics,* 7C-111 (1930)... (95)

687. Spoelstra, H. J., *Arch. Suikerind.*, vol. 3, No. 23, p. 903 (1931)... 256, 276

688. Stamsvik Heat Exchanger, Penn Grove Mfg. Co., Penn Grove, Pa... 207

689. Standard Oil Development Company, personal communication, 1928.. 395

690. Stanton, T. E., *Trans. Roy. Soc.* (*London*), **A190,** 67 (1897).149, 179

691. Stanton, T. E., *Proc. Roy. Soc.* (*London*), **A85,** 366 (1911); reprinted in *Collected Researches, Nat. Phys. Lab.* (Teddington, Eng.), **8,** 75 (1912) and **9,** 1 (1913); abstr. in *Trans. Inst. Nav. Arch.*, **54,** 48 (1912)..................................... 104, 107, 108

692. Stanton, T. E., *Brit. Advisory Comm. Aeronaut., Tech. Rept.*, p. 31, 1916–1917.. 179

693. Stanton, T. E., R. Booth, and D. Marshall, *Brit. Aeronaut. Research Comm., Rept. and Memo.* 271, 1917................. 235

PAGE

694. Stanton, T. E., D. Marshall, and C. N. Bryant, *Proc. Roy. Soc.*
(London), **A97,** 413 (1920); reprinted in *Collected Researches,*
Nat. Phys. Lab. (Teddington, Eng.), **16,** 1 (1921)............. 104

695. Stanton, T. E., and J. R. Pannell, *Trans. Roy. Soc. (London)*, **A214,**
199–224 (1914); reprinted in *Collected Researches, Nat. Phys.*
Lab. (Teddington, Eng.), **11,** 295 (1914)................. 87, 105

696. Stender, W., "Der Wärmeubergang und stromendes Wasser in
vertikalen Rohren," Springer, Berlin, 1924.................. 179

697. Stender, W., *Z. Ver. deut. Ing.*, **69,** 905 (1925)............. 259, 279

698. Stender, W., *Wiss. Veröffentl. Siemens-Konzern,* **9,** Part II, p. 88
(1930)... 185

699. Stewart, R. W., *Trans. Roy. Soc. (London)*, **A184,** 569–590
(1893).. 232, 233

700. Stewart, F. C., and F. G. Hechler, *Refrig. Eng.,* **31,** 107–111
(1936); *Ice and Cold Storage,* **39,** 126–127 (1936); *Ice and*
Refrig., **90,** 3 (1936)...................................... 321

701. Stodola, A., "Steam and Gas Turbines," Vol. II, McGraw-Hill,
New York, 1927... 16

702. Stokes, G. G., "Mathematical and Physical Papers," Vol. V,
pp. 95, 104, Cambridge, London, 1905...................... 87

703. Stoll, K. E., *Power,* vol. 75, No. 5, p. 168 (1932)............... 279

704. Stone, J. H., *Refrig. Eng.,* **10,** 137 (1923)...................... 345

705. Stose, C. W., and C. W. Whittemore, Thesis in Chemical Engineering, Massachusetts Institute of Technology, 1922............ 249

706. Stroebe, G. W., E. M. Baker, and W. L. Badger, *Trans. Am.*
Inst. Chem. Engrs., **35,** 17–41 (1939); *Ind. Eng. Chem.,* **31,** 200–
206 (1939)............................. 321, 324, 325, 331, 332

707. Stuckle, R., and W. Emendorfer, *Kälte,* **6,** 49 (1930)......... (185)

708. Sucksmith, W., *Phil. Mag.* (6), **43,** 223–240 (1922)............. 149

708a. Suydam, V. A., *Phys. Rev.,* (2) **5,** 497–509 (1915)..........393, 394

709. Taylor, G. I., *Brit. Advisory Comm. Aeronaut., Rept. and Memo.*
272, 31, pp. 423–429 (1916)................................ 163

710. Taylor, G. I., *Proc. Roy. Soc. (London)*, **A124,** 243 (1929)........ 122

711. Taylor, T. S., *Trans. Am. Soc. Mech. Engrs.,* **41,** 605 (1919);
Refrig. Eng., **10,** 179 (1923).............................. (24)

712. Taylor, C. F., and A. Rehbock, *Nat. Advisory Comm. Aeronaut.,*
Tech. Memo., Notes 331, 1930, Government Printing Office,
Washington, D.C..................................... 207, 232

713. Ten Bosch, M., "Die Wärmeubertragung," Springer, Berlin,
1922.. 259, 266

714. Theodorsen, T., and W. C. Clay, *Nat. Advisory Comm. Aeronaut.,*
Rept. 403, 1932, Government Printing Office, Washington, D.C. 236

715. Thoma, H., "Hochleistungskessel," Springer, Berlin, 1921. (215), 216

716. Thomson, A. K. G., *J. Soc. Chem. Ind.,* **56,** 380T–384T (1937)... 205

717. Thornton, W. W., *Phil. Mag.,* **38,** 705 (1919)................. 8

718. Thwing, C. B., *Phys. Rev.,* **26,** 190 (1908).................... 394

719. Townshend, B., and E. R. Williams, *Chem. Met. Eng.,* **39,** 219–222
(1932)............................... 382, 383, 388

PAGE

720. Trahey, J. C., and W. S. Smith, S.M. Thesis in Chemical Engineering, Massachusetts Institute of Technology, 1930......... 124
721. Trinks, W., "Industrial Furnaces," Vol. I, p. 152, Wiley, New York, 1926... 43
722. Tsao, U., Ph.D. Dissertation, University of Michigan, 1941...... 263
722a. Tubular Exchanger Manufacturers Assoc., Standards TEMA, New York, 1941....................... 138, 346, 350, 352, 353
722b. Tucker, W. B., S. M. Thesis in Chemical Engineering, Massachusetts Institute of Technology, 1936.................. 227, 229
722c. Tuve, G. L., and L. J. Siegel, *Trans. Am. Soc. Heating Ventilating Engrs.*, **44**, 523 (1938).................................... (284)
723. Ulloch, D. S., and W. L. Badger, *Trans. Am. Inst. Chem. Engrs.*, **33**, 417–440 (1937); *Ind. Eng. Chem.*, **29**, 905–910 (1937)... 193–195, 267
724. Ullrich, W., Sc.D. Thesis in Chemical Engineering, Massachusetts Institute of Technology, 1935........................ 72
725. Ulsamer, J., *Forsch. Gebiete Ingenieurw.*, **3**, 94 (1932)....... 220, 225
726. Ulsamer, J., *Z. Ver. deut. Ing.*, **80**, 537–543 (1936)............ (391)
727. Underwood, A. J. V., *J. Inst. Petroleum Tech.*, **20**, 145–158 (1934) 145
728. *Nat. Bur. Standards*, *Circ.* 227, Apr. 19, 1927.............. 386, 388
729. Van der Hegge Zijen, B. G., "Measurements of the Velocity Distribution in the Boundary Layer along a Plane Surface," Thesis, Delft, 1924; printed by J. Waltman, Jr., Delft.... 102, 104
730. Van der Hegge Zijnen, B. G., *Proc. Acad. Sci. Amsterdam*, **31**, 500 (1928)... 106
730a. Van Dusen, M. S., *J. Am. Soc. Refrig. Eng.*, **7**, 202 (1920)..... 388
731. Van Dusen, M. S., and J. L. Finck, *Nat. Bur. Standards J. Research*, **6**, Paper 291, pp. 493–522 (1931).................. 24
732. Van Marle, D. J., *Ind. Eng. Chem.*, **16**, 458–459 (1924).... 332, 333
733. Vargaftik, N., *J. Tech. Phys.* (U.S.S.R.), **4**, 341–360 (1937)...... 243
734. Vargaftik, N., and W. Paquenov, *J. Expt. Theoret. Phys.* (U.S.-S.R.), **8**, 189 (1938) .... (391)
735. Vargaftik, N., and J. Timrot, *J. Tech. Phys.* (U.S.S.R.), **9**, 963–970 (1939)... 392
736. Verschoor, H., *Trans. Inst. Chem. Engrs.* (*London*), **16**, 66–76 (1938).. 266
737. Vornehm, L., data given in ref. 725...................... 219, 221
738. Vyroubov, V., *J. Tech. Phys.* (U.S.S.R.), **9**, 1923–1931 (1939). 236, 237
739. Wagener, G., *Gesundh.-Ing.*, Beiheft, Reihe 1, Heft 24, p. 5, 1929...................................... 207, 232, 235
740. Walker, W. H., W. K. Lewis, and W. H. McAdams, "Principles of Chemical Engineering," 2d ed., McGraw-Hill, New York, 1927... 10
741. Walker, W. H., W. K. Lewis, W. H. McAdams, and E. R. Gilliland, "Principles of Chemical Engineering," 3d ed., p. 136, McGraw-Hill, New York, 1937..... 52, 92, 261, 286, 288, 292, 295
742. Wallace, J. L., and A. W. Davison, *Ind. Eng. Chem.*, **30**, 948–953 (1938)................................. 263, 265, 281, 282

PAGE

743. Wamsler, F., *Mitt. Forsch.*, Hefte 98 and 99, 1 (1911) 243, 244

744. Wamsler, F., *Z. Ver. deut. Ing.* **55**, 599–605 (1911); *Mitt. Forsch.*, **98**, 1–45 (1911) 393, 394, 396

745. Washington, L., and W. M. Marks, *Ind. Eng. Chem.*, **29**, 337–345 (1937) 198

746. Watzinger, A., and D. G. Johnson, *Forsch. Gebiete Ingenieurw.*, **10**, 182–196 (1939) 191, 194

747. Weber, H. C., Thesis in Chemical Engineering, Massachusetts Institute of Technology, 1919; discussed in ref. 433 173

748. Weber, H. C., personal communication, 1921 175

749. Webre, A. L., and C. S. Robinson, "Evaporation," Chemical Catalog Co., New York, 1926 .... 295, 313, 317

750. Webster, G. C., *Trans. Inst. Engrs. Shipbuilders Scot.*, **57**, 58–105 (1913–1914) 179

751. Wedmore, E. B., *J. Inst. Elec. Engrs. (London)*, **61**, App. IV (1923); **68**, App. I (1930) 16

752. Weidlein, E. R., *Trans. Am. Inst. Chem. Engrs.*, **13**, Part II, pp. 25–42 (1920–1921) 345

753. Weise, R., *Forsch. Gebiete Ingenieurw.*, **6**, 281–292 (1935) 248

754. Wells, W. C., "Essay on Dew," Constable, London, 1818 224

755. Wenzl, M., and F. Morawe, *Stahl u. Eisen*, **47**, 867–871 (1927) ... 395

756. Westphal, W., *Verhandl. deut. physik. Ges.*, **10**, 987–1012 (1912) 393

757. Westphal, W., *Verhandl. deut. physik. Ges.*, **11**, 897–902 (1913) ... 395

758. Wetzler, K., Dissertation, Darmstadt 396

759. Wiegand, J. H., Ph.D. Thesis in Chemical Engineering, University of Michigan, 1941 .... (290)

760. White, C. M., *Proc. Roy. Soc. (London)*, **A123**, 645 (1929) 122

761. White, J. B., S.M. Thesis in Chemical Engineering, Massachusetts Institute of Technology, 1928; data are given in ref. 192 .... 120, 193

762. Whitman, W. G., and J. L. Keats, *Ind. Eng. Chem.*, **14**, 186–191 (1922) .... (284)

762a. Wiebe, R., and M. J. Brevoort, *J. Am. Chem. Soc.*, **52**, 622 (1930) 400

763. Wiedmann, G., and R. Franz, *Ann. Physik*, **89**, 497–531 (1853) .. 8

764. Wilkes, G. B., *Ind. Eng. Chem.*, **31**, 832–838 (1939) 9

765. Wilkes, G. B., F. G. Hechler, and E. R. Queer, *Heating, Piping Air Conditioning*, **12**, 68–72 (1940) 9

766. Wilkes, G. B., and C. M. F. Peterson, *Heating, Piping Air Conditioning*, **9**, 505–510 (1937); **10**, 477–480 (1938) 240

767. Williams, G. C., personal communication, 1941 .... 236, 237

768. Williamson, E. D., and L. H. Adams, *Phys. Rev.* **14**, 99–114 (1919) 30, 37

769. Wilson, E. E., *Trans. Am. Soc. Mech. Engrs.*, **37**, 47 (1915) 272

770. Wilson, D. W., W. E. Lobo, and H. C. Hottel, *Ind. Eng. Chem.*, **24**, 486 (1932) 81

770a. Wilson, R. E., W. H. McAdams, and M. Seltzer, *Ind. Eng. Chem.*, **14**, 105–119 (1922); abstr. in *Eng. News-Record*, **89**, 690 (1922) 120

771. Winding, C. C., *Ind. Eng. Chem.*, **30**, 942–947 (1938) ... 227, 228, 237

PAGE

772. Winkler, K., *Forsch. Gebiete Ingenieurw.*, **6**, 261–268 (1935).... (180)

773. Wirka, J., *Proc. Am. Wood Preservers' Assoc.*, p. 285, 1924; p. 271, 1925.. 43

774. Wohlenberg, W. J., and R. L. Anthony, *Trans. Am. Soc. Mech. Engrs.*, FSP **51**, 235–246 (1929)........................ 76

775. Wohlenberg, W. J., and E. L. Lindseth, *Trans. Am. Soc. Mech. Engrs.*, **48**, 849–937 (1926)............................ 76

776. Wohlenberg, W. J., and D. G. Morrow, *Trans. Am. Soc. Mech. Engrs.*, **47**, 127–176 (1925)............................ 76, 82

777. Wohlenberg, W. J., and H. F. Mullikin, *Trans. Am. Soc. Mech. Engrs.*, **57**, 531–540 (1935) 82

778. Wohlenberg, W. J., H. F. Mullikin, W. H. Armacost, and C. W. Gordon, *Trans. Am. Soc. Mech. Engrs.*, **57**, 541–554 (1935)... (82)

779. Wood, A. J., and P. X. Rice, *Trans. Am. Soc. Mech. Engrs.*, **45**, 497 (1923); *Refrig. Eng.*, **10**, 357 (1924).................... 345

779a. Woods, W. K., Sc.D. Thesis in Chemical Engineering, Massachusetts Institute of Technology, 1940................. 325, 328–330

780. Woolfenden, L. B., Thesis in Chemical Engineering, Massachusetts Institute of Technology, 1927........................ 160

781. Worthing, A. G., *Phys. Rev.*, **28**, 190 (1926)................... 394

782. Worthington, H., and C. B. Malone, *J. Franklin Inst.*, **184**, 115 (1917)... 225

783. Wüllner, A., *Ann. Physik*, **4**, 321–341 (1878)............... (391)

784. Wunderlich, M. S., *J. Am. Soc. Heating Ventilating Engrs.*, **34**, 189 (1928)... 345

784a. Young, F. L., and W. J. Wohlenberg, *Amer. Soc. Mech. Engrs.*, Advance Paper, New York, 1942........................ 262

785. Zarnite, *Wärme*, **54**, 756–761 (1931).................... 316

786. Zeiner, E. F., *Power*, **73**, 957 (1931)..................... 345

787. Zinn, R. E., H. G. Theoming, and C. G. Duncan-Clark, *Trans. Am. Inst. Chem. Engrs.*, **37**, 399–412 (1941).............. (202)

788. Zumbro, F. R., *Refrig. Eng.*, **13**, 49–63 (1926)................ 272

789. Zwikker, C., *Arch. néerland. sci.*, **9**, Part IIIA, 207 (1925)...... 394

SUBJECT INDEX

Bold-faced type is used to indicate the pages containing the more important equations or relations for heat transfer.

A

Absolute temperature, definition, 47
Absorption strength of luminous flames, 74–76
Absorptivity, definition, 48
Acetone, 168, 169, 181, 275, 307
Acoustic velocity, 19, 120
Aerofoil, 236
Air, conditioning of, 285–292
  over finned tubes, 234–235
  free convection, 237–250
  friction (*see* Friction)
  gaps, 24
  normal to banks, **226–230**
  normal to single cylinder, **221**
  in pipes, recommended equation for, **174**
  over plates, **206**
  specific heat of, 406
  in steam, effect of, 283–285
  (*See also* Gas, Gases)
Alcohol, butyl, 168, 169, 181, 263, 275, 307, 310, 311, 315, 316
  ethyl, 263, 275, 307, 310, 315
  methyl, 263, 310, 312, 315
  pentyl, 275
  propyl, 263, 275, 307, 310, 315
Algae, prevention of growth of, 279
Alloys, thermal conductivities of, 380–381
Aluminum foil, 9
Ammonia, condensation of, 271–274
  radiation from, **72**
Analogies, between conduction of electricity and heat, 43
  between heat transfer and friction, 162–164

Aniline, free-convection data for, 243
Annealing furnace, 85
Annular spaces, friction in, 123–124
  heat transfer in, 200–202
  hydraulic radius of, 200
  radiation in, 59, 200–201
Aqueous solutions, calcium sulphate, 318
  gelatin, 323
  glycerine, 309, 311
  molasses, 311, 323
  sodium chloride, 309, 311, 318
  sodium hydroxide, 323
  sodium sulphate, 309, 311, 318
  sugar, 309, 312, 317, 326
  sulphite liquor, 331
Area, Areas, arithmetic mean, 12
  average, for hollow cylinder, 11–12, 344
    for hollow parallelepiped, 13–15
    for hollow sphere, 13
    for radiation, 59–60
  geometric mean, 13
  of heating surface, 134–137
  logarithmic mean, 12, 344
  for pipes, tubes, 417, 418
Asphalt, heating of, 191
Average temperature, of fluids, 133–144, 183
  of gas, 70, 127
Average temperature difference, 141–149, 188, 261, 356

B

Baffles, 230, 346–354, **357**
Bar fins, 231–236
Bare pipes, heat loss from, **245–247**

Beam length, 69
Benzene, 168, 169, 181, 263, 275, 283, 312, 315, 330
Benzyl mercaptan, 276
Bernoulli's theorem, 116–131
Billet reheating furnace, 80
Biot number, 95
Bituminous coal, 81
Black body, 49
Blast-furnace stoves, 49, 175
Boiler furnace, 81–84
Boilers, gases in (*see* Gas, Gases)
Boiling liquids (*see* Evaporation)
Boltzmann, 49
Boundary layer, 101–111, 158–164
Buffer layer, 101, 109, 158
Building materials, thermal conductivities of, **382–388**

C

Carbon dioxide, 65, 72, 82, 165, 171, 174, 243
Carbon tetrachloride, 243, 263, 308, 311, 315
Carborundum muffle, 61–62
Caustic soda solutions, evaporation of water from, 323
Cellular motion, 240
Centigrade heat unit, 379
Centipoise, 407
Chlorbenzene, 283
Chlorination of cooling water, 279
Chromium alloys, thermal conductivities of, 381
Cleaning heating surface, 279, 317, 350
Clouds of particles, radiation from, 73
Coal, powdered, 73, 77
Coal gas, *h* for, 165, 171
Coefficient of heat transfer, calculation of, 24, 136, 176, 191, 296
  individual, definition, 135
  over-all, definition, 134
Coils (*see* Curved pipe)
Coils in liquids, 249
Coke deposits, 139–140, 197
Colloidal particles, 101, 215

Color band, 101, 122
Color screens, in radiation, 74
Combustion chamber, radiation in, 77
Condensation, dropwise, 255, 275–279
  film forming, 255–282
    data for, 263–290
    dimensional analysis in, 95, 260
    outside horizontal tube, equation for, 261–262
    nomenclature for, 256
    recommended curves for, **268**
    theory of, 259
    on vertical wall, 259–261
      chart for, **269**
  graphical analysis of *U* for, 271, 275
  mechanism of, 255, 275
  of mixed vapors, 280
  number, 95
  over-all resistances plotted, 275
  in presence of gas, 285–292
  scale coefficients for, 138, 274
Condenser tubing, standard dimensions of, 417
Condensers, surface, calculation of *U* for, 136
  cleaning of, 279
  scale coefficient in, **138,** 274
  steam-side coefficient in, **268**
  water-side coefficient in, **184,** 273
Conditioning of air, 283–292
Conductance, definition, 25
Conduction, 5–44, 343–346
  definition, 1
  Fourier equation for, **7**
  periodic, 43
  steady, definition, **7**
    effect of ribs in, 16–17
    examples, 10, 23
    through flat walls, 10
    in fluids, 18–22
    graphical method for, 16
    through hollow cylinder, 11, 22, 343
    nomenclature for, 5
    through nonhomogeneous material, 8
    through pipe covering, 11, 343
    through porous materials, 8
    problems in, **25–26**

Conduction, steady, resistance concept
of, 22–24
in solids, 8–18, 22–26, 343
temperature gradient for, 7–22
three dimensional, 18
unsteady, 27–44
approximate method for, 39
in brick-shaped solid, 38
in cube, 37
in cylinder, 36, 37
definition, 7
dimensionless ratios in, 31–38
examples, 34, 40, 41
mid-plane, definition, 32
nomenclature table for, 31
problems in, **44**
Schmidt method, 39–43
in semi-infinite solid, 37
in slab, 32–35
in sphere, 36
in square bar, 37
theory of, 28–30
Conductivity, thermal (*see* Thermal
conductivity)
Conservation, of energy, 111–116
of matter, 111
Consistent units, 5, 31, 46, 88, 91, **96,**
112, 151, 156, 218, 256, 294, 341
Contact resistance, 24
Continuity, equation of, 111
Contraction loss, 122, 360
Convection, definition, 1
Conversion factors, for coefficient of
heat transfer, 392
for Reynolds number. 88
for thermal conductivity, 379
for viscosity, 407
Cooling towers, 285–292
Core, resistance of, 163
Cosine law, 52–54
Costs, 132, 344, 351, 352, 365, 371–374
Countercurrent, 141
Critical radius, 345–346
Critical Δt, 315
Critical velocity, 101
Cross-flow heat exchanger, 147
Curved pipe, friction in, 122
heat transfer in, 177, 184
Curvilinear square, 17

D

Dehumidification, 283–285
Design of exchangers, 346–374
Diameter, equivalent, 119, 124, **197,**
200, 203, 234–237
Diameters of pipes and tubes, table of,
416, 417
Diathermanous, 9
Dichlorodifluoromethane, 274
Dichloromethane, 274
Diffusion of vapor through gas, 280–
290
Diffusivity, thermal, 30
of vapors through gas, 256, 258
Dimensional analysis, 87–98
in fluid dynamics, 87–90
in heat transfer, 90–95, 164–415
limitations of, 95
nomenclature for, 88, 91, 95
pi theorem in, 89
problems in, 97–98
theory of models, 95
Dimensional constant, 88
Dimensionless groups, ratios, 95
Diphenyl, condensation of, 263
Diphenyl oxide, heating of, 193, 263
Direct contact of liquid and gas, 283
Dirt deposits, 138, 175, 273, 279, 316
Double pipe condenser, 271
Drip coolers, 202–206
Drip type condenser, 271
Dropwise condensation, promoters for,
256, 275–278, 323, 331
Ducts, friction in, 123
heat transfer in, 197–200
Dynamics of fluids, 99–132

E

Economic frequency of cleaning con-
densers and evaporators, 279, 318
Economic temperature difference in
exchangers, 144, 370–373
Economic thickness of insulation, 344
Economic velocity in exchangers,
141, 363–370
Eddy viscosity, 163
Effective thickness, of fluid film, 222

Emissivity, definition, 49
  discussion of, 49–51
  tables of, 393–396
Enameled apparatus, 250, 334
Energy balance, 111–116
Enlargement loss, 121, 128, 360
Enthalpy, definition, 114
  table for steam, 397
Enthalpy potential, 285–292
Entropy, of steam and water, 397
Equivalent diameter, 123, 197–203, 237
Ethyl acetate, 298, 315
Ethyl alcohol, 263, 275, 307–315
Ethyl ether, 275
Evaporation, of boiling liquids, 294–339
  apparent coefficient of, 296, 322
  in basket type evaporator, 326
  effect, of air adsorbed on heating surface, 301
    of arrangement, 313
    of diameter, 314
    of hydrostatic head, 327
    of physical properties, 311–313
    of roughness, 299
    of scale, 316–319
    of solute, 311
    of stirring, 313
    of surface tension at interface, 301–304, 325
    of temperature in, 308–311
    of temperature difference, 319, 333
  energy balance for, 115
  over horizontal tubes, 295–321
  individual coefficients of, 296–337
  inside tubes, 321–334
  mechanism in, 295–303, 321
    photographs, 298, 301, 302
  optimum cleaning cycle, 318
  over-all coefficients of, 314–319, 323, 326–337
  recommended procedure for, 334
  superheated liquids in, 299
  temperature gradient in liquids in tubes, 321–334

Evaporation, of liquid into noncondensable gas, 285–292
Extended heating surfaces, **231–236**

F

Factor of safety, 177, 357
Fanning equation, 118–121
Fictive viscosity, 162
Film, resistance of, 163
Film coefficient (*see* name of fluid)
Film concept, 101–111, 134–141
Film temperature, 167, 218, 257, 271
Film type coolers, 202–205
Finned surfaces, **231–236**, 290
Fittings, resistance of, 121
Flames (*see* Radiation)
Flow of fluids, 99–132
  Bernoulli's theorem, 116, 127
    examples, 129–132
  dimensional analysis applied to, 87–90
  mechanisms of, 99–111
    streamline, 99–101
    turbulent, 101–111
  pressure changes due to friction, 116–132
  Reynolds' criterion of, 99–131
  velocity distribution in, 100–111
    (*See also* Friction)
Flue gas, cooling of, 173
Forced convection, definition, 1
  (*See also* Gases; Liquids; name of fluid or of apparatus)
Fouling factors, 137, 175, 197, 273, 316
Fourier equation, 6
Fourier number, 95
Fourier series, 30
Free convection, 170, 185, 189–191, 197, **237–251**
  definition, 1
  from horizontal cylinder, 241
    calculations for, 245
    data for, 243
    recommended procedure for, **244**
  inside horizontal pipes, 185–186
  mechanisms of, 211, 237
  photographs, 211, 238
  from planes, 240, 248

Free convection, simplified relations for, 240–241
simultaneous radiation loss in, 240, 246
calculations, 247
temperature distribution in, 213, 237–240
inside tubes, 170, 185, 191
velocity distribution in, 238
from vertical cylinders, 241
from wires, 243
Freezing of fruit juices, 43
Friction, analogy to heat transfer, 162–164
in annular sections, 123–124
contraction loss, 128–131
in curved pipes, 122–123
definition, 116
enlargement loss, 128–131
for fluid flow, 116–131
in packed tubes, 124–125
in rectangular sections, 123, 198
in straight pipes, 118
effect of heat transmission on, 120, 129–131
across tube banks, 126, 358
Friction factors, 117–131, 358
Fromm waffle plate, 106
Froude number, 101
Furnace design, 77–84
example, 82
Fused salts, 196

G

Gas, Gases, in annular spaces, 123, 200
effect of temperature on $c_p\mu/k$, 415
table of data for, 169
free convection, 170, 185, 191, 240
liquefied, specific heat of, 402
over plane surfaces, 205–207
radiation from, 64–73
specific heat of, 406
temperature of, errors due to radiation, 223–225
thermal conductivity of, 391–392
viscosity *vs.* temperature of, 410
Gases outside banks of tubes, data for, 227
recommended relation for, **229**

Gases outside banks of tubes, forced convection, 226–230
Gases outside single tubes, forced convection, data, 219
dimensional analysis, 217
mechanism, 211–217
nomenclature, 218
recommended relation for, **220–223**
approximate equations for, 223
simultaneous radiation, 217, 223–225
Gases in tubes, heating and cooling of, 168–179
approximate relations for (charts), **174–176**
calculations for, 176, 177
in coils, 177
condensation of (*see* Condensation)
effect, of diameter, 166
of dust, 175
of length, 172
of mass velocity, 165
of temperature, 173
in packed tubes, 178
recommended equation for, **168**
simplified equation for diatomic, 174
for superheated steam, 172
summary of data for, 169
transitional velocity for, 170
vs. Prandtl equation, 171
vs. Reynolds equation, 171
Gelatin solutions, 323
Geometric mean area, 13
Geometrical factors, 10–18, 57
Glycerine, free-convection data for, 243
heating of, 190
solutions, boiling of, 309, 311
Graetz number, 95, 188
Grashof number, 95, 170, 191, 197, 242
Gurney-Lurie charts, 32–37

H

h, individual coefficient of heat transfer, definition, 135, 137

Heat, mechanical equivalent of, 114
  total (*see* Enthalpy)
Heat capacity, 399–406
Heat content (*see* Enthalpy)
Heat economizers, 141
Heat loss, bare pipe, coefficient for, **247**
Heat meter, 24
Heat regenerators, 43
Heat transfer, analogy to fluid friction, 162–164
  coefficient of, individual definition, 135
    over-all, definition, 134
    range of, 4, 251
  effect on fluid friction, 120–121
Heating and cooling, recommended equations for, **154, 210**
Heptane, 315
Hexane, 275
Hot-wire anemometer, 102, 243
Humidification, 292
Hydraulic radius, 119, 124, 197, 200, 203
Hydrocal, 43
Hydrocarbon oils (*see* Oils).
Hydrogen, 169, 171, 197, 243, 246

I

Ice formation, 43, 85
Illuminating gas, heating of, 165
Insulating materials, thermal conductivity of, 382–388
Insulation, heat loss decreased by, 12
  heat loss increased by, 345
Intensity of radiation, definition, 53
Interference fringes, 213
Iron pipe, dimensions of, 416

J

Jacketed vessels, **250**

K

Karman analogy, 163–164
Kerosene, 168, 169, 181, 194, 310, 311
Kinematic viscosity, 113

Kinetic energy, discussion of, 114
Kirchhoff's law, 48

L

Laminar flow film, 101, 164
Laminar motion, 99, 186
Latent heat of vaporization, of liquids, 398
  of water, 397
Linseed oil, 195
Liquids, heating and cooling of, forced convection, annular spaces, 201
    baffled exchangers, **230**
    drip coolers, 202–205
    normal to single tubes, 226
    plates, **205**
    in tubes, streamline flow, **190**
      turbulent flow, **168, 195**–**197**
  free convection, 241–251
    (*See also* Oils; Water)
  latent heat of vaporization of, 398
  specific heat of, 400–405
  thermal conductivity of, 389–390
  viscosity *vs.* temperature of, 408
Logarithmic mean area, 12
Logarithmic mean temperature difference, 142, 356
Luminous flames, radiation from, 73–77
Lungstrom preheater, 43

M

Mass transmission coefficient, 284–292
Mass velocity, definition, 111, 166, 226
Material balance, 111
Mean mixing length, 162
Mean temperature, 144, 271
Mean temperature difference, 141–149
Mechanical equivalent of heat, 114
Mercury, 197, 304
Metals, thermal conductivity of, 380–381
Meter, heat, 24
Methyl alcohol, 263, 310–315
Midplane, definition, 32
Mineral oils (*see* Oils)

Models, theory of, 95
Molasses, 311, 323
Motion, cellular, 240
  streamline *vs.* turbulent, 99
Muffle furnace, example, 61
Multipass heat exchanger, 146, 348

N

Naphtha, 263
Natural convection (*see* Free convection)
Natural gas, 82
Newton's law, of cooling, 3, 135
  of motion, 88
Nitrogen, 243
Nomenclature, for boiling, 294
  for condensing, 256
  for convection, 151
  for design, 341
  for dimensional analysis, 88, 91
  for fluid dynamics, 112
  for heat transfer, inside tubes, 156
    outside tubes, 218
  for radiation, 46
  for steady conduction, 5
  for unsteady conduction, 31
Nonluminous gases, radiation due to, 64–73
Nonuniformity, in temperature distribution, 156
  in velocity distribution, 160
Nusselt number, 95

O

Octane, 275
Octyl thiocyanate, 323, 331
Oil, mineral, thermal conductivity of, 389–390
Oil heater, calculation of pressure drop, 129
Oils, free convection for, 243, 250
  in tubes, heating and cooling of, streamline flow, **190**
    determination of specific heat, 189
    distortion of streamlines, 186
    Graetz number, 95, 188

Oils, in tubes, mechanism, 186
    recommended relation, for heating, **190**
  for streamline flow, **190**
  summary data, 193–195
  theory, 187–188
  for transition region, **196**
  turbulent flow, **192–197**
    effect of length, 190, 196
    fouling of tubes, 138, 197
    nomenclature table, 156
    recommended relation for, **195**
Oleic acid, 276, 278, 323
Olive oil, free-convection data for, 243
Optimum amount of coolant, 370
Optimum frequency of cleaning condenser and evaporator, 279, 318
Optimum temperature difference in exchangers, 141, 370–374
Optimum thickness of insulation, 12, 344
Optimum velocities in exchangers, 139, **363–370**
Over-all coefficient, definition, 134, 136
  graphical analysis of, 271
  ordinary ranges of, 251
  tables of, 249, 250
Oxide films, 22, 45
Oxygen, free-convection data for, 246

P

Packed tubes, friction in, 124–125
  heat transfer in, 178
Parallel plates, fluid friction, 124
Peclet number, 95
  vs. Reynolds number, 172
Pentane, 275
Perfect gas law, 115
Periodic conduction, 43
Petroleum oils (*see* Oils)
Photographs, of boiling, 298, 301, 302, 329
  of condensation, 255
  of finned tubes, 231–233
  of flow, across tubes, 211–215, 328
    over plates, 107

Photographs, of scale deposits, 139, 140

Pi theorem, 89

Pipe, banks of, 126, 230
dimensions of, 416
friction in, 118
photographs of, 215

Pipe stills, 80

Pitot tube, 103

Planck equation, 50

Poiseuille's law, 90, 120

Powdered coal, radiation from, 76

Prandtl analogy, 163, 169, 171

Prandtl number, 21, 95

Pressure, effect, upon free convection, 242, 243
upon transitional velocity, 170
upon viscosity, 120

Pulverized coal flame, radiation from, 76

R

Radiation, of heat, 45–86
absorptivity for, 48
black body, 49
coefficient of heat transfer (chart), 63
constant, 49
cosine law, 52–54
definition, 1
emissivity for, 49, 393
errors in pyrometry, due to, 223–225
geometrical factors, 55
intensity of, definition, 53
Planck equation, 50
plus convection, coefficients for pipes, **247**
problems, 84–85
reflectivity for, 49
simplified equation for, 63, 224
Stefan-Boltzmann equation for, 49
total emissive power of, 48
total hemispherical intensity of, 48
vs. convection, 45
to wall tubes, 58–62

Radiation, from luminous flames, 73–77
absorption strength, 75–76
methods of attack, 73
powdered coal, 73, 76–77
through nonabsorbing media, 51–64
between adjacent rectangles, 56
between disks, 57
examples, 60–62
between planes, 57
recommended equation, 15
from nonluminous gases, 64–73
ammonia, 72
average temperature of gas, 70
example, 72–73
carbon dioxide, 65
carbon monoxide, 72
flue gas, 64–73
example, 72–73
sulphur dioxide, 71–72
water vapor, 66–68

Raschig rings, 290

Recovery of waste heat, 43, 141

Reflectivity, definition, 49

Refrigerants, 271–275, 307–315

Regenerators, 43–44

Reheating furnace, 80

Resistance, thermal, contact, 24
graphical analysis of, 271–275
individual, definition, 23, 137
over-all, definition, 137
total, definition, 23

Resistances, in parallel, 25
in series, 22–24
example, 23

Reynolds analogy, 162, 171

Reynolds number, 95, 96, 99
critical value, 101, 118, 193

Ribs, conduction in, 16

Ripples, 261

Roofs, conduction through, 43

Roughness, 90, 107, 120, 175

Rubber, heating of, 34–35, 43

S

Safety, factor of, 154, 177, 210, 357

Saturation pressure of water, 397

Scale deposits, 137–139, 197, 273–275, 316–319
  removing, 140, 279, 318
Schlieren photograph, 111
Schmidt method, 39–43
Schmidt number, 95
Shadow photograph, 212
Shape factors, for steady conduction, 11–18
Shell-and-tube condensers, 272
Shell-and-tube exchangers, 230, 346
  data, 227–229
  mean-temperature difference, 141–149
  recommended procedure, **230, 357**
Similarity, principle of (*see* Dimensional analysis)
Simplified equation for radiation, 62–64, 224
Slag on boiler tubes, 138–139
Sodium chloride solution, evaporation of water from, 309, 311, 318
Sodium sulphate solution, evaporation of water from, 309, 311, 318
Solids, specific heat of, 399
  thermal conductivity of, 380–388
Sonic velocity, 19, 120
Specific heat, 115, 399–406
  of gases, 406
  of liquefied gases, 402
  of liquids, 400–401
  of solids, 399
Spheres, forced convection with, 237
Spray ponds, 290
Stanton number, 95
Steady state, definition, 7
Steam, condensation of, 254–280
  superheated, cooling of, 172, 208
Steam boilers, 81–84
Steam table, 397
Steaming of wood, 27, 43
Steel pipe, dimensions of, 416
Stefan-Boltzmann equation, 49
Stethoscope, 101
Stoves, blast furnace, 43
Stratification, 160
Streamline flow, 100, 186
Streamline shapes, 236
Subcooling, 270

Submerged conductors, 15
Sucrose solution, evaporation of water from, 309, 312, 326
Sugar solution, evaporation of water from, 311, 323, 326
Sulphite liquor, evaporation of water from, 331
Sulphur dioxide, radiation due to, 71–72
Superheat in vapors, removal of, 279
Superheated steam, condensing of, 279
  cooling of, 172
Surface condensers, 254–283
Surface temperature, measurement of, 149, 264
Surface tension, 93, 301, 303, 325
Sutherland constant, 21

T

Tables, nomenclature (*see* Nomenclature)
  of beam lengths, 69
  of consistent units for Reynolds number, 412
  of conversion factors, for h and U, 392
    for Reynolds number, 88
    for thermal conductivity, 379
    for viscosity, 407
  of emissivities, 393–396
  of enthalpy of steam, 397
  of latent heats of vaporization, 398
  of over-all coefficients, 249–251
  of pipe dimensions, 416
  of ratio $c_p\mu/k$ for gases, 415
  of specific heats, 399–406
  of surface tensions, 415
  of thermal conductivities, 380–392
  of tube dimensions, 417
  of vapor pressure of water, 397
  of viscosities, 407–412
Temperature, mean value in gas radiation calculations, 70
Temperature difference, mean, 141–149
Temperature distribution, in moving fluids, 158–161, 186, 211–213, 238–239
  in solids (*see* Conduction)

Temperature stresses in tubes, 152
Thawing fruit juices, 43
Theory of models, 95
Thermal conductivity, 4–44, 380–392
　of alloys, 380–381
　average temperature for, 10
　of building and insulating materials, 382–388
　conversion of units for, 379
　effect, of density, 8–9
　　of porosity, 9
　　of temperature, 8
　of gases, 20–22, 391–392
　of liquids, 18–20, 389–390
　　empirical equation for, 20
　of solids, 8–9
　temperature coefficient of, 9
　units, 7
Thermal diffusivity, 30
　of wood, 43
Thermocouples, 149–152
　disturbance due to, 107
　error due to radiation, 223–225
　traveling, 150, 321
Toluene, 243, 263, 275, 283, 312
Total emissive power, definition, 48
Total heat of steam and water, 397
Total hemispherical intensity, definition, 48
Towers, heat transfer to gases in, 178
　packed, friction in, 125
Transition region, 192–197
Transitional velocity, definition, 170
　effect of pressure upon, 170
Trichloro-ethylene, 263, 283
Tubes, dimensions of, 417
　temperature stresses in, 152
　(*See also* Pipe)
Turbulent motion, 99, 193
Turpentine, 263

U

U, over-all coefficient of heat transfer, definition, 134, 136
Units, consistent, 5, 31, 46, 88, **97,** 112, 151, 156, 218, 256, 294, 341
　conversion of, for coefficient of heat transfer, 392

Units, conversion of, for thermal conductivity, 379
　for viscosity, 407
Unsteady conduction (*see* Conduction, unsteady)
Unsteady state, definition 7, 27

V

Vacuum, evaporation under, 309
Valves, resistance of, 121
Vapor-diffusion theory, 283–292
Vapor pressure, of water, 397
Vaporization, due to boiling (*see* Evaporation)
　latent heat of, 398
Vapors, condensation of mixed, 280
　desuperheating of, with condensation, 279
　　without condensation, 172, 279
Velocity, effect upon heat transfer, 139, 154–251
　mass, weight, definition, 111, 166
　maximum, 100, 158–161
　　vs. average, 106
　optimum, 139, **363–370**
Velocity distribution, isothermal, over rough surfaces, 106–108
　in smooth pipes, 104
　nonisothermal, 158–161, 186, 211–215, 238
Viscosity, conversion factor for, 407
　defined, 120
　eddy, 162–163
　effect of pressure on, 120
　fictive, 162
　of gases *vs.* temperature (chart), 411
　of liquids *vs.* temperature (chart), 409
　units, 407
　of water, 407
Viscous motion (*see* Streamline flow)

W

Waste-heat recovery, 373
Water, chlorination of, 279
　enthalpy of, 397
　entropy of, 397

Water, evaporation of, 296–337
    into air, 285–292
    heating and cooling of, forced convection, annular spaces, 201–202
      baffled exchangers, 230
      drip coolers, 202–205
      normal to single tubes, 226
      plates, 207, 248
      in tubes (*see* Water in pipes)
      free convection, 242–251
      (*See also* Liquids)
    latent heat of vaporization, 398
    optimum amount of, 370
    specific volume of liquid, 397
      of vapor, 397
    thermal conductivity of, 389
    vapor pressure of, 397
    viscosity *vs.* temperature, 407
Water in pipes, cleaning of tubes, 274, 279
    heating and cooling of, 179–186, 191

Water in pipes, heating and cooling of, in coils, 184
    effect, of diameter, 166, 184
      of length, 179, 180
      of temperature, 184
    flow in films, 202–205
    at low velocities, 185, 191
    nomenclature table for, 156
    recommended equation for, **168**
    scale deposits, 138
    simplified equation for, 183–184
    use of chlorine in, 279
    in vertical pipes, 185, 191
Water vapor, radiation due to, 66
    saturated temperature of, 397
Wood, steaming of, 27, 43
Wrought-iron pipe, table of dimensions, 416

Y

Yaryan evaporator, 330–332